POLLEN GRAINS

POLLEN GRAINS

Their structure,
identification and significance
in science and medicine

BY

R. P. WODEHOUSE, Ph.D.

Scientific Director of the Hayfever Laboratory
The Arlington Chemical Company
Yonkers, New York

HAFNER PUBLISHING CO.

NEW YORK

1959

COPYRIGHT, 1935, BY THE

MCGRAW-HILL BOOK COMPANY, INC.

REPRINTED BY ARRANGEMENT

PUBLISHED BY

HAFNER PUBLISHING CO., INC.

31 EAST 10TH STREET

NEW YORK 3, N. Y.

LIBRARY OF CONGRESS CATALOG CARD NO.: 59-15783

1-16-61

Printed in the U.S.A.

NOBLE OFFSET PRINTERS, INC.

NEW YORK 3, N. Y.

To

ROBERT A. HARPER

PREFACE

The morphology of pollen grains is as old as most other branches of botanical science; historically, we find that it started at the same time as those which require the use of the microscope, but, through the years which followed—and, indeed, until very recently—it has been neglected to such an extent that it has lagged far behind all other branches of botanical science. At the present time the discovered is but a small part of the discoverable in pollen morphology. The present work, therefore, cannot be a compendium of much knowledge, if, indeed, such were desirable. Though it presents as far as possible what is known about pollen grains, it does so primarily with the object of bringing out the principles involved in their study, of showing where new discoveries may be made, and of furnishing a reliable method of approach.

In the preparation of the material, I have written the sections regarding the pollen grains of the different families and those regarding the evolutionary tendencies as I came to them separately and, for the most part, independently of each other. Consequently they may be read in the same way. Nevertheless, as the different families were finished it was found that they would fit together, quite naturally, in a sequence corresponding, for the most part, to the system of Engler and Prantl. In a few instances, however, in which continuity of the story of the pollen-grain forms demanded a deviation from this sequence, concession was made to the morphology of the pollen grains. Though the story presented here is only fragmentary, its underlying continuity will be better appreciated if approached in the sequence in which it is presented. And this will have the added advantage of emphasizing the huge gaps that remain unfilled and so lend stimulus to their filling which is, perhaps, the most valuable purpose of this book.

In selecting the species of pollen for study, I have kept in mind those of my readers who wish to be able to identify pollen found in the air—and possibly causing hayfever—also those who study pollen fossilized in peats and other sediments. I have included most of the wind-pollinated species known to me as such; also I have included such insect-pollinated species as are known or believed to contribute to the production of hayfever and those which are likely to be found in the fossil records. Nevertheless, the number of species included has had to be greatly extended beyond these limits; otherwise the primary purpose of these studies would be defeated, because morphology is a comparative science. A true understanding of the form of a pollen grain cannot be gained without comparing it with its allied forms; and any deductions drawn concerning it are likely to be misleading without such comparisons. Particularly is this true of the grains of wind-borne pollen, since they are almost invariably reduced in form. Therefore, wherever an anemophilous species is selected for study, as many as possible of its allies are also included. Frequently these are rare and often grow in distant countries, but they are included for the sake of completing the story.

The materials upon which the story of the morphology of pollen grains is based are presented in the specific and, to a certain extent, in the generic descriptions. Like similar descriptions in ordinary botany manuals, these constitute a catalogue of pollen grains, together with the characters by which they may be recognized, and are intended only for reference. In presenting this part of the material I have adopted the language of the taxonomist, characterized by its terse and formal brevity. It is fitting that these descriptions should be couched in the language of the taxonomist, for they rightfully belong to his field; pollen grains are as much a part of the plant as the various organs upon which he has drawn to build his imaginative and surprisingly beautiful classification. But in this he has consistently ignored the pollen grains. In his rejection of them he has thrown away, perhaps, the richest part of his heritage, for in no other part of the plant are to be found packed in so small a space so many readily available phylogenetic characters.

In the discussions of the families are described the form of grain that is basic for the family and from which the others might have been derived and, as far as known, the interrelationships of the various forms to each other and the evolutionary tendencies manifest in the group. The story as a whole is, therefore, best approached through a consideration of the family discussions, with reference to the generic and specific descriptions only when necessary.

Keys to the genera and species are provided wherever this is deemed advisable. These are not intended for identification, though it is conceivable that in some cases they may be used for such a purpose. They are summaries of the distinguishing characters. The same data could have been presented in tables, but the key is deemed preferable, because it eliminates repetition, and data so presented are more compact and readily available. Though these keys must not be regarded as natural, I have taken advantage of the great flexibility inherent in keys to bring out the characters according to their relative importance and to arrange the different forms according to their natural sequence as far as the limitations of the available data permit their understanding.

The illustrations are all original and entirely the work of the author, except where otherwise indicated. All drawings, except the diagrams, are freehand from studies made with a Zeiss binocular microscope, generally using a magnification of 900 or 1,300, obtained with a 3-mm. apochromatic objective, n.a. 1.4, or with a 2-mm. apochromatic objective, n.a. 1.3, together with paired 15 × oculars.

The greater part of both the written material and the illustrations was prepared especially for this book and appears here for the first time. To the following journals, however, I am indebted for permission to reprint parts of my articles which have already been published: *Bulletin of the Torrey Botanical Club*, *American Journal of Botany*, *The Scientific Monthly*, *The Journal of Allergy*, and *Hygeia;* and to *Practical Microscopy* for permission to reprint some of the figures used in my article on the "Shapes of Pollen Grains," which was published therein.

I am also greatly indebted to many friends for help in various ways and am pleased to take this opportunity of expressing my thanks and appreciation. Particularly is this true of Prof. R. A. Harper, without whose encouragement and kindly criticism this book might never have been written. To Prof. F. A. McClure of Lingnan University, Canton, China, I am indebted for the pollen of *Glyptostrobus;* and to Dr. I. B. Pole-Evans of Pretoria, South

Africa, and to the Royal Botanical Gardens, Kew, for the pollen of *Welwitschia*. The pollen of plants which grow locally was collected by the author, but practically all other material used in the preparation of these pages was obtained from the New York Botanical Garden, and I am indebted to Dr. E. D. Merrill, the director in chief, for many courtesies in the use of the herbarium and library.

R. P. Wodehouse.

Yonkers, New York,
   September, 1935.

CONTENTS

xi

LIST OF PLATES

INTRODUCTION

We are accustomed to think of pollen as the fertilizing dust of plants, the yellow powder that forms in the middles of most flowers. In fact, the name pollen just means dust. But, as seen with the microscope's eye, it is a vast assemblage of independent organisms. There are hundreds or thousands of them in the least smear of pollen, but each one is an individual and as much entitled to individual consideration as the plant which produced it.

Pollen grains are small, so small that they cannot be seen with the naked eye; nevertheless, each is a phase in the life cycle of the flowering plant, the point in the cycle where all the potentialities and characters of the plant, be they the beauty of the rose, the majesty and dignity of the oak or the grace and elegance of the vine, are distilled into a tiny cell and cast with millions of others to the winds.

Pollen Grains Are Spores.—They correspond to the small or male spores of the ferns. It is even a little difficult to draw a hard-and-fast line between pollen grains and other kinds of spores. Perhaps the best distinction is this: When a spore, like the fern spore, germinates, it ruptures its wall, and the developing prothallus emerges; when a pollen grain germinates, the young prothallus, which is only rudimentary does not rupture the spore wall but is entirely contained within it. Of course, the word germination, used in this sense with pollen grains, has nothing to do with tube formation, which takes place later. Though the latter is also called germination, the two processes are quite distinct, and the word germination would better be reserved for the first division of the protoplast in the formation of the prothallus.

Pollination.—The problem that confronts pollen grains is that of reaching the pistil of another flower. It is well known that it is toward the achievement of this result that the many different colors and structures of flowers have been developed; it is likewise true that to the same end many of the varied and beautiful forms of pollen grains have been evolved.

1

Wind Pollination.—Evidently the most primitive method of pollination was the simple and direct method of dispersal by wind. Since pollen grains are ordinarily small enough to float almost indefinitely in the air, provided that it possesses any movement at all, they may simply be cast off on the chance that some will reach their goal. The chances are extremely slight that any one pollen grain will ever reach its destination in another flower by this method, so when wind is the agency employed, the remoteness of the possibility must be compensated by the liberation of an enormous amount of pollen. The most primitive flowering plants are all wind pollinated, *e.g.*, the cycads, the maidenhair tree, and the pines and their allies. The method was eminently successful, for all three of these groups of trees came to dominate the plant societies of past geological ages, though now they have for the most part dwindled to mere fragments of their former grandeur. But the method is extravagant; it is safe to say that for every grain which reaches its goal there are many thousands which are carried astray. Indeed, it is these misdirected wanderers that are the cause of most hayfever.

It is not exactly known how the angiosperms came to abandon wind pollination, but it was probably because insects at some very early period developed the habit of feeding on pollen. This we may see going on today. For example, the corn plant, which is wind pollinated, is freely visited by bees which rob it of its pollen. The gymnosperms, like the maidenhair tree and the pines, appear to have been able to fortify their pollen against this menace, possibly by producing unpalatable pollen or producing it so fast that they get it matured and shed before the insects can breed their numbers up sufficiently to devour it. This appears to be the primary reason why the majority of anemophilous plants have only a brief flowering period.

Insect Pollination.—Other plants appear to have turned this adversity to their advantage; instead of combating the onslaught of insects, they encouraged their visits because the uneaten pollen which they accidentally carried from flower to flower proved to be quite as effective in achieving pollination as vast quantities discharged into the air. Through a long process of evolution, the plants appear to have developed nectar to supply the insects, that they might spare their pollen, and by concealing the nectar in devious ways and placing the pollen at certain vantage points in the flowers much pollen was saved at the cost of only a little nectar. But in order that this method may succeed it is necessary to have the right kinds of insects visit the flowers at the right time. It is obviously to secure this end that the elaborate and beautiful structures of flowers have been developed, always directed towards the most effective pollination with the minimum expenditure of pollen.

Successful as the method of pollination by insects has proved to be with many thousands of plants, undoubtedly success has not been universal. Plants with flowers specialized to pollination by a limited number of kinds of insects must inevitably be restricted in their range to that of the insects which can pollinate them. Their number must, likewise, be restricted by the size of the population of the particular kind of insects required for pollination, and this, in turn, may be limited by the available food supply for the larvae of the insects, or by their natural enemies. Also, sometimes even the flowers most elaborately devised for securing the visits of only beneficial insects must have failed. If we examine almost any patch of squirrel-corn, for example, a large number of the flowers will be found to have been bitten open by some insect which, being unable to secure the nectar in the normal way, has adopted the method of biting a hole in the side of each spur. Also, when bumble bees visit these flowers and thrust their large heads in at the tiny orifice they split the flower wide open, apparently without effecting pollination. So this flower, which is highly specialized for insect pollination, has apparently failed to a large extent, having at least two kinds of insects which defeat its elaborate devices for preserving its nectar for only those insects which can effect pollination.

Return to Wind Pollination.—So we are not surprised to find that during the evolutionary period when the majority of flowering plants were developing many marvelous and beautiful adaptations to insect pollination, to others it became necessary to abandon insect pollination and return to the old extravagant method of wind pollination. To this category belong the families of the grasses and sedges and the majority of, if indeed not all, other angiosperms which are wind pollinated. The flowers of the grasses and sedges possess what are believed to be vestiges of petals and sepals, which seem to show that they are related to the lilies and amaryllis. Having given up insect pollination, they no longer have need of the showy colors of their ancestors and have abandoned them. But they were successful upon their return to their old ways; the grasses cover many square miles of prairies and plains, which, it seems, would be impossible for them to do if they were compelled to rely upon insects for their pollination. The enormous hordes of insects that would be required to pollinate the grasses of the Kansas prairies or the Texas hills or even all the grasses of an ordinary hayfield are almost unthinkable.

Wind-pollinated flowers can generally be distinguished from those that are insect pollinated by their lack of qualities attractive to insects—such as color, perfume, and nectar—, by the relatively much larger quantity of pollen which they shed, and by their protruding anthers designed to scatter the pollen to the wind. Associated with wind pollination there is also generally found a more or less complete separation of sexes, the stamens and pistils being born in different flowers, and the staminate and pistillate flowers on different parts of the plant or even on different plants. For example, the wind-pollinated ragweeds bear staminate flowers in spikes with the pistillate flowers at their bases, and the cattails bear the staminate and pistillate flowers both in the same long spike but separated from each other. A more complete separation is found in the ash and poplar trees, in which each tree bears only staminate or only pistillate flowers.

In their pollination the poplars and willows offer an interesting comparison. They both belong to the same family and are certainly closely related. The willows, however, differ from the poplars in being primarily insect pollinated, possibly in the transition stage, on the way to becoming wind pollinated, while the poplars are entirely wind pollinated. The flowers of both are borne in catkins, the male and female on different trees. Those of the willow, however, are yellowish, sweet scented and provided with nectar, and they prove attractive to insects for they are visited by them in large numbers, while the flowers of poplars are much less conspicuous, without fragrance or nectar, and are of no interest to insects. Though the willows certainly secure pollination by insects, they just as certainly secure it also by wind. They produce an unusually large amount of pollen, for insect-pollinated plants, and if insects fail to carry it away, it is scattered freely in the air. It can easily be detected by appropriate means several miles from the trees, and sometimes occurs in sufficient abundance to cause hayfever. It is quite possible, therefore, that willow should be regarded as in the transition stage, changing from insect to wind pollination.

It is a curious fact that plants which have abandoned insect pollination and returned to the method of pollination by wind, though they may seem to have failed in their venture in entomophily, they are in no way failures upon their return to the old method. The fact is attested by the extraordinary success of the ragweeds, the grasses, the sagebrushes, many farm and garden weeds like the pigweeds and lamb's-quarters, and most of our forest trees, which are anemophilous. Certainly they are more successful as wind-pollinated plants than are the pines and their relatives and the maidenhair tree, which stuck rigidly all the time to the old-fashioned method, never trying the experiment of entomophily. Though the experiment in itself was a failure with some, it certainly did no harm to those plants which tried and abandoned it, and may even have endowed them with a superior vigor.

Fertilization.—When the pollen grain reaches the pistil, it has already germinated, in the sense that a fern spore germinates. Though the pollen coats are not broken, and from outward appearance the grain is still a single cell, at this stage there are within a number of cells, either actually formed or represented in some way, corresponding in an abbreviated and sketchy fashion to the fern prothallus. When the grain comes to rest on the stigma of another flower the moist secretion which it encounters there stimulates the prothallus to renewed growth, and a slender tube emerges. There may be special pores provided for its emergence, especially if the outer coat of the grain is thick, or the exine may simply rupture. The pollen tube penetrates the tissues of the stigma and style, finally reaching one of the ovules where it discharges two male gametes which were produced by the prothallus of the pollen grain, and fertilization is effected.

WORLDS OF DIFFERENT SIZES

Perhaps the first question that one is going to ask upon approaching the subject of pollen morphology is: Why are the forms of pollen grains so odd and strange—so different from the things that we are accustomed to seeing in everyday life? It is true they are not all alike; unrelated species can easily be told apart, and often the differences between them are very great. Nevertheless, great as these differences are, they are trifling compared with those that exist between pollen grains and the things that we are accustomed to seeing without a microscope. The microscope shows us another world. And truly this is the answer to our question. Pollen grains belong to a world of another size.

The World of Gravity Walkers.—There is a law of nature that places a handicap on bigness; the larger an animal is the greater its difficulty in moving. Mathematicians have a more exact way of stating this law. They say that the surface area, and the cross-sectional area or strength, of a thing are functions of the square of its linear dimensions, while its volume or weight is a function of the cube of the same dimensions. Among the everyday things that we know, this disproportionate increase of volume or weight over surface area or strength that is encountered as an object increases in length and breadth limits the size of animals that, for example, may walk comfortably bearing their weight on their feet to about the size of an elephant. Animals very much larger, like the whales, must live in an aquatic medium that supports their bulk, for it would be totally unmanageable on land. At the other end of the series, a mouse is perhaps the smallest animal that has weight enough to get traction for its feet; and even it freely uses its claws for that purpose. This is the world of our size, bounded at the top by about the size of an elephant and at the bottom by that of a mouse. It is the world in which we perform most of our activities and to which we are best adapted. We need no lenses to see all of it, and we need no mechanical aids to handle things in it, hence our feeling of being at home in it.

In this world of elephants, men, and mice, animals walk on four or two feet, and the bearing of their weight, particularly among those near the upper limit, is perhaps their most serious structural problem. All beings, both plants and animals, which inhabit this size-world are primarily shaped by the asymmetrical or one-directional pull of gravity. The plant directs its stalk upward against the force of gravity and its roots downward with the force of gravity, while its branches may be symmetrically arranged around the vertical axis; and for the same reason animals differentiate an upper and lower side. But the forces of this size-world tend to impose a further limitation of symmetry on all beings in it which move; for in response to a motion which is always at right angles to the gravitational pull, front and back ends are likewise clearly differentiated. Nature's tendency to make all things as symmetrical as possible is thus thwarted in all directions except laterally, but here it asserts itself. Thus it is that beings which move in this world are characterized by a right and left or bilateral symmetry, which is the only one possible to them.

Among animals which move in this world, flight is seldom undertaken and is hazardous, except toward its lower limit. It may be called the world of gravity walkers. Within it forms of things may be very different, yet, when compared with those of either the world of larger things, which is perhaps the world of planets and solar systems, or with those of the world of next smaller things, to which the insects belong, they seem much alike.

The World of Easy Flight.—Within this world of smaller things gravity and movement impose the same type of bilateral symmetry, as before, upon the beings which inhabit it, but its lessened effect brings about some curious results. The support of bodily weight is not a problem; instead, the effect of gravity is too weak to give sufficient traction for convenient walking on four or two feet in the usual way. Feet must be provided with suction disks or with hooks. In this world of lessened gravitational effect it is nearly as easy to walk across a ceiling or up a vertical wall as it is along the floor. In it flight is the rule and not the exception, and flight is attended with no hazards. So much is this so, that it may be called the world of easy flight. It is a world in which we are not at all adapted and can play no part without special aids. Even for us to observe most of it, a good lens is a help; and to handle objects in it, forceps and other instruments are necessary. Among its inhabitants insects predominate, for their structure, which is far different from that of elephants, men, and mice, is beautifully adapted to movements within its size limits.

Though the effect of gravity is so far reduced that flight is easy, its accomplishment requires muscular effort. Only the smallest inhabitants of this size-world attempt to float without muscular effort, and when they do they must devise some special floating mechanism, such as the tuft of silk of the balloon spider or the crown of pappus of the thistle seed.

World of Floating and Sticking.—In the world of next smaller size, the one to which spores and pollen grains belong, floating is easily accomplished. No wings are used, because none are needed. It is a world of objects so small that when they are free they float, for the effect of gravity is not strong enough to pull them down against the slightest current of air; and when they touch they stick, for the effect of gravity is not strong enough to pull them loose again. But the lack of gravitational effect has an even more important influence, that is, upon the symmetry of the beings of this world; as a consequence of it, their top and bottom sides are not differentiated. Moreover, they do not have an independent forward motion with its consequent differentiation of front and back ends, and they are, therefore, rarely bilaterally symmetrical, and when they are, it is for reasons of another category. With organisms of this size-world, symmetry, which in nature tends ever to be as complete as possible, has much fuller sway and reaches a much fuller expression. Since the sphere is the most perfectly symmetrical figure, it is not surprising to find that beings of this world are basically spherical; it could, indeed, be called the world of spheres. That is, perhaps, the most outstanding character of pollen grains— they tend to be spherical, and their sculpturing is nearly always of a much higher order of symmetry than the bilateral to which we have become accustomed in our world and in the world of easy flight. Is it any wonder that the forms of pollen grains look odd and strange to us?

The range in size of pollen grains does not exactly coincide with the range of the world of floating and sticking. It extends, perhaps, a little beyond at the upper end but falls far short at the lower, for there are spores which are far smaller than pollen grains and still float freely in the air. The largest pollen grains, as, for example, those of the pumpkin, which are about 200 μ in diameter, are so large that they cannot float easily, but they can stick, with the help of a little oily adhesive, so they travel by sticking to insects. From this size pollen grains range downward to about that of the forget-me-not which is $4\frac{1}{2}$ μ in diameter. But it, too, travels by sticking to insects. It is an interesting fact that among pollen grains only those of intermediate sizes are the best floaters. Invariably both the very large and the very small are exclusively stickers. Only those between 58 and 17 μ, with one notable exception, are good floaters. The reason that those above this range are exclusively stickers is obvious— they are just a little beyond the size range of easy floating but still within the range of moderately easy sticking. But the reason that those below this size range are also almost exclusively stickers is not so easy to see. It may be that their small size, with its attendant disproportionately large surface area, is a hindrance to them in leaving their anthers or in separating from each other. That this is so seems likely from the exceptional case of the pollen of the paper mulberry. It is air borne, yet its grains are only 13 μ in diameter, which is well below the size range of most air-borne pollen. It is, however, forcibly ejected from the anthers in a rather spectacular manner. If a flowering branch of the paper mulberry is kept in water, its pollen will be seen to puff out from the flowers, like puffs of smoke. Also, the many fungi, whose spores are even smaller—yet are floaters par excellence—are provided with an efficient mechanism for throwing the spores clear of the plant and of each other. The reason that only moderately large pollen grains are floaters is probably to be found in the inability of most plants to develop a satisfactory ejecting mechanism.

Resemblances of Pollen Grains to Protozoa.—Many people have marveled at the resemblances between pollen grains and such minute aquatic organisms as the Radiolaria and Heliozoa. The shells of these animals are generally made of some silicious or calcareous material, chemically entirely unrelated to the exine of pollen grains, yet they appear to bear a quite remarkable resemblance to them. Their basic form is spherical, and their sculptured patterns are similar to those of pollen grains in their symmetrical completeness. The question naturally arises: How do these organisms come to resemble pollen grains, since their shells are of an entirely different composition and they live in an aquatic medium? The resemblance that they bear to pollen grains is due solely to the fact that they live in a similar size-world. They are floaters and stickers without independent movement in an aquatic medium, just as pollen grains are in an aerial medium. And, freed from the asymmetrical influence of a one-directional gravity and of one-directional movement, they have become as nearly perfectly symmetrical as pollen grains, assuming the spherical form and somewhat similar sculptured patterns. Looked at more closely, however, they are seen to have no more resemblance than this; their sculptured patterns are composed of different elements of symmetry, belonging to different mathematical series. For example, the underlying series among the patterns of pollen grains is that of the tetrahedron, cube, and pentagonal dodecahedron, always with three equal angles coming together at a point; while the patterns of the most similar protozoa, *e.g.*, *Circoporus* and *Circogonia*, are built on the plan of the octahedron and icosahedron, which have four angles coming together at a point, a condition almost never encountered among pollen grains. Such differences as these are basic and, measured in terms of the world of floating and sticking objects, are far greater than, let us say, the difference between a man and a crocodile, measured in terms of our world of gravity walkers.

The actual similarity that the inhabitants of the world of floating and sticking usually bear to each other is due to the fact that within the size limits of such tiny objects as spores, pollen grains and protozoa, much less diversity of form is possible than within the worlds of larger objects. It is true that at its upper end and, in fact, through the greater part of its range, which is occupied by pollen grains, considerable diversification of form is possible. The large pumpkin pollen grain, those of the Malvaceae, with a diameter of about 153 μ, and of the four-o'clock, with a diameter of about 180 μ, are elaborate and beautiful objects. Nowhere among the grains of smaller orders of magnitude do we find anything approaching the multiplicity of their detail and beauty of pattern. As we pass downward in the series of grains arranged according to their size, they become less and less ornate. The smaller pollen grains are practically without decorations, excepting germinal apertures of the simplest kind or germinal furrows of an equally simple kind; and as we pass over into the domain of spores which are still smaller even these are missing. Indeed, the smaller spores in their simplicity and plainness of form are quite like bacteria which are the inhabitants of the next smaller size world.

In the world of bacteria and organisms of similar size the forms are all so simple that it is difficult to distinguish most of them by their morphological characters. For that reason the bacteriologist must rely mainly upon physiological characters for purposes of classification and identification.

We shall not dwell longer upon this size-world, or upon those which lie still lower in the scale, than to point out that as the size of the particle diminishes and, as a consequence, the proportion of the surface area increases, new and unfamiliar properties are encountered, and the old familiar ones lost. For example, the world next in size below that of bacteria is perhaps the world of colloid chemistry. In this world particles are too small for us to see even with a microscope; but if we could see them, they would probably be found to be perfect spheres and all look much alike. The properties which distinguish colloids are mainly those which have to do with surface areas, for truly this is a world of enormous surface areas.

A consideration of objects and organisms of these different size classes furnishes a suitable background against which to view pollen grains. Their most striking and fundamental characters are those of the size-class to which they belong and do not lend themselves to ready comparison with objects of other size-classes. Underlying this is the old familiar law which says that the surface area of an object is a function of the square of its linear dimensions while its volume is a function of the cube of the same dimensions.

PART I
GENERAL

CHAPTER I

HISTORICAL REVIEW

The history of pollen morphology is necessarily associated with the development of the microscope. On account of the small size of pollen grains not even the first beginnings of their study could be made until the microscope had reached a fairly high stage in its development, and each notable improvement in the construction of the microscope has always been reflected in a corresponding advance in pollen morphology. Though the microscope as we now know it is distinctly a modern instrument, its origin is lost in antiquity. There is even some evidence that the ancient Greeks had simple lenses and understood the principles of magnifications, but not until the middle of the seventeenth century, when Hooke gave the world his compound microscope, was an instrument constructed of sufficient power to reveal anything of the shapes of pollen grains.

Hooke's microscope is described and illustrated in the preface to his "Micrographia," which is dated London, 1665. It consists of a tapering brass tube with a single objective at the small end, a large eyepiece at the opposite end, and between these two a third lens could be inserted; but, he states, he did not use this lens, because the fewer the refractions used the clearer the image. The tube was also provided with an opening whereby it could be filled with water, which Hooke states caused the image to appear sharper but was too troublesome to use.

Though such an instrument would appear crude and useless to us, it is hard to estimate its importance in the seventeenth century. From it emerged a whole host of discoveries. The work that Hooke himself did with his microscope, now preserved in his "Micrographia," was in many ways remarkable, but it was too discursive and entirely lacking in unity of purpose, except possibly to demonstrate the beauty and achievements of his microscopes, of which he seems to have been justly proud. But of much farther reaching effect was the work of his contemporary microscopists Malpighi, Grew, and Swammerdam, who with van Leeuwenhoek, using a simple microscope, were really the founders of microscopic anatomy.

Of these, only Grew and Malpighi have had anything to say about pollen. Almost simultaneously they observed and described pollen grains, pointing out that, while those of the same species were alike, those of different species were different. It is

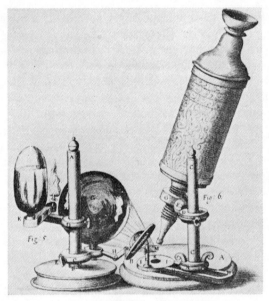

Fig. 1.—Hooke's microscope.

not a matter of any importance to us which of them was the first to describe pollen grains, though most historians seem to think that it is incumbent upon them to settle the question of the priority of these two men, and much bitterness has resulted from the fruitless discussions centering around this question. Though Malpighi lived in Italy, and Grew in England, each was quite familiar with the other's work and borrowed freely from the other but always with acknowledgment as complete as was customary in those days. The question of priority seems not to have interested them at all then—and no more need it interest us now. Malpighi and Grew are recognized as the cofounders of microscopic plant anatomy and so it is that they are cofounders of pollen-grain morphology. But, the contribution of Grew to the latter greatly outranks that of Malpighi, though possibly the reverse is the case with their contributions to plant anatomy in general. The difference between the work of the two men is perhaps more a matter of character than of merit. And, though they were cofounders of pollen morphology, it will perhaps be better to discuss their lives and work separately.

Nehemiah Grew.—Nehemiah Grew was born in 1641 at Atherstone, Warwickshire, the only son of Obediah Grew, a schoolmaster who afterward be-came the nonconformist vicar of St. Michael's Coventry, where Nehemiah spent his youth. Grew's life extends through some of the most troublous times that England has ever experienced. Born the year before Charles I proclaimed war upon the Parliamentary forces, he witnessed the fall and execution of Charles I, the establishment of Cromwell as Protector, and the reigns of Charles II, James II, William and Mary, and the greater part of that of Queen Anne. Yet all the turmoil

FIG. 2.—Nehemiah Grew (1701) after the portrait by R. White.

going on about him seems to have left his life singularly unruffled. He attended Cambridge University, where his acquaintance with John Ray first stimulated his interest in botany. On leaving Cambridge, Grew went to Leyden, where he received the degree of M. D. in 1664, after which he returned to Coventry to practice medicine.

He turned to the study of vegetable anatomy and physiology in the hope of gaining a clearer understanding of the anatomy and physiological processes taking place in the human body, because, he says: "Upon reading some of the many curious Inventions of Learned men, in the *Bodies* of *Animals*. For considering that both of them came first out of the same *Hand* and were therefore the contrivances of the same wisdom I thense fully assured my self that it could not be a vain Design; to seek it in both." And indeed all of Grew's work is colored by this conception of the analogy between animals and plants in their structure and physiological processes.

All Grew's botanical work is bound in a single volume—"The Anatomy of Plants," published in London in 1682, though some of it had been published 11 years earlier. The first of his essays, "The Anatomy of Vegetables Begun," was published by the Royal Society of London in 1671, the same year that Malpighi's "Idea" was submitted to the Royal Society in manuscript form. Since the present discussion is concerned mainly with the history of pollen morphology, it is necessary to refrain from going deeply into this great work, which in many ways seems amazingly modern. Agnes Arber, in her delightful essay in "The makers of British Botany" (1912), truly says:

It is no less than two hundred and forty years since Grew sent his first treatise to the Royal Society, so it is scarcely wonderful that a number of his results have been rejected in the course of time. It is far more remarkable that far more of his conclusions—and those the more essential ones—have been merely confirmed and extended by later work.

In his description of the flower, after describing in a manner which would do credit to a modern textbook of botany the various ways in which the anther may be articulated with its filament and the ways in which dehiscence may take place, he says: "At these clefts it is that they disburse their powders; which as they start out, and stand betwixt the two lips of each cleft have some resemblance to the common sculpture of a Pomegranate with its seeds looking out at the cleft of its Rind." In speaking of the anthers elsewhere, he says: "These parts are hollow; each being the Theca or Case of a great many extreme small Particles either globular or otherwise convex. . . . They are all crowded together and fastened in close ranks without any pedicils, to the sides of the Theca." His descriptions are always concise and vividly pictorial in effect. Knowing full well that his reader was unlikely to be possessed of a magnifying glass and totally ignorant of its possibilities, he compares what he saw through his glass with familiar objects seen with the unaided eye:

The Particles of these powders, though like those of Meal or Dust, they appear not easily to have any regular shape; yet upon strict observation, especially with the assistance of an indifferent Glass, it doth appear, that they are a Congeries, usually of so many perfect Globes or Globulets; sometimes of other Figure, but always regular. That which obscures their Figure is their being so small: In Dogs-Mercury, Borage, and very many other Plants, they are extremely so. In Mallows, and some others, more fairly visible.

The Colour of these small Particles contained in the Theca is also different. But as that is usually white or yellow, so are these: sometimes Blewish; but never Red. And sometimes not of the same Colour with that of the Theca. Which further shows how scrupulous Nature is in differentiating the Tincture of the several Parts.

They are also of different Bigness and Figure. Those in Snap-dragon, are of the smallest size I have seen; being no bigger through a good Microscope, than the least Cheese-Mite to the naked Eye. In Plantain, also through a Glass, like a Scurvy-grass-Seed. In Bears-foot, like a Mustard-seed. In Carnation like a Turnip-seed. In Bind-weed like a Pepper-Corn. In all these of a Globular Figure.

In Devils-bit, they are also round, but depressed, like the seed of Goose-grass, or a Holland cheese. In the Bean and all sorts of Puls, and Trefoyls, also in Blew-bottle, &c. they are Cylindrick. In Orange Lilly, Oval, one 5th of an Inch long, like an Ants-Egg. In Deadly-Nightshade, also Oval, but smaller at both Ends. And those of Pancy, Cubick. In all these and the former, they are Smooth.

But in Mallow, Holyoak, and all that Kind, they are beset round about with little Thorns; whereby each looks like the Seed-Ball of Roman Nettle, or like the Fruit of Thorn-Apple, or the Fish called Piscis arbis minor, or the Murices, used anciently in Wars. They are also very great, showing, through a Glass, of the bigness of a large White Pease; being 200 or 300 times biger than those of Snapdragon; of which there are about a Thousand in each Theca, that is in the space of about 1000th Cubical Part of an Inch.

The grains described above are all illustrated in a plate that follows their description; but the figures are disappointing, falling far short of his graphical descriptions, and in no way bear comparison with his anatomical drawings.

Whether or not Grew understood the fertilizing function of pollen is not quite certain. He is sometimes credited with priority in the sexual theory of plants, since he stated somewhat vaguely that he believed that fertilization was one of the several functions of pollen. However, the credit for its discovery belongs more properly to Camerarius, who some years later (1694) established with abundant evidence the existence of sexuality in plants. The question of the usefulness of pollen clearly

caused Grew considerable concern.   He feels that the beauty of
the petals and sepals of the flowers is their justification.   And
this, he thinks, may also be true of the stamens.   But, if so, why
do their anthers split open?   For this really destroys their beauty.
But he noticed that flowers are nearly always occupied by insect
"guests."   So, attributing to flowers the same generosity of soul
that he himself is known to have possessed, he concludes that the
pollen grains in the anthers are to provide food for "these vast
numbers of little animals," each flower "thus becomming their
Lodging and their Dining-Room both in one."   Yet he is not
quite sure whether they "only suck from hence some juices . . .
or also carry some of the Parts, as of the Globulets, wholly
away."   It is truly quite remarkable how near he came to
discovering insect pollination, but this remained for Kölreuter
about a hundred years later.   That Grew was far from satisfied
with his explanation of the usefulness of pollen to the plant is
quite certain, for he closes his discussion of the matter with
these words: "Or lastly what may be the Primary and private
use of the Attire [stamens] (for even this above-said, though
great, yet is but secondary) I now determine not."   Elsewhere
he says: "It would appear that the attire serves to remove some
superfluous parts of the sap, as a preparatory process to the
production of seed."   This idea seems to have been borrowed
from Malpighi and is hard to reconcile with his statement, made
somewhat earlier in the "Anatomy of Plants," in which he says:

In conversation with our learned Savilian Professor, Sir Thomas
Millington, he told me he was of the opinion that the attire served as the
male organ in the production of seed.   I replied at once, that I was of
the same opinion, and gave him some reasons for it, answering at the
same time some objections that might be brought against it.

Though Grew was halting and uncertain in his statements
regarding the usefulness of the anthers and pollen, in describing
pollen grains he paints the picture with a few bold strokes; and
he clearly states that, though pollen grains tend to be spherical
or globular in form, they are of different size and form in different
species but those of the same species are all alike.   In this he
may be said to have laid the foundation of pollen morphology.

Malpighi.—Cofounder with Grew of the science of plant
morphology, Marcello Malpighi, was born at Crevalcore near

Bologna, Mar. 10, 1628. His parents were farmers, enjoying an independence in financial matters. Studying at the university he became doctor of medicine in 1653 and taught for two years, until he was appointed to the chair of theoretical medicine at Pisa. But, never of robust health, he was forced to leave Pisa on account of the climate after three years, whereupon he went to Messina in 1662 as professor of medicine, returning to Bologna in 1666. In 1667 he was made a fellow of the Royal Society of London, publishing his treatise on the silkworm, which was the first of a long series of papers on zoology, medicine, and botany, eventually collected and published by the society as the well-known volume "Opera omnia" (1687). In 1691, at the age of sixty-three, he became private physician to Innocent XII, but before he had long held this position he died of apoplexy (1694).

FIG. 3.—Marcello Malpighi after the portrait by Tabor.

"Malpighi was primarily physician, as we must perforce acknowledge, yet nothing, we find, is beyond the curiosity of Malpighi the botanist." He says that he began his studies with human anatomy but being unable to understand what he found there turned to the study of higher animals; he gained from them nothing, so, for the sake of further comparisons, turned to the world of insects and finally to plants in his search for simpler structures, for, as he says, "I thought that if I mastered these I might retrace my steps upwards to the higher forms, and clear the path of my earliest studies."

Though Malpighi was on an equal footing with Grew, or possibly even superior, as the founder of microscopic plant anatomy, his contributions to pollen morphology fell far short of those of Grew. Nevertheless, he revealed the basic principles in much the same way that Grew did. He says that "the chambers of the stamens are packed with a mass of globulets almost atomic." His expression *globulorum congerie, quasi atomorum* is surprisingly like that used by Grew in describing the pollen in the anthers. Continuing, he says, "These are of various color and shape, generally yellow as in the lily and rose, but generally white and transparent in the mallow and plantain.   Likewise of various form.   That of the lily is distinctly oval but pointed at its ends, and throughout its length, as in a wheat seed, extends a furrow."   This mention of the single furrow of the lily pollen is apparently the first observation of the principal characteristic of the pollen of most monocotyledons.   The very few figures of pollen that he gives are, like those of Grew, disappointing, but he shows quite correctly the single furrow of the lily grain.

In all his observations Malpighi was obsessed with the idea that every part of the plant had its counterpart, both in form and function, in the animal body, and this led him to the most surprising conclusions, considering his remarkably accurate observations.   Regarding the pollen, he says:

> The plant egg or ovum is concealed in the ovary . . . surrounded by stamens and a floral envelope.   Aeration of the egg may be facilitated by the hollowness of the style, and the entrance of noxious insects prevented by the secretion of a sticky fluid . . . in this fluid are secreted also the impurities of the sap.   The pollen dust is likewise a mere secretion . . . prior to the maturation of the ovum . . . and may be compared perhaps to the menstrual discharge of women.

At the time when Malpighi wrote this, Camerarius had already correctly interpreted the organs of the flower, including the pollen, but Malpighi could not have known it, for Camerarius' work was not published until after Malpighi's death.

An interesting comparison is drawn between the works of Malpighi and Grew by Sachs in his history of botany: "If Malpighi's work reads like a masterly sketch in which the author is bent only on giving the outlines of the architecture of plants, the much more comprehensive work of Grew has the appearance of a text-book of the subject. . . . The tasteful elegance of Malpighi is here replaced by a copiousness of minute detail."

With the passing of these two great pioneers the study of botany stagnated for about 150 years.   Possibly it was because these men had reached so far ahead of their time that no one was able to follow them; or it may have been that the capabilities of the microscope, as it existed then, had been exhausted, and the stimulus of the invention of the compound instrument had worn out.   Whatever the cause, the science of pollen morphology received no contributions of note until well into the nineteenth century, when with a sudden re-awakening appeared, almost simultaneously, the works of Mirbel, von Mohl, Purkinje, Fritzsche, and others. Before we bridge this gap, which takes us into work of a decidedly modern aspect, it will be well to pause a little to consider the problem of the sexuality of plants, because of its necessarily close association with pollen morphology.

SEXUALITY IN PLANTS

The Assyrians.—The earliest known recognition of sex in plants is attributable to the ancient Assyrians, who, it is fairly certain, practiced hand pollination of the date palm. Among the many carvings and examples of glazed brickwork that have been recovered from their ancient civilization are a number which have been interpreted to represent this practice. But the theme is always mythological, and its representation so highly stylized as to leave its basic origin uncertain. Thus, in the palace of Ashur-nasi-apal, who was the worshiped deified ruler of the Assyrian empire from 885 to 860 B.C., have been found carved slabs of stone representing this theme. These are described by A. T. Olmstead, who, in his history of Assyria (1923), writes as follows of the carvings which decorated the altars at the gate of the palace:

The middle one represents eagle headed beings with huge beaks, lolling red tongues, stiff high crests, their dress and posture like that of their more human companions, save that their weapon was a knife stuck into their girdle; their right hand held aloft the spathe which was to fertilize the palm, in the left was a small basket.

Some of the best of these sculptures are preserved in the Metropolitan Museum of Art. These show the same theme repeated again and again, with slight variation, in the different parts of the temple. Always the beings are gigantic, both actually and as compared with the palms which they are believed to be pollinating; always they have large, widespread wings; and always the posture is the same, with the upraised right hand bearing the spathe, which is sometimes smooth and sometimes imbricated, and the left hand hanging at the side bearing a basket. The head is sometimes that of an eagle with partly open beak and protruding tongue and sometimes that of a man with plaited beard, and into the girdle are always thrust two or three knives with the handles showing, that of the third knife, when present,

FIG. 4.—Assyrian winged being pollinating the date palm. (*Courtesy of Metropolitan Museum of Art, New York City.*)

bearing the head of an animal. "In the room itself," Olmstead tells us, "were sculptured figures of Ea, the fish god. He, too, raised the fertilizing palm spathe. And over the figures of the king and his chancellor, themselves 8 ft. high, towered to twice the height a gigantic, winged genius with the fertilizing palm spathe." Again, from the palace of Sargon, 717 B.C., has been recovered a beautiful relief in glazed brick of a winged being somewhat similar though differently attired bearing in his hand the same object which is believed to be a spathe and with which he appears to be pollinating a date palm.

Some doubt has been cast upon the interpretation of these figures as representing pollination. L. Legrain states that they "do not represent the pollination of the date palm. The stylized trees, and the mythologic guardians are watching the tree of 'fortune,' happiness, and good luck and keeping the fruits for the king."

Whatever the correct interpretation of the Assyrian winged beings may be, it is recorded that Herodotus,* in the middle of the fifth century B.C., brought back from his travels in the East the information that the date palm is of two sexes and that in Assyria the female tree is fertilized by dusting it with branches of the male. But this was not followed up, for we find Aristotle, the founder of natural history in the middle of the fourth century B.C., categorically denying the existence of sex in plants because they are nonmotile, and he believed that, as in animals, the sexes were separate only in species which were free to move about. His pupil Theophrastus was somewhat better informed, for he at least suspected the truth. He says that terebinths are some male and some female and that the former are barren and are therefore called male. However, he was more of a philosopher than a naturalist and dismisses the subject thus:

What men say, that the fruit of the female date palm does not perfect itself unless the blossom of the male with its dust is shaken over it, is indeed wonderful, but resembles the caprification of the fig, and it might almost be concluded that the female plant is not by itself for perfecting the foetus; but this cannot be the case in one genus or two, but either in all or in many.

* In this discussion of the early development of the sexual theory I have followed Miall and Sachs.

Pliny.—Little is known of the development of the sexual theory of plants from this time until that of Pliny, about 350 years later, but in the meantime it must have become well established, for Pliny, himself not a naturalist but rather a "compiler of anecdotes," calls the pollen dust the material of fertilization and says that naturalists tell us that all trees and even herbs have the two sexes.   After this, for nearly 16 centuries, the question excited little interest among naturalists.   The idea was accepted and made use of by Konrad von Gesner and de l'Ecluse, early herbalists of the sixteenth century.   Prosper Alpino in 1592 had observed the pollination of dates in Egypt, but Jung and Cesalpino regarded the sexuality of plants as an absurdity, and, as we have seen, Malpighi, who gave the first careful study of the seed and development of the embryo, rejected entirely the idea of sex in plants.   The next advance was the simple statement of Sir Thomas Millington, reported by Grew, which we have already seen above.   But this was thrown out only as a suggestion, and, while Grew stated that he believed Millington's conjecture that the stamens are the male organs, he did not follow up the suggestion and the other functions which he ascribed to the stamens showed how little the idea of their sexual significance had aroused his interest.   Ray, in his "Historia plantarum" (1693), reinforces the conjecture of Millington and Grew by citing once more the example of the date palm.   "In the desert," says Ray, "when artificial pollination cannot take place, the wind may possibly answer the same purpose."   It remained, however, for Camerarius to put the question to the test.

Camerarius.—Rudolph   Jacob   Camerarius   was   born   in Tübingen in 1665 and died there in 1721.   In 1688 he became director of the botanical garden in Tübingen and in 1695 first professor of the university, succeeding his father, Elias Rudolph Camerarius.   Camerarius' work is known to us principally through his famous letter "De sexu plantarum" addressed to Valentine, professor of Giessen, dated 1694, some years after his observations had been made.   He observed that a female mulberry tree, growing with no male tree near, bore fruits which contained only abortive seeds.   This aroused his interest so much that he took female plants of *Mercurialis annua* and kept them in pots apart from the others; he found that, though the plants throve and produced fruits, not one produced a fertile seed.   His communication on this subject was the beginning of the large number of experiments which were described in detail in his letter to Valentine. He carefully describes the flower, the anthers, the pollen, and the behavior of the ovules and then proceeds to the experimental part. He removed the male flowers of *Ricinus* and found that he got no seeds. From this he concluded that no ovules of plants could ever develop into seeds without first being prepared by the pollen which is borne in the stamens. "It therefore follows," said he, "that the stamens are the male sexual organs in which that powder which is the most subtle part of the plant, is secreted and collected, to afterwards be supplied from thence." Finding that most flowers are hermaphroditic, he concluded that they were always self-fertilizing, but he thought it strange by comparison with fertilization in snails which are hermaphroditic animals. The complete explanation, however, remained for Kölreuter and Sprengel nearly three quarters of a century later. Among Camerarius' many experiments were several failures, which, in his scientific way, he

FIG. 5.—Rudolph Jacob Camerarius (1665–1721).

took pains to report. He was much disturbed to find that three plants of hemp taken from the field and planted in the garden produced fertile seeds, and upon repeating the experiment by growing the plants indoors in pots he obtained the same results. In this case it appears that he left to some one else the cutting out of the male plants.

James Logan.—The importance of Camerarius' discoveries soon became appreciated by other investigators. Some denied them; others declared that they knew them all the time; but others were sufficiently aroused to put them to the test. Among the latter was James Logan, governor of Pennsylvania. He set some plants of corn at opposite ends of a plot of ground, about 80 ft. apart. In one group he left the plants intact, but from the others he removed the male panicles. Later in the summer he observed that the ears of the hills in which the plants had been decapitated were all sterile except "one large ear which grew out somewhat further from the stalk than usual, and on that side too, which faced another hillock in a quarter from whence our strongest winds most commonly blew." An ear among the unmutilated group, which had been wrapped in muslin, remained without a fertile seed. It thus appears that Logan may be credited with the first appreciation of wind pollination. The exact date of this work is not known, but it appears to have been published at the Hague in 1739.

Miller.—The credit for the recognition of insects as an agency in pollination appears to belong to Philip Miller. In 1751 he planted 12 tulips about 20 ft. apart and attempted to prevent fertilization by removing all their stamens as soon as the flowers began to open. Some days later, however, he saw some bees load themselves with pollen at an ordinary tulip bed, fly over to the flowers upon which he had operated, and when they had gone he observed that they had left on the stigmas sufficient pollen for fertilization and these flowers later produced seeds.

Gleditsch.—The argument for the necessity of pollination was clinched by a series of masterly experiments by J. G. Gleditsch in 1749. Gleditsch had already observed that the spores of fungi were disseminated everywhere by the air. He had observed that a female date palm (*Chamaerops humilis*) which had been brought to Berlin from Africa had never been known to produce seed, though it was about eighty years old, and he himself had observed it for 15 years. There was no male tree in Berlin, so he procured part of a male inflorescence from a tree growing in Leipzig which he dusted over the female flowers of the Berlin tree and tied on to the inflorescence. The result was that fruit ripened the following winter and germinated in the spring. Though this was only doing once more what Herodotus had reported the Assyrians as doing in the fifth century B.C., it was the only experimental proof since that of Logan of the sexuality of plants and cleared the ground for Kölreuter and Sprengel.

Kölreuter.—It was about 12 years later that the memorable work of Joseph Gottlieb Kölreuter was done. His report, "Verläufiger Nachricht vom einigen das Geschlecht des Pflanzen betreffenden Versuchen und Beobachtungen," was published in four parts, between the years 1761 and 1766. The work has been summarized for us by Sachs in his history of botany, from which the following account is drawn. Kölreuter recognized the importance of insects in flower pollination. He had observed that many flowers had something within them that was attractive to insects. From this he concluded that flowers which were incapable of pollinating themselves were pollinated by insects. He collected nectar from many flowers and found that upon evaporation it gave a sweet substance like honey; from this discovery he concluded that bees made honey from nectar. In order to discover how effective insects were in the fertilization of flowers, he pollinated 310 with a brush, leaving the same number to be pollinated by insects. The number of seeds formed in the latter case was only a little less than in the former.

His contributions to the morphology of pollen grains were notable, despite the fact that his microscopes were very imperfect. He discovered that the outer covering of pollen grains consisted of two distinct coats and noticed in some species the spines and sculpturing on the outer coat and its elasticity. He observed the orifices and their lids in the exine of pollen grains of *Passiflora*. He noticed that when the grains were made wet the inner coat would protrude through the apertures of these grains, standing out as rounded papillae, which in some cases eventually ruptured and allowed the contents to escape. He correctly interpreted the formation of papillae through the protrusion of the inner coat through the pores as permitting some expansion of the grain without the rupture of the wall. Yet Sachs, in summary, regards this as a mistake on Kölreuter's part, pointing out that these papillae are really the beginnings of pollen tubes of which Kölreuter was unaware. It is true that Kölreuter did not understand the function of pollen tubes in fertilization. It was, perhaps, on this account that he was able to recognize the much more subtle function of the papillae in volume-change accommodation, which is unquestionably a necessary, though perhaps secondary, function, in all those grains which have heavy walls and have no furrows which may accommodate changes in volume.

Gleichen and others thought that the grains contained spermatozoa and must burst to discharge them in order to effect fertilization. But Kölreuter did not regard the bursting of the grains as a natural process, since they obviously possessed devices for its prevention. Instead, he started with the hypothesis that the oil on the surface combined with the moisture of the stigma forming a new substance, in the same way that an acid and an alkali unite to form a salt, and that this substance, if fertilization is to ensue, must be absorbed by the stigma and conveyed through the style to the ovules. But he later abandoned this idea, for experience taught him that if he exchanged the moisture of a stigma for that of an allied species, then dusted the stigma with its own pollen, he got no hybrid.

Kölreuter's most important contribution to the development of the sexual theory was his artificial production of hybrids. He produced hybrids of *Nicotiana, Dianthus, Mathiola, Hyoscyamus,* and others. He showed by experiment that if a stigma received the pollen of its own species and that of another at the same time, only the former is effective, and he drew the logical conclusion that that is why hybrids are rare in nature, though they can easily be produced artificially.

Sprengel and Flower Pollination.—The next important contributions to the sexual theory are the brilliant researches of Konrad Sprengel (1812). He showed that cross pollination was the rule and not the exception and stated that "Since very many flowers are dioecious, and probably at least as many hermaphroditic flowers are dichogamous, Nature appears not to have intended that any flower should be fertilized by its own pollen." Dichogamy, the maturing of the stamens and pistils at different times, had previously been noted by Kölreuter without appreciation of its significance. The importance of insects in pollination was brought out forcibly by Sprengel. He says:

In the summer of 1787 I was attentively examining the flowers of *Geranium sylvaticum,* and observed that the lower part of the petals was provided with slender rough hairs on the inside and on both edges. Convinced that the wise framer of nature produced not a single hair without a definite purpose, I considered what end these hairs might be intended to serve. And it soon occurred to me, that on the supposition that the five drops of juice which are secreted by the same number of glands are intended for the food of certain insects, it is not unlikely that there is some provision for protecting this juice from being spoiled by rain, and that the hairs might have been placed where they are for this purpose. Since the flower is upright, and tolerably large, drops of rain must fall into it when it rains. But no drops can reach one of the drops of juice and mix with it, because it is stopped by the hairs, which are over the juice drops, just as a drop of sweat falling down a man's brow is stopped by the eye-brow and eye-lash, and hindered from running into the eye. An insect is not hindered by these hairs from getting at the juice. I examined other flowers and found that several of them had something in their structure, which seemed exactly to serve this end. The longer I continued this investigation, the more I saw that flowers which contained this kind of juice are so contrived that insects can reach it, but that the rain can not spoil it; but I gathered from this that it is for the sake of the insects that these flowers secrete the juice, and that it is secured against the rain that they may be able to enjoy it unspoilt.

Sprengel noticed that the markings of petals and their colors could serve to guide the insects to where the nectar was. He observed dichogamy in *Epilobium angustifolium* and found that the older flowers were fertilized by pollen brought to them from the younger. He found the same thing in *Nigella* but the opposite in a species of *Euphorbia*. He showed that in protandrous flowers—those in which the stamens mature first—the exact place which was occupied by the stamens is subsequently occupied by the stigma so as to be in position to remove the pollen from the body of an insect which has just left a younger flower. From such observations he concluded that the whole structure of flowers was an adaptation to secure pollination by one or several species of insects.

Sprengel clearly distinguished between anemophily and entomophily. He showed that all flowers "which are without a proper corolla and have no calyx in its place, are destitute of nectar and are not fertilized by insects, but by some mechanical means as by the wind." He also observed that such flowers produced light pollen and in large amounts, while with insect-pollinated flowers the reverse is the case. He showed that all the devices of flowers, whether for insect pollination or for wind pollination, pointed indubitably to the fact that nature avoided, as far as possible, self-pollination. It remained only for Knight, Herbert, and Gärtner to show that crossing of flowers produced more numerous and more vigorous progeny and that repeated self-fertilization led to a weakening of successive generations.

In spite of the many proofs of sexuality in plants, there were still many people who doubted and attacked the theory bitterly.

But Karl Friedrich Gärtner published, in 1849, his "Versuch und Beobachtungen über die Bastardzeungung," a masterly review of the whole subject in all its phases, the result of an investigation which lasted 25 years. This was really the final confirmation of the doctrine of the sexuality of plants so brilliantly initiated by Camerarius.

SHAPES OF POLLEN GRAINS

Francis Bauer.—Returning to the morphology of pollen grains, which we left with the brilliant researches of Grew and Malpighi to trace the development of the sexual theory, we find the next important work to be that of Francis Bauer, the artist. Unfortunately, however, most of Bauer's work was never published and consequently had no effect on the development of the science. Many years after Bauer's death we find investigators rediscovering certain points showing themselves to be in complete ignorance of others which were well known to him. He had seen and drawn well-developed pollen tubes, probably before the close of the eighteenth century, yet Amici is credited with their discovery in 1830. Of course it is far from certain that Bauer understood the function of pollen tubes because he wrote nothing about them. He recognized the extent to which family likenesses are borne by pollen grains and other points which were not cleared up until nearly half a century later. I believe that if Bauer's work could have been published during his lifetime, the science of pollen morphology would now be considerably in advance of what it is today.

The greater part of Bauer's work is bound in a single volume at the British Museum (Natural History) at South Kensington. This work consists of numerous drawings, illustrating more than 175 species, in 120 genera and 57 families. All except a few of these are in the form of pencil sketches in an unfinished condition and with no verbal description. Most of the figures are small and crowded together on sheets of cross-section paper which was obviously used as a scale of dimensions and which he varied to suit the size of the grains being depicted. The whole appearance of the unfinished sketches suggests great haste; only the essential features are recorded and the name, with occasionally a word or two about the color. Nevertheless, the sketches are surprisingly accurate, and the fact that Bauer was generally able so readily to single out the essential features shows that he had an understanding of pollen morphology far in advance of his time. His method of working appears to have been to sketch the grains as circumstances afforded opportunity, probably in connection with his illustrations of the plants themselves drawn for other purposes, for there is no order in their arrangement. It was apparently his intention to redraw these with all their details at a later date. This was, however, fulfilled in only a very few cases. But there are in the collection a few finished drawings, and these are of great beauty, clarity, and accuracy of detail and frequently colored. They are much larger than the sketches and usually drawn only one to a page.

On account of the inaccessibility and great interest to all students of pollen morphology which attach to the drawings of Bauer's, most of the species represented in his collection in the British Museum have been classified and listed below. The time when Bauer made the drawings is not exactly known, for none bears a date. But the evidence of the few drawings of this kind which were published in connection with his illustrations of plants suggests that the work extended over a long period of time, possibly the greater part of Bauer's stay at Kew, from 1790 until his death in 1840.

LIST OF POLLEN SPECIES SKETCHED BY BAUER

Coniferae
Pinus uncinata
　　nigra
　　sp.

Araceae
Arum Colocasia

Commelinaceae
Tradescantia sp.

Liliaceae
Lilium tigrinum
　　bulbiferum
　　candidum
Asphodelus hirsutus
Brodiaea congesta
Yucca gloriosa

Amaryllidaceae
Hemerocallis caerulea
　　　　　sp.

Amaryllis sp.

Iridaceae
Sisyrinchium californi-
　　cum
Tigridia Pavonia

Musaceae
Musa rosacea

Cannaceae
Canna indica

Orchidaceae
Ophrys nyodes
　　　Nidus-avis
　　　apifera
Orchis mascula
　　　maculata
Listera ovata
Epipactus pallens
　　　palustris

Cymbodium aloëfolium
Neottia sp.
Limodorum sp.
Epidendron elegans
Gymnadenia confusa
Cryptostylis sp.

Proteaceae
Banksia speciosa
　　media
　　ericaefolia
　　Cunninghamii
　　marginata
Dryandra formosa
　　floribunda
Leucadendron grandi-
　　florum
Protea sp.
Hakea acicularis

Aristolochiaceae

List of Pollen Species Sketched by Bauer.—(*Continued*)

Aristolochia Sipho

Amaranthaceae
Amaranthus caudatus

Caryophyllaceae
Dianthus barbatus

Nymphaeaceae
Nymphaea advena

Magnoliaceae
Magnolia grandiflora
   glauca

Ranunculaceae
Anemone hortensis
Caltha palustris

Berberidaceae
Berberis asiatica

Papaveraceae
Eschscholtzia califor-
   nica

Fumariaceae
Fumaria parviflora
   sp.

Cruciferae
Arabis alpina

Saxifragaceae
Hydrangea hortensis
Ribes sp.

Rosaceae
Geum chiloënse
Agrimonia mexicana

Mimosaceae
Mimosa pudica
Acacia ciliata
   marginata
   longifolia
   sp.

Leguminosae
Lupinus luteus
   sp.
Lathyrus odoratus
Erythrina laurifolia
Pisum nigrum

Geraniaceae
Pelargonium sang-
   guinium
   inguinalis
   sp.
Geranium Robertianum
Oxalis Bowiei

Tropaeolaceae
Tropaeolum majus

Polygalaceae
Polygala sp.

Malvaceae
Althaea rosea
Malva aphila
   sylvestris

Hypericaceae
Hypericum calycinum

Violaceae
Viola tricolor
   odorata

Passifloriaceae
Passiflora sp.
   quadrangu-
      laris
   minima
   lunata
   holosericea
   Herbertiana
   serrata

Thymelaeaceae
Pimelea decussata

Melastomaceae
Melastoma sp.

Begoniaceae
Begonia hirusta
   nitida

Combretaceae
Combretum purpureum
   sp.

Myrtaceae
Eucalyptus pelis-
      siodora

   pulveru-
      lenta
   sp.
Melaleuca fulgens
   pulchella

Onagraceae
Oenothera speciosis-
      sima
   Lindleyana
   densiflora
Clarkia pulchella
   acicularia
Fuchsia coccinea
   sp.
Epilobium palustre

Umbelliferae
Eryngium alpinum

Ericaceae
Andromeda calyculata
   polifolia
   empetri-
      folia
   buxifolia
Kalmia angustifolia
Rhododendron dauri-
   cum
Ledum palustre
Erica media
   discolor
   versicolor

Plumbaginaceae
Statice Armeria

Loganiaceae
Logania floribunda

Asclepiadaceae
Periploca graeca

Convolvulaceae
Convolvulus sepium

Polemoniaceae
Cobaea scandens
Gila tricolor

Boraginaceae
Myosotis scorpioides

LIST OF POLLEN SPECIES SKETCHED BY BAUER.—*(Continued)*

Hookeri sp.	Veronica sp.	Leontodon Taraxacum
		Cichorium Intybus
	Bignoniaceae	Sonchus hispanicus
Verbenaceae	Bignonia sp.	palustris
Lantana trifolia	Capreolata	Doronicum sp.
Verbena (blue)		Gnaphalis sp.
Stachytarpheta muta-	Acanthaceae	Aster fruticulosus
bilis	Thunbergia alata	chinensis
Labietae	Dipsaceae	Madia elegans
Salvia splendens	Scabiosa atropurpurea	Anthemis Cotula
Solanaceae	Cucurbitaceae	Achillea Millefolium
Franciscea calycina	Cucumis sativus	Rudbeckia digitata
	Cucurbita sp.	Dahlia frustranea
Hopeana	Rubiaceae	Cineraria glauca
Solanum nigrum	Oxyanthus speciosus	Gaillardia bicolor
Petunia phoenicea	Manettia sp.	Cladanthus arabicus
Scrophulariaceae		Centaurea cyanus
Calceolaria	Lobeliaceae	Seratula quinquefolia
Verbascum virgatum	Lobelia gigantea	Calendula officinalis
Antirrhinum majus	sp.	Zinnia elegans
Pentstemon sp.	Compositae	Tagetes sp.

Besides these unpublished pollen figures some of Bauer's published drawings of plants are accompanied by figures of their pollen grains. For example, the *Curtis Botanical Magazine* for 1832 carries, as No. 3172, an illustration by Bauer of an orchid, the large-leaved pterostylis (*Pterostylis Banksii*). It consists of a beautiful colored picture of the whole plant, an enlarged flower, enlarged dissections, and a group of seven pollen grains, six in water and expanded and the seventh apparently dry and in air, consequently not expanded. These grains he found to be quite different from those of other orchidaceous plants. Of them he says:

I have now, on the second of May, examined the pollen grains with Ploessel's grand microscope, and to my great surprise, have found a total deviation from those of all the hundreds of specimens of orchidaceous plants I have yet investigated. These grains in their ordinary form consist of three- or four-celled corpuscles. . . . This I consider an important circumstance, and could not be detected by botanists possessed only of a glass of moderate power.

In this connection it is interesting to note that in Bauer's British Museum collection are illustrated grains of 15 species of Orchidaceae and that, of these, all except one (*Epipactis pallens*) are represented as four- or occasionally three-celled.   So one is at a loss to explain his surprise at finding the grains of pterostylis to be three- or four-celled, unless the figures of the British Museum collection were all drawn subsequently to that of pterostylis, which would require the entire collection to have been done during the last eight years of Bauer's life, which seems improbable.   It is true, however, that his figures of the grains of pterostylis do not resemble those of any other orchidaceous plants, nor do they answer his description.

Bauer wrote nothing more about multiple-celled pollen grains, but if one can judge from the mute evidence of his drawings they intrigued him greatly, for among his collection are found far more than the normal proportion of such forms.   Furthermore, those which he chose to draw appear not to have been taken entirely at random but selected rather to cover the whole field of such forms as far as possible, and never did he let an unusual form escape him.   The 16-celled grains of the acacias in their characteristic geometrical arrangement are shown again and again, but along with them are the exceedingly rare forms of *A. ciliata* with 12 cells and of *A. marginata* with 10.   Besides these he showed the 16-celled *Acacia* grains in most of their irregular arrangements. One wonders, in looking over his sketches, if he understood that the normal 16-celled grain possessed its peculiar-looking arrangement because it is made up of four tetrahedral tetrads.   It is likely that he did, for his drawings show that he knew that the grains of *Mimosa*, which is closely related to *Acacia*, occur only in fours—always in tetrahedral tetrads.   He showed in the four-celled grains of *Epilobium palustre* and in 10 different species of Ericaceae that the grains are always four-celled and that the cells are in the tetrahedral arrangement.   In the latter he quite correctly interpreted the furrows, but in neither case does it appear that he understood the spatial relation that the pores of three-pored grains bear to the pores of their three neighbors in such tetrads.   Perhaps the microscope which he praised so highly was not quite equal to the task.   Or was it because his interest in the multiple-celled grains was occupied with the mathematics of their arrangements to such an extent that other details slipped by him?   At any rate, when he came to the four-celled grains of *Periploca graeca* he found and interpreted all the curious arrangements in which these grains occur, but in none

of his numerous drawings of them did he show the germ pores
which face each other across the sutures between the adjoining
cells. He found that the grains of *Oxyanthus speciosus* are in
fours and that those of *Myosotus scorpioides* may be two-celled.
With the consideration therefore, that multiple-celled grains are
relatively scarce among pollen grains in general, it seems that
Bauer must have carefully recorded all such, whenever encountered, on account of an innate interest in the curious. In this he
expressed a scientific curiosity scarcely at all appreciated in his
day, for his contempories seem to have regarded him always as
Francis Bauer the Artist, paying scant heed to Francis Bauer the
Scientist.

This is interestingly brought out in the many illustrations
which Bauer made in fulfillment of his office of "botanical
painter to His Majesty, George III." His floral dissections which
accompany these pictures, besides being works of art, are scien-
tifically accurate, and with many of the illustrations he showed
the pollen grains as with his pictures of pterostylis. This plan
of showing figures of the pollen grains along with each species
illustrated was not new with Bauer. It had already been
adopted by William von Gleichen in "Das Neueste aus dem
Reiche der Pflanzen," in 1764. Gleichen always showed his
pollen grains in a circular inset, one-half of each grain drawn in
its dry condition and the other in its wet condition, which
showed that he understood the difference between the two and the
importance of recognizing both. Unfortunately, however,
Gleichen's figures were not drawn by himself. It is true that
they appear to have been done by an excellent artist, but since, as
Sachs says, microscopic drawings cannot pretend to take the place
of the object itself but are rather intended to show to another
person what passed through the mind of the observer, they fail
in their purpose, appearing merely as unnecessary ornaments.
With Bauer the case was somewhat different, for throughout the
greater part of his career at Kew, Bauer was closely associated
with the great English botanist Robert Brown, since they were
both subsidized in their work by Sir Joseph Banks. And from
this union of an excellent botanist with an inimitable artist of
keen botanical understanding were born some notable results.
Much of Brown's work was illustrated by Bauer. This is true,
for instance, of Brown's memoir "On the Proteaceae of Jussieu,"

which was published in the *Transactions of the Linnaean Society* in 1809. In speaking of the pollen of this family Brown says, "I am inclined to think, not only from its consideration in this family, but in many others, that it [the pollen] may be consulted with advantage in fixing our notions of limits of genera." And he incorporated in his diagnosis of the family a description of the pollen grains: "pollen triangulare, angulis subsecernentibus, quandoque ellipticum v. lunatum raro sphaericum." The figures by Bauer illustrating the triangular, elliptical, lunate, and spherical forms of pollen grains bear out the diagnosis and testify to the value of pollen-grain forms in classification. And one cannot suppress a sigh of regret that the example here so admirably set by Brown and Bauer has not been followed in other taxonomic work.

It is quite plain that in this case the idea of the importance of pollen characters came from Bauer rather than from Brown. As a matter of fact, in some of Brown's publications the work is almost entirely that of Bauer, the name of Brown, the botanist, merely giving botanical sanction to the work of Bauer, the artist. This is true of Brown's report "An Account of a New Genus of Plants Named *Rafflesia*," which was published by Brown in the *Transactions* for 1820 and consists entirely of the beautiful illustrations, one of them colored, by Bauer. In this, however, the pollen grains are drawn with insufficient magnification to show any detail. Perhaps a better example of Bauer's work is found in Brown's report on the fertilization of orchids and milkweeds, published in the *Transactions of the Linnaean Society* for 1833. The chief value of this paper lies in its truly masterly illustrations by Bauer, which are certainly among the best of this great artist's work now extant. Accompanying those of *Asclepias purpurescens* and *A. phytolaccoides* are figures of the dissected flowers and their pollinia. These latter are shown in their various stages of development, in their ordinary condition of maturity and germinating, both on the stigma and in vitro. His figures of the germinating pollinia with the pollen tubes streaming out, one from each pollen cell, are marvels of beauty and accuracy and would do credit to any textbook of botany today. Brown tells us that when he discovered, in 1830, the significance of the pollinia of the milkweeds, he communicated his findings to Bauer and found that Bauer had already (in 1805) discovered and illustrated the germination of these pollinia but kindly permitted Brown to use the illustrations. The keen understanding shown in this work shows that Bauer the botanist was the peer of Bauer the artist, who was recognized by all as supreme.

The story of Bauer's life is simply and beautifully told in the epitaph on his tomb in the church at Kew where he lived and did his work. It reads:

In memory of Francis Bauer, Esq., F. R. S., F. L. S. &c., Botanical Painter to His Majesty George III, and resident draughtsman for fifty years to the Royal Botanic Gardens at Kew, where he devoted himself to the advancement of natural science; under the munificent patronage of Sir Joseph Banks, Bart., the president of the Royal Society. In the delineation of plants he united the accuracy of a profound natural- ist with the skill of an accomplished artist, to a degree which has only been equalled by his brother Ferdinand. In microscopical drawing he was altogether unrivalled, and science will be ever indebted for his elaborate illustrations of animal and vegetable structures, of which invaluable specimens are preserved at the British Museum and in the University of Göttingen. He was born at Felsperg in Austria, on the 4th. of October 1758 and accompanied his friend the Baron Joseph Jacquin to England in 1788. He settled at Kew in 1790 where he lived admired, loved and respected. He died on the 11th. of December 1840, aged 82 years. The *works* of Francis Bauer are his best *monument*. Friendship inscribed this record on his honoured tomb.

Before Bauer's death there had already appeared a sudden burst of interest in pollen morphology. Almost every botanist of note was intrigued by it, and his interest held for a little time. This was probably due to the fact that the period at the beginning of the century was marked by great improvement in the micro- scope. "In 1824 Selligue exhibited to the Academy of Paris an excellent microscope with double lenses, several of which could be screwed on one over the other, with a magnifying power of five hundred times; in 1827 Amici made the first achromatic and aplanatic objectives with three double lenses screwed on one over the other," and it was about this time that the microscopes by Ploessel referred to by Bauer were made. Sachs in his history of botany says, "How rapid the progress was before and after 1830 is shown by comparing von Mohl's work on climbing plants of 1827 and its antiquated illustrations, with his publica- tions of 1831 and 1833, when the figures have a thoroughly modern appearance."

Of the investigators following Bauer a few stand out for their contributions to the morphology of pollen grains; Purkinje, von Mohl, Mirbel, Fritzsche, and Meyen. The pollen works of these were produced more or less simultaneously between the years 1830 and 1839, so that it is difficult for the chronicler to present them in their proper order. The work of all except Purkinje has a decidedly modern aspect. Purkinje, whose work slightly antedates those of the others, appears, therefore, to have been unable to avail himself of the most recent improvements in the microscope. Nevertheless, his observations and interpretations are so far in advance of those of his predecessors

that he must needs be credited with a large share in the advances made, though they were so soon to be eclipsed by those of von Mohl and Fritzsche. Purkinje's work on pollen appeared in 1830 while that of von Mohl appeared five years later, and that of Fritzsche in several parts was given to the world 4 to 7 years later.

Johannes Evangelista Purkinje.—On account of his Bohemian birth and isolated position in the scientific world, the works of Purkinje, who was born in 1787 in the village of Libochowitz on the Elbe, are but little known. During his lifetime they did not have the effect upon the general current of scientific thought to which their originality and keen understanding entitled them.

FIG. 6.—Johannes Evangelista Purkinje, by Joseph Mánes. *Reproduced from the Scientific Monthly by kind permission of Dr. Victor Robinson.*)

Likewise his work on pollen is entirely unaffected by the hot disputes that were being carried on in France, Italy, and England. But he was not born in a peasant hut, as has sometimes been stated. He was born in the castle of Baron Herberstein for whom his father was agricultural official.

The young Purkinje attended school in his native village, going later to the Piarists in Moravia where he studied philology. Upon his graduation he entered the order of the Piarists as a teacher of ancient languages. Later he went to Prague, his native capital, where he occupied himself with literature and teaching, and in 1819 at the age of thirty two he turned to the study of medicine. In this he specialized in physiological optics, graduating with a thesis on the subjective aspects of vision. His thesis was read by Goethe at Weimar, and so impressed was the great German poet with the rare scientific ability of its author that a lasting friendship grew up between the two men, a friendship which shaped the whole subsequent career of Purkinje, for when he applied for the chair of physiology at Breslau it was through the influence of Goethe, coupled with that of Alexander von Humboldt, that he was successful in his candidacy in 1823.

At Breslau he found himself in a decidedly hostile and unsympathetic atmosphere. When he required a microscope the idea was scoffed at. For, why should a physiologist need a microscope? He was forced to carry on his experiments in an unequipped corner of the laboratory, and later he even found it necessary to transfer them to his own home. In the meantime his classes dwindled away. But it was amidst such surroundings that Purkinje did his greatest work. Gradually, however, his exceptional attainments became recognized at Breslau. Students began coming again to his classes, and later the Prussian government erected for him a building devoted exclusively to physiology, which was opened in 1839 as the first Physiological Institute. But these latter years at Breslau were for Purkinje largely sterile of scientific achievement.

In 1850 he returned to Prague as professor of physiology. His return to his native country was celebrated not alone in Prague but throughout the provinces, and the government gave him a splendid laboratory with a capable assistant and adequate salary; here he remained until his death in 1869. But these years, though supplied with everything that he needed, like his latter years at Breslau, were without notable contributions to science. It was amidst the hostile surroundings during earlier days at Breslau and with improvised apparatus that his greatest work was done. His biographer, Dr. Robinson, says, "It is the glory of Purkinje that he holds a foremost place among the investigators who found physiology a speculative subject and left it an experimental science."

Purkinje was primarily a physiologist. His first work was in physiological optics. His method of lighting the retina, his measurements of the lens and cornea, and measurements of the refracting surfaces of the eye made the ophthalmoscope of Helmholtz possible. He studied fingerprints and was the first to recognize their permanent and distinguishing character. He will always be remembered for the Purkinjean nerve cells which form a characteristic feature of the cerebellum and for the Purkinjean fibers of the cardiac muscle. In botany he introduced the terms *cambium* and *protoplasm* and others. And, before Schleiden and Schwan, he taught that organs consist of cells and nuclei. But, like most investigators of first rank, he conducted many minor researches, and among them was his study of pollen grains.

Purkinje's work on pollen is embodied in the single volume "De cellulis antherarum fibrosis nec non de granorum pollinarum formis, commentationis phytotomica," Breslau (1830). The first part of this work is devoted to a profusely illustrated discussion of the microscopic appearances of anther walls, in which he attempted to bring out their specific differences, a subject which appears never to have been adequately studied since. The second part of the book, entitled "De formis granorum pollinis relate ad familias naturales adnota nonulla," begins his discussion of the pollen grains of the same species of which he had studied the microscopic characters of the anthers.

In the preliminary discussion he tells us that the forms of pollen grains may be spherical or triangular and all in between and that these forms are distributed among the most diverse families so that some have one form, some another, and other families both. He then proceeds to characterize the pollen grains of the different families. Grains, simply smooth spheres, he says, are encountered in the Alismaceae and, principally so, in the Gramineae and Juncaceae and many others which he names. Smooth spheres and oblong spheres are found in the aroids, Iridaceae, etc., also the primitive asclepiads. But in the cucurbits and Malvaceae they are hispid spheres. The characteristic forms of many groups are thus given, and when families cannot be so characterized he gives the forms by genera, pointing out that the basic characters of pollen grains may be family or generic. And, while he never attempted to construct a key for identification, as most subsequent investigators have done, in his classification of the characters of pollen grains he provided the materials for such a key. His recognition of the characters of pollen grains possessing phylogenetic distribution was a decided step in advance of his predecessors.

His descriptions show that he examined his pollen grains in the moist and expanded condition, yet in none of his figures are the grains burst or extruding their contents, as they are in most of those of Bauer. It therefore appears that Purkinje had found a suitable technique for expanding the grains without bursting them, and it is quite evident that he regarded this as the proper condition to reveal their characters. He had at his disposal methods of preparing them in a dry condition had he wished to do so; indeed, he was the discoverer of the use of balsam as a mounting medium, and it is known that in technical ability he was unsurpassed in his time.

Purkinje believed that the various forms of pollen grains were largely the result of their development while in contact with each other in the anther sac. If we look into the beginning of pollen grains, he says, we find that in the anthers while still in the bud they are generally appressed tetrahedral but that when their surrounding pressure is released they expand into spheres, or, if the pressure is longer continued and with less loosening, they keep their tetrahedral form. Compound grains remain in the condition in which they were in the bud. He believed that the positions of both the protuberances and the pores of the grains, which he calls *hila*, are the result of the contact and pressure relations of the grains with each other. The spines, etc., of rough or hispid grains, he states, are merely strongly developed intercellular fibrillae. In his study of the pollen of the passion flower he described the large, operculate pores, stating that the opercula are nothing but the sides of a plane tetrahedron, presumably arising from its tetrahedral contacts with the neighboring grains in the anther. And in other grains which do not have opercula, these contact points, when the grains are torn apart, leave weakened spots through which the inner coat bulges out, forming the familiar germinal papillae. That such is actually the case with the spores of some fungi has recently been shown by B. O. Dodge. And with pollen grains it is true that of those which have their pores or furrows in the trischistoclasic system the system is generally, if indeed not always, initiated by just such contacts with two or three of the neighboring cells of the tetrad. Purkinje's statement is as close to the actual truth as he could possibly have come in the light of the then current cytology. Undoubtedly the whole truth of the situation would have been clear to him had the karyokinesis of the reduction divisions of pollen mother-cells been then understood.

Purkinje made the first attempt to build up a system of nomenclature for the description of pollen grains. His terms generally clearly and accurately described the structures to which they were applied, and many of them are so appropriate that they might be advantageously adopted even today. The germ pores he called hila, apparently borrowing the term from the name denoting the point of attachment of a seed to its pod, having in mind the former attachment which he believed the grains to have had with each other in the anther, for he knew quite well that pollen grains are never attached to their anther sacs in the way that seeds are attached to their placenta. In some ways this term is fully as good as the modern term germ pore, which is faulty because it draws attention to only one function of the pore—a function which only one pore in a grain generally serves—and so directs attention away from an equally important function, that of volume-change accommodation, a function which generally requires more than one pore or furrow in each grain. When the pores are surrounded by a thickening, as in the grains of *Nerium*, Purkinje called them halonate; when borne on horn-like projections, as in the grains of *Oenothera*, he called them corniculate; when sunken in pits, as in the grains of *Tilia*, he called them pariform. The pine grains, with their lateral bladders, he called myocephalic; and the grains of *Saxifraga* he described as meridionate, yet even today writers frequently describe the meridionally arranged furrows of such grains as parallel, which, of course, is self-contradictory when used in connection with a sphere. Such grains as those of the mints, which have banded furrows, he called zonate. The compound grains he described as conglobate, which is perhaps a more appropriate term than the current word compound, for it clearly designates an assemblage of *individuals*. It also has a variety of convenient usages which the other has not; for example, if there were three grains joined together, which he stated to be the case with the Epacridaceae, he described them as triglobate; or if four are joined together, as with the grains of *Bignonia* and *Catalpa*, he described them as "grana quaterne conglobata." Of the *Acacia* grains he says that there are 6, 7, 8 or, more frequently, 16 "in orbicula conglobata." Purkinje's system of nomenclature deserved much more attention than was ever given to it by subsequent investigators. A system of this kind, had it been put into use, would have saved much confusion, for to give a thing a name is to recognize its existence, thereby directing attention to it—the first and most essential step toward its explanation. These are only a few of his terms, but the fact that he felt the need of them shows that he saw clearly and that the characters of pollen grains and their significance had for him a vivid reality. This we may regard as Purkinje's great contribution to the morphology of pollen grains.

Purkinje's botanical work is curiously detached and self-sufficient, as if he were a lone invader of the botanical field. This, as we have already seen, was due to his geographically isolated position. As a matter of fact, the time when Purkinje's paper on pollen was published was a period of unprecedented botanical activity, and, though we find no contributions of a purely morphological character before von Mohl and Fritzsche in 1832–1837, there were many investigations on pollen which, while centering mainly on the problem of fertilization, had a profound effect upon the development of our science. We must, therefore, digress a moment and examine some of these.

"FERTILIZING" GRANULES

Needham (1740) had discovered that many pollen grains, upon being brought into contact with water, expand, extruding papillae at their pores, and eventually burst, discharging their contents. The contents, consisting of a viscous fluid charged with granules, he believed to be the fertilizing material, supposing that, in nature, when discharged on the stigma, the granules made their way through channels in the style to the ovules. An entirely different view was held by Kölreuter (1761), who believed pollen grains to consist of a cellular core covered by a thin, delicate inner membrane and a tough, elastic outer coat. The bursting of the latter in contact with water he regarded, as we have seen, as unnatural and guarded against in nature by the extreme elasticity of the inner coat, which could bulge through the pores as the grain expanded and so act as safety valves to keep the grain from bursting. The fertilizing substance, he thought, was secreted from the pollen grains in the form of the oily fluid commonly found on the surface and was required to mingle with a similar secretion from the stigma to form a new substance which flowed through the style to the ovule where it initiated the formation of the embryo. This view, of the combining of two substances on the stigma, however, he later retracted, finding that it was irreconcilable with the facts revealed by his experiments in hybridization.

Baron von Gleichen Russworm, in "Das Neueste aus dem Reiche der Pflanzen" (1764), attacked Kölreuter on all points and stated that the granules which Needham had observed pollen grains to discharge, upon being immersed in water, moved like animate bodies. He therefore considered that they were endowed with life and were comparable to animal spermatozoa. He thought that one of these entered the ovule and became the embryo. This was in conformity with the current theory of "evolution" and was really a modification of that theory as put forward by Moreland in 1702, who believed that the pollen grain contained the embryo and that the whole grain must pass from the stigma through a tube in the style to the embryo sac where it became implanted. This theory, as stated later by Christian Wolff (1723), hypothesized the presence of embryos borne by the sap throughout the plant, eventually becoming lodged at the leaf bases to form buds or at the base of the stem to form bulbs—so why not in the pollen grains, eventually to be implanted in the embryo sac, to form seeds? The bursting of the pollen grains with the emission of granules which appeared to be endowed with independent movement, to Gleichen, was evidence that the pollen grain contained not one but many such prospective embryos.

The matter was studied by Turpin (1820), who was the first to draw attention to the formation of the pollen tube. He stated that the pollen wall consisted of two layers which he called the exhymenium and the endhymenium (*exhyménie* and *endhyménie*) and that the fertilizing fluid or fovilla is contained within the latter. When such a pollen grain is placed in water the outer membrane ruptures, and the inner extends, forming a thin-walled intestinal-like tube bearing the fertilizing fluid from the grain. Soon this tube, he said, breaks up, and the fluid is discharged bearing its excessively small granules, which are endowed with independent movement and are comparable to animal spermatozoa. It is not entirely certain if what Turpin saw was really a pollen tube, or if it was just the contents of the pollen grain streaming out into the water and assuming the form of a tube.

To Giovanni Battista Amici, professor of mathematics at Modena in 1824 more properly belongs the credit for the discovery of the *pollen tube.* He appears to have first appreciated its significance, though his remarkable discovery was made quite by accident. He had found that the stigma of *Portulaca oleracea* was covered with hairs which contained granules, and he wanted to see if they moved as he had seen similar granules move in the cells of *Chara;* he found that they did. His statement of the way in which they move is meticulously concise and accurate, contrasting sharply with the statements of most authors of the time, and, therefore, immediately commands respect. Repeating the observation, he accidentally found a hair with a pollen grain attached, and while he was watching the movements of the granules in the hair, the pollen grain suddenly split open and sent out a kind of tube which was somewhat transparent. Growing along the side of the hair, it entered the tissue of the stigma. He described it as a simple tube filled with granules which circulated in and out of the grain. This, he found, continued for nearly three hours, ending in the disappearance of the granules, but he was not able to tell whether they returned to the grain, entered the stigma, or dissolved away bit by bit. He allows the reader to infer, however, that the prolific humor or fertilizing fluid was carried into the stigma by the pollen tube, for he states that Kölreuter and Gärtner believed that the splitting open of a pollen tube is an unnatural process, the result of an excess of moisture, and that the prolific humor, residing on the inside of the inner elastic membrane, filters through only bit by bit. "We have, therefore," Amici says, "observed an exception to their opinion in the pollen of *Portulaca oleracea.*" One wonders if he really regarded the behavior of the pollen of *P. oleracea* as an exception or as an example of the rule itself.

In following the story of pollen morphology through this period, one wonders at how firmly the belief in the independent

existence of spermatic granules, animalcules, or plant spermatozoa, as they were called, had become entrenched in men's
minds. But no less curious were some of the beliefs entertained
regarding the structure of the grain itself, as bit by bit its structure became revealed. The two layers of the wall and their
remarkable differences from each other had become generally
accepted, though Gleichen (1764) and Hedwig still believed that
there was only one layer in the wall. As we have seen, Robert
Brown, in generalizing the form of the grains of the Proteacea,
says that they are triangular with secreting angles, which
compensate for the lack of secretion of the stigma.

Guillemin.—It is unfortunate that Brown mistook the
germinal papillae, which bulge prominently from the germ pores
in these grains, for glands, for the idea was picked up and extended
by Jean Baptiste Guillemin (1825), who, in his "Recherches
microscopiques sur le pollen," based a classification of pollen on
their supposedly secreting organs. He said that pollen grains
derive their color from a sticky fluid on the surface, which might
be mistaken for an outer coat but may be removed by alcohol, for
it is only the product of the papillae, mammillae, and other projections of the outer membrane, which are in reality organs of
secretion. Some grains, like those of *Cobaea scandens*, which
we now know are coarsely reticulate and covered with an abundance of oil, he described as cellular and having a nipple in each
cell secreting the viscous material. This type of grain he
consequently called mammillary. He classified pollen grains
"according to the presence or absence of secreting organs" as
viscous and nonviscous. The former class he divided according
to the nature of the supposed secreting organs, whether they were
papillae or mammillae. These groups he further divided according to the number and arrangement of the secreting organs. The
echinate grains of the Compositae he characterized as papillate;
and the lophate grains of the Cichorieae as having facets or
flattened mammillae (*mamelons*), taking exception, in this, to the
descriptions of Mirbel and Amici who had already more nearly
correctly described grains of this character. The latter author,
in a short paragraph appended to the story of his observation
of the germinating pollen grain of *Portulaca oleracea*, had stated
that the grains of *Cichorium Intybus* were spheroidal, with faces
corresponding to those of the pentagonal dodecahedron, a

statement which, though not entirely correct, is much closer to an actual expression of fact than that of Guillemin.

Perhaps the most interesting part of Guillemin's paper is his description of the response of pollen grains to moisture, for the phenomenon is but little known and scarcely at all understood even today. He says, "All smooth, nonviscous elliptical pollen grains, in contact with water, absorb this fluid almost instantly (never later than a second) by a suture or longitudinal cleft by which they are marked. A rapid movement of separation is seen in this suture; the grain swells and becomes perfectly spherical." This is an accurate description of what takes place in practically all pollen grains which are provided with germinal furrows, but it is not necessarily confined to nonviscous, smooth grains.

Brongniart.—The remarkable discovery of Amici and the curious conception prevalent at this time regarding the spermatic granules and the secreting glands of pollen grains excited the interest of the young botanist Adolph Brongniart, who undertook to straighten out the problem of fertilization in flowering plants. How comprehensive his study was intended to be may be seen from the following problems which he set himself: (1) the structure and development of pollen; (2) the interaction of pollen and the stigma; (3) the means of communication between the stigma and ovule; (4) the structure of the ovule; (5) the introduction of the fertilizing substance into the ovule; (6) the development of the ovule and its interaction (*rapport*) with its surrounding tissue. His paper was read before the Paris Academy of Sciences in 1826 and published a year later as "Mémoire sur la génération et le développement d'embryon dans les végétaux phanérogamiques" (1827). How successful he was in convincing the academy that he had solved all these problems is seen by the fact that they awarded him the prize for experimental physiology.

He accepted the current conception of a pollen grain as a vesicle filled with fine granules which escape from it when moistened. He was at first unable to decide whether the granules are absorbed by the grain during its development or are generated within but concluded that they are most likely absorbed and that in the grains of *Oenothera* the angles with their bulbous projections are absorbing organs and not, as Brown

had said, organs for secreting oil. In fact, he states that all
pores and furrows, whatever their form, are organs for absorbing
the pollen granules during development and for their emission
at maturity. The walls of the grain he described as consisting
of two layers, of which the outer is thick and often cellular, as,
for example, in those of *Cobaea*, *Ipomoea*, *Datura*, and *Mirabilis*,
mistaking in these the reticulate surface pattern for cells. He
repeated the experiments which Amici had done with the pollen
of *Portulaca;* he found that he was able to get pollen tubes in
the same way from all kinds of pollen, and he saw clearly that
an extension of the inner coat covered the tube as it grew out.
He found that some grains, such as those of *Oenothera*, put forth
tubes from two or more of their pores. The tubes, he thought,
bore the spermatic granules which he considered to be the most
important part of the grain and undoubtedly analogous to animal
spermatozoa because they appeared to have an independent
movement. He found that their movements were slowed down
by lowering the temperature, and this, in turn, he considered
to be the cause of the inability of some plants to set seed in
cold weather. Also, he found that the granules were of different
sizes and shapes in different species. He undertook to measure
them, in spite of their extremely small size, and furnished tables
of their measurements in many different species.

Setting himself to the second problem—the action of pollen
on the stigma—he accepted Amici's discovery of the pollen tube
penetrating the stigma, at the same time rejecting the theory of
Kölreuter, Link, and Gärtner, who supposed that fertilization
is accomplished by the slow seepage of a resinous material through
the pollen membrane. But where Amici's observations left off,
Brongniart's imagination carried on. The whole stigma, he
said, is designed to absorb the fertilizing fluid. The stigma is
covered with transparent vesicles, the stigmatic hairs, which in
most cases are prolongations of the cells or vesicles of which the
stigma and style are composed. The pollen tube or spermatic
tubule, as he called it, penetrates deeply into the tissue of the
stigma, becoming expanded at its distal end. At this stage it
may be dissected out. Brongniart's observations and his accurate
figures, if they had stopped here, could have constituted an
important step toward the solution of the problem of fertilization, though but a slight step beyond Amici; but his lively

imagination, ever ready to supply where observation failed, led him to see the pollen tube burst and discharge its vibrating "spermatic granules" among the cells of the stigma and to see them migrate down the whole length of the style and enter the placenta and embryo sac. His illustrations of their progression are quite convincing.

In some kinds of plants, like *Hibiscus* and *Nuphar*, the stigma, he said, is provided with an epidermis which underlies the stigmatic hairs. This epidermis he believed to be a thin homogeneous membrane of a noncellular nature. The pollen grains he found to be caught by the projecting stigmatic hairs which prevent them from coming in contact with the membrane. He said:

It appears to me that in the case of these, the pollen grain sends out from its interior a prolongation of the inner membrane or spermatic sac; this membranous tube applies itself to the epidermis of the stigma, which is equally membranous, the two uniting at their surfaces, thus establishing a direct communication between the spermatic cavity of the grain and the space beneath the epidermis of the stigma, in the same way as between the tubes of such Algae as *Spirogyra* at the time of conjugation. Thus the spermatic granules pass from the pollen grain into the stigma. The spermatic granules themselves then penetrate the stigma and are really the active part in fertilization.

Brownian Movement.—At about the time when this remarkable paper of Brongniart's was being awarded a prize by the Paris Academy of Sciences, Raspail, in his studies of the structure and development of pollen, concluded that movements of the pollen granules were due to external causes, and that they were not endowed with life. The question of this phenomenon was taken up by Robert Brown (1828), who observed the movements of the granules in the pollen of *Clarkia* and satisfied himself that they were not due to extraneous causes, such as evaporation and convection currents, concluding that the movements were inherent in the particles themselves. Having observed this movement in the pollen of most diverse plants, he sought it among the spores of mosses and *Equisetum* and then in the leaves and other parts of plants, finding it just the same. Then he looked in the pollen from herbarium specimens that had been dried for 20 and 100 years. He thought that in the pollen of the old herbarium specimens the movement was a little slower, but he doubted if the particles could live so long, so he examined oölite fossil wood, which could be burned, and found that when he ground it up fine enough the particles vibrated just like those of pollen grains. Then he examined silicified wood and finally stones which bore no fossils, with the same result. From these experiments he came to the conclusion that the vibration of particles was the property of nearly all material of whatever origin but that it was inherent in the particles themselves and not, as Raspail had asserted, due to extraneous causes. It is from these researches of Brown's that the phenomenon—Brownian movement—bears his name. He did not think that the discovery of the almost universal presence of this property militated against the theory of pollen spermatozoa, though, in the meantime, Raspail had brought further evidence in support of his contention that the vibrations of pollen granules were due to external causes and that the particles were not living animalcules.

Raspail's charges were regarded seriously enough by the Paris Academy to cause them to appoint a committee to investigate the phenomenon. The committee consisted of Cassini, Desfontains, Mirbel, and de Blainville. Its report is interesting. Cassini, after summarizing the statements set forth in the memoirs of Raspail, Brown, and Brongniart, expressed the opinion of the committee as follows:

Your commissionaires, after devoting themselves to the observation of the facts with all the care of which they are capable, and discarding from their minds all prejudices, have unanimously agreed with M. Brongniart and M. Brown that the extraneous causes to which M. Raspail attributes the movement of the granules do not have anything to do with it.

On the other hand we recognize with M. Brown that various inorganic substances ground in water, offer, if not always, at least sometimes, bodies of which the size, shape and movement are almost the same as those of the pollen granules: such are the outward appearances. But must it necessarily follow that the inner nature, all the properties and functions, are absolutely the same in these bodies of such diverse origins? This we shall not have the temerity to decide, and cannot with assurance until after much more numerous researches and more profound than those which we have made.

Nevertheless, the committee agreed that the pollen granules pass into the stigma and, traversing the style, accomplish fertilization, as described by Brongniart. As a further expression of their faith in the author of the prize essay, they recommended Brongniart for membership in the Academy.

Brongniart immediately responded with another memoir— "Nouvelles recherches sur le pollen et les granules spermatiques des végétaux" (1828)—reasserting all his claims and stating that pollen granules differ from those of lifeless material in that the former not only move but also change their shape as they do so. Having settled this question to his own satisfaction and to that of the Paris Academy, he made one of the most surprising statements:

> By the action of water or the humidity of the stigma the external membrane [of the pollen grain] *contracts* and pushes out the inner membrane, which emerges as a projection through the pores by which the outer membrane is pierced, causing the formation of one or more tubes which finally burst, setting free the granules which penetrate into the stigma.

It is difficult to understand how Brongniart could have thought that pollen grains behaved in such an anomalous fashion when moistened, for their sudden *expansion* under this condition is one of their most striking characteristics, one that can easily be seen even with low magnification and which had been adequately described by Guillemin three years earlier.

On account of the sanction and acclaim that Brongniart's work received from the Academy, it came to have a profound influence upon the development of the science. In the same year we find Mayen, in his "Anatomische-physiologische Untersuchungen über den Inhalt der Pflanzen-zellen (1828)," making essentially the same statements regarding pollen spermatozoa, and, as we shall see later, even the careful Hugo von Mohl was not entirely immune to Brongniart's influence, though he, from the first, vigorously denied the spermatozoon-like character of the pollen granules.

Amici.—It appears, however, that Amici was not convinced, for we find him two years later (1830) writing a note "sur le mode d'action du pollen sur le stigmate" to Mirbel on the same subject. He says that one can see the circulation of the prolific humor in the pollen tubes of many grains besides that of *Portulaca* in which he had made his original observation, but that it is seen best in the grains of *Hibiscus syriacus*. In these he saw generally

2 or 3 tubes coming out of the grain at the same time and in other species of Malvaceae as many as 20 or 30 from a single grain. He states that the tube or tubes, as the case may be, emerge from the grain and penetrate into the stigma.

This is quite certain and can be shown with many plants: but is the prolific humor passed out in the interstices of the conducting tissue as M. Brongniart saw and drew it, to be next transported right to the ovule, as supposed by that author? No; it is the tube which elongates bit by bit, the whole length of the style and comes in contact with the ovule, to each ovule corresponds a tube.

He says that, of course, the pollen grain could not provide enough nourishment for the tube to traverse the length of the style; therefore it must receive its nourishment from the tissues of the style; but his caution prevented him from committing himself on this point for which he had only indirect evidence. However, he observed that the pollen granules traverse the tube and continue to circulate all the time.

In these few words Amici contributed more toward the development of our science than possibly all other investigators of his period put together. If we are to draw a lesson from this, it is surely that one careful observation, accurately recorded, is worth more than numerous argumentative discussions and that the offering of a prize is not a good way to uncover the truth in a controversial matter.

While these researches were being directed to the discovery of the structure and function of pollen grains, but little was done that was strictly morphological, that is, of a comparative nature, or in the way of furnishing material for a comparative morphology. Kölreuter (1761) had pointed out that plants which are related ordinarily have similar pollen but that as much similarity may sometimes occur among the pollen of plants which are only very distantly related. Brown (1809) set an excellent example in his taxonomic discussions of the Proteaceae by including descriptions of the pollen-grain forms in his diagnoses. Sprengel (1812) announced for the first time that the pollen grains of many dicotyledons have three furrows, a fact the recognition of which is as important in morphology as the discovery by Malpighi of the single furrow among the grains of most monocotyledons. Amici, as we have seen, in 1824 correctly interpreted the form of the grain of *Cichorium Intybus*, describing the faces as corresponding to those of a pentagonal dodecahedron, which, in effect, they do, except that their arrangement is disturbed by the presence of three germ pores. The apparently faceted nature of the grains of the Cichorieae had already been noted by Mirbel, but he had failed to recognize the geometrical relation of the facets to each other. In this respect Amici had a decided advantage in that he was a profound mathematician. Guillemin, in 1825, believed that the forms of pollen grains could be as useful in the classification of plants as the seeds which had been used by Gärtner and Richard. But Guillemin's attempt to classify pollen-grain forms on the ill-conceived basis of the nature and function of what he took to be their secreting glands did not substantiate his contention. Of greater moment was his accurate description of the vicin threads (*fils visqueux*) which he found on the grains of *Oenothera*, the curiously interesting, delicate threads which hold the pollen grains of *Oenothera* and many Ericaceae, etc., together in a cobwebby mass. They have to this day not been satisfactorily explained.

Mirbel.—The next important advance in morphology is that of Charles François Brisseau-Mirbel, in 1833, in his studies of the pollen of *Cucurbita Pepo, Hyoscyamus alba, Cobaea scandens, Passiflora brasiliensis,* and *Lilium superbum.* This work is but little known, because it is appended to his much larger work on *Marchantia polymorpha.* Yet it is the most exhaustive and accurate study of its kind that had been made up to that time. He treated the development of the pollen mother-cells of *Cucurbita* from their first anlaga, and the formation of the tetrads, which must be regarded as the most important advance in this direction since 1820, when Brown and Bauer in their study of *Rafflesia* had discovered that pollen grains were developed in special cells and not just in the anther cavity, as formerly believed and asserted by Turpin in the same year. But of still greater importance were Mirbel's descriptions and figures of the mature grains, for these are accurate and at the same time interpret the meaning of the structures represented. Mirbel had been an artist but was early introduced to the study of botany by Desfontaines, with the result that we find in him that rare combination of artist and scientist which we have already seen produced such remarkable results in Bauer and seems to be essential to the development of a morphological science in its formative stages. The value of correct drawings is generally greatly underestimated, many people even assuming that good photographs must be more reliable.   In making microscopical drawings the eye is compelled to dwell upon the contours and minute detail of the object. At first these appear to be without arrangement, but after the eye has studied them and put them accurately together on paper an underlying plan is revealed, and from the apparent chaos gradually emerges the plan of the whole which may then be resolved into its structural elements.   These may be captured and retained only as dictated to the mind by the trained eye and skillful hand.   As more forms are examined the same structural elements are found to occur again and again in different combinations, and different but related plans are revealed.   In this way the morphological science is built up as a visual structure.   It is only after the units of this structure have become fixed by repeated examination and recording and become accepted by others that they may be given names.   At this stage which is relatively far along in the development of a science, and scarcely yet attained in the development of the morphology of pollen grains, a system of nomenclature may gradually take over a part, at least, of the burden of drawings.   Mirbel had already, in his "Anatomie végétale" (1802), attempted such a system of nomenclature by furnishing a glossary of descriptive pollen terms, but this was destined to fail because it had outrun his knowledge of pollen structures.   And we find him, in his description of the *Cucurbita* pollen grain, making little use of his own glossary, relying, instead, upon his truly superb drawings.   These show the grains unexpanded, expanded with the germinal papillae protruding, and with the wall ruptured so as to display its inner and outer coats

Classifications Based on Pollen Characters.—The first successful use of pollen characters in classification appears to be that of John Lindley in 1830, in his genera and species of orchidaceous plants.   In these the pollen grains are always shed united in masses of varying sizes, shapes, and degrees of compactness. The pollen masses are webby in appearance in some species and waxy in others.   When the latter, they have a sticky gland whereby they may become attached to the bodies of insects. In some species the sticky gland is borne on a long stalk or caudicle, in some on a short stalk, and in others the gland is unstalked. These characters form the basis for the establishment of four tribes in Lindley's monograph. Julius Fritzsche, in his "Beiträge zur Kenntniss des Pollen" (1833), showed for the first time the possibility of classifying pollen-grain forms extending over a large number of families. But his classification, while fairly comprehensive, is entirely artificial. He divided all forms of pollen grains into those with single grains and those with compound grains, which at once splits such families as the Onagarceae, Typhaceae, and Mimosaceae into two, because in each case it is only some of their members which have compound grains. His next divisions were those with furrows and those without. That Fritzsche made no attempt to make his classification approximate the natural system seems evident from this, for the presence of a single furrow in the pollen grains of most monocotyledons and of three in most of the dicotyledons had already been noticed by several authors. This work of Fritzsche's must be regarded as only introductory to his much larger work "Ueber den Pollen," which appeared 4 years later, after the great work of von Mohl's "Ueber den Bau und die Formen der Pollenkörner," which followed closely after Fritzsche's first paper and covered the entire field, giving to pollen morphology, for the first time, the dignity of a science.

Von Mohl.—Born in Stuttgart, Apr. 8, 1805, Hugo von Mohl came of an illustrious family. His father, Ferdinand von Mohl, was a man of great ability and activity and at different times held important political offices. His mother, a daughter of the Finance Minister of Würtemberg, was an accomplished woman, and to her the young Hugo was indebted for much of his early education. He had three brothers—Robert, who became prominent in government service; Julius, an oriental scholar; and Moritz, a political economist.

For 12 years the young Hugo received formal education at the Stuttgart gymnasium, specializing in classical languages; but while there he occupied his leisure in the study of botany and mineralogy, guided somewhat by the botanist Frölich, and in the study of mathematics, especially optics, in which he became remarkably proficient. In 1823 he went to Tübingen to study medicine, graduating in 1828. His father wanted him to adopt medicine as a profession, but he, preferring botany, prevailed upon his father to let him go to Munich where he furthered his botanical studies in the society of Schrank, von Martius, Zaccharini, and Steinheil, devoting himself mainly to a study of the anatomy of palms, ferns, and cycads. In 1832 he became professor of physiology at Bern, and it was while there (1834), at the age of twenty-nine, that he published his, "Über den Bau

Fig. 7.—Hugo von Mohl, after the portrait by Cederquist.

und die Formen der Pollenkörner," his only work devoted entirely to the study of pollen.

In 1835 he returned to Tübingen as professor of botany, succeeding Schübler, where he remained practically continuously till the end of his life, excepting the year 1843 when on account of illness he made a protracted stay in the southern Tirol and in Italy which restored him to health. His constitution was generally rugged and vigorous; he frequently made long collecting trips on foot and was seldom troubled by ill health, except toward the end of his life. He never married. He lived a lonely life but was a cheerful and congenial companion to those who knew him well. He was learned in literature and the arts, except music, for which he had a decided aversion. He died suddenly at Tübingen in 1872 in his sixty-seventh year.

There is an excellent short biography of von Mohl by de Bary in the *Botanische Zeitung*,* with a complete bibliography includ-

* **1872**: 561.

ing 90 citations. This has been translated, slightly abridged and omitting the bibliography, in the *Proceedings of the Royal Society of London.** To this I am largely indebted for the above short sketch.

Von Mohl belongs to the richest period of botanical history and lived in an atmosphere of botanical investigation. He was contemporary with Unger, Schleiden, Hoffmeister, Pringsheim, Nägeli, and others equally illustrious. And it is hard to imagine the development of botany during this period without the firmly laid foundations of von Mohl. It has been said that "to give anything like a full account of von Mohl's writings would be to write a history of vegetable physiology." Yet he never composed a connected account of his subject and published only two books, his "Micrographia" (an introduction to the knowledge and use of the microscope) and the "Vegetable Cell." "His efforts as a writer were confined to monographs usually connected with questions of the day or suggested by the state of the literature. In these he collected all that had been published on some point, examined it critically, and ended by getting at the heart of the question which he then endeavored to answer from his own observations. He was usually satisfied with establishing separate facts and in his conclusions kept as closely as possible to what he had actually seen. In scattered monographs of this kind he treated conclusively all the more important questions of phytotomy. Much of his work is found in the *Botanische Zeitung*, which, with Schlectendahl, he founded in 1843 and in which he maintained a constant and active interest throughout his career.

Though his works dealt principally with the solid framework of plants, they were mainly based upon the cell as the unit of structure. He was the first to take up the view that vessels of wood are made up of cells, having observed for the first time their formation from rows of closed cells. And he was the first to appreciate the significance of the plasma membrane, which he called the "primordial utricle," recognizing, however, that it was of the same substance as the rest of the mucilaginous mass which enclosed the nucleus. He later gave to it the name "protoplasm," adopting Purkinje's name for the formative substance within the eggs of animals and cells of embryos, but von Mohl defined it, distinguishing it from the cell sap, and

* **23**: 61–64, 1875.

showed that it was the substance which contained the chloroplasts and carried out the circulation which had long been observed in plant cells.

On the basis of the structure of cell walls, to which the greater part of von Mohl's work was directed, he worked out a classification of tissues, distinguishing for the first time wood, bast, vascular bundles, etc., thus making possible a comparative anatomy of tissues. The more important of his monographs on these various subjects have been collected and published as "Vermischte Schriften."

All through his career von Mohl was much interested in the microscope and microtechnique. He was able to polish and set lenses, and the modern microscope owes much to him for his inventions and improvements of methods for making microscopical measurements. In his "Micrographia" he gave many practical hints to opticians on the construction of the microscope. No less important were his contributions to microtechnique. It was the custom of his time to crush, tear, or macerate the objects for microscopic observation, but von Mohl introduced the preparation of thin transverse and longitudinal sections. In drawing from the microscope he despised the finished drawing which purports to be an accurate and detailed representation of the object. All his drawings he made himself, contrary to the prevailing custom, and in them he showed only the points under discussion, striving merely to make them expressions of his opinions; in his later works, having gained greater facility and clarity in verbal description, he almost entirely dispensed with illustrations.

The greater part of von Mohl's work on pollen was published as "Über den Bau und die Formen der Pollenkörner" at Bern in 1834, among his earliest works. This publication is now extremely rare and hard to come by, so I have had to content myself with the French extract by Leret (1835). The extract, however, is virtually a complete translation, except that the historical part is abridged and the six plates of the original are reduced to three.

When von Mohl set himself the task of bringing order out of the chaos that existed in men's minds regarding pollen grains, he began by critically reviewing most of the work that had already been written on the subject. Much of this he discredited, but it cannot be said that his pollen work was entirely uninfluenced by current beliefs and theories, though in his later works he gained a notorious independence of thought. It should be said, however, that it was only in his conception of the cellular structure of the pollen wall that he shows any such bias. In this he is a composite of his predecessors, and for this he has been severely criticized by later botanists who came to treat his whole pollen work with scorn, overlooking the great wealth of material that it contains aside from this curious misconception.

Von Mohl approached the study of the morphology of pollen grains imbued with the idea that the outer wall was of a cellular structure. This viewpoint was apparently partly gained from analogy with tissues which he had already been able to prove to be of a cellular nature in most cases. Moreover, Meyen (1828) and others had already stated that the outer coats of such grains as those of *Hemerocallis* and *Amaryllis* were made up of a large number of flattened oil-filled cells. In reality these grains are merely reticulate, the " cells " being the spaces between a system of net-like thickenings which anastomose over the surface of the grain. This bias of von Mohl is one of the very few instances when he allowed a preconceived notion to befog his ordinarily keen powers of intellect and observation. He stated that the cells which make up the outer coat of such grains are five-, six-, or seven-angled like those of ordinary epidermis but very much smaller than any tissue cells. He saw that the dissepiments between them were single-walled, unlike those of tissue cells each of which has its own wall so that the separating partitions between them are double. He found that the walls of these supposed cells were generally thin and smooth and pointed out that they often present the appearance of a network of vessels anastomosing over the surface of the grain and that they were mistaken for such by Kölreuter and Hedwig. But, he pointed out, they do not always have such an appearance, for in the rather exceptional grains of *Cobaea scandens* the walls are thick and appear to be composed of perpendicular fibers. Whatever their form or size, these cells, von Mohl stated, are always filled with a yellow or red oil which he said is not found in noncellular pollen grains. In this von Mohl was obviously following the current opinion, but it appears that his observations did not always bear out this statement, for he goes on to point out that those grains which are not

obviously cellular may be as oily as the others but that they are
generally more or less granular, though the granules are often so
small that they can scarcely be seen even with the best microscope.   These granules, he reasoned, must be in reality minute
cells, because the grains have oil, and the oily material is formed
and retained in the outer wall and is not secreted on to it by
glands or papillae, as asserted by Brown to be the case among
the grains of the Proteaceae.   Indeed, in some grains, like those
of *Pitcairnia latifolia*, he found an actual transition between what
appeared to be an obviously cellular condition at the equator
to a granular condition at the poles.   The granules, he thought,
must, therefore, be the same as the cells, only smaller.

Following the same reasoning and finding transitions from
granular walls to more finely granular, even to completely
homogeneous walls, in such grains as those of *Araucaria*, *Rumex*,
the Boraginaceae, and the Gramineae, he concluded that in the
walls of such grains the cells have so nearly disappeared that the
walls present only little obscure points which, though they can
scarcely be seen, must exist because the walls have a faint yellow
color due to oil which could be produced only by such cells.

Though the outer wall of such grains may often look like the wall of an
ordinary plant cell [he says], the comparison of the external membrane
with that of a vegetable cell is entirely inexact, and one should regard it
as an organ composed of cells or rudiments of cells and a homogeneous
element which unites them and, for that reason, compare it not with the
simple membrane of a tissue cell but with such compound membranes,
as, for example, the membrane of the ovule.

Carrying on this reasoning, he fell into the error which he had
condemned in Brown and tells us that the appendages of the
external membrane, such as the spines and papillae, are really
excessively developed cells which appear to exude oil at their
points in the same way that glandular cells do on other parts
of the plant and that that is the reason why spiny and papillate
grains are generally more oily than those which are smooth.
But he correctly points out that this is not a universal correlation,
as supposed by Guillemin, for some grains are spiny and have
little oil, while others lacking spines have an abundance of oil,
and, strange as it may seem, he attributes Guillemin's failure to
observe this to his failure to recognize the cellular nature of the

membrane in some grains and its transition through granular to almost smooth in others. Von Mohl returns to this theme again and again, repeatedly asserting that "the cells, spines and granules of the external membrane ought to be considered as secretory organs and reservoirs of viscous oil." The idea permeates his whole conception of pollen structure. In a less gifted observer it could have rendered his whole work valueless, but in von Mohl it was relatively much less serious. Sachs says of von Mohl, "He generally connected his researches into structural relations with physiological questions; but . . . he never forgot that the interpretations of visible structure must not be disturbed by physiological views. . . . He used his thorough physiological knowledge chiefly to give a more definite direction to his anatomical researches." Never did he let a preconceived notion disturb his vision, as, for example, did Brongniart. Pollen morphology is a descriptive science, so it is much less serious to misinterpret what is seen than to see awry what has previously been misinterpreted, provided that the observations are correctly and accurately reported. Remove this curious misconception from von Mohl's pollen work, and we have a reliable and accurate guide which could serve us today in almost all other particulars, so it will pay us to pursue the work further.

Regarding the pores, he says, in the grains of some species they occur one in each furrow. In grains without furrows they occur sometimes on the equator, sometimes regularly and sometimes irregularly arranged. As for the shape of the pores, he points out that they are usually round; but those that are situated on the equator are often elongate. "Are these pores real openings," he says, "or are they thinner spots in the membrane like the pores of cellular tissue? This is a question that I cannot answer for the smallest pores, but when they are larger I have been able to convince myself, by separating the membranes, that they are not real openings but are closed by a membrane which is generally thin." In some species he found the pore membrane to be thicker even than the external membrane of the rest of the grain. Such, for example, is the case with the grains of squash, passionflower, and others in which the pore is really closed by a little lid which is pushed to one side or up on top of the tube as it emerges. Often the pore is surrounded by a halo, he points out, which may be less distinctly granular than the rest of the grain. The halo is generally round, but in the grains in which the pores are hidden in the furrows the pore may be surrounded by an elliptical halo, transversely arranged and often longer than the width of the furrow.

Regarding the origin of pollen, von Mohl tells us that the grains are borne in cells, nearly always four in each. "One sees the granular contents of the cells parted into four little masses; in consequence of development, these masses are replaced by four grains of pollen which adhere more or less strongly to each other. Later the grains separate and, finally when the cells which contained them have disappeared, remain free in the cavity of the anther." He also noticed that the arrangement of the four cells was sometimes according to the four angles of a tetrahedron and sometimes all in one plane; in the dicotyledons tetrahedral in all species which he had observed, but in the monocotyledons he found them arranged both ways. Though this is not the whole story, it is a remarkable advance over Brown's discovery in 1820 that pollen grains were formed in special cells.

The greater part of von Mohl's study of pollen grains is presented in the form of a descriptive classification of their forms. I have reproduced this here in an abbreviated form, because, though written 100 years ago, it still has value and has never been really superseded.

VON MOHL'S CLASSIFICATION

A. Coat of a single membrane—Asclepiads.
B. Coat of two membranes
   † Furrows and pores absent
       i. Surface granular—*Calla, Crocus, Sagittaria, Ranunculus,* etc.
       ii. Surface papillate—*Canna, Gaertnera paniculata, Bauhinia,* etc.
       iii. Surface cellular—*Phlox, Ruellia, Aleurites,* etc.
          Derivative forms—grains in fours
            a. Tetrads in one plane—*Apocynum, Vellosia, Periploca.*
            b. Tetrads tetrahedral—*Juncus, Luzula.*
    †† Longitudinal furrows present
       A. Furrow one (most Monocotyledons)
          I. Surface granular, without adornments
            a. Furrow membranes (*Streifen*) granular—many Monocotyledons and *Myristica.*
            b. Furrow membranes smooth—Monocotyledons, *Ginkgo, Liriodendron,* and *Magnolia.*
          II. Surface granular, with spines—*Nymphaea alba, N. advena*

   III. Surface cellular—Hemerocallis and other Monocotyledons

   IV. Surface reticulate—*Alstroemeria.*

   Derivative forms, grains united in fours—Orchids.

B. Furrows two—*Cypripedium, Amaryllis, Calceolus, Pontederia cordata, Tamus, Dioscorea, Tigridia, Watsonia, Micranthus, Calycanthus* (rare and always flat with the furrows on the edges).

C. Furrows three, longitudinal

   I. Surface granular, furrow membranes granular—Several Dicotyledons.

   II. Surface granular, furrow membranes smooth—*Lacis fucoides, Balanophoreae,* Cynomorium. *Nelumbo* and many other Dicotyledons, the commonest form.

D. Furrows more than three

   I. Furrows four—*Houstonia, Sideritis, Cedrela, Platonia, Blackwellia,* and many others which are normally three-furrowed.

   II. Furrows six—Some Labaetae, Ephedra, *Sanguisorba,* Passiflores.

   III. Furrows many—Rubiaceae, *Penaea, Sesamum.*

   Derivative forms:—(*a*) form of *Pinus* (intermediate between the one-furrowed Monocots and the three-furrowed Dicotyledons). (*b*) Form of *Lotus.* (*c*) Form of *Poinciana.* (*d*) Pollen prismatic—*Tropeolum majus, Ximensia.* (*e*) form of *Loranthus.* (*f*) Polyhedral, such as *Corydalis, Fumaria, Clerodendron, Rivina.* (*g*) Spiral:—*Thunbergia, Mimulus, Hypericum.*

††† Outer coat with pores

   Primitive forms:—

A. One pore—Gramineae, Cyperaceae, *Typha angustifolia, Spargainum, Restio, Cecropia, Anona.*

B. Two pores—*Colchicum, Broussonetia* and several Monocotyledons and Dicotyledons.

C. Three pores

   I. Surface granular—*Oenothera,* Amentiferae, Urticaceae and other Dicotyledons.

   II. Surface cellular—many Passiflores.

D. Four pores

   I. Pores on the equator—*Myriophyllum, Boehmeria, Campanula rotundifolia, Trigonia,* etc.

   II. Pores not on the equator, *Passiflora, Impatiens, Balsamina.*

E. More than four pores

   † Pores distributed regularly

     (*a*) On the equator—*Alnus, Betula, Ulmus, Goniocarpus, Campanula, Thryallis* (in the last more or less towards one pole).

     (*b*) Over all the surface—*Basella alba,* etc.

   †† Pores scattered irregularly

(a) Outer coat granular, smooth—Nyctaginaceae, Thymeli-
aceae, Convolvulaceae, Chenopodiaceae, *Alisma Plantago, Celtis australis, Plantago lanceolata.*

(b) Outer coat granular and spiny.—Malvacelae, *Cucurbita,
Ipomoea.*

(c) Outer coat cellular.—*Polygonum orientale, Persicaria,
Cobaea.*

Derivative forms (i.e., of †††, outer coat with pores)

(a) Grains in tetrahedral tetrads, *Jussieua erecta, Drimys Winteri* etc.

(c) Form of Mimosaceae.—*Inga, Acacia* etc.

†††† Outer coat with longitudinal furrows and pores

Primitive forms

A. Round with three pits and three pores.—Dipsicaceae, Geraniaceae.

B. With three furrows and three pores

(a) Outer coat granular—Common in Dicotyledons.

(b) Outer coat with spines—Most Compositae.

(c) Outer coat cellular—*Turnera, Grewia, Stackhousia, Syringa,
Ligustrum, Celastrus.*

C. Outer coat with more than three furrows, each with a pore.—
Boraginaceae, Polygalaceae etc. and exceptions among the
three-furrowed forms.

D. Six to 9 furrows, of which three contain one pore each *Vinca rosea.*

E. Three or four furrows, and three pores not in the furrows.—
Carolinea campestris, C. longiflora, Eriodendron.

Derivative forms

(a) Tetrahedral tetrads.—Epacridaceae, Vacciniaceae.

(b) Cubic and dodecahedral forms.—Malpighiaceae—*e.g.,
Gaudichaudia.*

(b) Polyhedral with three pores and three furrows *Lactuca,
Vernonia montevidensis* (transition form).

F. Wall of three membranes.—Some conifers, *e.g., Taxus.*

It is evident that von Mohl recognized the furrows of the grains
to be their most important morphological features, a fact which
has often been overlooked by later investigators, particularly
those who insist upon examining pollen in its dried and shrunken
form. He points out that the arrangements of the furrows are
enormously varied, though they generally are meridionally
extended. But, whatever their arrangement, they are always
so formed that the folded part projects inwardly when the grain
is dry, "but when the grains are made wet they expand and the
part of the furrow which was hidden becomes a part of the
external surface of the grain . . . and the part which was hidden
in the folds always presents a different structure from the rest
of the outer membrane although it is in immediate continuity

with it." In their expanded form he calls the furrows *Streifen*, and states that they are generally transparent, though they may be granular, but if so the granules are quite different from those of the rest of the outer membrane and may have characteristic arrangements in different species.

Von Mohl recognized for the first time the geometrical configurations that the furrows assume and their importance to his classification. He noticed that three furrows arranged meridionally was the commonest condition among the dicotyledons but that there are also many other numbers and arrangements among them. He found that in the grains of *Corydalis lutea*, for example, there were six furrows. The surface of these grains, he said, is found to be divided by six fissures into four triangles, or, in other words, the furrows correspond to the six edges of a tetrahedron. Other grains of this species he found to have nine furrows, corresponding to the edges of a triangular prism with its sides rounded out. And in the grains of two species of *Rivina* and one of *Fumaria* the furrows are so arranged that they divide the surface of the grain into pentagons, forming of it a pentagonal dodecahedron. In some species he found that a single furrow configuration was characteristic but that in others two or more configurations could be found even in the pollen from a single anther. Passing to the spiral forms, he found that he could establish a sequence of forms ranging from that with three furrows meridionally arranged to the strictly spiral forms, such as those found in the pollen of *Thunbergia* and *Mimulus* in which a single furrow follows a zigzag course over the surface of the grain. He therefore concluded that the spiral forms were derivatives of the ordinary three-furrowed configuration. His analysis of these furrow configurations was truly a remarkable feat, expressive of his great genius for interpreting what he saw. In his interpretation of *Pinus* pollen, however, he was somewhat less successful. He regarded it as a derivative from the one-furrowed form of the monocotyledons but at the same time intermediate between it and the three-furrowed form of the dicotyledons. The single longitudinal furrow which occupies the ventral side in the grain of *Pinus* he correctly interpreted as the functional furrow, but the two re-entrant angles that the bladders make with the cap at their dorsal roots (Fig. 78) he interpreted as additional rudimentary furrows, homologous with those of the three-furrowed dicotyledons. Apparently, in this grain he saw a connecting link between the monocotyledonous and the dicotyledonous form of grain.

The echinolophate forms of the Cichorieae he described as "polyhedric," with three pores and three furrows, approximating in form a pentagonal dodecahedron. And the pollen of *Vernonia montevidensis*, in which the lophate form is only partially expressed, he pointed out as intermediate between the polyhedric and the more usual echinate form of the Compositae.

A highly suggestive part of von Mohl's work is the portion containing his descriptions of the pollen forms by families; to give an example: "Gramineae, oval, glistening, nonviscous, outer coat finely granular, not separable from the inner; on one side a punctiform umbilicus with a small halo." In families where more than a single form was found: "Chenopodiaceae (*a*) cubic with blunt edges, in the middle of each face a nongranular part like a pore, *Basella alba*, (*b*) spherical, outer coat finely granular, provided with about twenty pores, *Blitum capitatum*, *Salsola scorparia*."

In this way he characterized the pollen of 211 families with the formal brevity of taxonomic diagnoses. It is a matter of interest that the genus *Basella*, regarded by the older taxonomists as belonging to the Chenopodiaceae—von Mohl states that he followed Bartling's "Ordines plantarum"—is now separated from the Chenopodiaceae and put in a family of its own. Nor is this an isolated example. As we read through von Mohl's pollen descriptions by families we encounter many violent breaks in the succession of forms. Some of these have since been smoothed out by improvements in the classification; others remain and stand today as challenges to taxonomy. The succinct way in which von Mohl put forth his descriptions suggests that he felt that they formed a part of the family or generic descriptions. At any rate, he presented them in a form which could easily have been taken over and put into the family diagnoses, but they have to this day been ignored, in spite of the enormous wealth of material which they present with their obvious implications.

Two years after the publication of this paper by von Mohl, Fritzsche read before the St. Petersburg Academy of Science his "Ueber den Pollen," pointing out the errors in von Mohl's conception of pollen structures. Even though von Mohl never actually retracted his views, they became greatly modified in later years. In his "Vegetabilischer Zelle" (1851, page 123), for example he says:

> The perfect pollen grain consists of a cell . . . covered on the outside by a membranous layer which owes its origin to a secretion, and, in particular cases, is separable into two or three superincumbent layers. The outermost layer, corresponding to a cuticle, is mostly rather tough, uniform, or covered with granules, spinules, projecting linear and often reticulated ridges, mostly colored and the seat of a more or less abundant secretion of a viscid oil.

Apart from this von Mohl seems never to have referred to the matter again.

It may have been the appearance of Fritzsche's immortal work, seeming to knock the theoretical foundations from under von Mohl's, which prevented him from returning to the subject, causing him to leave it in this unfinished condition. Whether or not this supposition is correct, the fact remains that, after immersing himself in the study of pollen morphology for many years and amassing enormous quantities of material in one of the richest fields of botany, von Mohl abruptly left it and busied himself with other subjects which seem to us distinctly less interesting. It is also probable that von Mohl's work, antedating that of Fritzsche by a little over a year, anticipating all his main results, had a similar effect on Fritzsche, for, as we shall see, he also dropped pollen morphology, never to return to it, after he had put into print his "Ueber den Pollen," thereafter directing his attention entirely to chemistry. It is seemingly to this circumstance that we still have the field of pollen morphology largely unworked before us; because either one of these great minds could have made such inroads upon it and would have provided such an enormous stimulus to further investigation that pollen morphology would by this time have advanced to a stage of completeness comparable to that of the other branches of science to which these two men lent the powers of their intellects.

Carl Julius Fritzsche.—Born on Oct. 29, 1808, in Neustadt, in Saxony, Fritzsche was the son of Christian Ferdinand Fritzsche, medical officer in charge of public health of Stolpen and

Hohenstein.   His mother came from the family of Struve.   Both
parents lived until the year 1833 to see their illustrious son given
the degree of Doctor of Philosophy in Berlin.

In Neustadt, where Fritzsche spent his childhood, there was no
school, so up to his fourteenth year he received private instruction
directed toward the study of pharmacy; and later he went for
the same purpose to Dresden, where he was employed for five
years in his uncle Struve's pharmacy.   From Dresden he went to
Berlin, where he superintended for $2\frac{1}{2}$ years the laboratory of the
pharmacy of Helming.   But finding this occupation clearly not
scientific, he took the assistantship at the chemical laboratory
of the famous chemist Eilhardt Mitscherlich, and this was the
most important event in Fritzsche's educational career.

Mitscherlich had been a student of Link and Berzelius and had
distinguished himself as the discoverer of dimorphism in crystals
and of benzene sulphonic acid and nitrobenzene.   Besides his
accomplishments as a scientist, he had published part of a
history of Persia in Latin and Persian.   Thus it happened that
Fritzsche's close association with Mitscherlich was of great
benefit to him.   The master shared his knowledge freely with
the young man, and in this position which he held for $2\frac{1}{2}$ years he
found in every nook and corner an unfolding of his leaning toward
the natural sciences.   Fritzsche reports this association with
Mitscherlich as his happiest recollection, and from his "Curriculum vitae" we fully understand the feeling that bound him
to his master.   In this he expresses himself in these words, "In
this time I hold the greatest affection for Mitscherlich.   With
the deepest gratitude will I remember him to my grave.   With
fatherly care he guided my work and made it possible for me to
round out my knowledge."

It was probably due to Mitscherlich's influence that Fritzsche
entered the faculty of philosophy in the university in 1831.   He
records in his *Vita* that there he attended the lectures of Mitscherlich and such other distinguished men as the two Roses, chemist
and mineralogist; Lichtenstein, the zoologist; and Kunth, the
botanist.   In 1832 he published his "Beiträge zur Kenntniss des
Pollen" and in 1833 took his degree of Doctor of Philosophy with
"De plantarum polline" as his inaugural dissertation.   In 1834
he published "Ueber den Pollen der Pflanzen und das Pollenin"
in Poggendorf's *Annalen*.

In the same year he moved to St. Petersburg where he became a member of the St. Petersburg Academy of Science, and his great work "Ueber den Pollen," read before the academy in 1836, was published in the "Mémoires des savants étrangers" of the Academy in the following year. After that time his publications, which are numerous—over 60 are recorded—dealt almost entirely with purely chemical subjects, principally organic. Among them we find treatises on uric acid, the anhydrides of potassium nitrate and nitrous acid, alkaloids, indigo derivatives, carbohydrates, and many others. Most of his papers dealt with fundamentals, and some of them constituted milestones in the progress of science, as, for instance, his discovery that murexides were ammonium salts of purpuric acid, the decomposition of anthranilic acid into aniline and carbon dioxide, the discovery of the isomers of nitrophenol, and others. Such achievements as these required patience, industry, and precision of observation. These attributes Fritzsche possessed to the highest degree; in fact, he has been criticized for his excessive attention to details. It was this character, however, which led him safely past the pitfalls into which von Mohl had stumbled in his morphology of pollen.

Much of Fritzsche's time was commandeered for purposes outside his beloved sciences. In 1848 he was made chief of the commission for the study and organization of the Caucasian mineral waters, of which he was conducting the analyses at the time. He was chemist of the medical department and advisory member of the medical council to the Minister of the Interior; also, he took part in many commissions, as that on household gas illumination, the commission for the introduction of electric illumination into Russia, and the building of St. Isaac's Cathedral. He had now become Staatsrath Fritzsche. But all his free time he spent in his laboratory; at first he had only a small one near his home, but later moved to the new and spacious chemical laboratory of the Academy which he directed in association with N. Zinn.

The home life of Fritzsche was on the whole peaceful and happy, but he was twice a widower, and after the death of his second wife he was left for 15 years with the care and responsibility of bringing up his son and daughter. His relations with his colleagues were of the happiest character. Often they searched him out in his laboratory in friendly visit, eagerly expecting to hear from him something new and strange, also because they regarded him as a man of amiable character and good heart, ever active in the accomplishment of good.

Up to his final sickness he enjoyed excellent health, but in the year 1869 he suffered an apoplectic stroke which made of him a crippled old man. Although he recovered somewhat from it, he remained lame, and speech and memory had almost left him.

The friends who had known him when he was hale and hearty were grieved to see him in these latter days; he himself preferred death to such a life. For only a very short time did he resume his scientific activity—long enough to finish his study of the molecular changes of tin.

In the following year he journeyed to his native land in search of physical and mental relief. The latter he found in the circle of his family, who eagerly welcomed him home. His illness, however, became steadily worse and on June 20, 1871, brought him the desired release from his sufferings. Nevertheless, he was happy on his deathbed,

Fig. 8.—Karl Julius Fritzsche. (*Courtesy of the Soviet Academy of Sciences, Leningrad.*)

knowing that he had not lived in vain and that his life had enriched those with whom he had come in contact as well as the science which he loved. Truly it has been said that "the name of Fritzsche is indelibly written in the annals of learning next to the facts with which he enriched Science."*

Fritzsche's Works.—Before the publication of von Mohl's work on pollen in 1834, Fritzsche as we have seen, had already published his "Beiträge zur Kenntniss des Pollen" and his "De plantarum polline," and in the same year as von Mohl's paper,

---

* The facts of Fritzsche's life are derived from A. Butlerow (1872) and from the Curriculum vitae in "De plantarum polline" (1833).

his "Ueber den Pollen der Pflanzen und das Pollenin" was published in Poggendorf's *Annalen*. Strictly speaking, therefore, he deserves priority over von Mohl, but these works were only preliminary to his principal one "Ueber den Pollen," which was published in 1837, 3 years after von Mohl's.

In his "Beiträge" Fritzsche pointed out that the recent improvements in the microscope called for further advances in the study of pollen. The instrument he used was by Pistor and Schick, which he regarded as even better than the very fine instruments by Amici, Chevalier, or Ploessel. With this microscope he was able to get a magnification higher than necessary, or even desirable for the study of pollen grains, and the high resolving power and brilliancy of illumination of this microscope, which are really more important than magnification, are abundantly attested by his studies with it of starch grains, in which he shows the concentric rings quite clearly.

Having such an instrument, Fritzsche stated that it was necessary only to devise appropriate methods of preparing the pollen to reveal their characters much more fully than had ever been done before. A large part of the Beiträge is taken up with a discussion of the various methods of expanding pollen grains and rendering them transparent, which he recognized as essential to their study. Of the different methods, he selected treatment with varying concentrations of acids as the best adapted to the purpose.

With deftness and precision he defined the problems in hand to be whether the pollen of a species is of an invariable form; whether the different species of a genus agree in their pollen forms as they do in their other characters; what rule governs the distribution of the different pollen forms in the natural system; and whether the more highly organized dicotyledons also have more highly organized pollen.

From a preliminary survey of his material he at once came to the conclusion that the different forms of pollen grain, while more or less constant within the species, do not correspond to the natural classification, nor do the more primitive plants have the more primitive forms of pollen. But, he concluded, a classification of pollen forms has just as much right and may be just as natural as the classification of the plants themselves. Accordingly, he laid out a classification in some respects superior to that of von Mohl. He took as his primary divisions, for simple grains, (1) those with and (2) those without furrows. Of the former he made eight subdivisions, according to the number of their furrows: (*a*) grains with 1 furrow, *e.g.*, *Amaryllis;* (*b*) with 2 furrows, only *Justicia adhatoda;* (*c*) with 3 furrows, the commonest form among the dicotyledons; (*d*) with 4 furrows, generally occurring in pollen of species which normally have other numbers of furrows; (*e*) with 6 furrows (in this group he includes only those with their furrows meridionally arranged); (*f*) with 8 furrows, *e.g.*, *Symphytum officinale*, with a structure similar to that of the 3-furrowed forms; (*g*) with 10 furrows, *e.g.*, *Penaea mucronata* and *Asperula taurina;* (*h*) with 20 furrows, *e.g.*, *Polygala latifolia*, of which the furrows are meridionally arranged and only 4 have germ pores.

The grains without furrows he subdivided into those with and those without pores. Those with pores he subdivided again into those with one pore—only the grasses—and those with several pores. The latter are again subdivided into those with pores arranged in a circle around the grain, *e.g.*, *Banksia* and *Sida;* and those with the pores equally distributed—smooth, *Ribes;* with spines, Malvaceae.

The compound grains he treated as a separate group, subdividing it into (1) 4 grains united, without pores, *e.g.*, *Luzula;* (2) 4 grains, each with three pores, *e.g.*, Ericaceae; and (3) 16 grains united, *e.g.*, *Acacia*.

This is only a brief outline of his classification but will serve to show how complete was his understanding of pollen. One cannot but be struck with the similarity between this classification and that of von Mohl, yet there is no reason to believe that either author was influenced by the other. The classifications of both probably had the germ of their origins in Purkinje.

"De plantarum polline," which Fritzsche presented in 1833 as his thesis in fulfillment of the requirements for the degree of Doctor of Philosophy to the Friedrich-Wilhelms University, offers little that is new; it is little more than a summary, in Latin and without illustrations, of the work already presented in the Beiträge. His "Theses defendae" are: (1) Pollen granules are nothing but droplets of oil and starch grains; (2) a blue color is effected in starch by iodine owing to a union resulting from a strong affinity between the two substances; (3) grains of starch consist of a gummy material, formed in several concentric layers of homogeneous substances, the whole enveloped by a membrane.

Fritzsche's next paper "Ueber den Pollen der Pflanzen und das Pollenin" (1834) is directed toward the elucidation of the nature and origin of *Pollenin*. This is a substance which may be extracted from pollen by water, alcohol, ether, or alkali. Upon evaporation of the extract a residue remains in which crystals of various form are found, showing that *Pollenin* is not a single substance but a mixture of several. He pointed out that neither the external morphology nor the contents of the grains are greatly changed by the removal of *Pollenin*.

In order to clarify this latter statement a large part of the paper is devoted to the examination of the internal and external morphology. The contents of pollen grains, he stated, consist of three substances: (1) *Schleim*, which occurs in a half-fluid state, becomes dispersed in water without dissolving, is coagulated by weak acid, and is stained brown with iodine; (2) an oil-like substance which is distributed as very fine droplets throughout the whole *Schleim* mass. The droplets do not stain with iodine and can be made to run together into larger masses; (3) small starch grains which may not always be present but may easily be recognized because they turn blue with iodine.

The external morphology of many grains is described in great detail, and Fritzsche pointed out that some of them are strikingly similar to certain crystal forms. For example, the pollen grains of the Cichorieae are six-sided prisms and rhombohedra, and the grains of many Caryophyllaceae are pentagonal dodecahedra. But whatever the nature of the contents or the form of the grains may be, when the pollen is extracted with any of the reagents mentioned above, the grains remain unchanged, except for the removal of the soluble material on the surface. This then must be the source of *Pollenin*. Its chemical nature, however, Fritzsche was not able to discover beyond the fact that it is a mixture of several substances.

In this paper we see the trend of Fritzsche's mind toward chemistry. We also feel that he had at his command a large fund of knowledge of pollen structures. His knowledge of all the principal pollen forms of the Cichorieae and of the Caryophyllaceae, which enabled him to make the statements that he did about their crystal-like forms, suggests that this was the case.   As a matter of fact, at this time he knew much more about pollen than he had ever written.   The three papers which we have mentioned above told merely of side lights or interesting laws which had come out incidental to his main work, the heroic task of a complete analysis of the pollen forms of all the known plants.   We can imagine him carefully building up the structure of his science, block by block, and making each secure before adding the next.   It is likely that it would have been many years before the whole structure assumed a form to his liking, so meticulous was he and critical of his own work.   But this was abruptly changed by the appearance in 1834 of von Mohl's "Ueber den Bau und die Formen der Pollenkörner," for Fritzsche found in it that von Mohl had anticipated most of his work.   So he put together his own results and presented them to the St. Petersburg Academy of Science in 1836.

In "Ueber den Pollen," which was Fritzsche's answer to von Mohl, he stated that he published his results as much to confirm those of von Mohl as for their own worth.   But some of his results, he found, were quite different from those of von Mohl, and, besides that, the field recently opened up by the new developments of the microscope he considered so vast that a detailed knowledge at all commensurate with the number of known plants could be achieved only by the co-operation of many workers, whom he hoped that his work would encourage to enter the field.   It so happens, however, that Fritzsche set such a high standard of accuracy and keenness of understanding that few have been able to follow him, and no one has ever approached him in the beauty and accuracy of his drawings.

Regarding the contents of pollen grains—the *Schleim*, oil, and starch already referred to—only the last was known chemically; the other two, he stated, are mixtures.   But the *Schleim* has the property of absorbing water and swelling enormously. It is this property of the *Schleim*, he said, which causes the grain to crack open when the extent of the swelling exceeds the elasticity of the wall.   The contents then become extruded in the water, owing to a contraction of the grain due to the elasticity of the wall upon the release of pressure.   The extruded *Schleim* may be stained brown with iodine or coagulated with weak acids.   But if the grains have once been dried, the *Schleim* loses much of its capacity for absorbing water.

The oil drops and starch grains, he pointed out, as did von Mohl, make up the so-called pollen granules, and their movements, as shown by Brown, are of a molecular nature and common to all small bodies, though they were mistaken for animalcules. But, he said, it is only the starch grains which could thus deceive, for the oil occurs in spheroidal droplets or fluid masses, while the starch grains are of almost as many different forms as there are kinds of plants; they may be any shape but always turn intensely blue with iodine. It is through their turning endwise, crosswise, and getting out of focus that they give the appearance of changing their shape. Besides, he said, infusoria do not take the least bit of color with iodine; instead it is fatal to the existence of all lower forms of life. In these words he effectively disposed of the fetish of the independent existence of pollen granules.

Intine and Exine.—In discussing the integuments of pollen grains, Fritzsche pointed out that the majority have two coats. A few have one, in which case the outer is lacking; a few have more than two, in which case one or the other is doubled. Therefore, he considered, these coats should be named. "The ending *-ine* seems to me to be the most convenient, as chosen by Mirbel for the integuments of the egg, for it permits itself to be easily modified into German, Latin or French. I therefore name the inner pollen wall the *intine* and the outer the *exine*. When these layers are doubled they may be named accordingly as *exintine* and *intexine*." As Fritzsche had foreseen, the terms have been widely adopted, and we cannot now speak of pollen in any language without using them.

The intine he found to be always the same, consisting of a closed hyaline, colorless membrane which takes no color with iodine and is destroyed by strong sulphuric acid. It is the essential layer; when only one is present it is always the intine. The exine, on the other hand, though not essential and playing no part in fertilization, is complex and enormously various, and it is by it alone that we are able to distinguish the different species of pollen. It is not destroyed by concentrated sulphuric acid, merely turning purplish-red in this reagent.

The foundation of the exine, Fritzsche pointed out, is always a simple membrane and not, as von Mohl had stated, a cellular layer. He went to enormous pains to establish this point. He found that, by treating the grains with sulphuric acid, to dissolve out the contents and the intine, and rolling them between glass plates, he was able to isolate small pieces of the exine, and in some case he actually isolated the granules of the exine. From these experiments he came to the conclusion that the basic structure of the exine consists of a homogeneous matrix in which granules are embedded. These may be of various sizes and shapes, spaced closely together or far apart, or they may be entirely absent. They may be in rows which anastomose, forming a network over the surface of the grain, in which case the homogeneous material may be absent between the rows, nevertheless binding the palisade-like granules together in their rows. A striking example of this he showed in the grains of *Ruellia formosa*, in which the surface is heavily reticulate and presents a decidedly cellular appearance. This is likewise true of the grains of *Eranthemum strictum*, but here in the middle of each space of the net stands a spine or group of spines.

The question of the nature of the spines was next taken up. By the same process as before Fritzsche succeeded in isolating single spines from the exine of a grain of *Ipomoea* and others and came to the conclusion that the spines are the highest development of the granules. Von Mohl had considered that the granules and spines of the exine were reservoirs and secretory organs for oil, but Fritzsche demonstrated by numerous experiments that in no case were they reservoirs for oil; but in the spines he was nearly always able to see a dark streak, like a central core, which he concluded must be an oil canal. "For," said he, "the flowing out of an oily liquid from the majority of different kinds of pollen species through contact with water, which takes place especially strongly with those provided with spines, necessitates passages for this oil, since we cannot believe that it simply adheres to the outside of the grain." It should be stated, however, that the dark central cores which Fritzsche saw in the larger spines were probably merely the result of diffraction of light brought about by the convergence of the rays in passing through the highly refractive material of the spines.

Fritzsche stated that the relation of granules to spines is brought out in the grains of *Ipomoea purpurea*. Here the surface is covered with a network of rows of palisade-like granules, inclosing angular spaces on the surface of the grain, giving it a cellular appearance; and wherever the rows come together there is always a spine which seems to contain a canal.

The spines of the Cichorieae are, he said, the most remarkable of all, but unfortunately he found them so small and fragile that he was not able to isolate them and only once was he able to secure a section vertically through a spine. Of this he furnished a picture, as he said, for what it may be worth, fearful himself to draw conclusions from a single observation. These spines, he wrote, stand in single rows, united by a binding material, and the rows anastomose in such a way as to mark off the surface of the grain into a regular pattern resembling certain crystal forms. Observing the spine rows in side view he was able to see running up into each the same dark streaks which he took for canals.

As an example of a grain which was supposed to have a cellular exine he took that of *Cobaea scandens*. No one has before or since so accurately described this type of grain or figured it half so perfectly. Here, he said, walls stand up on the outer membrane, enclosing on it five- or six-angled spaces all over the surface of the grain. These walls are broken through and have the appearance of a bridge resting on piers. There is no membrane over the spaces or across the gaps in the vertical walls, as there would have to be if they actually enclosed cells, as von Mohl supposed. Furthermore, he continued, the walls cannot without tearing it be separated from the membrane upon which they rest. "It appears to me, therefore, that their nature can only be explained as thickenings of the membrane, which, after they have grown to a certain height, begin to form gaps at their bases."

Although such a pattern is widespread and always suggestive of a cellular structure, Fritzsche said, "An organization of a kind that is truly cellular, I have nowhere been able to perceive with certainty in the exine." And, although this point cannot be regarded as settled for all kinds of grains, he had little hope of ever finding a grain with an exine of a cellular structure.

Turning to such grains as those of *Gilia tricolor* and *Collomia grandiflora,* he described them as having a wickerwork exine, provided with regularly arranged pores. These, he stated, were not admitted by von Mohl to be true openings but were regarded as merely thin spots in the exine. He believed that von Mohl was led to misinterpret these openings by the presence below each of a small body which Fritzsche called *Zwischenkörper*, acting as a plug to close the hole from the inside. It was probably these, Fritzsche thought, which led von Mohl to believe that the germ pores of these and most other grains were not true openings.

The *Zwischenkörper* form the subject of an extensive investigation by Fritzsche. He found that they were hyalin, mostly lens-shaped bodies lying one beneath each pore between the exine and intine. When the grain is moistened they protrude through the pore in the form of a bubble. By rolling and crushing the grains and treating them with suitable reagents he was able to isolate them from the grains of *Astrapaea, Ruellia, Sida,* and others. In the grains of the Malvaceae, which have numerous pores, the *Zwischenkörper* could not be isolated, but he was able to remove a piece of the exine and showed that under each pore lay a small *Zwischenkörper*. And he concluded that, though they could not always be demonstrated, they must be present in all pored grains.

Fritzsche's Classification.—The second part of Fritzsche's book deals with the different forms of grains throughout the flowering plants. He stated that it had already been sufficiently shown from previous researches that no law governs the distribution of the forms of pollen in the natural classification of plants, nor does the form of the pollen grain always bear any relation to the lower or higher rank that we have assigned to it. But he believed that one could attain a natural classification of pollen forms if one began with the simplest and sought always the next most complex. Such a statement seems strange to us; today if we failed to see any parallelism between the pollen forms and the relationships of the plants we should naturally assume that the fault lay in our inability to interpret the pollen forms or possibly in the classification of the plants. But Fritzsche's idea that two systems of classification running contrary to each other could both be natural shows that he had no appreciation of the significance of the classification of plants. To him it was just a convenient arrangement of forms, as one might classify crystals by the number of their faces, their interfacial angles, their cleavage planes, or however one wished. This was probably because Fritzsche was primarily a chemist; and before

Darwin's time the idea of a natural classification among living things was not the underlying principle of all biological studies, as it is today.

Accordingly, he followed the classification of pollen forms already laid down in his "Beiträge." He began his system with the compound grains: "For," he says, "the compound pollen masses of the Asclepiads and Orchids stand indisputably at a lower stage, in all respects, than free grains." The compound grains of *Inga* he included here, but he regarded them as somewhat higher than those of the orchids and asclepiads because they have two coats while the latter have only one.

The major divisions of the single-grained group, he believed, should be drawn according to the number of coats that they have. In Group I, pollen with only one coat, are included *Caulinia fragilis*, *Zannichellia pedunculata*, and *Zostera marina*. *Zostera* pollen he found to be the most exceptional among all pollen, occurring in long, filamentous tubes occasionally branched and filled with granular fovilla which circulates in the tubes, just as Amici had seen it do in pollen tubes. Indeed, he concludes, the filamentous pollen grains correspond to the pollen tubes of most other plants.

In Group II, pollen with two coats, are included the great majority of known forms. Throughout the group, Fritzsche stated, the fovilla and intine are virtually uniform, the enormous variation in the forms of the grains having to do exclusively with the exine. The simplest and, therefore, the most primitive grains, according to Fritzsche, are those without structural openings, *e.g.*, those of *Ruppia*. Then he says, "Next follows a form very widespread among the monocotyledons which consists of an ellipsoid with a longitudinal strip of exine which is naked, representing a longitudinal furrow." In discussing this form of grain he stated that in much of the pollen of *Lilium candidum* he found grains of this character united in pairs, back to back with the furrows facing outward. In the pollen of *Phillydrum* he found similar grains united in fours, likewise with their furrows facing outward, but in the pollen of *Annona tripetala* he found four grains united face to face, *i.e.*, with the furrows inward. When these latter are separated from each other it is true that their contact faces are found to be thin-walled, as would be expected, but they do not possess the form of structural furrows.

It is doubtful, therefore, if Fritzsche was justified in assuming that they were true furrows. On the contrary, it appears to be invariably true that furrows are situated on the outer side of one-furrowed grains in relation to their tetrads. Fritzsche appears to have just missed the significance of this fact.

Continuing with his classified descriptions of pollen, he described grains with spiral bands from several species of *Thunbergia*, but he failed to relate these forms with those with three furrows, as had von Mohl.

Fritzsche's study of the pollen of the various species of passion-flower, however, is much superior to that of von Mohl and has never been equaled since. He recognized the pores at once for what they are, large germ pores, each covered with a lid of the same material and structure as the exine. He described in the minutest detail grains from this genus with three, four, and six pores and grains with three, four, and other numbers of furrows in a variety of arrangements. His beautiful figures of these must be seen to be appreciated.

Furrow Configurations.—Fritzsche fully understood the various furrow configurations. He recognized three meridionally arranged furrows as the basic arrangement among dicotyledons. Six-furrowed grains he found in the pollen of *Corydalis*, and he pointed out that the six furrows were arranged according to the six edges of a tetrahedron. The grains of *Corydalis* are spherical, smooth-walled, and transparent, and the furrows may be seen with great clarity. In the grains of *Basella alba*, however, Fritzsche also found six furrows, but here the grains are cubical in shape and exceedingly thick-walled and rather opaque, with a short furrow arranged diagonally on each of the six faces of the cube. In spite of this, Fritzsche recognized this furrow configuration as also corresponding to the edges of a tetrahedron and analogous to that of *Corydalis*, whereas von Mohl had failed to recognize this, relating, instead, the furrows to the faces of a cube. In the grains of *Talinum patens* Fritzsche found 12 furrows corresponding in configuration to the 12 edges of a cube, and in those of *Polygonum amphibium* he found 30 furrows. Here they are very short—little more than elliptical pores—and the grain is heavily reticulate with high vertical ridges, yet he was able to relate these furrows in their spacial orientation to the 30 edges of a pentagonal dodecahedron.

The grass grains, he showed, have one pore surrounded by a marked thickening of the exine. When dry the grains are cone-shaped, but when made wet they become spherical, with the fovilla protruding in the form of a bubble from the pore, ultimately bursting and discharging into the water, owing to the presence of a *Zwischenkörper*, which Fritzsche did not see but assumed must be present. If he had not made this assumption but had hunted out the *Zwischenkörper*—if, indeed, it may be called that—he would have found that it lies not between the intine and exine but in the body of the grain, generally remote from the pore. When made wet it expands, rapidly filling the entire cavity of the grain, thrusting the other contents out through the pore.

He found that the grains of a great many species have three furrows, with a pore in each furrow. When dry such grains are generally elliptical, and the pores cannot be seen, and, if made transparent by placing them in oil, a complicated internal structure is seen which is due to the marginal thickenings of the inturned furrows and the rims of the pores. This is the condition in most fossil grains, and Fritzsche's figures of grains in oil resemble closely those found in fossil studies. When made wet, however, these elliptical grains expand and become spherical, and the furrows with all their attendant structures may easily be seen.

Pollen-grain Patterns.—In the Compositae, Fritzsche recognized that the basic form was a spiny sphere with three furrows and a pore in each; but in those of *Centaurea*, he found that the spines were so small that they could be seen only with great difficulty. Among the Cichorieae he picked out all the different patterns and described their faces or units which make up the patterns.

Pine pollen, which had so confused von Mohl, Fritzsche examined both wet and dry and after the removal of the exine. He came to the conclusion that its internal structure was the same as that of *Larix*, though the latter possessed no bladders and presented an entirely different appearance superficially. The walls of both, he said, are three-layered, owing to a doubling of the intine. In *Pinus* the exintine is separated from the intine on both sides of the furrow and puffed out to form the two bladders. This, I believe, is the first nearly correct interpretation of the bladders of the grains of *Pinus*.

In reviewing this work of Fritzsche I have mentioned only a few of his statements, selected because they seem to be of special interest, frequently because they have to do with things which von Mohl had failed to notice or had interpreted differently. It is true that when Fritzsche differed from von Mohl, Fritzsche was more often correct, but for the most part the two authors agree, and their work together constitutes the most brilliant chapter in the history of pollen morphology. The two investigators approached the same subject with entirely different intellectual backgrounds. Von Mohl had just discovered that the tracheids of plants were modified cells and he had classified the tissues of stems and satisfied himself that they were all cellular and that the entire plant body was of a cellular structure. What more natural than that he should conclude that pollen grains were likewise cellular structures and regard the reticulate exines, which often have a decidedly cellular appearance, as a confirmation of this view? Fritzsche, on the other hand, was not primarily a botanist and had no preconceived notions of what any of the structures should be, but he had an extraordinary capacity for taking pains. He was much more interested in making observations than in drawing conclusions from them, whereas the reverse is true of von Mohl. The result is that Fritzsche's observations and his extraordinarily beautiful figures are more accurate and more reliable than those of von Mohl, but his reports of them are often wearisome, for in them we miss the brilliancy and purposefulness which characterize von Mohl. In fact, these two authors—Fritzsche, the plodding, painstaking observer, always accurate; and von Mohl, the brilliant theorist, always with a purpose—were by nature and training complementary to each other. It is with a sigh of regret that we must leave them now, for the paths of these two great investigators diverged in the earliest years of their productive period, Fritzsche to become one of the great chemists of his time and von Mohl certainly the greatest botanist of his.

Later Botanists.—The period following von Mohl and Fritzsche up to 1890 when Fischer's "Beiträge" was published, saw the attention of many young botanists directed to the study of pollen. In fact, nearly every botanist and writer on botanical subjects, under the stimulus supplied by the two preceding investigators, referred to the subject in some way; but most of them either quoted the earlier works without adding anything new, as if the final chapter had been written, or else they investigated on their own initiative, heedless of their predecessors, often reporting observations wrongly that had been adequately dealt with by Purkinje, von Mohl, or Fritzsche. The English writers offended most in this direction, possibly because the stimulus from von Mohl and Fritzsche failed to reach across the Channel. On the Continent, however, the period saw considerable advancement; but most of the best investigations of this period were directed mainly toward the elucidation of the development of pollen which had been made possible by the improved methods of technique, and to this the advances that were made in pure morphology were only secondary.

The situation at this time was very well summarized by Franz Julius Ferdinand Meyen, in his "Pflanzenphysiologie" (1839). He himself contributed but little that was new beyond the assertion of doubtful value that most pollen grains possessed a third coat between the intine and exine, which covered the pollen tube during its emergence from the grain. But his work served to clarify the situation by reconciling or correcting to some extent the opposing views which were then extant, and it became the main source of material, and possibly the best available, for subsequent students until the publication of the very much superior work of Hermann Schacht 20 years later.

In order to throw some new light upon the curious pollen structures which had recently become known, Karl Wilhelm Nägeli (1842) undertook to discover the mode of their origins and development. "For," said he, "the correct understanding of a thing depends not only upon a knowledge of its completed form but also of its beginning." He therefore studied the origin and development of the pollen of *Lilium*, *Tradescantia*, *Cucurbita*, *Oenothera*, and *Althaea*. He found that in each loculus of the anther was differentiated a vertical chain of primordial cells which became the pollen mother-cells, through the nucleus (cytoblast) of each becoming resorbed and the development of thickened gelatinous layers on the inner face of the cell membrane. From this stage he found that there were two possible courses of development. In one of these two granular masses are formed in each cell, each with a cytoblast, and at the same time a transitory cell wall is formed; then each cytoblast builds on its outer surface a gelatinous membrane; these he called the primary special mother-cells; then the cytoblast of each cell becomes resorbed, its granular contents divide again into two parts each with a cytoblast, and around each of these arises a gelatinous membrane (secondary special mother-cell). Or, the other possibility, the granular contents of the mother-cell divide into four masses each with a cytoblast and connected with each other by "sap streaming." Around each cell arises a gelatinous membrane (special mother-cell).

This remarkable description has the advantage for us that it almost ignores the nuclear changes. Apparently his material was not stained in a way to render any but the fully organized nucleus visible, so the picture was not confused by the complicated phenomenon of karyokinesis upon which most subsequent investigators have focused their entire attention. To Nägeli, when the nuclear material formed into chromosomes, it seemed to be simply resorbed, and this left his attention free for the observation of other things, such as the arrangement of the newly formed cells and their connection with each other by phragmoplasts, which he called sap streaming (*Saftströmung*).

But, to continue with Nägeli's story, he tells us that within each of the four special mother-cells a pollen cell is formed by the building of a wall (intine) which shuts in its whole contents. Then, through an osmotic excretion, there form on the outside of the pollen cell one or two layers of a substance which is at first gelatinous but later solid and colored (exine), with peculiar modifications in certain places where the pollen tubes grow out (*Zwischenkörper*). Then, the mother-cell and special mother-cells become resorbed, and a viscous material appears which accumulates on the outer surface of the pollen grains.

In the monocotyledons, he says, the formation of the special mother-cells by two successive divisions is the most usual course of development, while in the dicotyledons the four daughter cytoblasts generally form their four special mother-cells simultaneously. This course of development, he says, generally results in a tetrahedral arrangement, but in *Althaea* both the tetrahedral and squared arrangements are found and all in between. This observation is of the utmost importance to the pollen morphologist, since, as we shall see later, the arrangement of the grains in their tetrads determines to a large extent the arrangement and number of the pores or furrows of the completed grain.

Theodor Weimel (1850) showed that in *Fuchsia* each pollen mother-cell may give rise to two to five pollen grains in all possible arrangements, even four cells in a chain. He also noticed that the mature pollen grains of *Fuchsia* had two, three, four, and six germ pores, but he failed to observe the connection between the two phenomena.

A further advance was made in the same direction by Pringsheim (1854). He showed that in the tetrad formation of *Althaea rosea* after the four daughter nuclei are formed, they may assume a tetrahedral arrangement, or, less frequently, they may be all in one plane arranged either as a rhombohedron or as a square. But in either case, he said, there are weakly developed walls thrown across separating the four nuclei almost as in ordinary cell division, but before the walls are completed they are resorbed and replaced by ingrowths of the gelatinous mother-cell which finally separates the whole into four special mother-cells. Precisely how this is done, however, Pringsheim did not explain, and it was not fully elucidated until Farr (1916) worked out the process described by him as simultaneous quadripartition by furrowing.

The whole pollen situation was excellently summarized again in 1860 by Schacht in his "Ueber den Bau einiger Pollenkörner." This work, compared with the earlier summary of Meyen, shows the strides that had been made during the intervening 20 years. But, besides summarizing and correctly evaluating the previous work, Schacht contributed some important new points. He stated, at the outset, that the grains contain a fluid material consisting of a cell nucleus and insoluble material such as starch grains, inulin, oil, and protein compounds, as well as soluble substances such as sugar and dextrin but no fertilizing bodies. The oil, he stated, is uncolored and not the same as that which is found on the outside of the grain. He described the quadripartition of the pollen mother-cells in mistletoe, essentially as Pringsheim had done for *Althaea*. After the young pollen grains are formed, one in each of the special mother-cells, he showed that three thin spots appear on the outer wall of each while it is still smooth. Soon small spines begin to form all over, except on the three thin spots where the wall does not increase in thickness.

While this is happening the mother-cell and special mother-cells are resorbed, after which the pollen grains lie free without filling the space so that they do not hinder each other in their development. This observation of Schacht's shows us clearly why it is that pollen grains do not have three flattened sides, as commonly found in fern spores, resulting from their being pressed against their three neighbors of the tetrad. It appears, however, that Schacht did not notice that the three thin places mark the three last points of contact that each grain made with its three neighbors of the tetrad.

At this time, as we have already seen, it was commonly believed that the oil which clings to the outside of pollen grains, giving them their yellow color, is a secretion from the interior of the grain. But Schacht found that such oil was entirely absent from the granular contents. "Accordingly," said he, "if it is a secretion of the latter it must be formed while passing through the membrane of the grain," which he rightly regarded as *reductio ad absurdum*, but he did not tell us where the oil comes from.

In the descriptive part of his work he touched upon most of the plant families, classifying the grains according to their characters, though not in the form of a key. For example, he stated that the exine may cover the intine as a uniform membrane (*Canna*, *Strelitizia*, *Musa*, *Persea*), but it more often possesses thin spots. These may be closed by lids (Cucurbita). In this way he showed the phyletic distribution of all the known pollen characters, but perhaps the most valuable part of his paper is his excellent original drawings which accompany these descriptions.

Most of the work up to this time had dealt with pollen in general, taking for comparative studies pollen of widely separated species, generally so widely separated that little hint was offered of the transitions of form which are now known to exist between the pollen of different families. The result was that much of the evidence pointed to an absence of any parallelism between pollen forms and phylogeny. This was quite contrary to what should have been expected, particularly in the light of a growing feeling for the evolutionary origin of different biological forms, which was so greatly stimulated at this time by the publication of Darwin's "Origin of Species."

In order to find out to what extent the pollen forms agreed among the species of a single family, Sergius Rosanoff (1866) undertook to study the pollen of the Mimosaceae. One of the outstanding characters of this group is that the grains have a tendency to become united in various numbers. Therefore, while it is an excellent field for learning the effects of contacts of grains with each other, until these have been learned it is not a happy choice for discovering the relation of phylogeny to pollen form. Rosanoff found that among the Mimosaceae the mature grains may be single or firmly united in groups of 4, 8, 16, or higher numbers of cells and that the single grains bear no resemblance to the components of the compound grains. From this he came to the conclusion that, as Kölreuter had already stated, the similarity of pollen grains of different species does not always agree with their closeness in relationship. The weakness in this argument, of course, lies in the fact that the effect of the contact relations of the cells with each other in these compound grains almost completely suppresses the expression of their innate characters, just as in the case of tissue cells. Wood cells are wood cells no matter what plant they come from and differ far more widely from bast or parenchyma cells in the same stem than they do from wood cells of other plants, however distantly related.

Rosanoff's paper, apart from this conclusion, contains much of value. He found that the Mimosaceae, like the orchids which also have compound grains, could be classed into three groups: Group 1, those with single-celled grains, including *Desmanthus, Prosopis*, two species of *Mimosa*, and two of *Acacia;* Group 2, with grains in octads, including *Schrankia* and three species of *Mimosa;* and Group 3, those with 8, 12, 16, and 32 cells, represented only by *Acacia*.

The breaking up of the genus *Acacia* among the three groups is partly explained by the fact that the two species of *Acacia* (*viz., A. leucocephala* and *A. latisiliqua*) having simple grains are not true acacias, the former being now referred to the genus *Leucaena*, and the latter to *Lysiloma*. It thus appears that all true species of *Acacia* have compound grains ranging from 4- to 16-celled and occasionally higher but generally in multiples of four.

Though he was able to discover no resemblance between the compound and the single grains, he did find that the single-grained forms have many similarities. All have a granular exine with the granules arranged in lines converging toward the poles; all have three longitudinal furrows equally spaced and converging toward the poles; and under the furrows are found conspicuous lumps of highly refractive material. In these characters they agree, which is strong argument in favor of the phylogenetic value of such characters.

Up to this time there had been minor disagreements among investigators as to the true nature of the openings in the exine or *Austrittsstellen*, as they had now come to be called with a full realization of their normal function as points of emergence for the pollen tubes. Von Mohl had regarded them as not true openings, citing the lids of the same material as the exine covering them in squash and passionflower pollen; Fritzsche had regarded them as true openings but closed from within by a *Zwischenkörper;* and Meyen had hypothesized the presence of a third layer which emerged under pressure from within to form the pollen tube. Though these differences of opinion were really not significant and were more a matter of the material under consideration than of any basic morphological character, Aloys Pollender (1867) undertook to settle the dispute.

He examined the early stages of developing pollen grains of *Cucurbita* and of some Onagraceae. In the former he observed that the positions of the future pores with their lids seemed to be clearly marked off on the exine, but when he put the grains in weak chromic acid, shrinking the contents away from the wall, the incipient pores disappeared (his figures are so drawn). From this he came to the conclusion that the appearance of pores on the grain had been caused by the flattened cells which he thought he saw underlying the exine and that it was their function to form the lid and eventually to push it off, permitting the egress of the pollen tube. He therefore named them lid cells, stating that Fritzsche had mistaken such for *Zwischenkörper.* In the Onagraceae he said that the bulging germinal papillae were the same cells under a slightly different guise.

Whether or not Pollender was fully aware of the revolutionary import of such a supposition, making of the pollen grain a pluricellular structure, is not clear, but it seems that such matters were of little concern to him. His chief interest seems to have been to show that von Mohl, Fritzsche, and Meyen had erred. His statements, however, did not stand long unchallenged, for Christian Luersen (1869) immediately grasped the import of

Pollender's statements and answered him in his "Zur Contro-verse über die Einzelligkeit oder Mehrzelligkeit des Pollens der Onagrarieen, Cucurbitaceen und Corylaceen." He made a lengthy and detailed study of the pollen of these groups, for the most part confirming the work of his predecessors and adding thereto. But of Pollender he was able to say without fear of contradiction that his conclusions were unjustified and entirely without foundation. He found that neither in pollen grains of the Onagraceae nor *Corylus* are separate cells present, nor are such cells found under the lids, as Pollender had pre-tended to discover. He concludes that, in the onagrads, Pol-lender probably mistook for a cell the space formed beneath the germ pore by the shrinkage of the contents, and in *Cucurbita* and *Corylus*, the thickening of the intine or *Zwischenkörper* underlying the pores. But perhaps more important was Luer-sen's discovery incidental to these studies that the pollen grains of *Epilobium* are frequently found in the anther firmly united in tetrads as they were formed in their mother-cells and correspond-ing in arrangement to the angles of a tetrahedron, always with the bulging germ pores of neighboring grains touching each other, in six pairs in the position of the faces of the tetrahedron. The importance of this lies in the fact that it shows that the three germ pores of such grains originate at the points of contact made by each grain with its three neighbors of the tetrad. This point is beautifully illustrated with original drawings. If Pollender's paper has any value, it lies in the retort that it called from Luersen.

In England at this time attempts were made by some investi-gators to comprehend the significance of the pollen forms which were being revealed by the recently improved microscopes, but these were for the most part frustrated by a total disregard on the part of these investigators for the work that had already been done on the Continent. Only one of these will be men-tioned, for the others played no part whatever in the develop-ment of our science. M. P. Edgeworth (1877) published from London a little book entitled "Pollen." It would not be men-tioned here at all, except that, strangely, it is today the most quoted of all the earlier works. The book purports to be a compendium of nearly all known pollen forms. Each species is described in cryptic form and illustrated. The descriptions are for the most part erroneous, and the figures are purely imaginary, having almost no basis in fact. Yet these bizarre and grotesque figures resembling nothing that could possibly exist in nature have been copied and recopied, published in journals, textbooks, and even in newspapers, to the great detriment of these vehicles. The book itself was republished in 1879.

It was well known at this time that an almost universal character of pollen grains was their great aptitude for absorbing water with a surprisingly large increase in their volume, but the mechanisms whereby such volume changes were accommodated had been entirely overlooked since the time when Kölreuter had stated that in certain types of grains the intine could bulge through round pores in the exine, so preventing the rupture of the latter as expansion took place. It remained, however, for the French investigator J. Vesque (1883), who thought of pollen grains as living dynamic entities and not just inert vehicles of fertilization, to explain the mechanical organizations of pollen grains for accommodating their ever changing volumes. He tells us that when a pollen grain loses water it shrinks. In the simplest cases it just contracts with the formation of surface cavities. This is what happens with the grains of grasses, for example, causing them to assume irregularly shaped pyramidal or conical shapes when dry. But in other kinds of pollen the structure of the grain is such that it retains its symmetry no matter how great the loss of water that it may undergo. This result is obtained by two different means: (1) by meridionally arranged, spindle-shaped areas where the membrane is thin and weak (He does not call these areas germinal furrows, nor does he say that they have anything to do with germination. That function—the only one which they were supposed, by all other investigators, to possess— did not even interest him. He says that when moist such a grain is spherical and the spindle-shaped areas are broad but that as the grain dries it becomes ellipsoidal and the thin-walled areas become narrower until finally their cutinized edges touch and transpiration is thereby greatly hindered. If a further loss of water continues, it makes the grain thinner and longer, at the same time inducing in its interior a proportionate negative tension which must eventually check the loss of water.); (2) by one or both polar surfaces, at first convex, tending to become flat or concave as water is lost, returning to their original convexity when a permiable part of the grain happens to come in contact with a moist surface. An example of this type of grain is beautifully illustrated by the grain of *Juglans*, in which one polar hemisphere bears the pores through which water may be transpired or absorbed, while the other polar hemisphere is covered only by a thin, flexible membrane which may be depressed or raised in compensation for loss or gain in volume.

Further on in the same paper Vesque makes the surprising statement that the arrangement of the spines and of the laminae and the networks, which decorate the surface of pollen grains, does not appear to depend upon the mode of development: "They seem to obey only a geometrical law which may be none other than the law of phyllotaxy extended to other projecting organs of the plant and to the law of economy for the net." Quite clearly he recognized the mathematical arrangements of the surface sculpturing and their underlying law of least surface configuration which is regarded as a very modern idea. "Nothing is easier," he says, "than to explain the complicated form of the grains of the Cichorieae in this way. These grains are covered with ridges perpendicular to the surface, which form a regular network of pentagonal and hexagonal spaces." He did not quite grasp the controlling mathematical proportion between the number of pentagons and of hexagons which may be placed on a spherical surface but thought that this relation had something to do with the deviation of the shape of the grain from the truly spherical form, stating that "the number of hexagonal spaces will be greater as the grain approaches the cylindrical form"—offering this as the explanation for the fact that, of the 21 faces on the grains of *Lactuca*, 9 are hexagonal, whereas, in reality, the proportion between the hexagonal and pentagonal faces is in this case one of the few choices which are mathematically possible on a sphere when the total number of faces is 21. Nevertheless, Vesque here introduced for the first time into the study of pollen grains the mechanistic conception that their underlying forms are controlled by purely physical and mathematical laws.

In the meantime, the subject of the development of pollen grains was being vigorously prosecuted by Eduard Strasburger. Following a number of short papers on the subject, he published a masterly sketch in his "Ueber den Bau und das Wachsthum der

Zellhäute" (1882).   He chose for study representative forms as
dissimilar as possible, so as to exhaust—as he says—the multiplicity of different combinations.   The pollen of *Malva* was
studied in the minutest detail, from the anlage of the mother-cells
up to the completed form and even to its germination and tube
formation.   Using this as a background, he made comparative
studies of *Geranium, Guarea, Oenothera, Clarkia, Epilobium,
Pinus, Larix*, and many others.   This work he extended and
greatly improved in "Ueber das Wachsthum vegetabilischer
Zellhäute" (1889).   These two works cleared up almost completely the perplexing subject of pollen development, and they
form the basis of our knowledge of it today.   But dealing mainly
with development they are somewhat aside from our central
theme so cannot be dwelt upon further at this time.   In passing,
however, it should be noticed that Strasburger here introduced a
curious conception of the exine: "I call *exinium* the first coat
entirely covering the whole spores and pollen grains, *intinium*, a
second inner coat which is separated from the first."   This was
not according to the conception which we have seen that Fritzsche
had when he coined the words exine and intine, and it led to some
confusion later on.

We must also pass by, with little more than a word of mention,
two very interesting papers by Louis Mangin (1886, 1889).
The first of these deals with the physiology and chemistry of the
germination and growth of pollen; the second, with its structure
and development, and seems to have been inspired by the work of
Strasburger.   Mangin states that the intine in most cases consists of cellulose and pectose.   These two substances may be
mixed in various proportions, but more often the cellulose is
concentrated in the inner layer, and the pectose in the outer
layer of the intine, the two merging in between.   Beneath the
Austrittsstellen, where the intine is generally greatly thickened,
it consists principally of pectose, such thickenings being the
Zwischenkörper of Fritzsche.   In this same paper Mangin takes
Strasburger to task for his statement that in the grains of *Allium
fistulosum* the intine is not formed.   Instead, says Strasburger,
the exine is continuous throughout and cutinized except in the
region of the single germinal furrow, where it is greatly thickened
but not cutinized.   This part which Strasburger regards as a
thickened, noncutinized part of the exine, he states, gives rise

to the pollen tube. Mangin stoutly contradicts this, stating that the intine is continuous and gives rise to the pollen tube, while the exine is a discontinuous layer, not covering the region of the germinal furrow. These differences of opinion caused a lengthy controversy between the two investigators. Strasburger's viewpoint, while decidedly heterodox, conformed to his conceptions of intine and exine which he had clearly defined some years previously, while Mangin's viewpoint conforms to the conception that was generally accepted and was clearly that intended by Fritzsche in his original definitions of the words.

While the works of Strasburger and Mangin were not in themselves strictly morphological, the light that they threw on pollen structures made possible further advances in pollen morphology. Most attempts at working out anything like a comparative morphology had hitherto failed, because the structures of pollen grains were not fully understood and had not been clearly defined. But the work of Strasburger and Mangin had so cleared the field that it now awaited a really comprehensive comparative morphological study. This hiatus was soon filled by Fischer in 1890.

Fischer.—This scientist Carl Albert Hugo Fischer was born in Breslau in 1865, the second son of Robert Fischer. His earliest education was received at a private school in his native city. From there he went, in 1875, to Michaeli where he attended the gymnasium of Maria Magdelena until 1883, when he reached his majority. Afterward he attended the University of Halle, coming under the tutelage of such men as Grenacher, Kirchhoff, and Kraus. In 1886 he returned to Breslau, and under the direction principally of F. Cohn but also of Engler and Heidenhain he took his degree of Doctor of Philosophy in 1889 with his thesis, "Beiträge zur vergleichenden Morphologie der Pollenkörner." After the publication of this work it appears that Fischer paid no further attention to pollen, his interests centering mainly around colloidal chemistry, plant nutrition, soil chemistry, and applied botany. In 1898 he published an article on inulin and, in 1927, 'Bau und Eigenschaften pflanzlicher Kolloïde," both in Cohn's "Beiträge für Biologie der Pflanzen." In 1930 he published "Landwirtschaftliche Bacterienkunde." He is at present living in Berlin and actively engaged in the study of plant physiology, floristics, and allied subjects.

In his "Beiträge" Fischer states that, finding the field of comparative morphology of pollen by no means exhausted, he set himself the two problems: (1) "How is the outer layer of a pollen grain formed?" and (2) "In what way do plants which are related in their outward form agree in their pollen-grain structures?"

Fig. 9.—Hugo Fischer, 1926.

But while he was busy with these subjects there came into his hands the second edition of Edgeworth's book (1879) and Strasburger's "Ueber das Wachsthum vegetabilischer Zellhäute" (1889). The second had so completely exhausted the subject of the development of pollen grains and in such a fashion that Fischer felt that no further study of that subject was necessary. Of Edgeworth's book, however, he says that it is quite worthless because the author makes so many mistakes that none of his work can be accepted without proof.

Fischer studied his grains both wet and dry in order to learn the effect of expansion on their shape, and many of the grains he embedded in gum arabic and sectioned with a razor staining with appropriate aniline dyes. In this thorough fashion he studied over 2,000 species of pollen in 158 families—a much more complete study than any which had hitherto been made.

He was impressed at the outset by the fact that pollen grains are always single cells. People sometimes speak of pluricellular or compound grains, he says, when what is really meant is "cells grown together." Like other cells, pollen grains have three principal parts—nucleus, plasma, and wall—and the characters whereby the different kinds of pollen are distinguished are cell characters, the properties of the wall or, more properly, of the exine.

The exine, he says, generally reveals the possession of a cuticle which, in its chemical reactions, shows much similarity to protein substances, staining an intense brown with iodine and taking aniline dyes in the same ways that proteins do. This substance also gives the xanthoproteic and Millon's reactions which characterize proteins but differs from most proteins in being insoluble in alkali. In this latter character, however, the cuticle differs from suberin and cutin, which it otherwise resembles very closely. Fischer states that the exine is insoluble in concentrated nitric, hydrochloric, or sulphuric acid. It also resists gastric digestion, for upon examining the excreta of chafers which had been feeding on pollen, he found grains with their exines intact though their nutrient contents and intines had been dissolved away. Almost the only chemicals that he could find which would dissolve the exine were eau de Javelle and chromic acid; and to these reagents the different species of pollen showed marked differences in their reactions; with some the exine dissolved easily, but with others, *e.g.*, *Pinus*, it could be dissolved only upon prolonged boiling. In concentrated sulphuric acid the exine turns red, and this, Fischer says, is due to the presence of sugar, as had already been pointed out by Strasburger (1887) in the case of proteins. Structurally, Fischer says, Fritzsche had already pointed out that the exine usually consists of two layers. The inner is more highly refractive to light and has a weaker affinity for aniline dyes than the outer which carries most of the sculpturing responsible for the diversity of pollen forms.

Fischer's classification of these forms is as follows:

I   A. Exine absent
       B. Exine present
II   a. Uniform throughout
              b. With *Austrittsstellen*
III   1. *Austrittsstellen* round
IV   2. *Austrittsstellen* as furrows
              c. With germ pores
V   1. in the furrows
VI   2. free on the surface
VII With one or more lids.

Fischer uses the word *Austrittsstellen* in a more restricted sense than did his predecessors, applying it only to thin spots in the surface as distinct from actual holes through the exine, the germ pores.

In his classification he makes no use of the compounding of grains, as previous investigators had done, for, he says, it has no significance—some species may have compound grains, while their nearest relatives may have single grains, *e.g.*, species of *Typha* and *Jussieua*.   But a most striking observation that he made in his study of compound grains was that in symmetrical tetrads grains with bipolar axes are so arranged in relation to one another that the axis of each grain is directed toward the middle of the group, (*e.g.*, Ericaceae, *Drosera*, and *Jussieua*).   When each grain has only one *Austrittsstelle* it faces outward from the other grains (*e.g.*, *Philydrum*, *Victoria*, and *Drimys*).   We may perhaps call this Fischer's law, for I believe that no one before had observed this important relation between the forms of grains and their spatial relations in their tetrads, though Fritzsche had come very close to doing so.   It is to this law that pollen grains owe most of their basic form characters.

The body of Fischer's work consists of a critical examination of the pollen of about 2,200 species arranged according to his classification given above.   And from these studies he was able to draw the following conclusions:

Pollen grains of related species are generally similar; indeed, a single form of grain often runs through the whole family, and the species of a genus can hardly ever be distinguished from each other by their form, though they may occasionally be by their color.

Some families have more than a single basic form. Sometimes unrelated plants have similar pollen.

In the general evolution of pollen grains there has been a progressive strengthening of the exine and, at the same time, the formation of prearranged places of exit for the pollen tube, but, in both of these, sometimes a reversion has occurred. The strengthening of the exine takes place not merely through the accumulation of thicker material but more especially through the addition to the ground membrane of spines and reticulations. Thus the grains of the gymnosperms and monocotyledons generally have an exine of simple structure, while those of the dicotyledons generally have an exine which is more complicated, culminating in the spine-covered grains of the Compositae and the reticulate grains of the Cichorieae.

The pollen grains of the gymnosperms, monocotyledons, and lower dicotyledons are generally monomerous, while those of the higher dicotyledons are generally trimerous. This condition results from their position in the tetrad, which is generally in one plane in the former and tetrahedral in the latter. But there are many exceptions, so this criterion may be employed only with caution in classification.

Adaptation to insect pollination is accomplished by the presence of oil, which Fischer believes is secreted through the exine, and by the formation of spines. But the pollen of those plants which have reverted to anemophily differs from that of their related entomophilous species in having grains with thinner and smoother exine but generally standing in other respects close to the pollen of their relatives, as, for example, the anemophilous pollen of *Thalictrum*, *Artemisia*, and *Ambrosia*, though they may be entirely different, for example, the smooth, furrowless grains of *Populus* as compared with the reticulate, three-furrowed grains of *Salix*.

These few very concise statements of Fischer's summarize briefly and adequately the phylogenetic value of pollen-grain characters. They were first noticed by Grew and Malpighi. One by one they were laboriously brought to light and sifted out by subsequent investigators. There were many apparent contradictions, and many mistakes were made. But through the brilliant researches of such men as Mirbel, Purkinje, von Mohl, and Fritzsche, to mention only a few of the leading names, our understanding of pollen forms gradually took shape; it remained, however, for Hugo Fischer, taking nothing for granted, going always back to nature, to round out our knowledge and give us the morphology of pollen grains in its modern form.

CHAPTER II

METHODS OF COLLECTING POLLEN IN LARGE AMOUNTS

When it is necessary to secure pollen in large amounts, as for the preparation of hayfever-pollen extracts or various other chemical work, special methods must be employed according to the nature of the plants from which the pollen is to be obtained.

In general, it may be said that *it is always best to collect from the first flowers to open* rather than from those that bloom toward the end of the flowering season, because the late flowers are usually less vigorous and are likely to be infested with insects. With flowers which are particularly susceptible to pollen-eating insects, *e.g.*, the oxeye daisy and sorrel dock, the first flowers may be nearly free from such insects, but as the flowering season advances they become more and more infested with them, finally reaching a stage where there are so many insects that practically all of the pollen is devoured as fast as it is released from the anthers. With most forest trees it is essential that the flowers be gathered as soon as the first of them open, because the flowering period is often so short and so much under the influence of local weather conditions that if the weather turns suddenly warm and dry, anthesis may be completed within two or three days. Thus it is with early flowering trees, such as the pines, junipers, elms, and poplars; unless advantage is taken of the first opportunity to collect their flowers, the opportunity is likely to be lost entirely for the season. With the early flowering trees the factors that finally bring about anthesis are generally temperature and humidity. The flowers reach the bursting point and remain in this condition until the arrival of a warm, dry day when they suddenly open and complete their pollination within one or a very few days. Advantage should be taken of this fact to collect the flowers of such plants in the cool, damp days immediately preceding anthesis.

101

The method employed in handling the flowers depends to a large extent upon whether they are wind- or insect-pollinated and whether they will continue to live and shed their pollen after cutting or whether, as sometimes happens, pollen shedding ceases as soon as the flowers are cut.

Natural Shedding.—Nearly all anemophilous, and a few entomophilous, plants can be made to shed their pollen quite naturally indoors. Such, for example, are the conifers and most other gymnosperms, the Gramineae, Cyperaceae, Typhaceae, Chenopodiaceae, Amaranthaceae, most of the early flowering trees, the Ambrosiaceae, and *Artemisia* and, among the entomophilous plants, some species of goldenrod, thistle, and sunflower. In dealing with plants of this class the flowering stems are cut off and placed in water in the shedding room. For this purpose it is convenient to use long, shallow pans about one foot wide in which a central bar has been arranged lengthwise to act as a catch to hold the cut ends of the stems beneath the water. The plants are placed in these pans in a nearly horizontal position so that the flowering tips lean out far enough to be clear of the edges of the pans. Sheets of paper are then placed under the flowers to catch the pollen. The flowers should be gently tapped once a day until the pollen ceases to drop off; then the papers should be drawn out, and the pollen removed.

Most of the grasses can be handled in this manner. They should be cut in the early morning—if possible while the dew is still on them. The leaves should be stripped off in the field, and the stems trimmed to the proper length to fit the shedding pans. They should then be bundled loosely together, and their stems kept moist by the addition of water or, during very dry weather, by keeping them immersed in buckets of water until the shedding room is reached. The cut plants should not be stacked together for a longer time than necessary, and on no account may they be bundled tightly, because respiration is rapid during this period of their growth, and so much heat and moisture are generated that the plants may be "burned" and completely destroyed in less than an hour.

Collecting should be done in the morning. Many grasses exhibit a marked periodicity in their shedding. Some, for example, orchard grass, shed most abundantly early each morning, beginning as soon as the warmth of the sun's rays is felt, falling off toward noon, and ceasing in the afternoon. Others begin late in the day; for example, redtop begins to pollinate rather suddenly at about three o'clock in the afternoon and continues for only an hour or two. In either case the plants should be collected in the morning and placed in the shedding pans as quickly as possible, because the drying that sets in as soon as they are cut accelerates the opening of the anthers and causes the bulk of the day's pollen to be shed soon after.

Some grasses, of which the Indian rice and tall oat grass are examples, will shed little or no pollen after being cut. Nevertheless, these should be placed in the shedding pans as described above. After two or three days most of the anthers will be found to have dropped off unopened, and the rest can be removed by gently shaking the inflorescences. These anthers should be brushed up, partly dried, and shaken on sieves to remove any pollen that might happen to be freed from them. In order to obtain the pollen still remaining in the anthers they should be passed through a coffee mill with the plates adjusted just tight enough to roll the anthers and loosen the pollen. If this is done properly and the anthers are not too dry and brittle, most of the pollen will be set free and may be separated from the crushed anthers by sifting.

Pollen obtained by this method always contains a large proportion of immature grains, which are said to be anaphylactogenically less active than those that are mature, and some fragments of anthers which are totally inactive. The proportion of these will depend upon the skill and care with which the grinding and sifting are done.

Plant-breeder's Method.—Grasses and other plants which fail to shed naturally indoors can sometimes be handled by a plant-breeder's method. This consists of tying paper bags over the inflorescences in the field, just as they are starting to pollinate. Special bags may be obtained for the purpose which are proof against destruction by moisture but porous enough to permit the escape of the moisture which otherwise tends to accumulate within. The bags can be left on for only a few hours, after which they must be removed, and the pollen emptied out and dried.

Most insect-pollinated flowers offer more difficulty than those that are wind-pollinated, except the very few kinds that will shed naturally from pans of water. For roses we may employ the following special method.   The flower buds are gathered just as they are about to open.   They are then dried slowly on sheets of paper in a warm, dry, and well-ventilated room.   The corollas, which still remain tightly closed, are pulled off from their receptacles, and the pollen emptied out on to a sieve and brushed through to separate it from the anthers and other floral parts which come with it.

Carbon Tetrachloride Method.—Most entomophilous plants, in which the pollen is sticky and remains enclosed within the flowers, will yield to the carbon tetrachloride method (Wodehouse, 1916), which is briefly as follows: The staminate flowers, after being dried but not completely desiccated, are removed from their floral receptacle and freed as far as possible from all extraneous material.   The mass of flowers is then soaked in carbon tetrachloride in an open pan or mortar and gently beaten with a pestle, to loosen the pollen from the anthers or pollen tubes; the whole is then emptied on to a piece of fine muslin stretched across another pan, and the carbon tetrachloride pressed out.   The liquid carries the pollen through the muslin, leaving the crushed flowers behind.   These should then be washed repeatedly until all the pollen is loosened and suspended in the carbon tetrachloride. The suspension is then poured on to a Büchner funnel to which a piece of smooth filter paper has been fitted, and the carbon tetrachloride drawn rapidly through by suction, leaving the pollen collected on the filter paper in a solid cake.   This should be washed with fresh carbon tetrachloride, to free it from lipoid substances, and dried by sucking air through it.   The cake is then broken up, and the pollen sifted through a 200-mesh sieve and completely desiccated.   Pollen prepared by this method is generally contaminated to some extent with pollen of foreign species and plant fragments, but under favorable conditions these occur   in   only   negligible   quantities.

Desiccation.—Complete and prolonged desiccation must never be omitted, by whatever method the pollen is obtained.   Pollen collected on the papers in the shedding rooms may appear to be° quite dry when brushed up but, if confined in glass jars without a preliminary complete desiccation, after a few days it becomes caked and useless.   Furthermore, there is evidence to show that even air-dried pollen deteriorates slowly, but this may be prevented by completely desiccating and enclosing it in airtight containers.

Therefore, as soon as possible the pollen should be brushed up, sifted, and dried in a vacuum desiccator over calcium chloride or sulphuric acid until no more moisture can be removed, when it should be transferred to airtight containers with as little exposure to the air as possible.   Even after desiccation pollen may take up moisture if exposed to the air.   Indeed, the absorption of moisture from the air is so rapid with some kinds of pollen that it is difficult to weigh them in ordinary atmosphere.

CHAPTER III

PREPARATION OF POLLEN FOR MICROSCOPIC EXAMINATION

Methyl-green Glycerin Jelly.—A small amount of pollen, about as much as can be picked up on the flat end of a toothpick, or less, is placed on the center of a microscope slide, and a drop of alcohol added and allowed partly to evaporate. A second and third or even fourth drop may be added if necessary. The alcohol spreads out as it evaporates and leaves the oily and resinous substances of the pollen deposited in a ring around the specimen. The oily ring is wiped off with cotton moistened with alcohol, and, before the specimen has had time to dry completely, a small drop of hot, melted methyl-green glycerin jelly is added, and the pollen stirred in with a needle and evenly distributed. During the process the jelly is kept hot by passing the slide over a small flame, heating it just enough to sting but not burn the knuckle, which may be used to test its temperature. A No. 0 cover glass, which has been passed several times through the flame while held vertically with the forceps, is then placed over the specimen, and the slide gently heated. If the amount of jelly has been judged correctly, the cover will settle into position, with the gelatin reaching its periphery just when the pressure of the cover begins to be taken up by the pollen grains. This amount must be learned by experience and accurately gauged, because a smaller amount leaves the grains crushed or flattened by the cover or the mount incompletely filled, and a larger amount causes the preparation to be too thick for use with oil-immersion lenses.

If naturally shed pollen is not available, satisfactory material can generally be obtained from herbarium specimens, provided they were quickly and completely dried. Often it is only necessary to tap the dry flowers over the slide or crush a few anthers on it. If pollen cannot be removed in this way, a few anthers or, with the Compositae, a few florets may be removed from the specimen and placed on the slide. These are then moistened with alcohol, followed by a drop of water, and heated to boiling. The pollen may then be teased out, and the anthers and other debris removed, leaving the pollen in the water. The water is then drawn off with cotton or filter paper, and the jelly added as before.

The glycerin jelly is prepared according to the method of Brandt* which is as follows: Soak some gelatin for 2 or 3 hr. in cold water, pour off the superfluous water, and heat until melted. To 1 part of this add 1½ parts of glycerin and, while still hot, filter through spun glass pressed into the lower part of a heated funnel. Add 2 or 3 per cent phenol. Still keeping the mixture hot and fluid, add drop by drop a saturated solution of methyl green in 50 per cent alcohol, until the glycerin jelly becomes fully as dark as green ink.

Methyl-green glycerin jelly may also be made by adding the dye, as indicated above, to a good commercial preparation of glycerin jelly, of which there are a number on the market.

The relative proportions of glycerin and water are so balanced in glycerin jelly that the majority of pollen grains when placed in it are fully but rarely over expanded, and they never burst and extrude their contents, as is usually the case with ordinary aqueous mediums.

Contrast Stain.—When treated as above, the methyl green stains only the exine, leaving the intine and cell contents uncolored. If it is desired to show a contrast between the exine and cell contents, the pollen may be given a preliminary staining on the slide with weak aqueous eosine. The contrast thus obtained is striking and brilliant and therefore excellent for demonstration purposes but of no other advantage.

Pollen grains mounted in glycerin jelly and stained with methyl green have a peculiar habit of developing greater brilliancy during the first few days after they are made, probably through a slow, selective adsorption of the dye from the embedding medium. It is therefore advantageous to make up the slides a day or two before they are required. They retain their brilliancy for several months unimpaired but unfortunately are not permanent, for the dye fades slowly out after a period varying from about 9 months to 2 years, after which they are

* Lee, "Microtomist's Vade Mecum, 7th ed., p. 242.

entirely bleached. Such preparations may always be restored, however. To do this the slide is heated, the cover glass removed, a small drop of hot methyl-green glycerin jelly is worked in with a needle, and the preparation covered with a fresh cover glass. Specimens so rejuvenated are just as good as new, but the labor of recovering them is perhaps a little more than would be required to make them anew from fresh pollen. Nevertheless, the method is valuable in cases where the pollen is no longer available.

Aqueous fuchsin has the same selective properties as methyl green, is much more vigorous in its action, and is *permanent*. The only objection to its use is that the red color is theoretically not quite so satisfactory for observation with high-power lenses as the blue color, though in actual practice there is little difference. It may be used in place of methyl green as above, or according to the method of Fischer (1890) as follows: After the pollen has been washed with alcohol on the slide, a drop of weak solution of basic fuchsin in water is added, and the pollen stirred in with a needle. As soon as the grains have taken up all the dye, the water is drawn off with cotton, and, without letting the preparation dry, a drop of melted glycerin jelly is added, and the pollen stirred in, keeping the slide warm. It is then covered with a No. 0 cover glass.*

Atmospheric Pollen Slides.—Methyl-green or fuchsin glycerin jelly serves very well for catching atmospheric pollen and making pollen counts and identifications. A small drop of the melted glycerin jelly with the dye added is placed on a slide, spread out to occupy an area about equal to, and of the same shape as, the cover glass which is to be used in finishing the mount. The slide is exposed in a horizontal position protected from rain and sun by a shelter raised at least 4 in. above it. After 24 or 48 hr. the slide is brought into the laboratory and examined with a hand lens, and any extraneous material, like soot or sand, which, if present, might prevent the cover glass from fitting into place, is removed. The slide is then heated, the temperature being controlled with the knuckle as before, until any excess moisture which may have accumulated during exposure is driven off. It is then covered with a No. 0 cover glass.

---

* A very satisfactory glycerin jelly for this purpose is that prepared by Eimer & Amend, New York.

In order to make the pollen count from such a slide, it is placed on a microscope provided with a mechanical stage and passed from left to right and from right to left, progressing the width of a single field in a forward direction with each passage from side to side. For this purpose it is most economical of time and labor to use a low magnification (about 150 diameters), and whenever a pollen grain is found that cannot be identified at that magnification, a higher objective is swung in, the identification made, the high objective then replaced by the low, and the counting continued until the entire surface has been covered.

Examination of Dry Pollen.—When it is desired to discover the unexpanded shapes of pollen grains they may be observed dry in air with or without a cover glass. Such observations are also useful in seeing how much oil naturally occurs on the surface of the grains, also as a check against the method to be described below. With dry pollen in air, magnifications much over 200 diameters can scarcely be used to advantage; nevertheless, even at this magnification the shapes of the grains can be learned and something of the mechanical action of their organs of volume-change accommodation. If, however, a detailed examination of the grains in their unexpanded condition is desired, they must be stained and brought into a medium of suitable refractive index. This may be done as follows:

Aniline-oil Gentian-violet Method.—Place the pollen on the slide as before and add two or three drops of aniline oil which has been tinted with gentian violet only to a pale-purple color. Heat gently over a small flame, controlling the temperature with the knuckle as before until the grains become deeply stained; allow the slide to cool to room temperature; draw off the excess oil with filter paper; wash by repeatedly adding xylol and drawing it off until all the oil and unabsorbed dye have been removed; then add a drop of Canada balsam and cover. This method presents the grains unexpanded but brilliantly stained and in a medium eminently suited for observation with high-power oil-immersion lenses.

CHAPTER IV

POLLEN STATISTICS

A BOTANICAL AND GEOLOGICAL RESEARCH METHOD

BY GUNNAR ERDTMAN, *Stockholm**

Pollen statistics is the method of tracing the history of forests by a study of the occurrence of fossil pollen grains in peats and sediments. The method was elaborated some 20 years ago by the late Prof. G. Lagerheim of the Department of Botany at the University of Stockholm and by Dr. L. von Post, now professor of geology at the same university.

Pollen statistical methods include work in both the field and the laboratory. The field work is done chiefly during the summer. During the winter, however, when the lakes are frozen over, samples of bottom sediments can be obtained from them by means of borings through the ice. Several types of auger are available; but of these the one that is coming into most general use is the Hiller peat auger, manufactured by Beus and Mattson Company, Mora, Sweden (Fig. 10). This company offers the auger in two different models—a smaller one, with the chamber in which the peat sample is collected 32 cm. long and extension rods 100 cm. each; and a larger model, with the chamber 40 cm. long and extension rods 150 cm. each. If the field work is to be carried out with the help of an assistant, preference should be given to the heavier auger, which is more reliable than the lighter one. The field apparatus also includes a spade, big knife, nickel-plated forceps with smooth ends, glass tubes in which to keep the peat samples (about 7.5 cm. long, 1.3 cm. inside diameter, and corked at both ends), diopter compass, and a geodetical set for taking levels and distances.

* The essential parts of this chapter were included in lectures given at the University of Chicago and the University of Michigan, July, 1931, and in a note in *Science*, March, 1931. The section on technique is an abridgment of an article by G. Erdtman and H. Erdtman (1933).

Peat samples should be taken from the cleaned walls of peat hags if such are available, but, if not, borings have to be made. To do this a big sod is removed from the surface of the bog with the spade. From the walls of the sod the first samples are taken, say, from 2, 5, 10, 15, and 20 cm. below the surface. Then the auger is put in the hole left by the sod and forced down into the peat. Meanwhile the handle of the auger should be kept turning slightly to the right (clockwise) to prevent the container from opening. When the desired depth is reached the container is opened, and a good compact core obtained, by turning the handle swiftly about four revolutions to the left. It is then closed again by two turns to the right, and the auger is pulled up out of the peat, giving it a slight continued revolution to the right to be sure that the chamber will stay closed until it reaches the surface. The core is then removed from the chamber, and the outer layer, which might have become contaminated with material from higher levels, is removed with the knife. Samples are then taken from the core with the forceps at regular intervals, *e.g.*, at every fifth centimeter.

It is sometimes advantageous, when working with an auger of the larger model, to place a thin, removable zinc lining inside the container (see Fig. 10). When a boring is made the lining gets filled. The lining

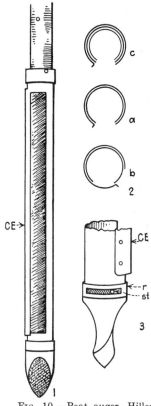

Fig. 10.—Peat auger, Hiller model. 1. Lower end of auger with chamber open. The cutting edge, *CE*, should be fairly sharp. The opposite edge may be marked at intervals of 5 cm. 2. Cross section of the chamber: *a*, open, *b*, closed, *c*, to show the position of the zinc lining which is represented in the sketch by the inner arc. 3. Lower part of the chamber and screw point. The outer sleeve of the chamber is riveted to the ring, *r*, but the inner is free to revolve within. *st* is a pin fastened to the inner sleeve; it can traverse the length of the slot in the ring, thus checking at the proper places the opening and closing movements of the sleeve. (*Adapted from Kräusel*, 1929.)

with the core of material enclosed is then removed from the
chamber of the auger and brought intact into the laboratory.
By the proper use of zinc linings a complete series of such cores
from the surface to the bottom of the bog can be obtained.
Drying and shrinkage of the material are prevented by glycerin,
and, from such cores, samples for pollen-statistical investigations
may be picked out at any time and from any part of the
cores. Sometimes one sample from every second foot of
the series of cores is sufficient; at other times a dozen samples
from one inch of core may be required. It is impossible in the
field to be sure of the best intervals at which the samples should
be taken; the use of the linings, however, solves the problem.

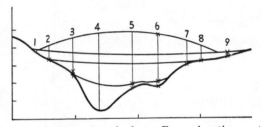

Fig. 11.—Cross section of a bog.   For explanation see text.

It is convenient to have the spade standing with its blade
thrust into the ground near the boring and to put the lower end
of the auger with its chamber through the handle of the spade
while the samples are being taken from the chamber.   Figure 11
shows, schematically, a section of a bog the stratification of
which has been made out from serial borings.   A complete series
of peat samples would most suitably be gathered from point 4,
and additional samples for the study of the growth of the bog
and the composition of the Sub-recent pollen flora, etc., from the
places marked with crosses.

When preparations for microscopical work are to be made, a
small amount of peat is taken from one of the samples, laid on
a slide, and mixed with 10 per cent caustic potash.   The slide is
then held with a clothespin, and the mixture carefully boiled over
a small alcohol flame until the greater part of the water has
evaporated.   Some drops of glycerin are then added and mixed
with the peat, and a part of the mixture is removed to another
slide and covered with a cover glass.   The pollen grains are then

counted by the use of a microscope with a mechanical stage. A magnification of about two hundred times is required for counting, and a high-power lens for the study of the finer structural details of the grains. Some sediments need no boiling, and preparations are made by simply mixing a part of the substance with distilled water. Calcareous material is treated with dilute hydrochloric acid and minerogene earths, and even rather coarse sand can be subjected to pollen analysis if centrifuged and treated with hydrofluoric acid. Trustworthy percentages are obtained, as has been proved for Sweden, by counting about 150 pollen grains. As to samples from northern Canada and other countries with only a few tree species of which pollen is preserved in bogs, fairly reliable percentages can be obtained by counting 100 or even fewer pollen grains. It is, on the other hand, desirable that more than 150 pollen grains should be counted in samples from districts with a great number of tree species (*e.g.*, great parts of the United States).

The frequency of the pollen grains of hazel, willow, and other species, which are more or less confined to the undergrowth of the forests and are not regarded in these studies as forest trees, is calculated separately and expressed as a percentage of the sum of the pollen grains of the forest trees proper. Thus a willow pollen frequency of 138 per cent indicates that the number of willow pollen grains in that sample was greater than the sum of the pollen grains of the forest trees. The frequency of *Sphagnum* spores, tetrads of Ericaceae, etc., is expressed in the same way. It is useful, too, to have a record of the *pollen frequency* per square centimeter, *P F*, from each preparation.

The percentages, *i.e.*, the relative frequency numbers, that are found for the pollen species in a sample constitute the *pollen spectrum* of the sample. The pollen spectrum shows to a certain extent the proportions of the different kinds of pollen grains which settled on the bog when the layer, from which the analyzed peat was taken, formed at the surface.

On the basis of a series of pollen spectra from a boring in a bog a *pollen diagram* may be constructed, with the depths of the peat plotted as ordinates and the pollen percentages as abcissas corresponding to those levels where the samples were taken. In a pollen diagram the curves for the single species or for a group of species give both a visual representation of the composition of the pollen flora and the oscillations with regard to frequency, which have taken place reciprocally between the pollen curves during the formation of the bog.

When a sufficiently close network of pollen-diagram stations has been completed for a country, and when the diagrams, with the aid of archeological data from the bogs or in other ways, have been properly dated, then it is possible, with practically the same accuracy as in the case of modern forests, to reconstruct on maps the distribution of the forest trees and the changes of the forest types from one area to another and from one region to another during different periods.

AN IMPROVED TECHNIQUE OF POLLEN ANALYSIS

The process of digesting peat by means of boiling with dilute alkalies, which at present is in general use, suffers from several sources of error, both theoretical and practical. Indeed, the composition of the fossil pollen content can be shown to vary according to the method of preparation of the samples for investigation.

If peat is prepared for microscopic investigation by boiling with alkali—rather a severe treatment—a source of error is introduced. Sometimes the peat is boiled with dilute alkali until most of the water has evaporated (this treatment may be repeated); sometimes it is boiled less intensively. According to the difference of treatment the results are often not strictly comparable. Furthermore, the peat is frequently inadequately digested by the alkali, and some pollen will consequently escape observation because partly or wholly obscured by undigested debris. Small pollen grains escape attention more readily than larger ones, which therefore tend to be overrepresented. This source of error is well known* and may in certain cases cause considerable distortion of the pollen percentages.

Another source of error is connected with the final covering of the slide with the cover glass. It is easy to demonstrate that the relative frequencies of the pollen grains in an artificial mixture of pollen grains (or in a peat preparation) may change to some extent according to the force with which the cover glass is pressed against the slide. This distortion will occur if some of the

---

* Cf.. *e.g.*, ASSARSSON and GRANLUND, pp. 80, 81, 1924.

material is squeezed out at the edges of the coverglass and seems to be due mainly to the varying sizes of the pollen grains.

Another drawback to the alkali method is, the difficulty of concentrating the pollen grains sufficiently for analyses of peat samples of low pollen content to be made reasonably quickly.

Among the constituents of peat are cellulose and hemicellulose, which on hydrolysis by acids are transformed into water-soluble products, *e.g.*, glucose. Other constituents are lignin and humic acids, both of which cannot be hydrolyzed by acids but are easily destroyed by oxidation. Combining the method of hydrolysis and oxidation we have been able to remove these constituents of peat and isolate the more resistant elements, *viz.*, pollen, spores, and fragments of cuticles. For the oxidative destruction of lignin and humic acids, treatment with chlorine dioxide* was found useful; the remainder of the peat was then treated with cold, strong sulphuric acid in order to hydrolyze the polysaccharides.

In our preliminary experiments we used a homogenous standard peat prepared from slightly moldered *Sphagnum* peat, the age of which is estimated to be about two thousand years. It was rather difficult to analyze by the alkali method, but when treated according to our acid-oxidation method the pollen grains and spores, etc., were obtained almost free from peaty debris.

The new method may perhaps at first seem to be rather complicated, since it involves the use of different chemicals and a centrifuge. In our opinion this is quite outweighed by its advantages, particularly the possibility of concentrating pollen grains and other microfossils to an extent far beyond reach of the alkali method. This advantage is particularly manifested in the study of any peats which for one reason or another have a low pollen content. In this connection some Canadian and other peats have already been mentioned, and others might be added, such as the Greenland peats which are situated beyond the distribution area of forest trees. With the use of the new method it has also been possible to establish the presence of pollen grains which are destroyed by the alkali treatment, or which, if not destroyed, it would have been very difficult and time wasting to have counted in a preparation made by the alkali method.

The Proposed New Method of Preparation of Peat for Pollen-statistical Purposes.—In order to obtain a homogeneous stock of

* SCHMIDT and GRAUMANN, 1921.

peat for a comparative study of methods dealing with the isolation of the pollen grains in peat, the sample of slightly moldered *Sphagnum* peat was mixed with cold 10 per cent sodium hydroxide solution and stirred until a semiliquid mass was obtained. After a few hours it was pressed through a metal net (meshes, 4 mm.) in order to remove coarse debris such as twigs, etc. After acidification with dilute hydrochloric acid (1:1) the peat was filtered with suction on a Büchner funnel and washed with water until the filtrate gave only a weak test for chlorine ions with silver nitrate. The peat was then spread on glass plates and dried at a temperature slightly above room temperature. The dried peat was carefully ground in a mortar and sifted (meshes, 0.4 mm.).

The peat thus obtained was used as a standard peat in our experiments and was first subjected to pollen analysis by means of the alkali method (boiling with 10 per cent sodium hydroxide until most of the water had evaporated, washing with distilled water, and centrifuging to remove the dark substances dissolved by the sodium hydroxide). Analyses showed the material to be homogenous enough to be used as a standard peat for methodological experiments (Table I). The uniformity of the five pollen

TABLE I

Pollen	Analyses					Extreme percentages	Average percentages
	1	2	3	4	5		
Alnus............	15	11.5	14	12.5	11.3	11.3 to 15	12.6
Betula............	45	43.5	45.5	45.5	45.7	43.5 to 45.7	45.1
Carpinus.........	.....	0.5	1	.....	0.3	0 to 1	0.4
Fagus............	0.5	0.5	1	0.5	1	0.5 to 1	0.8
Pinus............	30	35	29	32.5	34	29 to 35	32.2
Picea............	1	0.5	.....	trace	0.6	0 to 1	0.5
Quercus..........	7	8	8.5	7.5	5.7	5.7 to 8	7.1
Tilia.............	1	0.5	0.5	1	0.7	0.5 to 1	0.8
Ulmus...........	0.5	.....	0.5	0.5	0.7	0 to 0.7	0.5
Corylus..........	8	7	4	6	5	4 to 8	5.7
No. of pollen grains counted.	150	150	200	200	300		

spectra shown in Table I is rather remarkable, as coarse detritus, mainly leaves and stems of *Sphagnum*, was abundant in the preparations. Much care had to be taken to prevent pollen grains from being omitted or wrongly determined. The time required for each analysis was about 2 hr. In our attempts to get rid of the pollen-obscuring detritus, we proceeded in the following way:

Destruction of the Lignin and Humic Acid Components of the Peat.—In our first experiments we used alkaline oxidative agents, as boiling the peat in the solutions of potassium permanganate, sodium hypochlorite, or hypobromite. Although in some of these experiments a considerable concentration of the pollen was achieved, it was found difficult to avoid some destruction of pollen grains. For further experiments, therefore, an acid oxidizing agent, *viz.*, diaphanol (a solution of chlorine dioxide in acetic acid), was used. This, however, was found to act too slowly and not intensively enough. It was then replaced by a mixture of finely powdered potassium chlorate, acetic acid, and sulphuric acid. This method has the advantage over the diaphanol method in that the amount of the chlorine dioxide liberated by the reaction can be changed within wide limits. The method worked fairly well, but some difficulties were encountered from the slight solubility of the potassium chlorate. The best results were obtained when the potassium chlorate was replaced by the more easily soluble sodium chlorate.

In a Petri dish 0.2 g. standard peat was added to a mixture of 8 cc. glacial acetic acid and 4.5 cc. sodium chlorate solution (100 g. sodium chlorate and 200 cc. distilled water). One cubic centimeter sulphuric acid (80 per cent) was carefully added, drop by drop, and the Petri dish agitated to insure a thorough mixing of the fluids.* The whole was allowed to stand for 12 hr. at laboratory temperature after which the solution was diluted to about 40 cc., and the undissolved material collected by centrifuging. The sediment was washed once or twice in the centrifuge tubes with distilled water and again sedimented by centrifuging, then (to remove the water) washed in the same way twice with acetone and twice with ether (dried over calcium chloride). It was then spread out with a glass rod on the inner wall of the centrifuge tube, and the remaining ether evaporated by short heating on the water bath.

* Great care must be taken in adding the sulphuric acid, otherwise the reaction may become explosive resulting in serious burns to the operator.

Hydrolysis of the Polysaccharide Fraction of the Peat.—The material thus obtained consisted largely of cell walls and was of a faint, yellowish-white color. It was thoroughly mixed with sulphuric acid (1 cc. or less of an 80 per cent solution) and was allowed to stand for 3 hr., after which water was added, and the solid residue collected by centrifuging and thoroughly washed with distilled water as described above. The water was then poured off, and lactophenol (phenol crystals (20 g.), lactic acid (20 g.), glycerin (40 g.), aqua destillata (20 g.) added up to a certain volume, *e.g.*, 2 cc.). Staining was effected by adding a small drop of very dilute methylene blue. The whole was mixed carefully, and a certain quantity, *e.g.*, 0.1 cc., transferred to a counting chamber (Naumann, 1925). Here the pollen grains were counted, and the relative frequencies and the absolute pollen frequency calculated in the ordinary way.

A common blood-corpuscle counting apparatus (Bürker chamber, Thoma chamber, etc.) is too deep to allow a convenient examination of the preparations at the magnifications generally used in pollen statistical investigations. We have therefore devised a special counting chamber (capacity, 0.1 cc.; depth, 0.08 mm.) which is now on the market. It takes even the biggest pollen grains and at the same time allows the use of high-power objectives.

Results of analyses of standard peat treated in the way described above are practically identical with those obtained from peat treated with sodium hydroxide (Table I, page 116).

Everyone working with pollen statistics should have access to reference preparations of pollen grains from recent trees. Such preparations can be made directly from fresh material or from boiling stamens of herbarium specimens with 10 per cent caustic potash and mounting the pollen grains in glycerin jelly. After some practice it is possible even to identify pollen grains of different species within the same genus, for instance, to distinguish the pollen of *Picea canadensis* from the slightly smaller one of *P. mariana*, that of *Pinus Murrayana* from that of *P. Banksiana*, etc. It is often useful to calculate and record in a reference table the limits within which the dimensions of the pollen grains of closely related species vary. In the peat preparations some pollen grains are seen only from above, obliquely, contorted, or even in fragments or, in the case of pine and spruces, as isolated wings. Consequently, in studying the reference preparations, not only the breadth of the pollen grains should be measured, but also the length and depth of the pollen grain proper, and the breadth, length, and depth of the wings, when these are present. Notes on the finer structure are desirable, also notes on the color, which is variable according to the chemicals used in the preparation of the pollen for microscopical examination.

It is but natural that many difficulties will be encountered by those who venture in the study of pollen statistics. For example, it cannot always be assumed that where there was much pollen there was a correspondingly heavy growth of the trees that produced it—for pollen grains may be carried by the wind for hundreds of miles*—nor can it be assumed that where there are few or none there were few or no trees. If the bog into which the pollen fell was not in proper condition to receive and preserve pollen, it would be lost, and thus no record would remain. Such conditions include a chemical or bacterial state of the water which would cause the pollen grains to decay, a frozen surface over the bog at the time of pollen shedding, or a number of other circumstances.

To get an idea of the manner in which the fossil pollen record ought to be interpreted, samples from the surface of the bog should be examined for pollen grains, and the findings compared with the present distribution and abundance of the forest trees in the neighborhood. For that purpose the forests should be mapped, and their composition ascertained.

An investigation of this kind was carried out by the author of the present chapter in southwestern Sweden in 1920. The surface samples from the district investigated could be classed into two groups according to their pollen content: in the one dominated the pollen of conifers; in the other, that of deciduous trees. The samples of the first group came, as a rule, from the branches of living *Sphagnum* moss; those belonging to the second, from the wet, muddy hollows in the moss carpet. From these observations the question naturally arises: Were these groups of samples fairly contemporaneous in spite of the difference in their pollen content, which could be due to different physical and chemical conditions at the spots from which they were taken; or were they

* For example the pollen of pine and spruce from the continent to Greenland, as shown from analysis of peat from Greenland swamps.

not of the same age?   It was inferred that the samples from the hollows were older than those from the sphagnum branches, since the pollen spectra of the former appeared to be about the same as those from samples taken from within the *Sphagnum* peat at about the same levels as the samples from the hollows.

As to the dominance of the coniferous pollen grains in the samples taken from the living *Sphagnum* plants, one could suggest this to be due, at least in part, to the rain waters' having washed the small pollen grains of the deciduous trees farther down into the peat than the larger pollen grains of pine and spruce.   That pollen grains are sometimes washed down in this way has been shown by C. Malström of the Forest Service of Sweden.   In some laboratory experiments he used pollen of an easily recognizable species, allowing it to shed on the surface of a big sod of peat from a part of Sweden where pollen grains of the type used in the experiment could not be encountered and then pouring water in small portions on the peat.   In some of the cases pollen grains impregnated with colloidal gold to assure their recognition when encountered were used for experiments in the field.   The results of these experiments indicate that pollen grains are carried down by water *only within the unconsolidated debris* or litter which forms a layer from about 1 in. to 2 ft. thick on the surface of certain types of bogs and that pollen does not penetrate into the true peat.   Unconsolidated litter is largely absent from the bogs in southwestern Sweden: accordingly, pollen should not be expected to be carried down into it, in any amount, by water. This was proved by the fact that the pollen flora of the living *Sphagnum* in the bogs was practically identical with that of cushions of *Grimmia* and other mosses growing on rocks and old stumps or other places where the carrying down of pollen grains was impossible.

In the surface samples of *Sphagnum* the frequency of alder and birch pollen seems to bear a fairly close relationship to the actual distribution and abundance of these trees.   Both the alder and birch sometimes occur in greater quantities in the bogs than in the surrounding country.   This might cause a local overrepresentation of their pollen, making it appear that these species constitute a greater proportion of the forests as a whole than they actually do.

In one instance groves of hornbeam occurred about 100 miles south of the district under examination.   Pollen of this species was not found in the surface samples. It was found, however, fairly regularly, although with a low frequency, not far below the surface in some of the bogs. Hence it might be possible that not very long ago the hornbeam occurred farther north than now.

The frequency of beech pollen was fairly consistent with the recent occurrence of the beech. The same was true of spruce pollen. The spruce avoids the coast, and its range has a well-defined line of demarcation traversing the district, parallel to the coast. The spruce pollen frequency of surface samples from bogs at or near this limit is about 13 per cent; in the inland bogs it is higher; in the coastal bogs, lower.

The frequency of pine pollen varied between 49 and 66 per cent. The pine is a prolific pollen producer, and the pollen is easily carried by the wind and distributed over a wide area. The pine, therefore, is probably overrepresented in most of the pollen spectra. This is largely due to the pine forests in the country at large, as local stands of pine in the bogs seem not to affect the pollen spectra in the same degree as stands of alder and birch.

The pollen frequency of the willows was very low, presumably in accordance with the present distribution of the species belonging to this genus.

The mean oak pollen frequency was only 3 per cent, in striking contrast to the large oak forests of the district. The oak, therefore, had to be considered decidedly underrepresented in most of the pollen spectra. This was true both as compared with the conifers and as compared with some of the other deciduous trees, *i.e.*, the beech, the mean percentage of which is about two-thirds that of the oak, although the absolute frequency of the beech certainly is many times less than that of the oak.

Elm and basswood trees are found scattered all over the district. Only very few pollen grains of these species were seen in the surface samples. In spite of being entomophilous, *Tilia* does not seem to be underrepresented in the pollen diagrams: sometimes its pollen grains are found in great profusion in the peat, which might be due to flowers or whole inflorescences, becoming accidentally embedded in the peat.

The pollen of *Corylus*, or supposedly of this genus, has created quite a sensation during the progress of the pollen-statistical investigations. In certain older strata of many bogs in middle and western Europe it occurs in an abundance sometimes overtopping the total of all the other pollen grains; several theories have been put forward to explain these supposed "hazel forests." The identification of hazel pollen is not always easy: it is very similar to that of the birch, also to that of sweet gale (*Myrica*), which latter, however, is not believed to be subject to preservation in the bogs.   Its representation in the surface samples seems to be fairly consistent with the actual frequency of the hazel in the district under consideration.

Then there are some trees and shrubs in the district the pollen of which is not preserved in the bogs, for instance, aspen and several species belonging to the Rosaceae.   They are not very prominent in the vegetation, and their absence from the fossil pollen records accordingly is not of much importance.

For the sake of comparison will be added here some observations on the pollen content of the surface samples from a number of bogs or muskegs, made in Alberta, Canada, 1930 to 1931, where, contrary to the conditions of the previous district, trees the pollen of which is not preserved in peat are predominant. The greater part of the area investigated is situated in the wide transition zone, between the forest and the prairies, which stretches across central Alberta.   Originally this country was fairly consistently covered by various species of poplar and scrub thickets.   The dominant tree is the aspen, and, although much of the land has been cleared for agriculture, probably the major part of the area is still tree-clad.   The balsam poplar is locally abundant.   Thickets of willows are frequent, and throughout the country may be found *Picea albertiana*, the western form of *Picea canadensis*, occurring singly or in groups.   The coniferous covering is greatly extended by the numerous muskegs in certain regions.   The chief tree here is the black spruce, although the tamarack frequently accompanies it.   Birch is not abundant and occurs chiefly on the sides of some of the valleys and on muskegs. Groves of jack pine, *Pinus Banksiana*, are found in some of the sand-hill areas, whereas the lodge pole pine, *Pinus Murrayana*, is confined to the western extremity of the district close to the Rockies.

Pollen grains of *Populus*, the commonest of all the trees, do not occur in the surface samples.   On the other hand, jack pine contributes more than any other tree—about 50 per cent—to the average pollen spectrum of the surface samples, although it has such a local distribution that it might be concealed for weeks to a botanist roaming about in this vast district. Tamarack pollen has not been found, or only dubitably so, although there are hardly any muskegs without tamarack.

The birch pollen sometimes attains a frequency of 25 per cent or thereabout, owing to local overrepresentation caused by the pollen of *Betula glandulosa*. The pollen of the white spruce, the climax tree of the country, has a low frequency—up to 14 per cent. The frequency of the pollen of the black spruce is very variable: the highest percentages—about 50—were found in muskegs with a dense growth of black spruce.

The alders are decidedly less common than the willows, but their pollen, nevertheless, has nearly the same frequency as that of the willows or about 6 per cent. Out of 1,500 pollen grains counted, just 1 came from the hazel. The hazel seems to be fairly common, although it never appears in quantity.

We can infer from these observations that, if conclusions as to the composition of the present forests in Alberta should be drawn in the customary way of drawing conclusions regarding the forests of the past, speaking of a "birch time," a "pine time," a "spruce time," etc., on the basis of pollen statistics only, they would turn out to be entirely misleading. There is not a pine time in central Alberta at present, although the average pollen spectrum of the surface samples is that of a pine time. Moreover, in the surface samples there is no record of the dominating trees aspen and poplar, and likewise none, or only a scanty one, of such widely distributed trees as *Larix* and *Corylus*.

This shows that the problem essential to a successful start of pollen statistical investigations is one of ascertaining the composition of the present forests and of studying the processes connected with the catching and preservation of the pollen grains in peat and muck under formation (the "Actuopaleontology" of the bogs).

In the pollen statistical literature the term "pollen frequency" is often met with. Pollen frequency means the number of pollen grains per square centimeter of a preparation. The pollen frequency is by no means always proportional to the density of the forests that produced the pollen. A peat formed slowly would have a greater pollen frequency than one formed quickly, provided they both had the same capacity for catching and preserving pollen grains. In addition, a low pollen frequency might be encountered in peat from a well-wooded country, if the bog surfaces at the time of pollen shedding were not in proper condition to catch and preserve the pollen; and a relatively high pollen frequency could be found in bogs in districts void of forests if their surfaces could catch and preserve the pollen drifted there from a distance. But while it is realized that the pollen frequency figures are not direct indices and, unless properly interpreted, may even be misleading regarding the composition and density of the forests, it is believed that such figures, if calculated from a great number of localities in different countries and then compared with each other, could yield results that would show lines along which further research bearing on the theory of pollen statistics could be done.

The difference between the pollen frequency of bogs in the small and rather far-off Scottish islands and that of some high moors in northwestern Germany is very great, the figure from the Shetland Islands being about 8; that from Germany, about 330. The highest pollen frequency so far met with in Alberta was 90 (from bogs in the coniferous forests near the foothills of the mountains); the lowest, 14 (from a bog in the park land not far from the prairie). The highest pollen frequency from Alberta is three times less than that of some bogs near Achnasheen in the poorly wooded Rossshire in northern Scotland, and the lowest is about the same as that from the Orkney Islands, which are now practically treeless. The pollen frequency of the bogs in Alberta is thus on the whole strikingly low.

To get a clue to the explanation of this fact we must consider that "dead" bogs, *i.e.*, those where peat no longer forms, cannot catch and preserve pollen grains. This is also the case with living bogs during their inactive period, when the cold of the winter, exceptional drought, or, in some types of peat deposits, excessive rain puts a temporary stop to the formation of peat. As to the bogs in Alberta, long, cold winters and rainless springs would tend to retard the annual peat-forming activities to a considerable extent. Thus, for instance, the spring of 1931 was unusually dry in the district of Edmonton, and in the latter part of April and the first weeks of May when many trees and shrubs such as hazel, alder, birch, and poplar, were in bloom, the ground was still covered with yesteryear's dead plant remains, and hardly any green growth was in evidence. Certainly no formation of peat was going on at that time. Thus it might be fair to assume that the comparatively low pollen frequency of the bogs in Alberta is due to their low power of catching and preserving pollen grains, probably less than that of the bogs of oceanic western Europe, where the dead season of the bogs is shorter or, in some cases, possibly altogether absent.

The low pollen frequency in Alberta might be explained by the fact that, in spite of the short summers, peat is formed there very rapidly in most places; and trees, the pollen of which is not preserved in the bogs, play a much more important role in Alberta than in most parts of Europe. It is rather enticing to see the matter in this way; but then there is still to be explained the comparatively low pollen frequency of the bogs in the dense pine forests near the foothills of the Rocky Mountains, to which such an explanation could scarcely apply.

To ascertain the problems involved and their importance it is necessary to make experiments, chiefly in the field, extending over several years. Only in this way can knowledge of the actuopalaeontological processes be substantially promoted, and a more reliable key for unlocking of the palaeobiological problems be provided. This is urgently needed, as there is a tendency with many of those carrying out pollen statistical research to seek more and more distant objects for their studies, distant with regard both to time and to space. If the knowledge of the actuopalaeontological processes is not duly broadened at the same time as the pollen statistical research penetrates to such faraway regions, this kind of research will undoubtedly provide results of only illusory value.*

---

* For a bibliography of pollen statistics the reader is referred to Erdtman (1927, 1930, 1932, 1934b), and for a further discussion of methods to Kräusel (1929) and Erdtman (1933, 1934a).

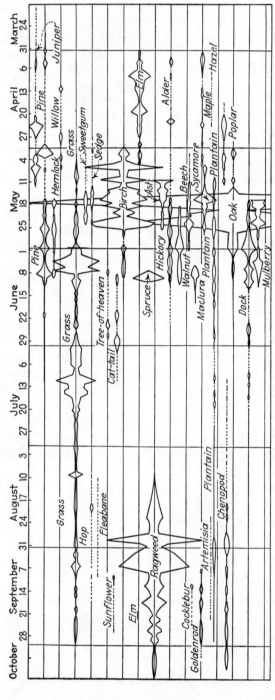

Chart I.—Record of the atmospheric pollen in the city of Yonkers, N. Y., during the year of 1932.   The horizontal distance between the vertical lines represents 50 grains of pollen caught on an area of 3.5 sq. cm. during 24 hours.   The graphs record the daily pollen counts, somewhat rounded out to eliminate the daily fluctuations.

CHAPTER V

ATMOSPHERIC POLLEN

A study of the atmospheric pollen forms an essential part of all pollen surveys. A single season's record of the succession of species of pollens which invade the atmosphere of any given locality furnishes valuable information regarding its hayfever potentialities. Each year the cycle faithfully repeats, with only such minor fluctuations as may be due to seasonal variations. Consequently, information gained in this way is of much more direct application to the handling of hayfever patients than even the most exhaustive botanical studies. Every community, therefore, should have its seasonal atmospheric pollen accurately determined and recorded in a readily available form.

The accompanying chart is a record of the atmospheric pollen for the city of Yonkers, New York, during the summer of 1932. This record is essentially the same as those of 1930 and 1931, except that the pollen of the early flowering trees reached their maxima a little earlier in 1931 than in 1932. For example, the deluge of oak pollen, always a conspicuous feature in these charts, took place on May 11 and 12 in 1931 instead of May 16 and 17, which is the time it occurred in 1932; also it was a little heavier in the latter year. As a rule, however, it is only among the early flowering trees that even such deviations as this in the time of pollination occur.

The pollen was caught from the air by exposing microscope slides coated with glycerin jelly, as already described.

The building where the slides were exposed is five stories high and stands on a slight eminence near the business center of the city. This elevation was chosen to gain general average conditions by avoiding the effect of the immediately local vegetation. It perhaps accounts for the relatively low grass count; for the grains of most kinds of grass are rather large, distinctly larger and less buoyant than those of the pollen of such plants as the ragweeds. However, this is perhaps less of a disadvantage than having the count overbalanced by the pollen from the plants of the immediate vicinity, as would be the case nearer to the ground level. Even at this elevation above the ground the immediately local flora is reflected to some extent in the pollen count. For example, several large trees of both Osage orange and mulberry are growing in the grounds of the laboratory. As a consequence, the pollen counts of both of these are obviously unduly high. Throughout the rest of the region these two species are relatively rare—much less abundant than sweet gum, for example, which their pollen counts outnumber on the chart.

The city of Yonkers is situated in the Hudson River valley, virtually at sea level. To the north and east, beyond the limits of the city, the country is partly built up and partly wild. The suburban sections are nicely cultivated, but the greater portion of the rest of the area is badly or not at all cultivated and is fully invaded by a diversified weed flora. The entire region appears to have been in the past a mixed forest of oaks. Of course, the majority of the trees have been destroyed, but many remain, some of great size and age. The commonest species of the oaks which remain are black, white, chestnut, scarlet, and swamp white. To the southeast and south lie the great metropolis of New York and its suburbs, covering a region of which the vegetation is for the most part reduced to a minimum. To the west lies the Hudson River, and on its opposite bank, which is the New Jersey shore, about a mile from the city, stand the Palisades, rising 500 ft. above the level of the river. Their tops are heavily wooded with a young second-growth mixed forest which extends westward only a short distance to be replaced by improperly cultivated farm land, harboring many weeds and extending many miles westward. To the south of the Palisades, in a southwesterly direction from the city, lie the famous New Jersey meadows. It appears that much of the pollen caught on the slides originated in these adjacent parts of New Jersey, because the count has a tendency to rise abruptly as the wind swings into a westerly direction. And the New Jersey meadows appear to have been the only possible source of the cattail pollen, which is that of *Typha angustifolia*, a species which, while abundant in the New Jersey meadows, is rare on the New York side of the river.

The first grains to be caught on the slides in the springtime were those of juniper. The different species of juniper cannot be distinguished in their pollen, but *Juniperus virginiana* is the only one common enough in the vicinity to produce the pollen recorded. The curious fluctuations represented in the bulges of the curve of this species on April 5 and 23 and May 6 are due to weather fluctuations. This is indicated by the fact that similar fluctuations occur in the curves of one or more of elm, alder, hazel, maple, poplar, and birch at the same times.

Birch pollen is represented throughout the month of May, extending even a little into June. Three species of birch are common in the vicinity of Yonkers—white, black, and yellow. Their pollens can be distinguished from each other only upon careful and minute examination of each grain, a task which is scarcely feasible in making pollen counts. The different species of birch pollinate in the succession named, generally with considerable overlapping. The first two bulges in the birch graph represent the flowering of the white birch, *Betula populifolia*. The third bulge, with its minor fluctuations which are due to weather variations, represents the flowering of the black birch, *B. lenta;* and the fourth represents the yellow birch, *B. lutea*.

Oak pollen began to be caught about the first of May and reached a count of about 20 grains on the second. Thereafter only occasional grains were caught, until May 16 and 17 when the count suddenly increased to 1,034 and 1,308, respectively, after which it dropped off considerably but rose again on May 23 to 644. These two major bulges in the graph repeat themselves from year to year and are undoubtedly due to different groups of species. At the time of the oak-pollen maxima the atmosphere is actually hazy with oak pollen. Nevertheless, in spite of its great abundance, which outnumbers all other species, oak pollen causes relatively little hayfever in the region.

In recording the pollen counts of the different grasses no attempt was made to distinguish the grains of the different species by their microscopic characters. But the different species can be separated out to some extent in the graph by taking into account their flowering periods. The first grains of grass appear toward the end of April, when the only species flowering was low spear grass, *Poa annua*. The count thereafter soon increased, reaching about 20 on May 8, as sweet vernal grass, *Anthoxanthum adoratum*, came into bloom. Toward the end of May, June grass, *P. pratensis*, quickly followed by orchard grass, *Dactylis glomerata*, began to flower. The maximum of their flowering is represented by the double-pointed bulge in the grass-pollen graph of June 4 and 7, when the counts reached about 140. As those two species completed their flowering, the grass-pollen count fell rapidly and continued low until the flowering period of timothy, *Phleum pratense*, which began about the end of June. This was soon followed by redtop, *Agrostis palustris*, and the bent grasses, *A. tenuis*, etc., whose maximum flowering period is reflected in the bulge of the grass-pollen graph occurring between July 11 and 15. This graph shows that timothy, in spite of the great emphasis that has been laid upon it in most hayfever literature, stands no better than fourth in the list of grasses for Yonkers; its pollen production is considerably less than that of June grass, orchard grass, and redtop. After the cessation of flowering of redtop and the bent grasses, with which early summer hayfever in Yonkers virtually ends, the grass count continued low, with a minor unexplained increase on Aug. 9, until the beginning of September when crab grass, *Syntherisma sanguinalis*, and goose grass, *Dactyloctinium aegyptium*, came into flower, causing the grass count to show a noticeable increase which reached a maximum on Sept. 6. After this final flare-up grass pollen continued to be caught, only two or three grains at a time, until the end of the season.

The first grain of ragweed, which proved upon examination to be of the giant ragweed, *Ambrosia trifida*, was caught on Aug. 8, only a few days after the first plants of that species were observed in flower. For about the first week thereafter the ragweed pollen caught proved to be entirely or predominantly of the giant species. But as the count increased, pollen of the dwarf species, *A. elatior*, was added, and throughout the greater part of the season the pollen of the two species appeared to be represented by about equal numbers of grains. The combined ragweed count gained rather steadily, reaching its maximum on Aug. 29. The diminution shown in the graph between Aug. 22 and 27 was due to unfavorable weather conditions, which were likewise reflected in the graphs of all other species recorded during that time. The sudden diminution occurring in the ragweed count on Sept. 1 is unexplained. It is apparently not due to unfavorable weather conditions, since it is accompanied by an increase in the pollen count of the other species. With other minor fluctuations the pollen of the ragweeds continued with dwindling count until well into October. In the Yonkers region the late summer hayfever, which is due almost entirely to the two ragweeds, starts between Aug. 15 and 20 and usually stops toward the end of September or early in October, and throughout the season its severity runs closely parallel with the pollen count of the two ragweeds.

Pine.—It is not possible to distinguish the different species by their pollen. Undoubtedly several are represented in the graph. The bulk of the pollen caught toward the end of May and the beginning of June corresponds to the flowering period of Austrian pine, *Pinus nigra* var. *austriaca,* which is extensively cultivated in and about Yonkers.

Hemlock, *Tsuga canadensis.*—Trees are scarce within the city limits but are fairly abundant outside.

Spruce.—Species unknown, but its pollen graph, extending over only 3 days, corresponds to the flowering of *Picea rubens.*

Sedge.—The different species are not easily distinguished in their pollen, but the first few grains caught in April and May correspond, in point of time, to the flowering period of *Carex pennsylvanica,* while those caught later in May correspond to *C. stricta.*

Willow.—The first grains caught correspond, in point of time, to the flowering period of pussy willow, *Salix discolor,* and the latter to crackle willow, *S. fragilis.*

Elm, *Ulmus americana,* is exceedingly abundant throughout the region. Several other species also occur sparingly, but no attempt was made to distinguish their pollen from each other. A single grain of elm pollen was caught on the slide late in September. This may have been from a tree of *Ulmus serotina,* a late-flowering species native of the south but occasionally planted northward.

Alder, *Alnus incana,* is abundant throughout the region.

Hazel.—The two native species *Corylus americana* and *C. rostrata,* and the European species *C. Avellana* occur sporadically throughout the region, but their pollen grains are not distinguishable from each other.

Maple.—The pollen grains of the different species are not distinguishable from each other; but the first occurrence of maple pollen on the slides corresponded to the flowering of silver maple, *Acer saccharinum,* which is much planted in and about the city and flowers ahead of all the others.   It is followed by red maple, *A. rubrum;* sugar maple, *A. saccharum;* sycamore maple, *A. Pseudoplatanus;* and Norway maple, *A. platanoides*, which probably all contributed to the maple-pollen count recorded in the graph.

Poplar.—The species of poplar were not determined. *Populus Eugenei* is the most abundant species within the city limits, but, being an artificially produced hybrid, it sheds but little pollen, and this mostly abortive, consisting of misshapen grains and empty skins.   A part of the pollen caught answered this description.   Beyond the limits of the city *P. deltoides* and *P. grandidentata* are abundant, and it is probably from them that most of the poplar pollen was derived.

Sycamore, *Platanus occidentalis*, is common throughout the region; two trees of this species grow within the laboratory grounds.

Ash, *Fraxinus americana*, is abundant throughout the region.

Beech.—The different species of beech pollen were not distinguished, but the long period over which beech pollen was caught suggests that more than one species was involved. Both the native species, *Fagus grandifolia*, and the introduced European species, *F. sylvatica*, in several varieties, are abundant.

Sweet gum, *Liquidambar Styraciflua*, is exceedingly abundant throughout the region.

Walnut.—Both the black walnut, *Juglans nigra*, and the butternut, *Juglans cinerea*, are found sparingly throughout the region.   Their grains can be distinguished from each other but were not separated in making the counts, though it was observed that both occurred.

Hickory.—The pollen grains of the local species of hickory cannot be readily distinguished from each other. *Carya ovata, C. alba, C. glabra*, and *C. cordiformis* are found in the region.

Tree of heaven, *Ailanthus glandulosa*, an Asiatic introduction, is abundant in the region.

Plantain.—The species recorded in the graph is entirely English plantain, *Plantago lanceolata*.   Grains of the two other species (*Plantago major* and *Plantago Rugelii*), which grow commonly in the region, were only occasionally caught on the slides, a grain or two at a time.   The pollens of these three species are easily distinguished from each other.

Chenopod.—Under this name are included the pollen of lamb's-quarters, *Chenopodium album;* Mexican tea, *C. ambrosioides;* and the pigweeds, *Amaranthus retroflexus* and *A. hybridus.* All four are common, and their pollen cannot be separated with certainty.

Artemisia, *Artemisia Absinthium,* is a recent introduction, adventive from Europe.

Goldenrod.—The different species of goldenrod cannot be distinguished in their pollen. Many species occur in the region, some of them in great abundance, but one species, *Solidago speciosa,* greatly outranks all others in its production of pollen.

Sunflower.—The fact that sunflower, *Helianthus annuus,* is cultivated in considerable quantities in the grounds of the laboratory probably explains the presence of sunflower pollen on the slides.

Fleabane.—*Erigeron canadensis* and *E. strigosus* are exceedingly common. Their pollen grains, however, are not distinguishable from each other.

Hop, *Humulus Lupulus,* occurs sporadically and grows sparingly in the laboratory grounds.

Linden, *Tilia americana,* occurs in several varieties. Though insect pollinated, its pollen was caught sparingly from June 22 to 30.

Besides the pollen species which are shown in the graph, a few grains of rush, wild cherry, privet, and sumac and the spores of horsetail, several ferns, and many fungi, including *Alternaria,* were caught.

After a hayfever patient has been properly typed, a glance at a chart of this kind will tell him whether or not, or just when, he is likely to have hayfever in the locality for which the chart has been prepared. It is therefore imperative that every locality, especially those that cater to the tourist traffic, and hayfever resorts in particular, should have such charts available for the inspection of prospective visitors who may be hayfever sufferers or for physicians who wish to learn the most favorable places to which to direct their patients.

CHAPTER VI

HAYFEVER

It is almost a tradition among hayfever sufferers that their malady is caused by roses, when it comes in the early summer, or by goldenrod, when it comes in the late summer. Usually such traditional bits of misinformation can be traced back to some half truth; in this case it is that both roses and goldenrod play minor parts in the production of hayfever. Nevertheless the hayfever that afflicts people in the early summer months when the roses are blooming is never caused primarily by roses; likewise that which afflicts people during the closing summer months when the goldenrod is blooming is never primarily due to goldenrod. Roses and goldenrod contribute so little that they need scarcely be considered as hayfever plants. The principal factor in the production of hayfever is not the beautiful or conspicuous flower, which is pollinated by insects, but the one that sheds most pollen, always drab and inconspicuous, and pollinated by wind. In a way, the amount of pollen that a plant can disseminate in the air is a measure of its ability to produce hayfever.

Though the flowers that cause hayfever are not objects of admiration and usually pass unnoticed, they are frequently associated with more conspicuous kinds, in both their habitat and time of flowering, with the result that the latter are sometimes blamed for the misdeeds of their less conspicuous cousins. Thus it is that when roses delight the eye and fill the air with their fragrance, the careful observer will always find near by species of grass with flowers neither beautiful nor fragrant but which cast to the winds enormously more pollen than is produced by the roses. In the same way when at the close of summer the many species of goldenrod garnish the fields and hills with their beautiful golden sprays there will always be found in the ditches along the roadside and in abandoned or poorly cultivated fields great masses of one or more species of ragweeds, filling the

134

atmosphere from inconspicuous greenish flowers with infinitely more pollen than is produced from their more showy neighbors.

Besides the grasses and ragweeds many other plants contribute to the production of hayfever. An analysis of these has shown that each climatic area has its own particular group of hayfever plants. These flower in most localities in three distinct seasons. The hayfever of the first season or *early spring* type is generally mild and of short duration, coinciding with the flowering of such trees as elm, oak, poplar, birch, maple, walnut, and willow, which, taking advantage of the leafless condition of the trees in the early spring, scatter enormous amounts of pollen to the winds. The duration of their flowering is relatively short; consequently this type of hayfever is less important than that of the two following seasons. The second or *early summer* hayfever season coincides with the flowering of the commoner grasses, which are its primary cause. The grasses begin to shed their pollen just when or even a little before the trees are completing their flowering, and continue until about haying time. The flowering period of most grasses, though generally short, is longer than that of most trees, and so many species with slightly different flowering periods are found associated that the season is considerably longer. And the irritation caused by their pollen much more intense than that caused by the tree pollen.

The third period corresponds with the flowering of the ragweeds, cockleburs, and goldenrods in the East and with the ragweeds, false ragweeds, cockleburs, sagebrushes, and many others in the West.

Early Spring Hayfever.—The trees which contribute their pollen to the cause of hayfever in the early spring are all wind pollinated, except the maples and willows. The *maples* undoubtedly employ insects to effect pollination. The flowers of the red maple, for example, are colored, sweet scented, and provided with nectar, offering every inducement to insects to visit them. Nevertheless, in most species of maple, adaptation to pollination by insects is rather imperfect; the anthers protrude beyond the floral envelopes so that when the insects clamber over the flower clusters in search of nectar a large amount of pollen is knocked loose and drifts away in the breeze. And some species of maple as, for example, the ash-leaved maple or box elder are entirely wind pollinated.

The *willows*, like the maples, are both wind and insect pollinated. Unlike most trees they have a long flowering period, and many species and varieties are found growing together and flowering at different times. As a consequence the blooming of all the willows together often covers a period extending from the time of the disappearance of the last snows when the first shrubby pussy willows flower while their branches are still leafless, to well into June when some of the larger tree forms complete their flowering after the leaves are fully developed. It is not known which of the numerous species and varieties of willow are the heaviest contributors to hayfever; probably they are not distinguishable in hayfever studies and, too, cases of willow hayfever are rather rare.

The *birches*, like the willows are generally represented by several species in the same locality. Thus in the northeastern United States the gray or poplar birch is generally found associated with the black and yellow birches, and, though each has a flowering period of scarcely over a week, that of the three together often extends over three or four weeks. Many more cases of birch hayfever than of willow have been recorded. This is in keeping with the fact that a larger amount of pollen is produced by the birches, and that wind is the sole agency employed in pollen transference.

The *elms* constitute a potential cause of hayfever, and severe cases of elm hayfever have been recorded. Though there are several species of elm in the United States, they are not commonly associated. Their flowering periods are usually less than a week, and the few cases of elm hayfever that have been reported, though frequently severe, are generally of short duration. The pollen of most elms is shed long before the leaves unfold, and the flowers are so small and inconspicuous that it is not surprising that they are seldom suspected of causing hayfever. When the flowers are shedding really prodigious quantities of pollen they look from the ground like rather large, dark reddish buds, swollen and about to burst.

The *poplars* or *cottonwoods*, like the birches, flower before the first unfolding of the leaves. They are frequently represented by several species in the same locality, but the one that is most commonly planted about city dwellings is *Populus Eugenei*, a hybrid produced in Germany by crossing the necklace poplar with the balsam poplar. It is always propagated by cuttings and exists only in the male or pollen producing sex. However, as with most hybrids, the pollen is largely abortive, represented in the anthers by empty skins, and most of the catkins fall prematurely from the trees. Few, if any authentic cases of poplar hayfever have been attributed to this or the various other species of poplar in the eastern states. In the western states, however, Arizona cottonwood, which is extensively planted in southern Arizona and California, is regarded by investigators as a frequent cause of hayfever; so also are the California cottonwood, western cottonwood, and the narrow-leaved cottonwood in regions of the West and Southwest, where they are abundant.

Of the many species of conifers, such as pines, spruces, and cedars, which are notorious for their large quantities of pollen and, consequently would be expected to cause hayfever, only the mountain cedar has definitely been shown to be a factor of importance. In the United States this species is confined to the limestone hills of southern Texas and to a lesser extent New Mexico. Flowering in December and January, it is said to be the cause of winter hayfever in these regions.

The *walnuts* of the East (black walnut and butternut), though they shed large quantities of light air-borne pollen, do not constitute a serious factor in hayfever. On the other hand, the California black walnut, which is much planted as a shade tree in the Sacramento, Napa, and Russian river valleys of California, is regarded as the most frequent cause of spring hayfever in those regions. It is interesting to note that the English walnut, also much grown in California and elsewhere and frequently associated with the California black walnut, is stated by eminent authorities to be of no consequence in hayfever.

The *oaks* which are among the last trees to come into leaf in the spring shed from their slender pendent green catkins an abundance of pollen just when the delicate bluish-green leaves are unfolding. Many cases of oak hayfever have been recorded, some of them very severe, but they are fewer than would be expected from the enormous quantities of pollen that these trees shed. In some regions where oak trees are abundant their pollen greatly outranks that of all other plants for a period of several weeks in May. In the eastern United States a large number of species are involved, including the white, black, red, chestnut, and swamp-white oaks. In the western and south-western parts of the United States other species are regarded as of considerable local importance. Thus the black oak of California and Oregon, and the live oak of California have been suspected of causing hayfever, and the black oak of western Texas, New Mexico, and Arizona and the white oaks of similar distribution are regarded as important in these regions.

Among the *sycamores* or *plane-trees* apparently our native species are quite harmless. In California, however, where an exotic species has been introduced and is extensively planted as a shade tree under the name of California sycamore, it is said to be a serious cause of early-spring hayfever.

The *hackberries* or *nettle-trees* have quite frequently been blamed for hayfever. They bloom early in spring when the leaves are beginning to unfold and shed large quantities of light, air-borne pollen, thus appearing to qualify for the production of hayfever. In the northeastern states, however, no cases of hayfever have been recorded for the species that grows there; but in the southern states, particularly in the Mississippi valley where a large form, *Celtis mississippiensis*, is abundant, it is probably the cause of some hayfever.

In general it may be said that trees with blossoms that are showy, sweet scented, or otherwise attractive to insects shed so little pollen that they need not seriously be considered as factors in hayfever. On the other hand, those that constitute the primary cause of early-spring hayfever have inconspicuous flowers, frequently pendent catkins, are without scent, and are rarely of any interest to insects. It is not safe, however, to say that only wind-pollinated trees can cause hayfever. Insect-pollinated trees that are not perfectly adapted to this mode of pollination may become a potential menace to hayfever sufferers, and this is a measure of the imperfection of their adaptation to insect pollination.

Early Summer Hayfever.—Following closely on the heels of the tree hayfever comes the early summer hayfever. In most places it begins before the close of the early spring hayfever season, but reaches its height in June when the roses are in bloom. On this account the malady is even sometimes called rose cold, an unfortunate name because roses rarely have anything to do with it.   Possibly the name was not originally intended to imply causal relationship, though in the past such a belief has been entertained by many.   *Roses* are poorly equipped to cause hayfever; they produce but little pollen, and this is not buoyant, instead it is adapted to insect transmission.   Besides this, most of the double roses in cultivation are of hybrid origin and produce little or no viable pollen, so that it is only from the wild species and some single-flowered cultivated varieties that any appreciable quantity of pollen may be obtained.   The hayfever of this period is caused almost entirely by the less conspicuous plants such as the grasses and plantain, which are associated with the roses in their habitat and time of flowering.

The *flowers of grasses* are small and inconspicuous and are not regarded as objects of beauty.   They are mostly green or greenish and so much less attractive then their more showy neighbors the roses and many other beautiful flowers of the summer garden, that they are nearly always overlooked.   The florets of grass lack entirely the conspicuously colored corolla and calyx familiar in the better known flowers, the place of these being taken by small green bracts.   The stamens, however, are well developed; each floret generally possesses three, appearing as double sacs. A number of florets open each day, sometimes with clock-like regularity.   The bracts spread apart; the anthers emerge, open, shed their pollen, wither, and die; and the green bracts close protectingly about the young seed.   The process is repeated each day, in many species always at precisely the same time, a fresh set of flowers coming into play at each opening until all the florets in the spike have opened, shed their pollen, and closed.

In the eastern United States the first species to flower is the *low spear grass* generally starting in April but continuing to flower throughout the greater part of the summer.   Low spear grass can generally be distinguished by its slender leaves of a yellowish green and its whitish flowering spikes.   The plants generally sprawl flat on the ground and show no tendency to stand erect unless crowded by each other or by other species. The species is abundant in lawns, and, owing to frequent cutting, its flowering period is generally prolonged until late in summer.

Apparently low spear grass contributes only little to hayfever because of its small size, low form, and the small amount of pollen produced.   At any rate, it usually starts to flower several weeks in advance of the appearance of early summer hayfever symptoms.

A more important species is the *sweet vernal grass*, which follows soon after the first flowering of low spear grass. The flowers are borne in compact, pointed spikes at the tops of erect stems. This species may usually be distinguished by its fragrant odor of cumarin, which can be detected upon drying or bruising the leaves. Sweet vernal grass was introduced from Europe as a meadow grass and has since become abundant throughout most of the northern part of North America. It dies soon after flowering, and its place in the meadows is taken by some of the late flowering grasses.

June grass and orchard grass follow closely on the heels of sweet vernal grass. Both flower at about the same time in May and June, and both are extremely abundant throughout the United States and most of Canada, except in very arid regions.

June grass is perhaps the commonest lawn grass. Though it is seldom permitted to flower in lawns, it has escaped from cultivation and is found everywhere. It flowers excessively in nearly all roadside ditches and waste places. When properly developed the plants stand about 2 ft. high and are distinguished by their soft, spreading, bluish panicles. This species is the favorite pasture grass throughout the more humid regions and is generally cultivated under the name of blue- or Kentucky bluegrass and is one of the most valuable and universally distributed grasses of the United States.

Orchard grass is about twice as tall as June grass and is coarse and stiff. It cannot be grown in lawns because it has a tendency to form tussocks. As a consequence of this habit it is sometimes called bunch grass. The flowering panicle stands erect, and when mature its branches stand almost straight out from the central axis; the lower branch is generally much larger than the others and, standing off abruptly from the central axis, causes the inflorescence to bear a remote resemblance to the foot of a cock, the enlarged lower side branch representing the spur; hence the name cocksfoot grass, by which it is frequently known, particularly in England.

Both June grass and orchard grass start to flower toward the end of May and continue through most of June, shedding large quantities of light, air-borne pollen.

Closely following these come redtop and timothy, which begin to flower late in June and continue through most of July. Both are cultivated in humid regions. Redtop is a valuable meadow and pasture grass frequently succeeding sweet vernal grass in its pollination in moist meadows. It is low, with soft, spreading panicles, somewhat resembling June grass, from which it can easily be distinguished by its later flowering period and the purple-reddish color developed by its panicles as they approach maturity. Though redtop resembles June grass in outward appearance, the two are seldom found together, because June grass does not thrive in acid soil which is favorable to the best development of redtop.

Timothy is the standard hay grass throughout the more humid parts of the United States. When made into hay it is cut at the height of its flowering season, while shedding an abundance of light, air-borne pollen. In many regions in which timothy is cultivated it covers large tracts of land and in these regions causes much of the hayfever occurring during the latter part of June and the early part of July. However, it is much less abundant in waste places, vacant lots, neglected fields, and along roadsides than are the other species and therefore is less productive of hayfever among suburban and city dwellers.

Though there are undoubtedly many other species of grass that contribute to the production of early summer hayfever, there is no doubt that the five species—sweet vernal, June grass, orchard grass, timothy, and redtop—are responsible for the greater part of the early summer hayfever. It is significant that hayfever of this type in the northeastern United States stops with the cessation of flowering of timothy and redtop; consequently, there is little need to consider such grasses as barnyard grass, crab grass, squirrel-tail grass, the witch grasses, and innumerable others that flower subsequently to this time.

There are, however, several others that should be mentioned; though a good deal less general in distribution and less abundant than the five species mentioned above, they should be regarded as contributory factors and sometimes as primary causes of hayfever.

For example, *meadow fescue* is frequently found associated with June grass; it flowers at about the same time. *Red fescue*, flowering a little later, is distinguished by its dark bluish-green, wiry leaves, forming basal rosettes in dry, sandy, or impoverished soils. *Velvet grass*, with its soft, velvety leaves and stems and purplish flower panicles, flowers in moist meadows and roadside ditches. *Tall oat grass*, with its graceful plumes, forms a conspicuous element of our roadside vegetation in July. *Meadow foxtail*, an old-fashioned grass formerly cultivated widely, now occurs only in isolated patches where it has been able to hold its own against its more hardy competitors. It is similar and closely related to timothy but can be distinguished from it by its early period of flowering.

In the warmer and more arid regions of the United States the hayfever sufferer has other species to contend with. Possibly the worst of these are *Bermuda grass* and *Johnson grass*. The former has a range extending from coast to coast in the southern part of the country, and the latter a range but little less extensive. Both were introduced from the Mediterranean region as forage grasses. Both are drought resistant and, once established, can scarcely be eradicated.

Of the two, *Bermuda grass* is the more important, because its pollen is the lighter and more easily dispersed by wind currents, and it has the longest flowering period of all the grasses, flowering from April to September and in some places practically throughout the year. When there is insufficient moisture it withers and dies to the ground but springs up again as soon as there is rain and bursts into flower.

Johnson grass is very different; the plants are tall and stout, usually reaching a height of 4 or 5 ft. or sometimes much more. The flowers are borne in large, open panicles but shed a disproportionately small amount of pollen of large and heavy grains. But what the pollen lacks in buoyancy and amount is largely compensated for by the height and abundance of the plants. In some parts of the Southwest it is a pernicious weed and has become so abundant that it has rendered farming unprofitable. In such localities it is said to be the worst hayfever weed that the sufferer encounters.

Farther west are other kinds of grass. Hall, (1922) in his catalogue of California plants, lists about 25 species that are to be regarded as at least contributory causes of hayfever. Besides these of the Pacific coast, there are many species in the Great Plains region deserving attention; but altogether they are so numerous that any adequate treatment of them is beyond the scope of this discussion. The reader who wishes to go more deeply into the subject is referred to Hall's list and other bulletins of the U. S. Department of Agriculture and bulletins issued by the various state departments.

Though the grasses are responsible for by far the greater part of early summer hayfever, there are several weeds that occasionally play an important part. For example, *English plantain,* a common weed of dooryards, vacant lots, and meadows, is frequently found associated with sweet vernal grass. It starts to flower at about the same time and continues, shedding large quantities of light, air-borne pollen well into July.

Of somewhat less importance are the several species of dock, as the yellow or curly dock and sheep sorrel. Besides these there are a number of plants characteristic of the Great Plains and of semiarid regions as, for example, Russian thistle, several kinds of salt bush, pigweeds, and various others which begin to flower in the early summer but reach their maximum development during the latter part of the summer and, therefore, more properly belong to the late summer group.

Late Summer Hayfever.—The expression, late summer hayfever, will call to the minds of many the goldenrods, sunflowers, and other gorgeous components of the waning summer's landscape, for the impression that these flowers must be the cause of their malady has become deeply fixed with many whose sufferings are ushered in with the appearance of such flowers. The term "goldenrod fever" has been popularly suggested to describe the form of hayfever occurring when the goldenrods bloom but with only the justification of coincidence in time.

Ragweeds are offenders in the East. Most of the hayfever occurring in the eastern part of the United States in the late summer is due to the ragweeds and their allies. All of them produce large quantities of pollen capable of being carried long distances by light winds. There are nearly 60 species in the ragweed family. The majority of these flower toward the end of summer, and, though there is considerable range in size and form of pollen grain in the different species, all possess in a high degree the characteristics of hayfever pollen. All are light and buoyant, they are shed in large quantities over long periods of time, and, as far as tests have been made, they are nearly all more or less toxic to hayfever patients. Thus the relative importance of the different species is largely a matter of their abundance and local distribution.

In the eastern states the common or dwarf ragweed and its near relative the giant ragweed are found growing in great profusion in roadside ditches and waste places. The *dwarf ragweed* can be distinguished by its finely divided leaf; each leaf is cut into many segments and each segment is again divided, giving it a fern-like appearance. The plants branch extensively and, when allowed to grow unhampered, assume a pyramidal form 4 or more ft. high, spreading at the base to 3 or 4 ft. They are so prolific that they are usually found growing in masses of hundreds or thousands together, often forming solid banks of vegetation. Toward the middle of August they become covered with the greenish-yellow flower spikes from which they shed their pollen.

The *giant ragweed* can easily be distinguished by its broad leaf, which is three-lobed or five-lobed or not divided at all; the blade of the leaf is carried down the leaf stalk as a narrow wing on each side. It also has the habit of branching extensively just above the ground, forming a more or less columnar bush frequently attaining a height of 12 or 13 ft.

Both species flower at almost the same time, the giant preceding the dwarf by only a few days. Many have observed the precision of the annual recurrence of their flowering period. Unlike the early spring flowers, which are frequently delayed in their appearance for several weeks by cold, rainy weather, the ragweeds are not influenced by weather conditions. It is now known that the principal factor governing their time of flowering is length of day, and thus it is that their reappearance can be predicted almost to a day in any given latitude.

The pollen-bearing flowers of the ragweed are extremely small and are borne in immense numbers in small heads, which are arranged in long spikes at the top of the plant and at the ends of the side branches, usually standing conspicuously out from the general mass of the bushes. These spiked flowers bear no seeds. Their entire effort is given to the production of pollen, which is shed in such enormous quantities that it rises up like clouds of smoke if the plant is shaken on a still day.

These two species are the only ragweeds found in northeastern United States. They have each about the same range reaching almost across the continent in the northern states and Canada.

They are much less abundant in the western part of their range and do not quite reach the Pacific coast. But these two species have their counterparts in the western ragweed and western giant ragweed.

The *western ragweed* is scarcely to be distinguished in outward appearance from the common or dwarf ragweed; they are about the same in size and habit, but the leaf of the western is not so consistently twice divided, and the plants spring anew each year from the same roots, while the eastern form must come afresh each year from seed. In southern California and throughout the Southwest the western ragweed is almost as abundant as the common ragweed is in the East and flowers at about the same time.

The *western giant ragweed* is likewise remarkably similar to the eastern giant ragweed; both have the same general habit and much the same shaped leaf. The western form differs, however, in showing a tendency to branch well above the ground— generally rising from the root on a central stalk—and the leaf blade is not carried down the sides of the leaf stalk, which is thus wingless. The western giant ragweed has a much more restricted range than have the other species mentioned; it is almost entirely confined to the southwestern states, from Louisiana to Arizona.

There are 11 other species of true ragweed in the United States, but of these possibly only the *southern* or *lance-leaved ragweed* is of importance in hayfever. This species is much smaller than the others and is distinguished by its slender lance-shaped leaves, with generally one or more large teeth near the base. It has a still less extensive range, being confined mainly to the central states, where it is known to cause some trouble to hayfever patients.

Scarcely less important than the ragweeds are the so-called *false ragweeds*, of which there are probably 25 species in the United States. They are similar in general appearance to the true ragweeds and are distinguished from them only on technical details such as their more spiny seed pods. Of these, the slender ragweed and bur ragweed are common in the Southwest and in Colorado; the latter also ranges northward into Alberta and Saskatchewan, where it is abundant in most arid regions, shedding large quantities of pollen during the latter part of the summer.

The *marsh elders* belong to the same family as the ragweeds and false ragweeds but are different from them, having the pollen-bearing and seed-bearing flowers in the same heads; they lack the long spikes of pollen-bearing flowers typical of other members of the family. Consequently they do not possess so efficient a pollen-dispersing apparatus. The high-water shrub or bushy marsh elder is common in tidal marshes along the Atlantic coast. It sheds large quantities of light, air-borne pollen in late summer, and clinical tests have shown that it is frequently active with hayfever cases but less so than the ragweed.

Other species of marsh elder, *e.g.*, poverty weed, prairie ragweed, and rough marsh elder—are found in moist, saline, or alkaline soils throughout most of the western part of the United States. They contribute to a certain extent to the production of hayfever.

The *cockleburs* constitute another group of plants related to the ragweeds. Fifteen species frequent waste places and impoverished ground. They are coarse, ill-smelling herbs with broad, bristly leaves. The staminate flowers are borne in comparatively large spheroidal heads, which are in turn arranged in elongate spikes standing conspicuously above the burs of the seed-bearing flowers. The pollen of the cockleburs has been shown to react with late summer hayfever patients, and in some regions they are troublesome hayfever plants.

The *sagebrushes* and *mugworts* constitute another important group of hayfever plants. There are about 200 species, of which nearly one-third are North American. Generally speaking, they are commonest in the arid and semiarid regions, reaching their greatest abundance in the Rocky Mountain states. The best known and commonest of these is the ordinary sagebrush. It is extremely abundant on the western slope of the Rocky Mountains and in the Great Basin. In some places the dusty, gray-green sagebrush plants are the only living things the eye can see for miles across the deserts.

Ordinarily, sagebrush reaches a height of only 3 or 4 ft., but under favorable conditions it may attain to 12 or 15 ft., assuming the form of a small tree with a fair-sized trunk distinctive for its shredding, reddish bark. The tree form is most commonly found in mountainous regions, where it sheds enormous quantities of light, air-borne pollen, which produces a type of hayfever known locally as mountain fever.

Of equal importance is the common mugwort, a herbaceous species which in its many varieties is found almost throughout the North American continent. One form of this species, known more especially as prairie sage, is common in the prairies of British Columbia, Washington, and southward; another slightly different form is common in the foothills of the mountains. Of the many other species perhaps the most important are the California mugwort and hill sage, both common in the Pacific coast states and in these regions serious causes of hayfever, and the silvery wormwood, which is widespread throughout the arid regions. In the Mesilla valley in southern New Mexico the silvery wormwood is a troublesome cause of hayfever. There are so many species and varieties involved, however, that any adequate consideration of them would be beyond the scope of this discussion. For a detailed account of the group and their relative importance in hayfever the reader is referred to the work of Hall and Clements (1923).

Among the Compositae are many other species which, like the goldenrods, sunflowers, and dahlias, may at times produce some hayfever symptoms but are frequently credited with much more than is their share. The pollen of all these is covered with long, sharp spines and is waxy, so that when shed the grains nearly all remain clumped together and can get into the atmosphere in only limited amounts. They can scarcely be counted as factors in hayfever unless brought in close proximity or actual contact with the sufferer. The pollen of such species frequently gives some reaction by the cutaneous test with ragweed patients, but this is probably solely on account of their biologic kinship with the ragweeds.

The groups of the *chenopods* and *amaranths* also contain many hayfever plants. One of the worst of these is Russian thistle or tumbleweed. It is of wide and ever increasing distribution, already covering nearly the whole of the United States. It is mainly in the western part of its range that it reaches its best development and becomes a hayfever menace.

Russian thistle must not be confused with the true thistles with which it has no kinship but to which it bears a certain resemblance in the sharp, spiny tips of its leaves. The plants branch excessively with long, slender branches, formed in such profusion that they fairly mat together. When fully developed they form compact, dome-shaped, and prickly bushes, which give off large quantities of pollen from July to September. After September they begin to dry up, and finally, breaking off at the root, they are rolled about the plains by the winds, distributing their seeds as they go, until they become entangled in a fence or some other obstruction, where they frequently accumulate in great masses. In eastern Washington and in Oregon, Idaho, Montana, and Wyoming Russian thistle is regarded as the worst of all hayfever plants. In the eastern part of its range it is comparatively harmless.

Also belonging to the chenopod family is the group of *salt bushes,* of which the desert holly, much used for Christmas decorations, is a well-known but harmless example. Many other species are important contributors to the production of hayfever. For example, the annual saltbush is said to be one of the worst causes of hayfever in southern Arizona. Also important through much of the Southwest are red orach, silver scale, all scale, and shad scale. These and the many other species inhabit mostly desert and semidesert regions in which the human population is sparse and scattered. Were it not for this fact it is likely that these plants would cause much hayfever, for the pollen of many species has been shown to be toxic to hayfever patients.

A close relative of the western salt bushes is greasewood. It is particularly abundant in saline situations in the Great Basin region, where it is often associated with sagebrush. It is generally a large, spiny, sprawling shrub, 4 or 5 ft. high or occasionally much higher, with small, narrow, fleshy leaves. The pollen-bearing flowers are borne in small, cone-like inflorescences standing upright at the ends of the spiny twigs. They shed large quantities of pollen from May to September. Greasewood is not regarded as a serious cause of hayfever, though its pollen has been shown to give cutaneous reactions with hayfever patients. There are other plants of the chenopod family, such as lamb's-quarters, winged pigweed, and poverty weed, which in some localities are of importance.

Among the *amaranths* the western water hemp is regarded as one of the worst hayfever plants when it is abundant. It is a tall, branching, coarse weed frequenting swampy or moist soils. The pollen-bearing flowers are borne in long, slender, or slightly drooping spikes, shedding large quantities of pollen from

July to September. Fortunately its range is restricted, being confined for the most part to the states of the Great Plains region. Similar to western water hemp and closely related to it are the various species of amaranth. These are mostly coarse weeds of gardens and ditches, as redroot pigweed and careless weed, and are frequent causes of hayfever in the Southwest.

Just how finely specific it is necessary to be in the diagnosis and treatment of hayfever is still an open question. Hall and Clements (1923), in speaking of the common mugwort, which, as regarded by them, includes 15 subspecies, almost all of which are considered as separate species by other authors, say: "Preliminary studies indicate that the pollens of the different subspecies all react alike. Therefore in testing and treating hayfever cases, the specialist need pay no attention to the complicated series of subspecies and minor variations."

Diagnosis.—The exact species of pollen, whether it be one or several which affect the hayfever sufferer, can be discovered by the hayfever specialist by means of the skin reaction at any time, because the abnormal sensitivity which hayfever sufferers possess to certain species of pollen exists as much in the skin of all parts of the body, and throughout the year regardless of season, as it does in the mucous membranes of the eyes and upper respiratory tract at the time when the pollen is in the air. Consequently, at any time of the year, whether the patient happens to exhibit hayfever symptoms or not, his sensitization may be determined by the appropriate application of the pollen to the skin.

The hayfever specialist provides himself with extracts of the pollen of all the different species of plants which are likely to cause hayfever in his vicinity. In making his collection of these, unless he has, as his guide, the results of a botanical survey of the region, the pollen of every wind-pollinated species and of the most abundant and copious pollen shedders among those that are insect pollinated should be included. From these he selects the extracts of the species which flower during the time that the patient has hayfever.

In making the skin test the application of the pollen is generally done by means of the scratch method. The flexor surface of the forearm is cleaned with 70 per cent alcohol, and the points at which the tests are to be made are marked by means of a skin

pencil.   These should be about ¾ in. apart, and since the average
arm is just broad enough to accommodate three such tests in a
row, they are generally arranged in transverse rows of three each,
starting with the first row at the proximal end of the forearm.
Done in this way the ordinary arm accommodates 8 to 10 rows,
i.e., 24 to 30 tests, which is generally quite sufficient.   Abrasions
are then made by lightly nicking the outer surface of the skin with
a medium-sized needle mounted in a handle or with the tip of a
fine, sharp scalpel.   The scarifier should penetrate only the outer
impervious layer of the skin and should not draw blood.   When
properly made, these abrasions do so little injury to the skin that
they can scarcely be detected; hence the necessity of previously
marking their positions.   To each is added a drop of the pollen
solution to be tested, reserving the first and last for control tests.
The most convenient way of applying the solutions is with a
capillary tube about 3 in. long.   This, when dipped in the solution in a slanting position, will draw it up by capillary force and,
when removed and turned in a vertical position, can be made to
release a drop on the abrasion.   Upon each of the controls is
similarly placed a drop of the solvent used to make the pollen
extracts.   Occasionally it is necessary to add a second drop to
each of the tests if the solution on them dries before the reactions
are obtained.   In any event each should be kept moist with the
pollen extract for about 15 min. or until the reactions appear,
after which the test material should be removed with cotton, and
the forearm wiped again with alcohol.

Typical skin reactions to pollen extracts are essentially the
same as the reactions of the same skin to mosquito bites.   There
generally appears a central whitish or yellowish edematous area
surrounded by a reddish areola (Fig. 12).   The edema may be
round in outline, or it may extend outward in irregularly shaped
pseudopodia of varying length, coming to resemble the form of an
Amoeba proteus.   These visual manifestations of the reaction are
generally accompanied by the same sort of itching as that of
mosquito bites.   There is much variation among different people
in their response to the test; occasionally, in highly sensitized
cases, the reactions may be very violent and, if obtained with
many of the tests at the same time, nearly the whole of the tested
surface may become edematous, with long pseudopodia coursing
upward on to the upper arm toward the axillary fossa.   On the

other hand, the reactions may be manifested only by a slight reddening about the scratches, occasionally even so small that it is necessary to compare them closely with the control tests to determine whether they are positive or not. Whether the reactions are large or small, both their visual manifestations and itching reach a maximum in about 20 min. and subside in an hour's time.

After the exact kind or kinds of pollen which cause the patient's hayfever have been determined by the skin test, the physician

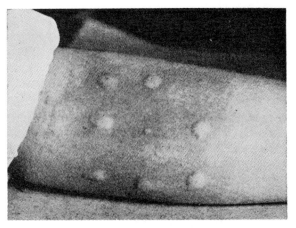

Fig. 12.—Arm of a hayfever patient, showing cutaneous reactions to pollen extracts, scratch test by pick method.

may institute a course of treatment. This consists of introducing subcutaneously minute but gradually increasing amounts of a specially prepared extract of the one or more species of pollen which cause the patient's hayfever. By so doing, a resistance to the toxicity of the pollen may be built up before the hayfever season opens, enabling the patient to resist the effect of the pollen when it is encountered in the atmosphere. Pollen extracts for this purpose can be prepared only by those thoroughly familiar both with the general sterility procedures observed in the preparation of vaccines and with the very special methods of handling pollen materials. There are many adequate pollen extracts on the market, and since the manufacturers of these always prescribe in great detail how their products must be used, a further discussion of them will not be entered into here.

A word of caution is, perhaps, necessary. In spite of the apparent simplicity of both the diagnosis and treatment of hayfever, and their complete harmlessness in the hands of trained specialists, both these procedures in the hands of the inexperienced are attended with very grave dangers and may even result in serious injury or death to the patient. Accordingly, neither should be attempted except by a qualified physician and with properly prepared materials.

CHAPTER VII

POLLEN-GRAIN CHARACTERS

I. GENERAL

The forces that shape pollen grains, as with other organisms, are hereditary and environmental. But, because pollen grains are generated generally in groups of four and set free generally as individuals to wander at great distances in the fulfillment of their destinies, their environmental influences come under two distinct categories—first, those of the prenatal or internal environment and, second, those of the postnatal or external environment. To the circumstance that pollen grains during their development are acted upon by their neighbors of the tetrad they owe such fundamental and conspicuous characters as the number and arrangement of their germinal furrows or the number of their germ pores, and the numerical type of symmetry of their sculptured patterns. And, when they reach maturity, they must be adapted to whatever means of transportation are available. Pollen grains are, therefore, unique in that the influences which determine their form are threefold—heredity, internal environment, and external environment. The effects of these three factors are inseparable but not indistinguishable.

Hereditary Characters.—As far as their hereditary characters are manifest, pollen grains of the same species and of closely related species tend to be alike, and, if the environmental factors are uniform, the degree of their similarity is a measure of their closeness of relationship. For example, the grains of tansy (Plate XIII, Figs. 1, 2), chrysanthemum, camomile, and daisy, which all belong to the same tribe of the Compositae, are so much alike that they can scarcely be distinguished from each other. They all have a thick, coarsely granular exine, bearing sharp conical spines, and their surface is covered with a copious layer of oil. They also have three characteristic germinal furrows, each enclosing a round germ pore. The similarity of the pollen grains of these three species is clearly a manifestation of the

153

closeness of their relationship, and such characters as the above
are purely hereditary or phylogenetic.

Internal Environmental Characters.—On the other hand, if the
internal environment is not uniform, striking differences may
result in the forms of the pollen grains, though they be closely
related or even of the same species. For example, the grains of
sunflower (Fig. 13) are provided with long, sharp spines and
three broad short germinal furrows in conformity with their

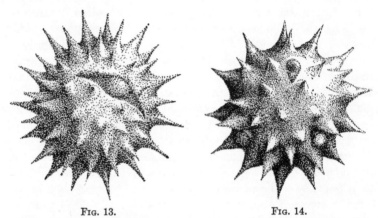

Fig. 13.   Fig. 14.

Figs. 13, 14.—Pollen grains of the sunflower tribe. Fig. 13, *Helianthus
annuus*, side view showing one of its three furrows; Fig. 14, *Dahlia excelsa*,
showing three of its six furrows, their major axes converging toward a point on
the upper hemisphere.

phylogenetic position in the tribe Heliantheae. But those of
Dahlia (Fig. 14), which belongs to the same tribe, have the same
sort of long, sharp spines and short germinal furrows, but instead
of three of these they always have six.   This is because the grains
of *Dahlia* do not form from the pollen mother-cell in the way that
is usual for the tribe (Wodehouse, 1931) but are formed in a way
distinctly aberrant and, thus, engendered under different conditions, the grains possess different internal environmental
characters.

External Environmental Characters.—In the same way, if
the external environmental factors are not uniform, pollen grains
may be extremely diverse in spite of a closeness in their relationship.   The tendency of related species to resemble each other
may be suppressed by the development of characters induced by

outside influences to such an extent that little similarity is recognizable. Thus it is that the pollen grain of tansy, which is insect pollinated, bears little resemblance to that of sagebrush (Plate XIII, Figs. 5, 6), which is wind pollinated. The grains of the latter have a thinner exine without spines, or with only minute vestiges of them, and are provided with only a trace of oil. Yet tansy is probably just as closely related to sagebrush as it is to the daisy with which its pollen-grain form is identical. The differences between the pollen grains of tansy and sagebrush are due to external environmental factors—tansy is pollinated by insects, while sagebrush is pollinated by wind.

From the above examples the conclusion may be drawn that, while heredity or phylogeny tends to dominate the basic form of pollen grains, the internal environment tends to control the number and arrangement of their germinal furrows and pores, and the external environment tends to modify their sculpturing. Accordingly, the characters of pollen grains may be classified as phyletic, internal environmental, and external environmental. The lines of demarcation between these classes of characters are often vague; the same character may even occur as much through one of the influences as through the other. For example, the smooth form of a grain may be either a family character inherent in the group, as with the pollen grains of rose (Plate IX, Fig. 4), mesquite (Plate IX, Fig. 1), and acacia (Plate IX, Fig. 3), which are smooth because smoothness is a character of the pollen grains of the Rosales, the order to which they belong. Or the same character might be induced by wind pollination, as we have seen was the case with the grains of sagebrush (Plate XIII, Fig. 5), which are almost perfectly smooth even though sagebrush belongs to a tribe of predominantly echinate-grained plants. Moreover, inherited characters may be expressed either as inherent per se or as the characteristic way in which the grains respond to their environmental stimuli. Though the results of these three influences are intimately bound together, they may generally be recognized and are frequently so marked that they form a natural basis for the classification of pollen-grain characters.

Characters of the Exine.—The morphological characters of pollen grains have to do principally with the exine and, to a lesser extent, with the intine. The function of the exine, like that of the skin of animals, is the protection of the organism from injury by external agencies, such as excessive desiccation, destruction by light, and mechanical injury. It is also called upon to perform two other functions which are the special properties of pollen grains. These are to provide for the emergence of the pollen tube at the time of fertilization and to accommodate changes in volume as the grain takes up and gives off moisture, which it readily does in response to the ever changing humidity of the atmosphere that it encounters as a free living organism. For the former function are provided germ pores; for the latter are provided furrows or harmomegathi.*

Germinal Furrows.—The form and character of the germinal furrows are generally rather strictly phyletic, tending to be constant throughout families and other large groups; but their number and arrangement are controlled to a large extent by their internal environment, which, in turn, is determined by the number and arrangement of the grains as they are formed from the pollen mother-cell, and may, therefore, be various even in grains from the same anther. Moreover, since the furrows are organs of the exine, which is subject to enormous external environmental modifications, they are indirectly subject to the same modifications. For example, the exine of the pollen grain of willow, which is primarily insect pollinated, is thick and provided with well-developed functional furrows, while that of the grain of the closely related poplar, which is wind pollinated, is thin and fragmentary and totally lacks furrows because the exine is so far reduced that it is incapable of supporting furrows. Thus it is that indirectly, through its effects on the exine, an external environmental influence, *viz.*, wind pollination, may completely banish the germinal furrows.

Germ Pores.—The furrows, besides accommodating changes in volume of the grain, always enclose the germ pores when the latter are present or, in the event of their absence, function directly as germ pores. A good example of the former condition is seen in the grains of goldenrod (Plate XII, Fig. 4). When such a grain is moistened and expands, the furrows gape widely open, and the germ pores bulge through the apertures which are situated in the middle of each furrow membrane; and when the grains dry, the furrows close tightly, hiding the germ pores from view. In such a form as that of maple (Plate X, Fig. 1), in

* See Glossary.

which furrows are present but without pores in their membranes, the furrows take over the function of the pores, serving both as *harmomegathi* and as places of exit for the pollen tube. This latter is suggested by the slight bulge that is generally seen in the center of the furrow membrane of such grains.

Many grains, such as those of the Chenopodiaceae and some Polygonaceae, entirely lack germinal furrows in the ordinary sense of the word but are provided, instead, with a number of rounded apertures in the exine. Functionally these are germ pores, since they permit the emergence of the pollen tube. They also permit a bulging out or a sucking in of the intine in accommodating volume changes. Though their shape, and their function of serving as places of exit for the pollen tube, prompt us to call them germ pores, there is much evidence to show that such apertures are morphologically furrows which have become so shortened that they coincide in extent with their enclosed germ pores. Their arrangement on the surface of the grain is that of furrows; and grains with furrows representing some of the various stages in the shortening process are found among the Polygonaceae. It may therefore be said that germ pores, when present, are always enclosed by germinal furrows and that the rounded apertures, such as those of the pollen of the Chenopodiaceae, are, in reality, shortened furrows.

Character of the Furrows.—The characters of furrows, whether they be long and tapering, as in the grains of goldenrod, or broad and short, as in the grains of sunflower, or circular and coinciding in extent with their contained germ pore, as in the grains of the Chenopodiaceae, are mainly hereditary and phyletic in their distribution, and are of the greatest value in the identification and classification of plants. Likewise, whether there be but a single furrow or a larger number of them is a character of the deepest phylogenetic significance. The presence of a single furrow is the sign of the monocotyledons, the primitive gymnosperms, or the primitive dicotyledons; while the presence of a larger number of furrows, whether it be 3 (only very rarely 2) on up to 30 or more, is a sign of the higher dicotyledons. On the other hand, *the number and arrangement of the furrows*, when more than one, are almost entirely internal environmental because they are the result of the number and arrangement of the pollen grains during their formation in the pollen mother-cell.

Origin of Pollen Characters

For our first clear understanding and concise statement of the origin of these classes of characters we are indebted to Harper (1918), who states that at least two sets of factors are involved in determining the form of cells, their internally determined or specifically inherited cell form—including their capacity to respond to stimuli—and their contact and other relations with their neighbors during growth. This latter involves especially the conflict between the laws of cell bipartition with rectangular intersection of the successive planes of division, on the one hand, and, on the other, the tendency of single cells and groups of cells to assume least-surface configurations.

The problem as to which of the great variety of characters found among pollen grains are specifically inherited and which are the result of interrelations with their neighbors is thus sharply defined; and since there appear to be no words to designate adequately these two classes of cell characters I propose to call those which are the result of specifically inherited cell form *emphytic;** and those which are due to contact and other relations with their neighbors during growth, *haptotypic.** Emphytic cell characters are usually strictly phylogenetic in distribution and consequently of high diagnostic value, while haptotypic cell characters are almost fortuitous in their phyletic distribution and of much less diagnostic value but are of the greatest histogenetic interest.

Though three is the characteristic number of germinal furrows among the higher dicotyledons, it is a significant fact that in the pollen of many plants are also found a varying number of grains with four, six, or two. Most frequently grains with aberrant numbers of furrows constitute only a small proportion of the total, but in some species, *e.g.*, the sorrel dock and white ash, almost one-half of the grains have four germinal furrows. In the grains of *Dahlia*, as already pointed out, the number of furrows is always six, despite the fact that three is almost the universal number throughout the Compositae; and in one specimen of tarweed (*Stenotus lanuginosus*) approximately one-half the grains have two germinal furrows.

---

* See Glossary.

Number of Furrows Due to Arrangement in Tetrad.—Why should three be the characteristic number of furrows among dicotyledonous pollen grains; and how do the other numbers originate? In the formation of pollen grains the pollen mother-cell nucleus always goes through two successive divisions and nearly always gives rise to four daughter-cells, producing in due course four mature pollen grains. In the dicotyledons these four cells are formed after two nuclear divisions which take place in rapid succession, at right angles to each other, without the dividing cell walls' forming until after the four daughter nuclei

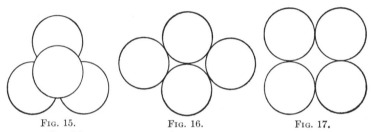

Fig. 15.   Fig. 16.   Fig. 17.

Figs. 15–17.—Diagrams of typical arrangements of four spheres in contact: Fig. 15, tetrahedral; Fig. 16, rhomboidal; Fig. 17, square.

have separated and reorganized. Regardless of the relative orientation of the spindles by which they were formed, the daughter nuclei generally tend to take up positions as far from each other as possible within the confines of the pollen mother-cell, which results in their being tetrahedrally arranged. Other arrangements sometimes occur; in fact, all possible arrangements of four cells in contact are found; but in the tetrads of dicotyledons the arrangement is prevailingly tetrahedral, and it is in this position that the phragmoplasts are formed, and the cells rounded off and separated.

If four spheres are placed together in the tetrahedral arrangement, it will be seen that each must make contact at one point with each of its three neighbors, giving each sphere three equally spaced contact points (Fig. 15). This suggests an explanation of the prevailingly tricolpate character of the dicotyledonous pollen grains.

For purposes of discussing the symmetry relations of these spheres it is convenient to speak of their polar axes as lines extending through the centers of the spheres and directed toward the center of the tetrad, where they would all four meet, if so extended, as stated by Fischer (1890). Thus each sphere comes to have an inner and an outer pole, a proximal and distal polar hemisphere, and the equator is the boundary between the two polar hemispheres. In the case of the four spheres, the three points of contact on each occupy the positions of the angles of an equilateral triangle, and all lie in the proximal polar hemisphere; whereas the three furrows in dicotyledonous pollen grains generally lie on the equator—midway between the poles.

Furrows Form at Points of Contact in the Tetrad.—Now let us see what the situation is when the four cells of the pollen tetrad remain united at maturity. Such is the case among most of the Ericaceae; for example, in the pollen of *Azalea* the four cells of the tetrad remain firmly united in the tetrahedral position, forming a four-celled compound pollen grain at maturity (Fig. 19). Each of the cells is

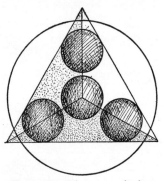

Fig. 18.—Diagram of four daughter nuclei in the tetrahedral arrangement showing their spacial relation to a tetrahedron, the mother-cell wall represented by the large circle.

much flattened against its three neighbors of the tetrad so that, instead of their contacts' being points, as in the case of spheres in this arrangement, they are broad, flat surfaces, the flattening extending very near, or even quite to, the equators of the grains. Each of the four cells has three germinal furrows contiguous and continuous with those of its three neighbors directly across the edges of their contact faces. Each furrow encloses a single germinal aperture at its point of contact with the furrow of the neighboring grain. Obviously, in this case the position of the furrows and apertures is determined by the tetrahedral arrangement of the grains in the tetrad group and is, therefore, a haptotypic character.

Another example of tetrad pollen grains is that of *Salpiglossis sinuata* (Fig. 20). The cells are in the tetrahedral position, but their union is looser than that of the grains of *Azalea*, as if formed under less pressure, and the contact faces are correspondingly less extended so that their edges do not nearly reach the equator. The furrows are spindle-shaped, broadening out in the middle to contain the germinal aperture and tapering toward their ends. Though they exactly meet each other on the line of contact between the flattened faces of the adjacent cells, their apertures are not at the edges of contact, as in those of *Azalea,* but are on the equators of the individual cells. This shows that in these grains the longitudinal positions of the furrows are controlled by the contacts between adjacent grains but that their latitudinal positions are independent of contacts with

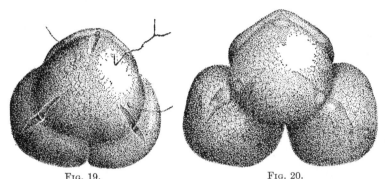

FIG. 19.   FIG. 20.

FIGS. 19, 20.—Mature pollen grains in tetrahedral tetrads: Fig. 19, *Azalea,* in which the four grains are closely packed; Fig. 20, *Salpiglossis sinuata,* in which the four grains are loosely attached.

neighboring grains; *i.e.,* they take symmetrical positions midway between the poles.

Tetrahedral Arrangement Due to Quadripartitioning by Furrowing.—When the grains remain united at maturity, as in *Azalea* and *Salpiglossis,* the relationship of the furrows to the arrangement of the grains in their tetrad is obvious. But when the grains are separate, as they much more often are, information of the same sort may be obtained by examining the pollen grains in the early stages of their development. After the two divisions of the pollen mother-cell nucleus are complete and the four nuclei have taken up positions as far apart as possible—consequently, in the tetrahedral arrangement—thickenings are formed on the inside of the pollen mother-cell wall in the regions of least pressure. This can perhaps be visualized if we think of the four nuclei contained within the spherical wall of the pollen mother-cell as being situated at the four angles of an imaginary tetrahedron (Fig. 18). Such a figure is bounded by four plane surfaces—each an equilateral triangle—six edges, and the four solid angles toward which the four nuclei have migrated. Now, when the soft, gelatinous inner layers of the mother-cell wall begin to swell, the viscous material is molded inwardly in the zones of least pressure which lie between each group of three nuclei. There are four such regions, each triangular and centering outside the centers of each of the triangular faces of such an imaginary tetrahedron. These four interior ridges of the mother-cell wall continue to develop inwardly until they meet in the center of the tetrahedron. At this stage each of the four daughter-cells is still connected with its neighbors through three broad channels, six in all. As the thickening of the mother-cell wall proceeds, the six, broad connecting channels are progressively narrowed until, at the last stage before complete separation, the cells remain united by pit connections which lie in the same planes as the six edges of the assumed tetrahedron and thus become the middle points of the contact faces of the four pollen cells. These pit connections are finally severed as the cells round up and become completely separated by the continued thickening of the pollen mother-cell wall. According to Farr (1916), Gates (1925), and others, this method of quadripartition by furrowing is prevalent among the dicotyledons.

Development of Sculpturing.—It is soon after the grains have separated that their sculpturing begins to appear. Its formation consists in the deposition in organized form of the material from outside and is not secreted by the grain. As a general rule, in normal grains little or no suggestion of the pattern or hint of the position of the germinal apertures is discernible until after the separation and rounding up of the daughter-cells are complete. Consequently, from an examination of normal material, the relation of the germ pores to the points of mutual contact is not generally apparent, except in grains which remain united.

In pollen grains which exhibit a complicated system of sculpturing this nearly always presents a radiosymmetrical pattern which is definitely related to the germinal apertures. For example, in the normal grains of chicory there are three apertures, and the pattern of the sculpturing is triradiate (Plate XI, Fig. 6); it is characterized by six prominent paraporal crests, so called because they are arranged one on each side of the germinal pores and their adjoining abporal lucanae. In aberrant grains in which there are more than three apertures the triradiate pattern is never found, which shows that the numerical type of the pattern is dependent upon the number of germinal apertures.

Fortunately, in the development of the pollen grains of some varieties of chicory there are encountered many irregular formations which show the nature of this relationship. In these the pollen mother-cells either fail entirely to divide, or their divisions are arrested before completion. For example, in the variety known as "red-leaved treviso"* a large proportion of the pollen mother-cells do not divide; in these the material of the special mother-cell walls is deposited in a granular concretion on the surface, but such cells appear to be deficient in power properly to organize it and become formless giants without germinal apertures, and with no suggestion of the symmetrical pattern characteristic of the normal grains. Yet, at least in some cases, spines are weakly developed, and they and the texture of the exine bear an unmistakable resemblance to those of the normal grains. The numerical symmetry of the triradiate pattern of chicory pollen is a haptotypic character and, in this case, lacking the contact stimuli, fails to develop; but the spines and texture are emphytic and develop, at least in part, independently of contact stimuli.

Abortive Tetrads.—In other anthers of the same chicory flowers the pollen mother-cells divide normally, but the four daughter-cells die without further growth and become quite empty; nevertheless, the pattern develops as typically on these small dead cells as on the normal grains. A similar condition has been described by Tischler (1908) and others among the grains of sterile hybrids; they state that, if a pollen cell dies after only the first rudiments of the sculpturing are laid down, the pattern continues to form and develops to completion even though the cell be dead and empty.

Symmetry Patterns Are Determined by Contact Points in the Tetrad.—Between these two extreme types of behavior are found

---

* I am indebted to Dr. A. B. Stout of the New York Botanical Garden for the use of the slides upon which these observations of the developing chicory pollen grains were made. The plants were grown from seed obtained from Dippe Brothers, Quedlinburg, Germany. It is interesting to note that they are characterized by excessive fasciation. See A. B. Stout, Duplication and cohesion in the main axis of *Cichorium Intybus*, *Mem. Brooklyn Bot. Gardens*, **1**: 480–485, 1918.

a few pollen mother-cells which appear to abort during the process of separation of the four daughter-cells. Occasionally this takes place when the furrowing has all but completed the separation of the cells; with the death of the protoplast they become "frozen," so to speak, in the final act of separation when each of the daughter-cells is still connected with its three neighbors by the pit connections which now become extended as six narrow tubes (Fig. 21). Though the process of division is arrested with the death of the cell, other processes continue; the special mother-

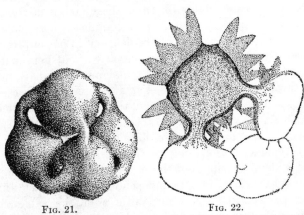

Fig. 21.   Fig. 22.

Figs. 21, 22.—Abnormal pollen grains of chicory, arrested in their development just before the final separation of the daughter-cells: Fig. 21, in the tetrahedral arrangement, with the external sculpturing omitted from the drawing; Fig. 22, in the square arrangement with the external sculpturing partly represented, in optical section.

cell walls thicken, and the pattern of the newly formed cells is carried nearly to completion, resulting in the phenomenon of four daughter-cells still united in the tetrad but with the pattern of the finished cells clearly defined. And in such cells the pattern exhibits triradiate symmetry, bearing the same relation to the three connecting tubes as in the normal grains it bears to the three germ pores.

Thus it is that in the grains of chicory the triradiate type of symmetry is determined by the number and position of the germinal apertures, and these, in turn, are formed at the last points of communication between the adjoining cells, the former sites of the three phragmoplasts which joined each cell to its three

neighbors of the tetard.   Since tetrad formation is prevailingly
tetrahedral among the dicotyledons, we have the explanation
of the fact that the patterns on the pollen grains of dicotyledons are prevailingly triradiate.   This fact is the more remarkable
since among floral and other symmetrical structures the pentagonal is the prevailing type of symmetry among the dicotyledons (see, for example, the many beautiful photographs by
Blossfeldt, 1928), while the triradiate or triangular and the
hexagonal symmetries are much less frequently encountered.
We are evidently dealing in this case with phenomena which are
to be classed in fundamentally different categories.

It has already been pointed out that in the pollen of many
species of dicotyledons varying proportions of the grains may
exhibit certain symmetries other than the triradiate.   Among
the grains of species which are typically tricolpate are frequently
found a few which are tetracolpate, hexacolpate, and occasionally
dicolpate.   How can these be related to tetrad formations?

Tetrad Arrangements.—It was well known to Nägeli (1842)
that, when pollen tetrads are formed, frequently there are a few
in which the cells fail to get into the tetrahedral position.   Two
other arrangements which they may assume are the square and
rhomboidal.   In the square (Fig. 17) all cells are in the same plane;
it is the arrangement which would result from bipartition with
rectangular intersection with no readjustment toward a least-
surface configuration.   In this grouping each cell makes only two
points of contact with its neighbors.   It is known to occur sometimes among dicotyledons and is normal for many monocotyledons.   In the rhomboidal arrangement (Fig. 16) all four cells are
in approximately the same plane, but two cells have two points
of contact, and two have three.   Such an arrangement would
result from bipartition with rectangular intersection followed
by a partially expressed tendency to assume the least-surface configuration.   This arrangement was called by Nägeli
the half tetrahedral.   These two types of divergence from
the tetrahedral arrangement cause either all four cells to have
two points of contact or two cells to have two and two to have
three.   But, experience shows that grains with two germinal furrows are the most rarely encountered of those with aberrant
numbers.   The commonest aberrant number of furrows is four—
a number which, if each furrow formed only at a contact point,

would require at least five cells in a group, which almost never occurs.

Four Furrows.—An explanation of the origin of four germinal furrows is found in the developing chicory pollen referred to above; among the irregular grains are occasionally found some "frozen" tetrads arrested in their development in the *square* arrangement with pit connections at only two points in each grain. In some few such cases the development of the external features of the grains has proceeded far enough to show quite definitely that two germ pores were forming at the two points of contact, as would be expected, but there were also two more, developing opposite these points (Fig. 22), thus giving each of these grains four germinal apertures and four furrows.

Thus we see that apertures and furrows are not confined exclusively to the points of contact or pit connections, but, when these are in such a position as to cause the cell to be asymmetrical, a degree of symmetry may be achieved by the development of supplementary furrows symmetrically placed.

Six Furrows.—The next most common aberrant number of furrows is six; this number is frequently found in grains of which the normal number of furrows is three. It is, as we have seen, characteristic of the grains of *Dahlia* (Fig. 14). The arrangement of these six furrows is always tetrahedral (Figs. 27, 28) in the sense that they occupy the same relative positions as those of the edges of a tetrahedron. It will readily be seen that in this arrangement each furrow is subtended on the other side of the grain by another which is exactly opposite and with its long axis at right angles to the first. In the grains of *Dahlia* the achievement of symmetry is carried a step farther than in those of chicory. Four furrows are formed from two points of contact in the same position and orientation as those of the grains of chicory, but two more furrows are developed in such positions and orientations as to complete the tetrahedral configuration. Consequently, the grain of *Dahlia* is more completely symmetrical than the four-furrowed grain of chicory.

In these two cases the two contact points, which induced the formation of four furrows in the one case and six in the other, were about one-quarter of the periphery or equator of the grain apart. When such is the case the addition of two supplementary furrows achieved symmetry partly, but it required the addition of four to achieve it completely. If the contact points are less than one-quarter of the equator apart, various other numbers of furrows would have to be supplied to complete the symmetry. As we shall see, this basic principle leads to the formation of a wide range of furrow patterns.

These observations lead us to the conclusion that the number and arrangement of the germinal furrows in the grains of most dicotyledons are determined by the tetrahedral or other arrangement incident to their formation in tetrad. And, inasmuch as the numerical type of symmetry of the pattern is determined by the position and number of the germinal apertures, it may be stated that the number and arrangement of the elements in the symmetry patterns of pollen grains are haptotypic characters, that is to say, are the result of their cellular interrelations and directly due to the conflict of the law of bipartition with rectangular intersection, in opposition to the tendency to assume the least-surface configuration.

FURROW PATTERNS

In the pollen of perhaps the majority of species of plants the haptotypic characters are constant, showing relatively minor deviations in the number and arrangement of the furrows in only a few exceptional grains. But in certain groups of plants it seems to be a prerogative for the pollen to exhibit an enormous range of variation in haptotypic characters, sometimes within a single or a few closely related species, running almost the entire gamut of possibilities. Such a group is the genus *Haplopappus*,* a large genus of Composites in the tribe Astereae. And, on account of the light which these grains throw on the general tendencies of furrow arrangement, they will repay our careful examination.

Tricolpate Grains.—The basic or typical form of the pollen grains of *Haplopappus* (Plate I, Fig. 10) is similar to that of the grains of most other Compositae. They are spherical or oblate spheroidal. The walls are thick and inflexible and are provided with germinal furrows. These are generally three, equally spaced around the equator, which they cross at right angles, converging along meridional lines toward two centers which, it follows, are triradiate and at opposite poles of the sphere. The axes of the furrows, if extended, would thus intersect at angles of

* The genus *Haplopappus* is used here as defined by Hall (1928).

PLATE I.—Pollen grains of *Haplopappus* and allied species, illustrating furrow configurations.   1, *H. MacLeanii*, dodecacolpate; 2, *H. MacLeanii*, nonacolpate; 3, *Erigeron strigosus*; octocolpate; 4, *H. acaulis*, hexacolpate; 5, *H. stenophyllus*, nonacolpate; 6, *H. MacLeanii*, dwarf; 7, *H. lanuginosus*, dicolpate; 8, *H. acaulis*, acolpate; 9, *H. MacLeanii*, tetracolpate; 10, *H. chrysanthemifolius*, tricolpate.

one-third of a circle or 120 deg. at each of the poles and thus divide the surface of the spheroid into three equal lunes. Though there is some variation in the lengths of the furrows, among the grains of different species, they never quite meet, always ending some distance short of the centers of convergence. Such a form of grain is called tricolpate.

The furrows appear as deep gashes cut into the exine. When the grain is moist they spread widely open and are seen to be crossed by a thin layer of the exine—the furrow membrane—which lacks the granular texture and characteristic sculpturing of the general exine. In the center of each is a rounded aperture or pore through which the pollen tube may grow at the time of germination and through which the germinal papilla always bulges when the grain is moist and expanded. The exine of the furrow membrane is elastic and permits the opening and closing of the furrow, thus accommodating changes in volume of the grain with the absorption and liberation of moisture.

In the pollen of many species of *Haplopappus* are found a varying proportion of grains with more or fewer than three furrows. Sometimes these present great irregularity and asymmetry in arrangement and form, but more often they are symmetrical, the various numbers of furrows forming characteristic patterns. These configurations are well defined, and, with some study, it is generally possible to assign patterns of any of the grains with supernumerary furrows to one or another of a rather small number of different type arrangements. The distribution of these aberrant configurations among the different species is quite fortuitous, the various forms occurring abundantly in the pollen of some specimens and being entirely absent from that of others of the same species. The most usual atypical numbers of furrows are 6 and 4. Other numbers of furrows encountered less frequently are 12, 9, and very rarely 2 and 8, and in one specimen none at all.

On account of the geometrical relations which the configurations of the atypical numbers of furrows bear to each other, it will be best to discuss them in the ascending order of their complexity.

Acolpate Grains.—Grains which apparently have no furrows have instead three germinal apertures (Plate I, Fig. 8). These apertures should probably be regarded as furrows which are so short that they coincide with the pores; nevertheless, they are quite round and without hint of meridional orientation. Only in the pollen of one specimen of *Haplopappus* was the acolpate form observed. In this all the grains are alike and differ from those of other species only in the notably larger size of their germ pores, which is obviously an adaptive response compensating for the loss of harmomegathy due to the absence of the

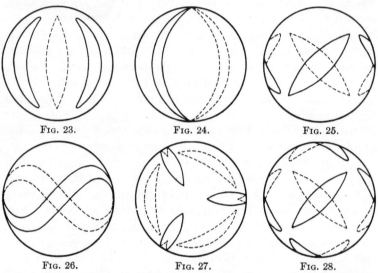

Fig. 23.   Fig. 24.   Fig. 25.

Fig. 26.   Fig. 27.   Fig. 28.

Figs. 23–28.—Diagrams of furrow arrangements: Fig. 23, tricolpate; Fig. 24, dicolpate with the two furrows opposite and united; Fig. 25, tetracolpate, the same as hexacolpate but lacking two furrows; Fig. 26, zigzag form, a tetracolpate derivative; Fig. 27, hexacolpate, one of the four centers of convergence uppermost; Fig. 28, hexacolpate, one of the six furrows uppermost.

furrows. In several other specimens of this species of which the pollen was examined it was found to be normal. The condition must, therefore, be regarded as exceptional.

Dicolpate Grains.—When the grains have only two furrows they are generally in the position of those of normal tricolpate grains, with their axes converging toward the poles at angles of 120 deg., as if one of the normal three had been dropped without otherwise disturbing the organization of the grain. When in this arrangement, the furrows have a tendency to be extended and become fused at one or both poles as if the absence of the third furrow led to the lengthening and fusion of the remaining two. This type of grain corresponds to Fig. 23, if we omit the furrow shown in dotted line on the underside of the grain. Occasionally a careful inspection of dicolpate grains with furrows in this position reveals a trace of the third furrow represented by a slight rift in the exine, suggesting that this form of dicolpate grain arises from the partial or complete suppression of one of the furrows. The furrows in dicolpate grains may also be exactly opposite each other. When so arranged they nearly always join together at both ends and completely encircle the grain as a single furrow (Fig. 24) but with two germinal pores opposite each other (Plate I, Fig. 7). Dicolpate grains of either form are rare but are found in the pollen of several species of *Haplopappus*.

Tetracolpate Grains.—When the grains have four furrows they are equally spaced on the equator (Fig. 25), but the axes of such furrows are never meridionally arranged; instead, they cross the equator obliquely and converge in pairs, at angles of 120 deg., toward four centers Plate I, Fig. 9). If such a grain is oriented under the microscope so that the center of one furrow with its germinal pore is uppermost, focusing down on the lower side of the grain will always reveal another furrow exactly opposite but with its long axis crossing that of the upper at right angles. The germinal pores of the other two furrows will be seen bulging out on opposite sides of the limb or the apparent boundary of the sphere. As the focus is changed (better seen with a binocular microscope giving stereoscopic vision) these two furrows will be seen to curve around the horizon and inward, with their axes approaching those of the upper and lower furrows, thus converging in pairs toward four centers, with angles of convergence of 120 deg. or one-third of a circle. This configuration suggests that from each center is missing a third furrow, which if restored would complete the hexacolpate configuration (Figs. 27, 28) to be discussed under the description of that type, and from which this may be regarded as a derived form.

In tetracolpate grains the furrows are often long and coalescent at their ends, thus traversing, as a single furrow, a zigzag course around the grain, crossing its equator four times. From such furrows any one or more of the germ pores may be absent, and the angles of convergence may be lost in broad, sweeping curves, causing the furrow to assume much the form of the curved seam in the fabric covering of a tennis ball (Fig. 26). The tetracolpate form, with furrows converging toward four centers, is quite common in this genus and is encountered in many different families.

Hexacolpate Grains.—When grains have six furrows, their usual configuration is such that they are equally distributed over the surface, with their long axes converging toward four centers, which are triradiate and equally spaced (Plate I, Fig. 4). This arrangement is perhaps best visualized by comparing the six furrow axes to the six edges of a tetrahedron and the points of convergence to the four solid angles of such a figure (Fig. 27). This configuration of furrows was observed by von Mohl (1835, page 225) in the pollen of several species of *Corydalis* and described by him as tetrahedral: "Toute la surface des grains se trouve ainsi partagée par six fissures en quatre triangles, ou en d'autres termes, les bandes de ce grain forment les arêtes d'un tétrahèdre." It was also described and illustrated by Fritzsche (1837, Plate VI, Fig. 5) in the grains of several species of *Corydalis* and of *Basella* and likewise regarded by him as the tetrahedral arrangement: "Mit sechs den Kanten des Tetraëders entsprechenden Spalten" (page 724).

When a hexacolpate grain is oriented so that one furrow is exactly uppermost, focusing down will reveal another furrow on the lower side, with its long axis directed at right angles to that of the upper; the four other furrows will be barely visible bending over the limb—the boundary of the median optical plane (Fig. 28)—but their four germinal pores can generally be seen bulging at four points equally spaced on the limb. If, on the other hand, the grain is so oriented that one of the centers of convergence is uppermost (Fig. 27), the three converging furrows will be almost wholly in view directed radially. And if now the microscope be focused on the lower surface, the three other furrows will be seen with their long axes directed tangentially, forming an equilateral triangle, and with their three apertures alternating with the three above. This form of hexacolpate pollen grain is exceedingly common. It constitutes a fair proportion of the pollen of most species of *Haplopappus*. It is likewise found here and there among all groups of Compositae and, as we have seen, is the characteristic form of the grains of *Dahlia* pollen. Outside the Compositae it is found regularly, and occasionally in the pollen of many different groups, including *Salpiglossis sinuata.* This latter is of peculiar interest because, as we have seen, its grains are shed united in their tetrads and so show the relation between this type of furrow configuration and the tetrad arrangement, a relation which will later be discussed at greater length (page 182).

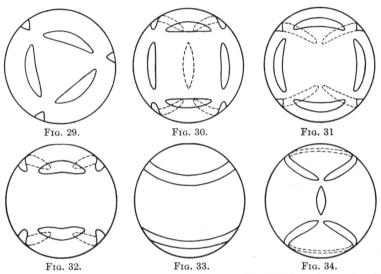

Fig. 29. Fig. 30. Fig. 31

Fig. 32. Fig. 33. Fig. 34.

Figs. 29–34.—Diagrams of furrow arrangements: Fig. 29, Nonacolpate, viewed with one of its spherical triangles uppermost; Fig. 30, nonacolpate, viewed with one of its spherical squares uppermost; Fig. 31, octacolpate, similar to the nonacolpate, except that one furrow is missing; Fig. 32, hexacolpate, derived form; Fig. 33, zonate; Fig. 34, half-zonate. The three latter are nonacolpate derivatives.

Grains are occasionally found with six furrows in an entirely different configuration which is not related to the tetrahedral. In this arrangement the furrows converge in pairs toward six centers, which are bilateral, instead of triradiate (Fig. 32), but with angles of convergence at least approximating 120 deg. This suggests that this form may be regarded as a derivative from the nonacolpate configuration to be described next, which likewise has six centers of convergence, and bears the same relation to the nonacolpate form that the tetracolpate configuration bears to the ordinary hexacolpate type. But this form is rare and is usually accompanied by ugly distortions of the grains, rendering them extremely difficult of analysis; usually some of the furrows lack apertures and are fused at one or more of their centers of convergence, thus traversing a more or less discontinuous course around the grain in each hemisphere between the equator and poles. Quite frequently grains are found with just two furrows completely encircling them in the position of the tropics on the terrestrial globe, and I believe that such zonate furrows represent the complete fusion and flattening out of the convergent angles of the six furrows of this form of hexacolpate configuration (Fig. 33).

This type of hexacolpate grain, which is perhaps best regarded as a nonacolpate derivative, is found occasionally in the pollen of *H. MacLeanii;* and its zonate derivative, which is much more easily recognized on account of its striking appearance, is found in the pollen of *H. stenophyllus* and outside the genus in the pollen of *Artemisia spinescens* in the Anthemideae and of *Limnia spathulata* in the Portulacaceae.

Nonacolpate Grains.—When grains have nine furrows they are as equally spaced as possible over the surface and are so arranged that their axes converge toward six centers which are triradiate (Plate I, Figs. 2, 5). This form bears the same relation to a form of pentahedron that the hexacolpate bears to the tetrahedron. This pentahedron is a right-triangular prism of which three sides are equal squares, and two, which are opposite, are similar equilateral triangles (Fig. 44). In the nonacolpate grain there are three viewpoints which show the four uppermost furrows with their axes forming the sides of a square (Fig. 30). Focusing down from any one of such reveals four more furrows curving around the limb of the sphere and converging toward the two ends of the ninth furrow, which subtends the upper square and is parallel to two of its sides. There are two views which show the axes of three furrows forming a triangle (Fig. 29; Plate I, Fig. 5). Focusing down from one of these brings into view three other furrows forming a triangle on the lower surface and exactly subtending that above; the three remaining furrows are seen curving over the limb from the angles of one triangle toward the corresponding angles of the subtending triangle. This type of grain is not common, having been found, in the present group, in the pollen of only two species, *Haplopappus stenophyllus* and *Erigeron strigosus,* but is fairly abundant in the latter. Outside this group it is occasionally found in the pollen of *Artemisia gnaphaloides* and *Rivina humilis* and is frequent among the grains of *Talinum multiflorum*. This type of furrow arrangement is stated by von Mohl (1835, page 225) to characterize some of the grains of the pollen of *Corydalis lutea*, of which he says, "Le grain représente un prisme triangulaire dont les faces latérales sont bombées, aussi bien que les terminales."

The nonacolpate type, besides giving rise to a certain form of hexacolpate and through this to the zonate type as noted above, apparently also gives rise to a curious half-zonate form (Fig. 34) by the dropping out of two furrows and the fusion of those remaining at their resulting bilateral centers of convergence. Grains of this form are of frequent occurrence among the pollen of *Limnia spathulata*, and it is likely that a further search will bring them to light in other species.

Octacolpate Grains.—When grains have eight furrows they present a very unusual symmetry; the axes of the furrows converge toward six centers, of which four are triradiate, and two bilateral (Fig. 31). If such a grain is oriented under the microscope with the four triradiate centers visible in the upper hemisphere, four furrows will be seen in the position of the sides of a square. Focusing downward will bring into view four other furrows appearing to start on the limb at the four angles of the square and converge in pairs toward two close but discrete centers in the lower hemisphere.

This form may be regarded as a derivative of the nonacolpate through the omission of one furrow and the moving together of the others partially to occupy its space. Occasionally the two bilateral centers approach very closely or actually coincide, producing a single tetraradiate center, but more often they are separated, presenting an appearance similar to that shown in Plate I, Fig. 9, of a tetracolpate grain.

The octacolpate form is rather rare; it has been found only in a few grains of *Fresenia fasciculata* and *Erigeron strigosus*. Outside the Astereae, it is common in pollen of *Artemisia spinescens* and *Talinum multiflorum*.

Dodecacolpate Grains.—When grains have 12 furrows they are equally spaced and so arranged that their axes converge toward eight triradiate centers, the furrows dividing the surface of the grain into six squares (Figs. 35, 36, Plate I, Fig. 1). This form bears the same relation to a cube that the hexacolpate form bears to the tetrahedron, and the nonacolpate form to the right-triangular prism. The form has been admirably described by Fritzsche (1837) for the pollen of *Talinum patens* in which it is clearly and beautifully seen on account of the absence of spines and the transparency and regularity of the grains. As Fritzsche says (page 725), "Die Anordnung der Spalten ist auch hier höchst regelmässig, indem sie den zwölf Kanten eines Würfels entsprechen; sie sind von ziemlich grosser Ausdehung und theilen die Exine in sechs viereckige, mit den Ecken zusammenhängende Stücken."

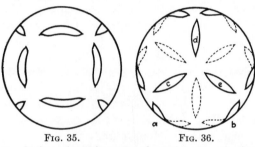

FIG. 35.   FIG. 36.

FIGS. 35, 36.—Dodecacolpate furrow configuration: Fig. 35, viewed with one of its four spherical squares uppermost; Fig. 36, viewed with one of its eight centers of convergence uppermost. (For further explanation see text.)

If such a grain is examined with any one of the centers of convergence exactly uppermost (Fig. 36), focusing downward will bring into view another center exactly below but with its radii alternating with those of the center above. Or, if the grain is oriented so that the axes of the furrows on the upper surface form a square (Fig. 35), focusing down will bring into view another square exactly subtending the one above, and four other furrows will be seen bending over the limb from the angles of one square toward the corresponding angles of the other square. In grains of this form the 12 furrows are never all occupied by pores; usually only four pores may be counted.

The dodecacolpate furrow configuration occurs among the grains of *Erigeron strigosus* and in those of *Haplopappus MacLeanii*. Outside the Astereae, besides being found in the pollen of some species of *Talinum* as noted above, it is occasionally found in the pollen of *Artemisia spinescens* and, in its various derivatives, in that of *Limnia spathulata*. It is said by Franz

(1908) to characterize the pollen of some species of Portulacaceae and is said by von Mohl (1835, page 225) to be found among the pollen of *Corydalis lutea* and *Clerodendron paniculatum*. It is also the characteristic form of the pollen of some species of Malpighiaceae.

Significance of Furrow Configurations

Recapitulation.—The study of the arrangement of the furrows of various numbers reveals controlling their configurations certain underlying laws, which may be deduced as follows: When a pollen grain forms in the tetrahedral arrangement, it makes three points of contact—one with each of its three neighbors of the tetrad—and consequently acquires three furrows equally spaced around the equator, and this explains the tricolpate form and triradiate patterns which characterize the majority of dicotyledonous pollen grains. But pollen grains do not always have three furrows, nor do they always form in the tetrahedral arrangement. When they form in some other arrangement with two unsymmetrical points of contact, two furrows are formed with orientation on the two points, but the cell maintains its symmetry in spite of this by the formation of symmetrically balancing furrows. Asymmetry in space relations among pollen grains, and perhaps among all cells, is avoided as far as possible. This is probably partly a matter of physical equilibrium, for, as Thompson (1917, page 209) notes, "in every symmetrical system any deformation that tends to destroy the symmetry is complemented by an equal and opposite deformation that tends to restore it."

Among the grains of the Astereae are many with four furrows which undoubtedly arose in this fashion; but there are even more grains with six and other numbers of furrows in which the symmetry is more complete than in those with four.

The Law of Equal Triconvergent Angles.—We have noticed that, in all the various configurations assumed by the furrows they tend to converge toward each other in threes with equal angles of convergence, which consequently tend to be 120 deg. This may be stated as the law of equal triconvergent angles. Occasionally, it is true, one of the furrows may be absent, leaving only two furrows converging toward a center, but in such cases one of the two convergent angles tends to be 120 deg. This law appears to be almost universal for grains which are spheroidal, as are those of the Astereae, but does not apply to grains which are much flattened or greatly elongated. Furthermore, when a furrow is missing from a center of convergence, the two remaining furrows have a strong tendency to coalesce at their ends, or sometimes such a condition may even lead to the total collapse of such defective configurations, resulting in sadly distorted and misshapen grains and suggesting an unstable condition at such biradiate centers. From this it becomes evident that, unless a grain have three furrows, or some multiple of three, it must have some biradiate centers of convergence, with their resulting lack of stability. "Die ganzen Zahl hat Gott gemacht; alles anders ist Menschenwerk."

Furrow Configurations and Polyhedrons.—The interesting relation between the various furrow configurations and certain polyhedrons will become clear if we consider the characters of polyhedrons in relation to the sphere as follows.   The tetrahedron (Fig. 43), for example, which is the simplest polyhedron, is bounded by four equal faces, each of which is an equilateral triangle with angles of 60 deg. If a sphere be circumscribed about a tetrahedron, and the four vertices joined by the shortest possible lines in the surface of the sphere subtending the edges of the tetrahedron, these lines will be arcs of great circles and will intersect at the four vertices in such a way as to make three equal convergent angles at each, and, incidentally, they divide the surface of the sphere into four equal spherical triangles whose angles are not 60 but 120 deg. The arrangement of such lines corresponds precisely to the furrows of a hexacolpate grain. In the same way if a sphere be circumscribed about a cube, and arcs of great circles passed through the vertices of the cube so as to correspond to its edges, these arcs will correspond in position to the 12 furrows of a dodecacolpate grain and will divide the surface of the sphere into six spherical squares, whose angles, since there are three, equal and convergent at each of the vertices, are 120 deg. These are the kind of square pieces that Fritzsche meant when he said, in speaking of the furrows of the grains of *Talinum patens*, "Sie . . . theilen die Exine in sechs viereckige . . . Stücken." In this connection the interesting geometrical observation comes to light that polygons, whether they be triangles, squares, or pentagons, when drawn over the surface of a sphere so as to divide the whole surface into equal parts, must always have their angles equal to 120 deg.

TABLE II.—COMMON FURROW CONFIGURATIONS

No. of faces	No. of edges or furrows	Furrow configuration	Corresponding polyhedron	Description of polyhedron	Example
3	0	Acolpate	None	None	Haplopappus (Pl. I, Fig. 8)
	3	Tricolpate	None	Three lunes	Rosa, Haplopappus (Pl. I, Fig. 10)
4	6	Hexacolpate	Tetrahedron	4 equilateral triangles	Dahlia; Haplopappus (Pl. I, Fig. 4)
5	9	Nonacolpate	Triangular prism	2 triangles and 3 squares	Haplopappus (Pl. I, Figs. 2, 5)
6	12	Dodecacolpate	Cube	6 squares	Haplopappus (Pl. I, Fig. 1)
7	15	Pentadecacolpate	Pentagonal prism or heptahedron	5 squares, 2 pentagons	Talinum patens
12	30	Triacontacolpate	Pentagonal dodecahedron	12 equal pentagons	Persicaria amphibium (Fig. 100) Fumaria spicata

If we write out the series of symmetrical furrow configurations commonly occurring in pollen grains, it is seen that to each of these corresponds a polyhedron; also, some other interesting facts become evident (Table II).

As the number of furrows increases by steps of three, the number of faces of the corresponding polyhedrons increases by steps of one, a relation which may be expressed by $E = 3F - 6$, where E is the number of edges or furrows, and F is the number of faces, an equation which expresses the series however far extended.

Obviously, there can be no polyhedron corresponding to grains with no furrows. Grains with three furrows, according to this equation, would require a polyhedron with three edges and three faces. No such polyhedron exists, because three planes cannot enclose space; but three curved faces can enclose a space, as they do in the simplest and commonest form the tricolpate, in which three arcs of great circles divide the surface of the grain into three equal lunes.

The largest number of furrows counted with any degree of certainty in the pollen grains of *Haplopappus* and the Astereae is 12. The higher numbers of furrows are difficult to count because of the nature of the grains; so whether or not numbers higher in the series than 12 exist among them is still uncertain. Outside the Astereae, however, 15 *furrows* are reported by Fischer (1890, page 56) for the grains of *Talinum patens* and *Montia fontana*, in which he says that their arrangement corresponds to the edges of a five-sided prism; also, in the pollen of *Platycapnos spicatus* (= *Fumaria spicata* L.) (page 37). The next number that, so far as I am aware, is recorded in the literature is 30 *furrows*, described by von Mohl for the grains of *Rivina brasiliensis*, *R. humilis*, and *Fumaria spicata*. In the last he states that the great transparency of the granular exine permits the distinction of areas marked off by the furrows and distributed in such a way that the whole surface of the grain is divided into pentagons which form a pentagonal dodecahedron (page 225). A similar configuration is described for the grains of *Polygonum amphibium* and *Alsine media* by Fritzsche (1837, page 725), who lays special emphasis upon the regularity of the pentagons and their arrangement. A similar figure is likewise described by Fischer 1890, (page 56) for the grains of *Portulaca oleracea* L. and *P. grandiflora*. Furthermore, in the Portulacaceae the dodecahedron is said by Franz (1908, page 33) to be the usual configuration for a large section of the family: "Die Grundform des Pollens ist in der ersten grossen Gruppe, bei den Portulacoideae, das Pentagondodekaeder."

The *pentagonal dodecahedron* with 12 faces and 30 edges fits into our series, fulfilling the requirements of $E = 3F - 6$, so it is not surprising that grains should be found with furrows conforming to this configuration. It is something more than a coincidence, however, that so many kinds of pollen grain exhibit the dodecahedron as the ground plan of their furrow arrangement, while apparently few exhibit the numbers of furrows intervening between 15 and 30. Why should the pentagonal dodecahedron be so favored among mathematical configurations, to the neglect of several simpler configurations involving fewer furrows? In the first place, the pentagonal dodecahedron is a striking and unique figure. It differs from the prisms and other polyhedrons which would accommodate the furrow numbers of our series between 12 and 30 *in being perfectly regular.* It is one of the five possible regular polyhedrons. All its faces are regular pentagons, with all their sides equal, all their angles 108 deg., and all their interfacial angles equal. The other regular polyhedrons are the tetrahedron, octahedron, icosahedron, and cube. Of these only the tetrahedron, which is bounded by four triangles, and the cube, which is bounded by six squares, share with the pentagonal dodecahedron the convergence of three and only three edges and angles at their vertices. The regular octahedron and icosahedron present four and five convergent angles at their vertices, a condition quite incompatible with the triconvergent angular pattern of pollen-grain-furrow configurations; consequently they may be dropped from further consideration.

When a sphere is circumscribed about a pentagonal dodecahedron and its vertices joined along the arcs of great circles, that is to say, when a pentagonal dodecahedron is constructed with its faces of spherical pentagons instead of plane pentagons, the convergent angles will be equal and exactly 120 deg. It thus becomes clear that perfect symmetry of configuration can be attained only when the furrows correspond in number and arrangement to the edges of regular polyhedrons having three equal convergent angles. It is such symmetry relations as these that account for the tetrahedron, cube, and pentagonal dodecahedron's being favored members of the numerical series of furrow configurations.

If, on the other hand, we draw a right-triangular prism, in its spherical form, equality of the three convergent angles at each of the centers of convergence cannot be attained, because in the plane-triangular prism the angles of the equilateral triangles are 60 deg., while those of the associated squares are 90 deg. When such a figure is adapted to the spherical curvature, and the edges take up the positions of arcs of great circles, the disproportion of these angles is further increased, though their total is now equal to four right angles. Thus we have a conflict between the law of equal triconvergent angles and the difference between the spherical values of a right angle and a 60-deg. angle. When the angles of the polyhedron are small, as 60 and 90 deg., an adjustment takes place. This is accomplished in various ways; sometimes a compromise is struck by a shift of the furrows which bound the triangle a little out of the paths of great circles,

tending to equalize the angles.   If this is carried far, the grain
sometimes shows a tendency to alter its shape, adapting the
surface curvature to that of the furrows in such a way as to
cause them to follow geodetic curves; the result is a slight bulge
through the triangular faces.   Such an adjustment, though
common in the grains of some plants, appears not to be found in
the grains of the Astereae; in these the adjustment is apparently
made mostly at the expense of the equality of the triconvergent
angles, with perhaps a little shifting of some of the furrows out
of the paths of great circles.   Seldom does the grain change
its shape.

The scarcity of the 15-furrowed grains and the still greater
scarcity of grains with furrows numbering between 15 and 30 is

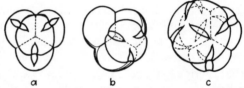

a   *b*   *c*

Fig. 37.—Arrangements of the four cells in *Salpiglossis* pollen, diagrammatic:
a, tetrahedral; *b*, half-tetrahedral, the upper cell with only two points of contact;
c, one cell a giant with only two points of contact which are about ¼ circumference apart.

apparently due to the difficulty or impossibility of making such
an adjustment.   All four of the polyhedrons missing from our
list (Table II) would have more than one kind of face; and, since
their internal angles are therefore different, this at once precludes
the possibility of equal triconvergent angles.   Such grains, with
furrow configurations corresponding to these missing numbers,
must be less symmetrical and consequently less stable than those
with the more perfect symmetry corresponding to the regular
polyhedrons, which have equal triconvergent angles and in
which there is no conflict between the angles of different types
of polygon.   There are only three such regular polyhedrons—the
tetrahedron, cube, and pentagonal dodecahedron.

**The Configuration Developed Depends upon the Contact
Points of the Grain in Its Tetrad.**—The question now arises:
What determines which one of these configurations shall be
adopted by the grain?   When a grain has three points of contact
in the normal tetrad, these points are equidistant, and such a

grain will acquire three furrows; but if it has only two points of contact, it may acquire a larger number. We have seen (page 166) that, in the dividing chicory pollen grain, two points of contact can result in four furrows. In the particular instance cited, the four cells of the tetrad were all of the same size but in the square instead of the tetrahedral arrangement. Further light is thrown on this point by a condition sometimes found in the grains of *Salpiglossis*. Its pollen, as we have already seen, is shed united in tetrads which are generally tetrahedral, and each grain tricolpate (Fig. 20). Occasionally, however, one finds tetrads in which one of the cells did not quite achieve the tetrahedral position, though approaching very closely to it but making only two points of contact (Fig. 37). Such cells may acquire three furrows in the ordinary tricolpate configuration (Fig. 37b), four furrows with their axes converging in pairs at 120 deg.; or more frequently two other furrows, generally without germ pores, are thrown in between the two biradiate centers (Fig. 37c). These bear a striking resemblance to the polar furrow or *Brechungslinie*, which is nearly always developed in segmenting eggs when four cells are formed in contact and which would otherwise all meet at a point (Fig. 38a, b). In the same way that the "breaking line" in the segmenting egg breaks the unstable tetraradiate center into two stable triradiate centers, thereby restoring the stability of the segmenting egg, these two connecting furrows in the pollen grain of *Salpiglossis* each join together two unstable biradiate centers and in so doing complete the tetrahedral hexacolpate configuration and thereby restore the symmetry and stability of the grain.

If two contact points can induce the formation of 3, 4, or 6 furrows, there seems no reason why two contact points could not likewise induce the formation of 9, 12, or more furrows, the choice depending upon the distance apart of such points in relation to the size of the grain. For example, if the formation of two furrows should be induced by contacts in such positions on the limb, as a and b (Fig. 36), so as to require four more to balance them symmetrically on the limb, these six furrows would converge in pairs and thus establish six unstable biradiate centers of convergence. From such an arrangement symmetry could be completed by the formation of three connecting furrows, as c, d, e, in each hemisphere. Our grounds for assuming that

three connecting furrows would form under these conditions
to join the six furrow ends in each hemisphere are again based
upon observations in developing embryos; for here when six cells
are formed in contact so that they would otherwise meet at a
point (Fig. 38c) they are always separated by the formation
of three intermediate walls or breaking lines, which are themselves frequently triradiate in arrangement and form with the
walls of the six cells three more triradiate centers with all the
angles 120 deg. (Fig. 38d).

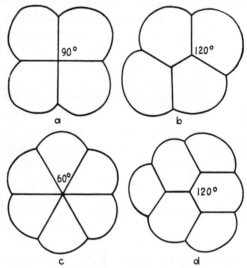

Fig. 38.—Arrangements of cells in one plane: *a*, four cells, unstable; *b*, four cells
stable; *c*, six cells, unstable; *d*, six cells, stable.

The distance apart of the initiating points must depend
partly upon the position of the grain in its tetrad but to a larger
extent upon its size in relation to that of its neighbors. It is
obvious that a shifting in the tetrad may change the distance
apart of the contact points, but much larger relative differences
are brought about by an increase in the size of one of the grains.
Thus it happens that grains of normal size may occasionally
bear four or six furrows, while the giants nearly always bear four,
six, or larger numbers of furrows; and likewise grains with
supernumerary furrows are most frequently giants.

It is interesting and perhaps not without profit to speculate
further as to the origin of the furrows. The unequivocal insist-

nce upon the 120-deg. angle and the almost equal insistence upon the triradiate centers of convergence of the furrow axes suggest that the furrows are the expression of stresses—whether they be pressure or tension, the orientation would be the same. In a plane surface, pressure between objects of similar size and offering similar resistance to the pressure results in a hexagonal configuration with internal angles of 120 deg. So familiar is this configuration that it is always recognized at once as the result of pressure. In soap films the configuration likewise tends to be hexagonal and with the same insistence upon the 120-deg. angle, and we recognize it at once as the result of tension.

On the sphere, hexagons of finite size are incompatible with equal convergent angles between furrows, for reasons which we have already seen. In the case of the segmenting embryo it is well known that the arrangement of the cells is brought about by the tendency to assume least-surface configurations, which in turn is the result of surface tension and, as Plateau has shown, is equally the property of oil drops and soap films. Consequently, it is reasonable to suppose that the furrow configurations are brought about by similar forces. But if we recognize the hexagonal system with its internal angle of 120 deg. as denoting relations of stress in a plane surface, by the same token we can recognize triangles, squares, and pentagons with angles of 120 deg. on a spherical surface as likewise denoting relations of stress. This being so, it follows that supernumerary furrows and their configuration on the surface of pollen grains are due to stresses set up in the grain by contact stimuli received at two points in the tetrad. And the particular type of configuration is determined by the distance apart of the two points relative to the size of the sphere. A critical study of the various furrow configurations viewed in this light shows that they are subject to the same laws as ordinary mud cracks or plaster cracks, and the many varied and complicated patterns which they describe are the result of their adaptation to a spherical surface.

II. THE TRISCHISTOCLASIC SYSTEM

When a layer of mud dries and shrinks, the shrinkage is manifest by the development of a system of small cracks (Fig. 39). Under favorable conditions such a system of cracks tends to divide the mud continuously into a number of hexagonal pieces.

It is true that such hexagonal cracking in mud is never exactly uniform. This is because the system is made up of a number of triradiate cracks of small extent which originate in random positions independently of each other and therefore must make rather violent adjustments as they merge together. Nevertheless, the system tends to approach an ideal, *i.e.*, the breaking of the surface into uniform hexagonal pieces. Such an ideal would be attained if, instead of a large number of independent triradiate cracks originating separately, there should start but a single one, and it should branch dichotomously with equal

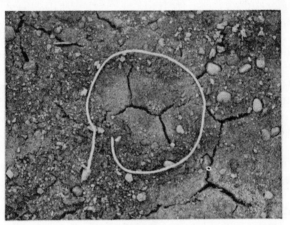

Fig. 39.—Mud cracks approximating the trischistoclasic system in their arrangement. Compare the part surrounded by a piece of string with Figs. 37c and 41.

triconvergent angles and cracks of equal lengths until the whole sheet of mud was cracked. Such an ideal may easily be imitated if, from a point a (Fig. 40) in a plane surface, three equal lines be drawn at equal angles (*i.e.*, 120 deg. each) ab_1, ab_2, ab_3; and from the ends of each of these be drawn in the same way two more lines equal to the first, b_1c_1, b_1c_2, b_2c_3, b_2c_4, etc.; then from the ends of each of these lines be drawn in the same way two more equal lines c_1d_1, c_1d_2, etc. Three equal hexagons will be completed, with six free lines and six apices in positions to form nine more hexagons surrounding the initial group of three, if the branching be repeated once more. Such a system of triradiate branching on a plane surface is open, and it may be continued indefinitely or until the entire available surface has been divided into equal hexagons.

Since the outstanding character of this system is its triradiate nature, I have designated it as the system of triradiate cracking or to use a single word, *trischistoclasic* (see Glossary). The system is extremely common. It may be stated as a law that the trischistoclasic system divides a plane surface continuously into equal hexagons, however far it may be extended. In its ideal form it is closely approached in the arrangement of the hexagonal cells of a honeycomb. In a cruder form, with imperfect adjustments between the different triradiate centers, it may be seen in mud cracking along the roadside and in plastered walls.

Due to Equilateral Stresses.—The conditions which bring it about are stresses equal in all directions. An interesting corollary to this is that if cracks appear in this system on a plastered wall, one may be reasonably sure that they penetrate only the plaster and not the body of the wall. The reason for this is that the plaster, being relatively light, is not influenced by gravity, so only the stress of its shrinkage, which is equal in all directions, is brought to bear on the formation of the cracks. If, on the other hand, the cracks in the wall tend to be vertical or parallel, one may be equally sure that they penetrate the body of the wall and are due to the lateral pull of the shrinking wall acting at right angles to the vertical thrust of gravity, two stresses which are unequal and, in this case, opposite in sign.

Since lateral stresses acting equally in all directions are the basic cause of the trischistoclasic system, another name for the system is naturally suggested, *viz.*, the system of equilateral stresses or, to use a single word, *isotasithynic* (see Glossary). This system stands in contrast to the system of vertical or parallel cracks which is due to unequal lateral stresses, and which therefore may be called *heterotasithynic* (see Glossary).

Furrow Patterns Isotasithynic.—In pollen grains of spheroidal form, in which all surface stresses naturally tend to be equal, the arrangement of the furrows always follows the trischistoclasic or isotasithynic system, unless there is some good reason why it should not do so, *e.g.*, in the tetracolpate grains of *Taraxacum*, q. v., and in the squarish grains of *Impatiens*, where it appears to follow the heterotasithynic system. Though on a plane surface the trischistoclasic system must be uniformly hexagonal if the individual lines composing it are of uniform length and angular deviation, when applied to the surface of a sphere of finite size and itself composed of lines of finite length, it can never be uniformly hexagonal. The numerous furrow patterns, which we have seen consist of triangles, squares, and pentagons, are various expressions of the trischistoclasic system in terms of the sphere. The explanation of this can readily be found if we try the experiment of drawing lines in the trischistoclasic system over the surface of a sphere in the same fashion as we drew them on a plane surface. When done on a sphere the system is closed. It does not stop with free lines and angles with the possibility

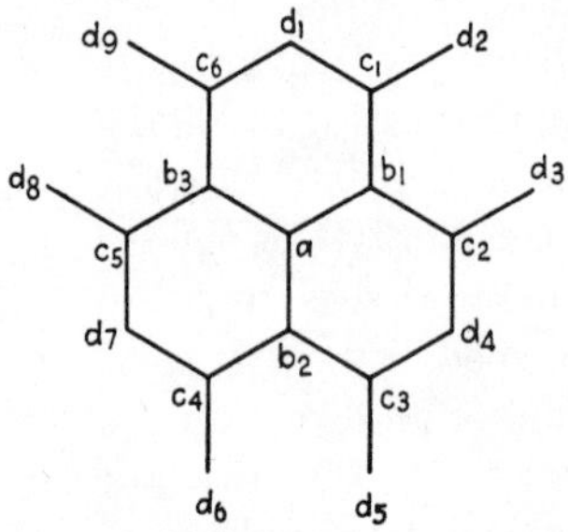

FIG. 40. 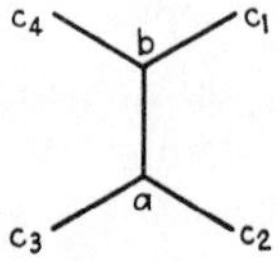   FIG. 41. 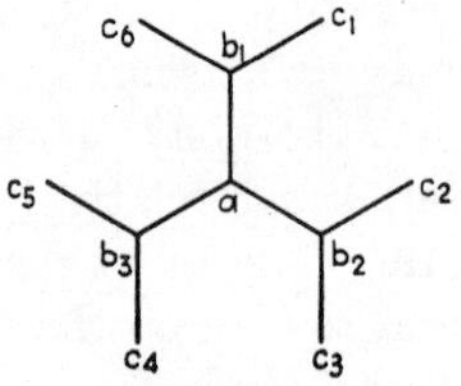   FIG. 42.

FIGS. 40–42.—The trischistoclasic system on a plane surface. Fig. 40 shows that it may be extended indefinitely; Fig. 41 represents the tricolpate furrow configuration; Fig. 42 the hexacolpate furrow configuration.

of being extended indefinitely, as on a plane surface. Instead, the number of its lines and, within certain limits, the character of the polygons which they will describe are fixed as soon as any single dimension of the system in relation to the size of the sphere is chosen, such as the length of the lines or the distance apart of their centers. On this account simplicity in the experiment is served if we start with the lines of the system instead of a triradiate center. But in doing so we must not lose sight of the fact that the system is still one of progressive branching.

The simplest expression of the trischistoclasic system in spherical terms is obtained if we select two points on a sphere spaced 120 deg. apart or one-third of the great circle upon which they happen to lie. The circle we shall call, for convenience, the equator; and the distance between the points, the interval of the system. Through these points draw two arcs of great circles in such a way that they meet at an angle of 120 deg. The point at which they meet will be found to be a pole of the sphere. Extended in the opposite direction these two lines will meet at the opposite pole of the sphere. Now, if each pole is made a triradiate center by drawing a third line at 120 deg. to the other two, they will coincide with each other, so that, in all, there will be only three lines. If lines were drawn in this way on a plane surface, they would appear as in Fig. 41; but since they are drawn on a sphere with their interval so chosen as to cause them to meet at the poles, they divide the sphere into three equal lunes. Such a system of lines is the lowest possible expression of the trischistoclasic system in spherical terms. It corresponds to the ordinary tricolpate furrow configuration, which is the commonest among pollen grains of the dicotyledons. Here, as we have seen, it is usually initiated by three contact points equally spaced on the equator, but it may also be initiated by two contact points one-third of the equator or 120 deg. apart.

In order to discover the next higher expression of the system in spherical terms, select two positions on the equator of the sphere one-quarter of the circle or 90 deg. apart, and draw lines through them converging toward each other at angles of 120 deg. as before. This time they will not meet at the poles but will meet at four points, two in the upper and two in the lower hemisphere. Such an arrangement corresponds to the ordinary tetracolpate furrow configuration. Now, make each of these points triradiate by joining together the two of the upper and the two of the lower hemisphere. The result will be six lines converging at four triradiate centers and marking the surface off into four equal equilateral triangles. This corresponds to the hexacolpate furrow configuration (Figs. 27, 28). The corresponding pattern on a plane surface is shown in Fig. 42. On a spherical surface, however, the number of lines is reduced, because b_1c_1 coincides with b_2c_2; b_2c_3, with b_3c_4; and b_3c_5, with b_1c_6.

The Series of Perfect Polyhedrons.—It will readily be seen that we may repeat the experiment of drawing lines in the trischistoclasic system over the sphere in as many different ways as we wish, selecting each time a shorter interval for the system; but only when we select an interval which permits the lines to assume a configuration corresponding to the edges of one of the perfect polyhedrons, the tetrahedron, cube, and pentagonal dodecahedron will it divide the surface of the sphere into polygons

all of the same kind.   The four equal equilateral triangles produced in the present instance, with an interval of 90 deg., correspond to the four faces of a tetrahedron (Fig. 43).   If drawn with
an interval of 60 deg. or one-sixth of the great circle, it would
divide the surface of the sphere into six equal squares corresponding to the six faces of a cube.   Drawn with an interval of 36 deg.
or one-tenth of the great circle, it would divide the surface of the
sphere into 12 equal pentagons, corresponding to the faces of a
pentagonal dodecahedron.   We thus see that the intervals of the
system that can produce perfectly symmetrical configurations
on the surface of a sphere are mathematically determined, as:

120 deg. or $\frac{1}{3}$ circle.........3 lunes corresponding to a 3-colpate grain
 90 deg. or $\frac{1}{4}$ circle......... 4 triangles corresponding to a tetrahedron or
                                                        6-colpate grain
 60 deg. or $\frac{1}{6}$ circle....... 6 squares corresponding to a cube or
                                                        12-colpate grain
 36 deg. or $\frac{1}{10}$ circle....... 12 pentagons corresponding to a pentagonal
                                                        dodecahedron or a 30-colpate grain

This series is mathematically fixed and cannot be extended in
either direction.   These four patterns are unique in that, with
each, the triconvergent angles are exactly equal, the lines are all
equal, and all are arcs of great circles.   All the patterns drawn
with other than these four cardinal intervals will be more or less
irregular and necessitate compensating adjustments of the lengths
of the lines, of their angular deviations, even of the intervals
themselves and compromises between the paths of the lines with
the arcs of great circles.   For example, if the interval of the
system lies between 90 and 60 deg., since the 90-deg. interval gives
a pattern of four triangles and the 60-deg. interval gives a pattern
of six squares, an interval between 90 and 60 deg. will necessarily
give a pattern composed of triangles and squares.   The ordinary
nonacolpate configuration presents such a pattern, obtained from
an interval of about 72 deg.   As we have seen, it consists of three
squares and two triangles corresponding to a right-triangular
prism (Fig. 44).   It is rare among furrow patterns of pollen grains.
If the interval of the system lies between 60 and 36 deg., since the
former gives a configuration consisting of squares, and the latter
of pentagons, a pattern drawn with an interval between these
two must be composed of pentagons and squares.   Such a pattern
is represented by the ordinary 15-colpate furrow configuration,

which is also rare among pollen grains. As we have seen, it consists of two pentagonal and five square faces and corresponds to the right-pentagonal prism (Fig. 47).

If we continue to draw trischistoclasic patterns over our sphere, choosing each time a smaller interval, after we pass the interval of 36 deg., which gives 30 furrows corresponding in arrangement to the edges of a pentagonal dodecahedron, an adjustment has to be made using tetragons (which may or may not be exactly square), pentagons, and hexagons; and, as the interval continues to decrease, *i.e.*, as the faces become more numerous, more and more hexagons are required in proportion to the tetragons and pentagons. And this greater proportion of hexagons over the other polygons will continue to increase as we approach a 0-deg. interval or an infinite number of polygons.

Possible Furrow Configurations.—It is interesting to examine in the light of the trischistoclasic system some of the polyhedrons which correspond to the rarer furrow configurations of this series up to and beyond the 30-colpate and to discover the possible extent of their variation within the trischistoclasic system (Table IV). For example, corresponding in number of edges and faces to the dodecacolpate configuration or *hexahedron* can be constructed another polyhedron quite different in form from the cube, yet possessing 6 faces and 12 edges as does the cube (Fig. 46). This figure is bounded by two triangles, two tetragons, and two pentagons. It is, of course, irregular and probably for this reason is less favored than the cube among pollen-grain furrow configurations.

The next figure in the series (Table IV) is the *heptahedron*, with seven faces and 15 edges. Three different forms of heptahedron can be constructed. The most obvious of these is the pentagonal prism (Fig. 47), which we have already seen is bounded by two pentagonal and five square or tetragonal faces. Another heptahedron is bounded by one triangular, three tetragonal, and three pentagonal faces (Fig. 48); and another by two triangular faces, two tetragonal, two pentagonal, and one hexagonal (Fig. 49).

The next numerical group of polyhedrons in the series is that of the *octahedrons*, with eight faces and 18 edges (Table IV). Several such figures can easily be constructed. The most obvious is the hexagonal prism (Fig. 50), possessing six tetragonal

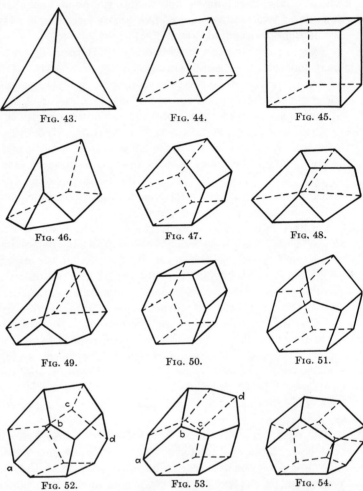

FIGS. 43–54.—Polyhedra which correspond to some pollen-grain furrow configurations: Fig. 43, tetrahedron, corresponding to the normal hexacolpate configuration; Fig. 44, pentahedron or right-triangular prism, corresponding to the nonacolpate furrow configuration; Fig. 45, hexahedron, in this case a cube, corresponding to the dodecacolpate furrow configuration; Fig. 46, hexahedron, in this case not a cube, but with the same number of edges and faces as a cube; Fig. 47, heptahedron or right-pentagonal prism, *cf.* Figs. 48 and 49; Fig. 48, heptahedron; Fig. 49, heptahedron; Fig. 50, octahedron or right-hexagonal prism, *cf.* Fig. 51; Fig. 51, octahedron; Fig. 52, nonahedron; Fig. 53, nonahedron; Fig. 54, decahedron.

and two hexagonal faces. Another octahedron can easily be constructed by simply dividing one of the two pentagonal faces of the pentagonal prism (Fig. 51) among the foregoing heptahedrons. A way in which this may be done is shown in Fig. 55, which represents a pentagonal prism opened up and laid on a flat surface. If the pentagon is divided by the line *ab*, there will be formed from the divided pentagon a tetragon and a pentagon. But as soon as this is done, if the medium in which we are working is as plastic as the exine of a developing pollen grain, a readjustment will take place, causing the new angles about the points *a* and *b* to approach as closely as possible to 120 deg., as indicated by the dotted lines. Thus the bisection of a pentagon flanked by two tetragons converts the flanking tetragons into pentagons. Accordingly, the new polyhedron now has eight faces, four of which are pentagons and four tetragons. Figure 51 represents such an octahedron. It was constructed from the pentagonal prism (Fig. 47), a heptahedron, by dividing its front pentagonal face into a tetragon and pentagon and thereby, through the action of the law of equal triconvergent angles in plastic material, converting the two adjacent tetragonal faces into pentagons. This figure has eight faces and 18 edges, and, therefore, it satisfies the equation $E = 3F - 6$, as required by the series.

In the same way a *nonahedron* may be derived from the preceding octahedron (Fig. 51) by dividing its back pentagonal face. In doing this there are obviously two choices. If the dividing line be drawn so that its ends impinge on two of the three tetragonal faces which surround this pentagonal face, these two tetragons will be converted, as before, into pentagons, and at the same time the divided pentagon will yield a pentagon and a tetragon. The total number of tetragons is, therefore, reduced by one, and the number of pentagons increased by two. Such a nonahedron is shown in Fig. 52. It has three tetragonal and six pentagonal faces. It also has 21 edges and therefore satisfies our equation as required by the series. This figure may be identified in Table IV by its designation three tetragons, six pentagons.

Quite a different kind of nonahedron is produced if, in dividing the back pentagonal face of the octahedron (Fig. 51), the dividing line is passed in such a direction that its ends impinge upon the edges of two pentagonal faces, instead of upon those of two tetragonal faces, converting the pentagons into hexagons.　This will become clear from Fig. 56, which shows the octahedron (Fig. 51) laid open on a plane surface with the back pentagonal face centrally placed.　If this face is now divided by the line *cd*, the divided pentagon yields a tetragon and a pentagon, thus increasing the total number of faces by one, and the adjoining pentagons are converted into hexagons, as indicated by the dotted lines.　Such a nonahedron has been constructed (Fig. 53). Two of its faces are hexagons, five are tetragons, and two are

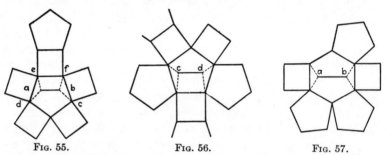

FIG. 55.　　　　　　　　FIG. 56.　　　　　　　　FIG. 57.

FIGS. 55–57.—Dissections of polyhedrons to show the effect of the division of their faces: Fig. 55, the division of a pentagonal face flanked by tetragonal faces; Fig. 56, the division of a pentagonal face flanked by two other pentagonal faces; Fig. 57, the division of a hexagonal face flanked by two tetragonal faces.

pentagons, *i.e.*, a total of nine, and it has 21 edges, thus satisfying the equation for the series.

The conversion of an octahedron into a nonahedron could be made equally well in a third way by dividing one of the pentagonal faces of the octahedron in such a way that the dividing line impinges upon a pentagonal face at one end and a tetragonal one at the other.　If this is done, the divided pentagonal face is made into a tetragon and pentagon as before, increasing the total number of faces by one, and at the same time the adjoining pentagon is converted into a hexagon, and the tetragon into a pentagon.　As a consequence, if the original octahedron had four pentagonal and four tetragonal faces, the resulting nonahedron would have four pentagonal, four tetragonal, and one hexagonal face.

Modes of Changing One Polyhedron into Another.—From these experiments the following generalization may be drawn for the *division of a pentagonal face* of a polyhedron surrounded

by tetragonal and pentagonal faces, assuming that the three
convergent angles at the points of impingement of the dividing
line become adjusted to approach equality: According to the
pentagon chosen for division and the orientation of the dividing
line, the total number of faces of a polyhedron will be increased
by one through the addition of hexagons, and the addition and
subtraction of tetragons and pentagons, in the following three
ways:

If the line dividing the pentagon impinge upon

a. Two tetragons, by	− 1 tetragon + 2 pentagons	
b. Two pentagons, by	+ 1 tetragon − 2 pentagons	+ 2 hexagons
c. A tetragon and pentagon, by		+ 1 hexagon

Another possibility is the *division of a tetragonal face.* In
this case it is itself converted into two tetragonal faces, but at
the same time, through the adjustment of the angles of impingement of the dividing line, it alters the flanking faces with the
three following results:

If the line dividing the tetragon impinge upon

d. Two tetragons, by	− 1 tetragon + 2 pentagons	
e. Two pentagons, by	+ 1 tetragon − 2 pentagons	+ 2 hexagons
f. A tetragon and pentagon		+ 1 hexagon

The *decahedrons,* which are the next group of polyhedrons in
our series, are of five different forms (Table IV), but all are
related to the nonahedrons in the same way that the latter are
related to the octahedrons. Some of the decahedrons may be
derived from the octahedrons by the division of a pentagonal
face as before. But other forms of the decahedron can be derived
from nonahedrons only by the division of a hexagonal face.
When this happens the divided hexagon yields two pentagons,
and at the same time one more side is added to each of the flanking faces. This will become clear from Fig. 57, which shows
such a hexagonal face of a nonahedron surrounded by some of its
flanking faces opened up along their edges and laid on a flat
surface. If the centrally placed hexagon be divided by the line
ab and the angles of impingement at *a* and *b* be equalized, the
two flanking tetragons will be thereby converted into pentagons.
In the same way if *ab* impinge on pentagons, the latter will be
converted into hexagons. Consequently, it may be stated that

the effect of the *division of a hexagonal face* upon the sum total of the faces of a polyhedron will be as follows:

If the line dividing the hexagon impinge upon

g. Two tetragons,	− 2 tetragons + 4 pentagons − 1 hexagon
h. Two pentagons,	+ 1 hexagon
i. A tetragon and pentagon	− 1 tetragon + 2 pentagons

We thus have nine ways of increasing the number of faces of a polyhedron by one, but it will be noted that the results of *a*, *d*, and *i* are alike, also of *b* and *e*, and of *c*, *f*, and *h*. Therefore, only four different results are obtained.

TABLE III.—FOUR POSSIBLE RESULTS OF INCREASING THE NUMBER OF FACES OF A POLYHEDRON BY ONE

Formula	Tetragons	Pentagons	Hexagons	Done by
(1)	−1	+2	0	Dividing a pentagon with a line impinging upon 2 tetragons or dividing a hexagon with a line impinging upon a tetragon and a pentagon or dividing a tetragon with a line impinging upon two tetragons
(2)	+1	−2	+2	Dividing a pentagon with a line impinging upon two pentagons or dividing a tetragon with a line impinging upon two pentagons
(3)	0	0	+1	Dividing a pentagon with a line impinging upon a tetragon and pentagon or dividing a hexagon with a line impinging upon two pentagons or dividing a tetragon with a line impinging upon a tetragon and pentagon
(4)	−2	+4	−1	Dividing a hexagon with a line impinging upon two tetragons

Applying these formulas to the nonahedrons of the table, we shall readily see that three of them may be applied to the first four of the nonahedrons there described, and all four to each of the succeeding nonahedrons, but this does not result in a total of 15 different decahedrons, for some of them are duplicates of the others. Of the 15 different ways in which decahedrons may be derived from nonahedrons only five give different results.

Figure 54 shows one of the possible decahedrons. This one was obtained from a nonahedron having three tetragonal and six pentagonal faces by dividing one of its pentagonal faces with the dividing line impinging upon two tetragonal faces [formula (2)]. The same figure could likewise be obtained from a nonahedron with four tetragonal faces, four pentagonal, and one hexagonal face, by dividing the hexagonal face and letting the dividing line impinge upon two tetragonal faces [formula (4)].

By applying our four formulas to the five different decahedrons we find that we are able to derive six different endecahedrons. And by applying the four formulas to these in turn we are able to obtain seven dodecahedrons. It is interesting here to note, in passing, that the pentagonal dodecahedron, one of the regular polyhedrons, is derived from an endecahedron having two tetragons, eight pentagons, and one hexagon, by dividing the hexagon so that the dividing line impinges upon the two flanking tetragons [formula (4)]. A glance at our four formulas and the five endecahedrons which have hexagonal faces will show that no other division of any of the faces of any other endecahedrons can produce it.

From the various dodecahedrons may be derived seven triskaidecahedrons, and from these in turn may be derived seven tetrakaidecahedrons. One of these, that having six tetragonal and eight hexagonal faces, is known as the orthic tetrakaidecahedron. It has recently acquired the reputation of being the only polyhedron which can uniformly partition space. For this reason it is worth while to note that it may be derived only from a triskaidecahedron having five tetragonal, two pentagonal, and six hexagonal faces, by dividing a tetragonal face with the dividing line impinging upon a tetragonal and a pentagonal face.

By continuing to divide the pentagons, tetragons, and hexagons in their various relations to the other faces we may extend this list of polyhedrons indefinitely. But it is without profit to extend it farther, for we are already in a position to predict what all the others will be. An inspection of Table IV shows that each addition of a face offers seven possibilities of combining tetragons, pentagons, and hexagons. In each numerical class of polyhedrons so obtained the tetragons range continuously from 0 to 6, while co-ordinately with them the pentagons range

from 12 to 0, by steps of two, and the hexagons range from
n to $n + 6$, where n is the smallest number of hexagons in the
numerical class of polyhedrons in question. Inspection of
Table IV shows that $n = F - 12$ (where F is the total number
of faces), since the smallest number of hexagonal faces in each
numerical class of polyhedrons is 12 less than the total number
of their faces. Hence the seven possible polyhedrons in any
numerical class are characterized as follows: They must have
0 to 6 tetragonal faces and co-ordinately 12 to 0 (by steps of
two) pentagonal faces and co-ordinately $F - 12$ to $F - 6$ hexagonal faces. This gives us a complete picture of all the possible
polyhedrons. For example, if we wish to discover what the
seven possible polyhedrons with 30 faces are like, by applying
the above formula the first of these will have as faces 0 tetragons,
12 pentagons, and 18 (*i.e.*, 30 − 12) hexagons. The second
will have 1 tetragon, 10 pentagons, and 19 hexagons; and so on
to the seventh and last, which will have 6 tetragons, 0 pentagons,
and 24 hexagons.

It will be noticed in the table that the number of hexagons in
the successive numerical classes increases with the number of
faces, while the numbers of tetragons and pentagons remain
within their respective ranges, with no increase as we progress in
the series. Consequently, when the number of faces reaches
infinity the hexagons will be infinitely more numerous than the
tetragons and pentagons, which is the same thing as saying
that if the faces of an infinitely large polyhedron are of a finite
size, they must be hexagonal. Since an infinitely large polyhedron with finite faces is a plane surface, we are brought to the
conclusion that the only polygon that can divide a plane surface
continuously is the hexagon, which, of course, is a recognized
fact and the basic principle of the trischistoclasic system.

In this series I have purposely omitted, for the sake of simplicity, the polyhedrons with triangular faces in the higher
numerical classes. Undoubtedly furrow configurations corresponding to these do occur. In fact they may occasionally be
found among the pollen grains of *Portulaca oleracea*, which have
as many as 30 furrows, but with grains of higher numerical
furrow configuration the triangular arrangement is extremely
rare, if indeed it ever occurs. The reason for this appears to be
that in a series of this kind triangles cannot be propagated, for

TABLE IV.—THEORETICALLY POSSIBLE FURROW CONFIGURATIONS

Faces	Furrows or edges	Polyhedron or numerical class of polyhedrons	Description of polyhedrons			
0	0	None	None, corresponds to acolpate grains			
3†	3	₃None	None, corresponds to three lunes in 3-colpate grains			
4	6	Tetrahedron*	4 triangles	0 tetragons	0 pentagons	0 hexagons
5	9	Pentahedron or triangular prism	2	3	0	0
6	12	Hexahedron, (cube)*	0 2	6 2	0 2	0 0
7	15	Heptahedron or pentagonal prism	0 1 2	5 3 2	2 3 2	0 0 1
8	18	Octahedron	0	4 5 6	4 2 0	0 1 2
9	21	Nonahedron		3 4 5 6	6 4 2 0	0 1 2 3
10	24	Decahedron		2 3 4 5 6	8 6 4 2 0	0 1 2 3 4
11	27	Endecahedron		1 2 3 4 5 6	10 8 6 4 2 0	0 1 2 3 4 5
12	30	Dodecahedron (pentagonal dodecahedron)*		0 1 2 3 4 5 6	12 10 8 6 4 2 0	0 1 2 3 4 5 6
13	33	Triskaidecahedron		0 1 2 3 4 5 6	12 10 8 6 4 2 0	1 2 3 4 5 6 7
14	36	Tetrakaidecahedron Orthic tetrakaidecahedron‡		0 1 2 3 4 5 6	12 10 8 6 4 2 0	2 3 4 5 6 7 8
15	39	Pentakaidecahedron		0 1 2 3 4 5 6	12 10 8 6 4 2 0	3 4 5 6 7 8 9

* Regular polyhedron.
† Appears to belong to the series, though it has no corresponding polyhedron.
‡ Orthic tetrakaidecahedron is supposed to be the only polyhedron that can partition space.

they are not formed from the divisions of the other polyhedrons; and when a triangle itself divides, the result is a triangle and a tetragon.   Moreover, the equalization of the angles of impingement, which must always take place, would in this case tend to obliterate the remaining triangle, reducing it to a line.   And if such a triangular face should escape obliteration by this means, it must inevitably sooner or later become converted into a tetragon through the impingement upon one of its sides of a dividing line of an adjacent polygon.   So the chances of a triangular face's surviving to one of the higher numerical classes of polyhedrons are extremely remote.

I have also omitted to give consideration to the division of a polygonal face with the dividing line impinging upon one or two hexagons.   If this should happen, it would convert the flanking hexagons into heptagons requiring internal angles greater than 120 deg., which is mathematically impossible in our series. Whether or not this is a valid reason for the nonoccurrence of heptagons I am unable to say.   At any rate it seems certain that the inherent tendency of the three convergent angles to be equal, and therefore not greater than 120 deg., would militate strongly against such an occurrence and probably force an impending division to some other region or delay it until the neighboring faces were ready to divide, resulting in simultaneous divisions in the one or more threatened hexagons, thus allowing the dividing lines to impinge upon the products of their division which are pentagons.   It is conceivable that in a region where the majority of faces are hexagonal the difficulty that each would experience in dividing in defiance of the law of equal triconvergent angles would delay their division until all were ready to divide, with the result that the divisions would be simultaneous throughout the region.   Since laws similar to these apply to the division of tissue cells, herein may lie the explanation of the simultaneous divisions which are occasionally encountered in tissue cells.

PART II
CLASSIFICATION

MASTER KEY*

I. GERMINAL APPARATUS CONSISTING OF A SINGLE FURROW OR PORE (MONOCOLPATE FORMS).

*Families without page references are not treated further in this work.

POLLEN GRAINS

b. Grains less than 200 μ in length and
without a triradiate crest. Cordaitales.........222 PAGE

2. Living or recent fossil forms.
   a. Exine thin and collapsing easily; intine thick and swelling (sometimes
   enormously) when moistened.
   (1) Exine flecked with granules or
   wart-like protuberances.
   (*a*) Grains 20 to 40 μ in diameter. Taxineae (Taxus)....283
   Cupressineae....247, 271
   Taxodineae.....247, 268

   (*b*) Grains 70 to 90 μ in diameter. Musaceae
   Cannaceae

   (2) Exine covered with short, conical spines.
   (*a*) Grains 30 to 70 μ in diameter, intine excessively
   thick and exine thin and
   transparent. Lauraceae
   (*b*) Grains 11 to 26 μ in diameter; intine not excessively
   thick, and exine not transparent. Gnetaceae (Gnetum) 292
   (3) Exine conspicuously reticulate. Naiadaceae.........297
   (4) Exine without spines or flecks or
   other decorations, sometimes
   fragmentary. Salicaceae (Populus). 350

   b. Exine thick and firm; intine not excessively thick.
   (1) Grains spheroidal, not grooved.
   (*a*) Exine quite smooth, grains
   60 to 105 μ in diameter. Abietineae (Larix,
   Pseudotsuga). 266, 268

   (*b*) Exine provided with well-
   developed spines or vestiges of them, 11 to 26 μ
   in diameter. Gnetaceae (Gnetum). 292
   (*c*) Exine pitted; grains about
   34 μ in diameter. Araucarineae
   (Agathis).........255

   (*d*) Exine very thick and rough;
   grains 60 to 90 μ in diameter. Abietineae (Tsuga).. 266
   (2) Grains elongate with longitudinal grooves. Gnetaceae (Ephedra) 283

III. Germinal Apparatus Consisting of Three or More (occasionally only two) Pores or Furrows or Both, in Which Case the Latter Enclosing the Pores. Occasionally the furrows may be rudimentary and nonfunctional.

[b] Texture of the exine only finely granular or nearly smooth. Spines short-conical.

Spines greatly reduced, sometimes rounded, but not vestigial.

(b) Exine with a well-marked lacunar pattern consisting of high, upstanding ridges, which bear the spines on their crests, enclosing polygonal lacunae (echinolophate).

(2) Exine not provided with spines.
 (a) Exine conspicuously reticulate.
  [1] Reticulations fine.
   [a] Grains less than 20 μ in diameter.

   [b] Grains more than 20 μ in diameter.

  [2] Reticulations coarse of high, upstanding ridges enclosing large polygonal lacunae.
   [a] Lacunae rather numerous, not forming a radiosymmetrical pattern.

   [b] Lacunae of finite number, forming a

FOSSIL GYMNOSPERMS

CYCADOFILICALES (Pteridosperms)

The most outstanding characters of the pollen grains of the Cycadofilicales are their large size and pluricellular structure. There is much variation in their size, ranging, in the different species that have been described, from 70 to 500 μ in diameter. There is also much variation in their cellular structure: in some the cavity of the grain contains only two cells, while in others it contains as many as 30. Nevertheless, it is almost universally true that the entire cavity is filled with cellular tissue with well-developed cell walls. Many of the pollen specimens that have been described from this group were found in the pollen chambers of their seeds, and there is no doubt that these grains increased in size after entering the pollen chamber, though the extent of this increase is not exactly known. In the pollen chamber of *Pachytesta*, Saporta and Marion (1885) describe pluricellular pollen grains which are 500 μ long. In the pollen chamber of *Aetheotesta*, Renault described similar grains about 400 μ long and without exines. It is hard to imagine, in the light of what we know of flower pollination of the present, any agency which could have effectively pollinated these two plants with such enormous pollen grains, many times larger than any known at the present time. It is therefore likely that these giant pollen grains made the trip from the anther to the ovule in a one-celled or few-celled form possessing an exine. But upon coming in contact with the nutrient fluid of the pollen chamber they germinated, developing prothallial tissue and throwing off their exine as they increased in size, just as the spores of ferns germinate when they meet with the proper conditions of moisture and temperature.

We have some direct information of the probable nature and condition of Cycadofilicinean pollen upon being shed, for the staminate inflorescences of two species of *Crossotheca* have been described by Kidston (1906), from which he dissected out pollen

211

grains. Under these conditions they are described as one-celled, and, in all their characters which have been preserved, they are remarkably like many of the fern spores of today. It seems likely that these may be taken as a fair example of what the Cycadofilicinean pollen grains looked like at time of pollination. And I doubt if they could be told from the spores of many of the contemporary ferns if encountered dissociated from the plants to which they belonged. That these grains were immature at the time when they were fossilized seems obvious to Kidston from their collapsed and crumpled condition. Nevertheless, had they been very immature, *e.g.*, still bathed in the tapetal fluid, at the time of their fossilization, they would probably all have stuck together in a solid mass and certainly could not now be dissected out separately, as Kidston succeeded in doing.

The only point upon which Kidston's *Crossotheca* pollen grains leave us in doubt is whether the prothallial tissue was to have been initiated in them before they left their anthers. However this may be, it seems certain that at least the major portion of the development of prothallial tissue in such grains took place in the pollen chamber. At any rate these grains as they occur in their anthers are of a size and character quite suitable to pollination by either wind or insects, comparing favorably in this respect with the grains of present-day conifers.

There is no evidence that the pollen grains of the Cycado-filicales produced pollen tubes, as do the conifers of the present, or even haustoria, as do those of the cycads and *Ginkgo;* but there is good evidence that some, at least, of the cells that formed in the interior of the grain were spermatogenous, producing motile antherozoids which they subsequently discharged into the pollen chamber. There appear to have been at least three ways in which the discharge was accomplished. In some of the grains their walls are said to be perforated, apparently to permit the passage of the antherozoids, and it was the discovery of this in the pollen grains found in the pollen chamber of *Aetheotesta* that led Renault to predict the finding of swimming antherozoids among the gymnosperms long before their discovery in *Ginkgo* by Hirasê. In others, for example, *Stephanospermum caryoides,* it seems likely that the grain underwent a sort of dehiscence, discharging into the pollen chamber a part or all its cellular contents; while in still others, for example, *Aetheotesta elliptica,* the grains appear to have thrown off their entire exine and continued their development as naked prothalli in the pollen chamber.

The Cycadofilicinean pollen grains are certainly the most primitive among those of all the gymnosperms. It is a notable fact that nowhere among the Cycadofilicales have there ever been described grains possessing anything akin to the broad, deep furrows which became so prevalent and came to play so important a role in the evolution of the pollen grains of all the later gymnosperms. In scarcely any way are they essentially different from the spores of ferns. And this is strange, because the seeds which were fertilized by them were themselves by no means primitive. They had already attained to a complexity and specialization of development which was but little short of that of the seeds of the conifers of the present. And yet the pollen grain of the Cycadofilicales runs true to form, for, as we shall see, in all its subsequent development, through the higher gymnosperms and the angiosperms, the pollen grain has lagged enormously far behind the seed with which it was associated.

It seems likely that in the Cycadofilicales the pollen grains left their anthers as single-celled spores, and germination,* or any extensive cellular proliferation, did not take place until after they arrived at their destination. As we shall see when we come to consider the Cordaitales and Bennettitales, the evolution of the pollen grain from the ordinary fern type of spore was accompanied first by a pushing back of its germination and cellular proliferation until a large part of this took place in the anther before shedding. It was then that the broad, deep furrow made its appearance, providing a proliferation chamber which appears to have accommodated the growth taking place within the grain without prematurely rupturing the exine. We shall see that the next stage of the evolution of the pollen grain was accompanied by a reduction of the prothallial tissue until it became represented by two or three nuclear divisions without the formation of any good cell walls, which took place prior to shedding—*e.g.*, in the grains of the cycads and *Ginkgo*—leaving

* In these studies I shall use the word germination to denote the first nuclear division of the microspore. This, of course, has nothing to do with the tube formation which takes place in the pollen grains of the angiosperms and is loosely called germination.

the broad furrow which had been provided to accommodate it a useless organ and very probably actually an encumbrance to the grain. And we shall see in the several different conifer groups several different ways in which the furrow was eliminated from grains which no longer had need of it.

The Cycadofilicales were a vast assemblage of "plants with the habit and certain of the anatomical features of the ferns, bearing on fronds only slightly differentiated from the vegetative foliage seeds of a cycadean type of structure." No cones were formed, and the anatomy of the stem and leaf was of a filicinean type. In fact, in none of their characters, other than those of their seeds, had this group advanced beyond the level of the ferns. They are unquestionably the most primitive known gymnosperms.

The group was called Cycadofilicales by Potonié (1899) without any knowledge that they bore seeds. When later it was discovered that some of their members bore seeds the name pteridosperms was proposed by Oliver and Scott (1903) to designate the seed-bearing Cycadofilicales. Subsequent investigations, however, have led to the conviction that all the Cycadofilicales were seed-bearing, and consequently the two groups are coextensive. For this reason it became necessary (Coulter and Chamberlain, 1917), in the interests of priority, to drop the more recent and certainly more descriptive term pteridosperms in favor of Potonié's original name.

The origin of the Cycadofilicales is still obscure. At one time it was thought that they were derived from the ferns. It now appears, however, that they are fully as old as the ferns, existing side by side with them in Devonian times. It is more likely that they were derived from some ancestral form which in the remote past gave rise to two divergent lines, one leading to the ferns and the other to the Cycadofilicales. They appear to have originated in the Devonian, and they culminated in the Carboniferous, assuming a dominant position among the vegetation of that period, but they did not extend upward into the Mesozoic. Nevertheless, at some time in their earlier history they probably gave rise to the next great group of gymnosperms which we have to consider, the Cordaitales, which did extend a little way into the Mesozoic; and later in their history, before they passed forever from the stage, they gave rise to the third great group, the Bennettitales or Hemicycadales, which became the dominant vegetation of the Mesozoic.

Fossil pollen grains rarely have names in their own right in paleobotanical literature, having nearly always been described in association with some other part of the plant, *e.g.*, the seeds or sporophyls. Consequently, rather than adopt a form genus for them, I shall call them by the name of the part of the plant with which they were described. In some instances the same pollen may have been described more than once and in different associations; under this system of nomenclature the pollen will come to have as many different names, but even this seems better than adopting a form genus which in this case would be meaningless.

Fossil pollen grains have received far less attention than their abundance and diversity in the Paleozoic and Mesozoic deposits deserve. Not only are they frequently found well preserved in the staminate inflorescences and in the pollen chambers of the plants to which they belong, but they frequently also occur in the general matrix. Renault (1879) states that "pollen grains scattered in the siliceous magmas are of a considerable number, and appear to have been shed in this epoque [Carboniferous] in as great profusion as the pollen of our Conifers of the present." Nathorst (1908) described a wonderful array of forms from Mesozoic deposits, mostly with a single furrow and some bearing bladders, as in the pollen of modern winged-grained Abietineae, probably members of Ginkgophytes, Cycadophytes, and Coniferae. If a full and accurate description together with adequate illustrations were available of all species found in connection with the parts of the plants to which they belong, many of the dissociated forms could be identified, and our knowledge of the ancient floras thereby greatly extended. The following brief discussion of the pollen of the Cycadofilicales and of the two following groups, the Bennettitales and Cordaitales, is intended to bring together only some of the descriptions of the more important species recorded in the literature in the hope that the very evident possibilities of such studies will induce others to devote their energies to this fascinating subject.

Crossotheca Höningshausi Brongt. (Fig. 58). Grains globular or slightly oval, 50 to 70 μ in diameter. Their outer surface roughened by numerous closely placed, very minute, blunt points.   Each grain is provided with a distinct triradiate crest (Fig. 58, Nos. 2, 3), though this is often difficult to see on account of the crumpling of the pollen-grain wall (Kidston, 1906). Kidston believes that the presence of the triradiate crest indicates that these grains were developed as members of tetrahedral tetrads.   No cellular tissue is observed in any of them, but this may be due to the fact that they were immature when fossilized, since they were dissected out of unopened anthers.

Crossotheca Höningshausi is known to be the staminate inflorescence of *Lyginodendron Oldhamium* Williamson.   The lygino-

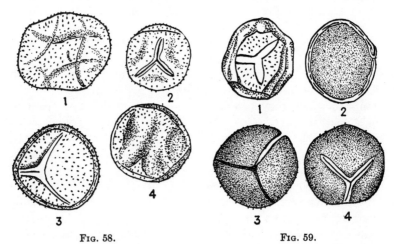

Fig. 58.   Fig. 59.

Figs. 58, 59.—Pollen grains of two species of Cycadofilicales, taken from unopened anthers, and possibly immature: Fig. 58, *Crossotheca Höningshausi;* Fig. 59, *Crossotheca Hughesiana*, both × 500.   (*After Kidston, 1906.*)

dendrons are common fossils in the English coal measures. They had the habit of tree ferns but bore highly developed seeds. *Lyginodendron Oldhamium* was a small plant with a slender, probably reclining, stem which bore at its top a crown of large and beautiful fern-like fronds.   The seeds, roots, leaves, and stems of many species of *Lyginodendron* have been found and described separately; only in relatively few species have all parts been united.

Crossotheca Hughesiana Kidston (Fig. 59).   Grains similar to those of the preceding species, including the slightly spiny nature of their exine.   When taken from the anthers they are mostly crumpled as if they had been immature when preserved. When expanded they are circular or slightly oval, measure 50 to 55 μ in diameter, and show the same sort of triradiate crest as those of the preceding species (Kidston, 1906).

Lagenostoma Lomaxi Oliver & Scott. Grains ovoid, 70 by 55 μ in diameter. Sometimes an internal cellular structure may be seen, though this is usually not the case, owing to the imperfect preservation of the pollen grains as found in the pollen chambers of the seeds (Oliver and Scott, 1904; Oliver, 1904). The seeds in which these pollen grains are found are abundant in the English coal measures and are known to belong to *Lyginodendron Oldhamium.*

Telangium Scotti Benson (Fig. 60). Grains found in the anther sacs of *Telangium Scotti*, the digitate clusters of sporangia

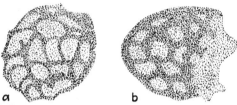

a   b

Fig. 60.—Pollen grains of *Telangium Scotti*, showing the reticulum of the coat; *a*, a grain taken from a section of inflorescence, and *b*, from the pollen chamber of *Lagenostoma ovoides*. (*After Benson, 1904.*)

attached to or associated with the leaves of *Sphenopteris.* The grains are ellipsoidal, 50 to 60 μ long and 40 to 45 μ broad, reticulately marked, and pluricellular. Grains found in the pollen chamber of *Lagenostoma ovoides* Williamson, which is the seed of *Telangium Scotti*, have the same general appearance but are somewhat larger—about 70 by 55 μ (Benson, 1904). The chief interest in these grains centers about the fact that associated with them in the pollen chamber of *Lagenostoma ovoides* have been found a number of smaller bodies which have been interpreted as antherozoids (Benson, 1908). It appears that certain of the cells of these large pollen grains discharged into the pollen chamber one or more antherozoids in something the same way as do the grains of *Cycas* and *Ginkgo.*

Lagenostoma ovoides is one of the commonest ovules occurring in the calcite nodules of the British coal measures but specifically distinct from *L. Lomaxi*, which has been attributed to *Lyginodendron Oldhamium.*

Physostoma elegans Williamson (Fig. 61). Grains ellipsoidal, about 55 by 45 μ, pluricellular, resembling those of *Stephanospermum*. In the pollen chambers associated with them are found small, kidney-shaped bodies which are interpreted by their discoverer as motile antherozoids produced by these grains.

Physostoma elegans is believed to be a species of *Lagenostoma*, though this has not yet been proved. The method of pollination is not known, but it must have been very effective, since 30 or more grains are included in a single section through the pollen chamber. Found in Lancas-Yorkshire coal fields (Oliver, 1909).

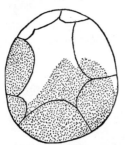

Fig. 61.— Pollen grain of *Physostoma elegans*. The dotted area represents the exospore where it has not been ground away in making the section, $\times 480$. (*After Oliver*, 1909.)

Stephanospermum akenioides Brongn. (Fig. 62). Grains, as found in the pollen chambers, ellipsoidal, 160 by 100 μ or occasionally 200 μ long. Texture of the outer coat finely granulated or sculptured, the interior of the grain divided into about 20 wedge-shaped cells disposed in five rows around the major axis of the grain. "The internal cells line the exospore everywhere, and surface views of the grain show the whole area mapped out by this internal tissue." The dissepiments are perforated by a large number of small holes, which Oliver believes may be utilized by the antherozoids in their escape from the cells in which they are formed, or else they may be due to bacterial action which took place after the death of the grain, in which case it shows that the partitioning walls were easily destructible.

Together with these large grains in the pollen chamber are found some which are smaller, averaging about 100 μ in length, which Oliver regards as grains which failed to germinate or were arrested in their growth in the pollen chamber. That the grains of this plant did grow after their arrival in the pollen chamber is demonstrated by the presence of pollen grains of the same general description trapped in the micropyle and measuring only about 66 μ in length. And pollen grains which are apparently of the same species, but found scattered in the matrix, measure only about 60 μ in length (Oliver, 1904).

Stephanospermum akenioides Brongn. (Fig. 63). Renault (1879) describes pollen grains found in the pollen chamber of

Stephanospermum akenioides, which according to his description are not the same as those described by Oliver above. The grains found by Renault are ellipsoidal, 170 by 100 μ, pluricellular, and the exine is covered with irregularly arranged short spines. The seed from which these grains were obtained was found associated

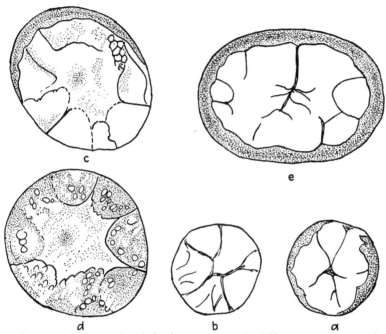

c

e

d

b

a

Fig. 62.—Pollen grain of *Stephanospermum akenioides*, *a*, a grain cut in transverse section showing the internal cell walls meeting in the center. The shaded portion represents the exine traversing obliquely the thickness of the section, *b*, the same section as seen at a deeper optical plane, *c*, *d*, two views of a grain cut in longitudinal section, *c*, the upper surface of the section, and *d*, an optical plane slightly lower. The cells of the grain have come apart leaving a space in which the remains of the axis of their former union is obscurely seen represented by the central darkened nodule. (*After Oliver*, 1904.)

with specimens of *Arthropitys* but apparently not organically connected with them.

Stephanospermum caryoides Oliver (Fig. 64). Grains as found in the pollen chambers ellipsoidal, flattened, 91 by 72 μ; provided with a wing-like bladder which completely encircles the grain. This, as shown in Oliver's figure, is almost exactly like the bladders found in the pollen grains of some of the Podocarpineae of the present time. Grains with this single encircling

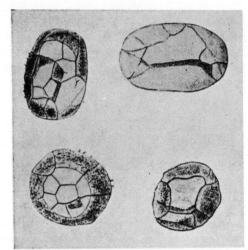

Fig. 63.—Pollen grains of *Stephanospermum akenioides*, taken from the interior of pollen chambers. The exine is covered with prickles and the interior of the grain is divided by partitions which form cells more or less regularly arranged and completely filling the cavity. (*After Renault*, 1879.)

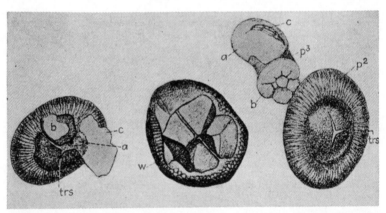

Fig. 64.—Pollen grains of *Stephanospermum caryoides*. The grains at the right and left in this figure each have a triradiate split and an encircling bladder. The central grain exhibits secondary internal cells which Oliver believes may be antherozoid mother-cells. The outer reticulate coat, *W*, is the exospore, × 650. (*After Oliver*, 1904.)

wing were common in the Paleozoic and appear to have been the prototypes of the winged-grained Abietineae and Podocarpineae. The body of the grain is marked by reticulate sculpturing, while the wing is radially striate. In the center of the grain is a triradiate slit, which suggests to Oliver that the grain had its origin as a member of a tetrad. The internal structure is pluricellular. Accompanying these grains in the pollen chambers are found groups of cells similar to those contained in the pollen grains. This suggests that some of the grains may have cast out their internal cellular tissue into the pollen chamber, either by dehiscence through the triradiate slit or by some sort of rudimentary pollen tube the presence of which is suggested in the appearance of one of the grains; then from this liberated tissue the antherozoids were developed and later discharged (Oliver, 1904).

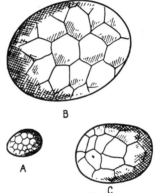

FIG. 65.—Pollen grains of Cycadofilicales, taken from pollen chambers, A, of *Aetheotesta elliptica*, and B and C, of *Pachytesta gigantea*. (*After Saporta and Marion*, 1885.)

Stephanospermum caryoides is a globular seed found at Grand'-Croix, larger than *S. akenioides*, which is about 15.5 by 12.5 mm. The nature of the plants that bore such seeds is not known, but the circumstance that they are found associated with *Alethropteris* and *Myeloxylon* favors the view that they were members of the Medullosae.

Pachytesta gigantea Grand'Eury (Fig. 65). Grains ellipsoidal, about 500 μ long, pluricellular. Found in the pollen chamber of *Pachytesta* (Saporta and Marion, 1885, page 64), a Permocarboniferous genus of seeds from the coal measures of France and elsewhere, distinguished for their large size, which is equal to that of a hen's egg. The plants which bore these seeds are not certainly known but probably belonged to the Medullosae (Seward, 1917).

Aetheotesta elliptica Renault (Fig. 65). Grains ellipsoidal, 320 to 400 μ long and 270 to 310 μ broad. "One sees in the interior a number of walls dividing the cavity into a certain number of cells. These walls are thin and flexible, resembling those of the grains of *Dolerophyllum*." These grains do not have any

exine. *Aetheotesta elliptica* is the name given by Renault to
seeds found in the Permian, of unknown affinities but, he thinks,
possibly belonging to *Dolerophyllum,* and the large, naked pollen
grains which he found in their pollen chambers which he calls
"Prépollinie." He states that these grains must have been very
numerous in the pollen chambers, since the section which he cut,
though only about $\frac{1}{10}$ mm. thick, retained five of them (Renault,
1876).

In his figure of *Aetheotesta* (Fig. 50, page 273) Renault shows,
caught in the mucilage at the orifice of the micropyle, a number of
small pollen grains which he says are of Cardaites, which have
kept their characteristic granular exine and familiar internal
structure. It seems to me, however, quite possible that the
appearance of these grains as he has described and drawn them,
might admit of another interpretation, *viz.,* that they are the
cast-off skins from the large, naked pollen grains which are found
inside the pollen chamber.

CORDAITALES

The pollen grains of the Cordaitales are generally ellipsoidal
in shape, rather large, measuring about 100 μ in length, and with
a characteristically roughened exine. They are always provided
with a single, deep, longitudinal furrow and exhibit a pluricellular
internal structure. As compared with the grains of the Cycadofilicales they possess certain rather striking differences. There is
generally a little less prothallial tissue, and its development takes
place earlier. In the Cycadofilicales there is some doubt if
germination* took place before the grain entered the pollen
chamber, but in the grains of the Cordaitales there remains no
doubt that germination took place prior to their release from the
anther. Correlated with this these grains possess a single
longitudinal furrow which appears to function as a proliferation
chamber, enabling the prothallus to develop without rupturing
the spore wall, as it did in the grains of the Cycadofilicales, which
were without a furrow. In the grains of the Cordaitales the
floor of the furrow became pushed up by the development of the
prothallus within, finally separating from the rest of the surface
of the grain along its rim and opening as a lid, permitting the
escape of the antherozoids.

* See footnote, p. 213.

In these characteristics the grains of the Cordaitales show a distinct advance over those of the Cycadofilicales, toward the form of the conifers and angiosperms. But they still differ from the grains of the conifers in their pluricellular internal structure with well-developed walls partitioning off the whole interior of the grain and in their lack of any protecting device for their wide-open furrow.

Perhaps it may be said that the outstanding advance of the cordaitalean pollen grain was its development of the broad, deep furrow which accommodated the growth of the prothallus within. But in these grains there had already been initiated a reduction of the prothallial tissue which, if continued, would be expected to do away with the necessity of the furrow. And, as we shall see, the evolution of the pollen grains of all the surviving descendants of the Cordaitales, except *Ginkgo*, was accompanied by a modification, protection, or

FIG. 66.—Pollen grain of *Cordaianthus Saportanus*, taken from an unopened anther. (*After Renault*, 1879.)

elimination of this very furrow which was the great achievement of the cordaitalean pollen grain.

These grains are extremely abundant in Carboniferous deposits. They are frequently found as "foreign" transgressors in the pollen chambers of many seeds of Cycadofilicales, where they are easily distinguished from the "native" pollen by their smaller size and by the fact that they did not continue their development in the unsuitable medium of the foreign pollen chamber. For example, Oliver (1904), in his discussion of the pollen chamber of *Stephanospermum*, states that "the upper left-hand grain shows a longitudinal furrow and is doubtless 'foreign' but referable to the cordaitean type. All these foreign pollen grains seem to agree in their arrested development, contrasting in this respect with the pollen of *Stephanospermum* which had undergone further development within the pollen chamber." Many of the grains which Renault (1879) saw scattered in silicious magmas of the Carboniferous deposits are, according to his description of them, undoubtedly referable to this group.

The Cordaitales were a large group of splendid tall trees which constituted an important part of the flora of the Carboniferous period. They were conifer-like in many respects, though they were not true conifers.   They had their origin in the late Devonian and became exceedingly abundant and widespread in the Carbon-iferous, but with the close of that period they practically dis-appeared, lingering on in only a few species until perhaps near the end of the Triassic (Knowlton, 1927).

On account of their many resemblances to the Cycadofilicales it seems likely that they originated directly from that group, but

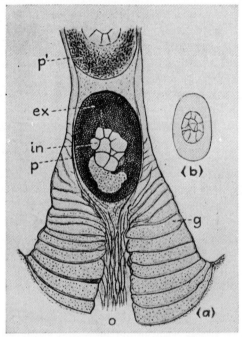

Fig. 67.—*Cordaianthus Grand'Euryi;* (*a*) a pollen canal with two pollen grains trapped in it; (*b*) a pollen grain removed from such a canal. (*After Renault*, 1869.)

if this is so their separation from them must have taken place in the very earliest history of the Cycadofilicales, for the two groups are practically coextensive both in time and in distribution. Another alternative is that both groups originated from a com-mon ancestor.   It really makes little difference which one of these hypotheses we accept.   Of much greater interest is the fact that the Cordaitales probably gave rise early in their history to the Ginkgoales and later to the various groups of the Coniferales.

Cordaianthus Saportanus Renault (Fig. 66). Grains ellipsoidal, large, measuring about 100 by 90 μ while still in the anther and 120 by 70 μ in the pollen chamber. The surface of the exine is finely reticulate owing to internal thickenings of the

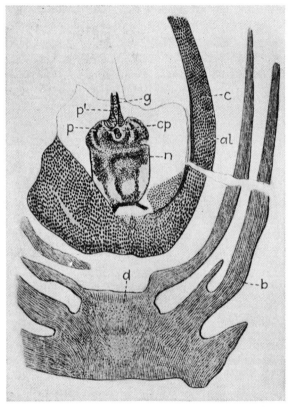

Fig. 68.—Longitudinal section of *Cordaianthus Grand'Euryi*, showing the seed with two pollen grains (*p*) in the chamber, and two others (*p'*) in the canal, shown enlarged in Fig. 67. (*After Renault, 1879.*)

outer wall, "provient d'un épaississement de la paroi qui se fait suivant les mailles d'un réseau" (Renault, 1879). This condition is indeed suggestive of the internal thickenings on the walls of the bladders of the winged grains of Podocarpineae and Abietineae.

The inflorescences which constitute this form species are encountered detached from the plants which bore them. They

are short cones bearing a few large, basal, sterile bracts comprising
a floral involucre and enveloping the centrally placed anther.

Cordaianthus Grand'Euryi Renault (Figs. 67, 68). Grains
ellipsoidal, about 300 μ long. Exine finely reticulate; the interior
of the grain partly filled with a few thin-walled cells, which
increased in number after the grain entered the pollen chamber
(Renault, 1879). Presumably from these cells spermatozoids
were developed (Seward, 1917).

Dolerophyllum fertile Renault (*Prépollinie*, Fig. 69). Grains
ellipsoidal, about 280 μ long. Exine finely roughened. On one

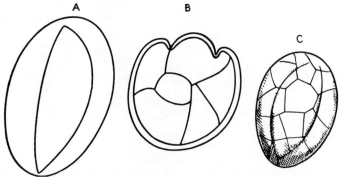

Fɪɢ. 69.—Pollen grains of *Dolerophyllum fertile: A*, a grain seen from above
showing two longitudinal grooves which facilitate dehiscence; *B*, a transverse
section of the same, showing the prothallial tissue dividing the contents into
cells; *C*, a surface view as in *A*, showing the underlying prothallial tissue. *A*
and *B* after Renault (1876), *C* after Saporta and Marion (1885).

side are two deep furrows joining together at one end and marking
out an elliptical-shaped operculum by which dehiscence may take
place. The interior of the grain is divided into 8 or 10 cells with
thin walls. Renault points out that these grains resemble those
found in the pollen chamber of *Stephanospermum* and other
members of the Cycadofilicales, except that the latter do not have
an operculum. It appears to me, however, both from Renault's
description and from his many beautiful drawings, that these
two furrows—*deux sillons*—are really the two grooves which
naturally form at the sides of an ordinary single deep furrow when
its floor is partly bulging out and becoming convex.

These grains were found by Renault (1876) in unopened anthers
and are described by him in elaborate detail and with profuse
illustrations.

It is not quite certain if the dolerophyllums should be regarded as belonging to the Cordaitales or to the Coniferales (Solms-Laubach, 1891). If they belong to the Coniferales, they are the only members of that order that have grains with an unprotected long, deep furrow, and a pluricellular interior. This seems to be conclusive evidence that these trees should not be regarded as Coniferales but should be assigned to the Cordaitales.

Whittleseya elegans Newberry (Fig. 70). Grains ellipsoidal, 210 to 222 μ long, with a long, deep furrow and pluricellular interior, essentially as in those of *Dolerophyllum* (Seward, 1917, Fig. 429, page 130, Vol. 3).

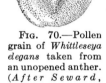

Whittleseya elegans is the name given to fossil leaves characteristically ribbed and resembling those of the Ginkgoales, to which group they were at one time referred. They are found in the coal measures of Ohio and in various places in Europe. The pollen is borne in longitudinal rows extending over most of the lamina. The plant which bore the leaves is otherwise unknown, and there is some doubt as to whether it should be associated with the

FIG. 70.—Pollen grain of *Whittleseya elegans* taken from an unopened anther. *(After Seward, 1917.)*

Cordaitales or with the Medullosae among the Cycadofilicales. The evidence of the pollen grain, however, in view of its single longitudinal furrow and comparatively reduced prothallial tissue, is strongly in favor of its cordaitalean association.

BENNETTITALES (Hemicycadales)

The grains of the Bennettitales are, with one or two exceptions, scarcely different from those of the cycads. They are boat shaped and provided with a single longitudinal furrow which appears to have been as ineffective in closing as that of the cycads and *Ginkgo*. Their prothallial tissue was much less extensive than in the grains of the Cycadofilicales, or even of the Cordaitales, but considerably more extensive than that of the Cycadales. In size they range from 20 to 67 μ in length, with the majority of them nearer the lower limit. They are thus generally a great deal smaller than those of the Cycadofilicales or even the Cordaitales but are larger than those of the Cycadales and the Ginkgoales. In the development of their prothallial tissue and their size they thus occupy a position intermediate between the Cycadofilicales and the Cycadales.

The Bennettitales occurred in some abundance in the Carboniferous period but in the Mesozoic became dominant; their remains are found in every country in the world where rocks of this age have been studied.* It has been estimated that there must

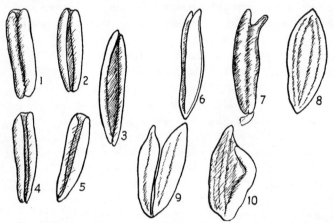

Fig. 71.—Pollen grains of Bennettitales: Nos. 1–5, those of *Cycadeoidea etrusca*, taken from a silicified strobile; Nos. 6, 7, *Williamsonia spectabilis;* Nos. 8–10, of *W. pecten.* Numbers 1–5 after Capellini and Solms (1892); Nos. 6–10 after Nathorst (1909).

have existed in the Mesozoic period 30,000 to 40,000 different species of them.

CYCADEOIDEA Buckland (*Bennettites* Carr.)

The pollen of *Cycadeoidea*, while far smaller than that of the Cordaites, is significantly larger than that of the living cycads. Whether or not there is a distinct increase in size at time of fertilization, as in the Cordaites, is still unknown since no section of seeds yet cut traverses a pollen chamber containing pollen.

Inside of these grains are seen markings which certainly represent internal cells. These are various in number; most frequently they are detached, rounded cells, not touching each other, in contact only with the inside of the spore wall, though occasionally, as shown in Fig. 72, No. 9, the whole of the interior of the grain is divided into a small number of angular cells. These are fewer than those of the Cordaitales but clearly more

* For an account of the fossil Bennettitales see Wieland (1906).

than three. Prothallial elimination had, therefore, proceeded farther than in the Cordaitales though not so far as in modern gymnosperms.

Cycadeoidea etrusca Cap. & Solms (Fig. 71, Nos. 1 to 5). These pollen grains are described as resembling little boats, their upturned sides naturally appearing as two darker lines. "I became convinced that they must represent elongate and collapsed pollen grains. And in the same section I noted finally

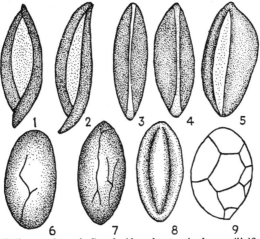

Fig. 72.—Pollen grains of *Cycadeoidea dacotensis* from silicified strobiles. Numbers 1 and 5 are shrunken, Nos. 6 and 7 fully expanded, No. 8 partly expanded, No. 9 in optical section showing the internal cellular structure. (*After Wieland*, 1906.)

a free thin-walled, obtusely ovoid, and still distended body which may likewise represent a better conserved uncollapsed pollen grain."

The specimen from which these grains were described is a silicified trunk found by one of the authors on a sepulchral chamber of the ancient necropolis at Marzabotto. It had been placed there with vases and other objects of reverence by the Etruscans, who obtained it from the Upper Jurassic scaly clays of the Apennine Hills more than 4,000 years ago. The specimen, sectioned and showing the pollen grains, is now in the museum at Bologna (Capellini and Solms, 1892; Wieland, 1906. The latter author includes a translation of Count Solms' description of this beautiful fossil).

Cycadeoidea dacotensis Wieland (*Bennettites dacotensis* Mc-Bride, *B. McBridei* Ward) (Figs. 72, 73). Grains ellipsoidal, about 67 μ long. The pollen is found in perfect preservation in sections cut through silicified cones. Grains in every stage of shrinking and distension are to be seen (Fig. 72), and in most a single longitudinal furrow is present. The grains present no other external markings, but occasionally internal markings may be observed which are undoubtedly cell walls (Fig. 72, No. 9, Fig. 73).

C. dacotensis is known in its fossil form as a large, globular trunk found in the Upper Jurassic Wealden or Lower Cretaceous

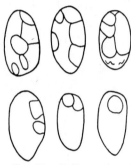

formations of the Black Hills of South Dakota and Wyoming. On a single specimen were counted 61 fruits, all at more or less the same stage of development, and from this Wieland regards the plant as monocarpic, fruiting once and then perishing, as is the case with some of the palms of the present day.

Fig. 73.—Pollen grains of *Cycadeoidea dacotensis*, showing the unusual appearance of the internal cellular structure. (*After Wieland,* 1906.)

WILLIAMSONIA Carr.

Grains ellipsoidal or boat-shaped, 25 to 65 μ long, with a single longitudinal furrow reaching from end to end, similar to those of *Cycadeoidea.*

Williamsonia spectabilis Nath. (Fig. 71, Nos, 6, 7). Grains narrowly elliptical, 58 to 65 μ long, with a single long and well-marked furrow, in all respects similar to those of *Cycadeoidea etrusca*. They are generally found jumbled together and twisted and bent into all sorts of shapes and positions. Sometimes they are splitting open and look like a pair of breeches. They may be curved, straight, or spindle-shaped and sometimes even egg-shaped.

The fossil from which these grains were obtained is described by Nathorst as occurring in large quantities in the Lower Estuarine series near Whitby, England. It has also been obtained from beds of the same age at Marske in the Cleveland district of Yorkshire. The flower has been restored by Hamshaw Thomas (Seward, 1917, Volume 3, Fig. 552). It has never been found associated with the rest of the plant, but Nathorst (1909, 1911) believes it to belong to the plant that bore the leaves known as *Ptilophyllum pecten*.

Williamsonia pecten (Leckenby) Carr. (*W. Leckenbyi* Nath.) (Fig. 71, Nos. 8 to 10). Grains similar to those of *W. spectabilis* but always smaller, generally 36 to 44, rarely 50 μ long. These grains were obtained by Nathorst from carbonized sporophyls which were discovered by Leckenby at Scarborough and which he erroneously believed to belong to the leaf of *Palaeozamia pecten*. The specimen is now in the Sedgwick Museum, Cam-

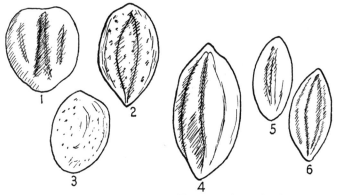

FIG. 74.—Pollen grains of Bennettitales: Nos. 1–3, those of *Wielandia angusti-folia*, Nos. 4–6, those of *W. punctata*. (*After Nathorst, 1909.*)

bridge (Nathorst, 1909, 1911). The plant is described by Bancroft (1913) from an Indian specimen believed to be referable to the same species. The stem was 5 to 6 cm. in diameter and clothed with an armor of leaf bases. The structure of the pinnae is in general agreement with that found in the Bennettiteae.

WILLIAMSONIELLA Thomas

Grains essentially the same as in other members of the Bennettitales.

In habit *Williamsoniella* resembles *Wielandiella*, but the leaves are more scattered on the stem, which is slender and freely branching dichotomously. The genus was founded for the reception of species found in the Middle Estuarine series of the Middle Jurassic plant beds at Gristhorpe, and Cleveland in Yorkshire.

Williamsoniella Lignieri (Nath.) Thomas (*Williamsonia* (?) *Lignieri* Nath.) (Fig. 75, No. 2).   Grains ellipsoidal or boat-shaped, 25 to 30 μ long (Nathorst, 1909).

Williamsoniella coronata Thomas.   Grains spheroidal or ellipsoidal, about 20 μ in diameter, provided with a single, well-marked furrow, similar to the grains of *W. Lignieri*.

Wielandia angustifolia Nath. (*Williamsonia angustifolia* Nath.) (Fig. 74, Nos. 1 to 3).   Grains ellipsoidal, with or without a furrow.   Not much reliance can be placed on these specimens, because, as Nathorst (1909) points out, the appearance of the

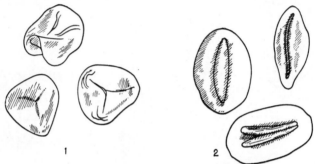

Fig. 75.—Pollen grains of Bennettitales: No. 1, a group of three grains of *Cycado-cephalus Sewardi*, No. 2, of *Williamsonia Lignieri*.   (*After Nathorst*, 1909.)

pollen grains suggests that they were immature at time of fossilization.

Wielandia punctata Nath. (Fig. 74, Nos. 4 to 6).   Grains ellipsoidal, about 58 μ long, with a single longitudinal furrow which is always more or less bulging outward (Nathorst, 1909).

Cycadocephalus Sewardii Nath. (Fig. 75, No. 1).   Grains rounded tetrahedral with the ordinary triradiate crest character-istic of fern spores.

This plant is believed to belong to the *Williamsonia* group, but its exact interpretation is doubtful.   The fossil is a large flower, entirely staminate, consisting of 17 or 18 sporophyls seated on a stout peduncle.   It was found in the Lower Rhaetic of Sweden.   Its fern-like spores, lacking the single longitudinal furrow which characterizes the grains of the Bennettitales, suggest that the plant may be wrongly associated with this group.

LIVING GYMNOSPERMS

KEY TO THE GENERA

I. With a single longitudinal germinal furrow.
  A. Furrow deep; without bladders and without longitudinal ridges; ellipsoidal.
    1. Grain almost as broad as long.
        a. Outer surface slightly warty-granular.　Cycas
        b. Outer surface smooth or slightly granular.　Zamia
          　　　　　　　　　　　　　　　　　Ceratozamia
        c. Outer surface finely reticulate pitted and wrinkled on the dorsal side.　Dioon
        d. Outer surface not pitted. Wrinkled on the dorsal side.　Microcycas
    2. Grain much longer than broad—about 29.6 by 18.2 μ.　Ginkgo
  B. Furrow shallow, flanked by bladders, generally normally 2, 1 on each side; occasionally normally 3 (a few abnormal grains may be present with other numbers); grain not generally ellipsoidal.
    1. Furrow not sharply defined; bladders normally 2, firm. Grains 45 to 109 μ in diameter.
        a. Bladders rounded at the ends, not flattened dorsoventrally.
          (1) Grains 45 to 57 μ in diameter; bladders large, about two-thirds the diameter of the body of the grain.　Pinus
          　　　　　　　　　　　　　　　　　Pseudolarix
          (2) Grains 96 to 110 μ in diameter, and bladders small in proportion to the grain.　Abies
        b. Bladders flattened dorsoventrally at their ends, thus appearing pointed when the grain is seen in end view.
          (1) Grains 50 to 60 μ in diameter.　Cedrus
          (2) Grains 65 to 90 μ in diameter.　Picea
    2. Furrow sharply defined, resembling that of *Cycas*, ventral roots of the bladders springing from the rim of the furrow, bladders mostly flaccid, except when there are 3. Grains small, 23 to 48 μ in diameter.
        a. Bladders normally 2, except in *Podocarpus dacrydioides*, their texture merging with that of the cap through their dorsal roots, various in size and shape in the different species.　Podocarpus
          　　　　　　　　　　　　　　　　　Dacrydium

        b. Bladders normally 3.
            (1) Bladders flattened, with internal reticulate thickenings, merging through their dorsal roots with the exine of the cap.   Podocarpus dacrydioides

            (2) Bladders more or less globular without internal reticulate thickenings, almost wholly ventral in origin.   Pherosphaera

    C. Furrow shallow, not flanked by bladders, with 19 or 20 longitudinal ridges; 51 to 57 μ long.   Welwitschia

II. Without a well-marked furrow and without bladders.
    A. Intine very thick; exine thin and flecked, easily ruptured, and cast off when the grain is moistened.
        1. Pore a well-marked papilla.
            a. Pore papilla straight or only slightly bent at its tip. 23.5 to 32 μ in diameter.   Cryptomeria
            b. Pore papilla bent sharply at right angles. 28.5 to 41 μ in diameter.
                (1) Pore papilla long and conspicuous.   Sequoia
                (2) Pore papilla short, almost vestigial.   Glyptostrobus
        2. Pore a low protuberance.   Taxodium
                                            Torreya
                                          Cunninghamia

        3. Pore entirely absent.
            a. Grains 34 to 40 μ in diameter.   Cunninghamia
            b. Grains 29.5 to 36.5 μ in diameter.   Libocedrus
            c. Grains 18 to 30 μ in diameter.   Taxus
                                          Juniperus
                                        Thuja
                                        Cupressus
                                          Chamaecyparus
                                          Callitris

    B. Intine not excessively thick; exine not very thin and not cast off when the grain is moistened.
        1. Exine smooth.   Larix
                                          Pseudotsuga
        2. Exine rough corrugated.   Tsuga
        3. Exine pitted.
            a. With an annular thickening in the exine, probably representing the furrow rim.   Araucaria
            b. Without an annular thickening.   Agathis

III. Without germinal furrows or bladders; ellipsoidal in shape with 6 to 8 (generally 7) high angular ridges with a zigzag hyaline streak in the grooves between them or with 11 to 15 low ridges without hyaline streaks.   Ephedra

IV. Without furrows, bladders, or ridges; tending to be
spheroidal in shape. Intine thick and hyaline,
expanding excessively when moistened. Exine
thin but not easily rupturing, provided with rudimentary or vestigial spines, otherwise smooth   Gnetum

CYCADALES

The grains of the Cycadales (Fig. 76) entirely lack prothallial
tissue. They are broadly ellipsoidal with a single deep, longitudinal furrow reaching from end to end, essentially as in the
grains of *Ginkgo* (Plate II, Fig. 6). Such a grain may be
described as boat-shaped. It is bilaterally symmetrical in the
sense that its two sides and its two ends are exactly alike; but its
remaining two sides are dissimilar, since one of them bears the
furrow and the other does not. The side which bears the furrow
is regarded as ventral, and its opposite convex side as dorsal.

This form of grain persists throughout the group without serious
modification except in the texture—more especially of its dorsal
side. Nevertheless, we can recognize foreshadowed in this
simple and unquestionably primitive grain the many varied and
elaborate forms found among the higher gymnosperms and some
of the lower angiosperms. In *Zamia* and *Ceratozamia* it is quite
smooth all over. In *Cycas* it is minutely warty on the outside,
suggesting the flecked surface of the grains of *Juniperus*. In
Microcycas it is somewhat wrinkled on the dorsal surface, suggesting the crinkly surface of the cap of the grain of *Pinus*, *Podocarpus*,
Tsuga, and others.

When this type of grain is dry the edges of the furrow arch
inward toward each other, tending to close the opening, and may
even touch in the middle; but at its two ends the furrow always
remains more or less open on account of the persistently rounded
shape of its ends. When the grain is moistened the furrow gapes
widely open, and this is the condition in which the grains are
generally found when mounted in glycerin jelly for microscopic
examination. Under certain conditions, however, they swell
excessively; the floor of the furrow rises and may frequently be
found protruding as a mound surrounded by a rim which is the
margin of the furrow, foreshadowing the form of the grain of
Araucaria in which the furrow is virtually absent, its rim alone
persisting as a ring-shaped thickening in the exine. Or the
furrow may be completely evaginated, causing the grain to assume

a spherical form. In this condition the grains are curiously suggestive of those among the Coniferales which are round and smooth, *e.g.*, that of *Larix*, except that in the grains of the cycads the exine of the evaginated part is a little thinner than that of the rest of the grain.

This one-furrowed or monocolpate type of grain, besides occurring throughout the Cycadales, is characteristic of many monocotyledons and primitive dicotyledons, *e.g.*, the Palmaceae, Magnoliaceae, and Nymphaeaceae. Its great stability and persistence in these divergent groups are in keeping with its antiquity.

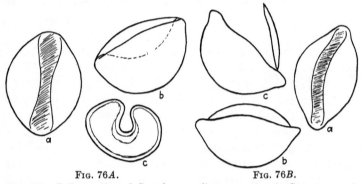

Fig. 76A.   Fig. 76B.

Fig. 76.—Pollen grains of Cycadaceae, diagrammatic, *A*, *Cycas*, *a*, ventral view; *b*, longitudinal; *c*, transverse optical section. *B*, *Zamia integrifolia;* *a*, unexpanded; *b*, ventral view partly expanded, side view; *c*, a similar grain with the floor of the furrow opening like a lid.

As we have already seen, it is characteristic of the Paleozoic Cordaitales and the Mesozoic Bennettitales; the grains of *Cycadeoidea* of the latter group, for example, were essentially the same as those of *Cycas* except that they were a little larger. Indeed, this type of grain appears to have been the starting point from which the many elaborate and varied forms of grain of both angiosperms and gymnosperms have evolved.

The living Cycadales are represented by nine genera consisting of less than a hundred species (Coulter, 1898). Besides the five genera of which the pollen is described in the following pages there are four others—*Microzamia* and *Bowenia* in Australia and *Encephalartos* and *Stengeria* of southeast Africa, of which no pollen was available for study. For a further discussion of the plants of this interesting family the reader is referred to the fascinating account of the "Living Cycads" (Chamberlain, 1919).

The cycads are the last remnants of a venerable and once prosperous race. They are believed to have originated from the Bennettitales during the Permian period, or possibly they originated from the Cycadofilicales, as a co-ordinate race with the Bennettitales, as early as the Devonian period. This interesting problem is discussed at great length by Chamberlain (1915). It is a noteworthy fact that "the nine genera of living cycads are so sharply defined that there is no difficulty in recognizing them," also that they are widely scattered and extremely isolated in distribution; they are found, seldom more than one genus growing in the same place, in such far-distant countries as Chile, Cuba, Mexico, Japan, Australia, and Africa. This is what would be expected of the vanishing remnants of a race of formerly world-wide distribution. In other words they are going the way of the Cordaitales, the Bennettitales, and the Ginkgoales, plants whose pollen grains were burdened with the single exaggerated furrow with no adequate method of closure. May it not be something more than a coincidence that these plants perish while the higher gymnosperms and the higher angiosperms, which, as we shall see, devised means of protecting or eliminating the primitive furrow, gained the ascendency?

CYCAS L. Cycad, Sago palm

Grains boat-shaped, broadly elliptical in outline when seen from the dorsal or ventral side, 25.1 to 32.5 μ in length. The single furrow tends to gape widely open when the grains are moistened, or, occasionally, the inner part completely evaginates, causing the grain to become nearly spherical in shape. The outer part of the exine is thin and minutely warty, especially on the dorsal surface, but the inrolled rim and floor of the furrow are quite smooth (Fig. 76). The grains of *Cycas* closely resemble those of *Ginkgo* (see Plate II, Fig. 6) but differ in the granular nature of their exine and the smooth margins of their furrows.

The genus includes about 16 species of low trees with columnar trunks, about 8 to 30 ft. high, topped by a crown of large pinnate leaves in the center of which are borne the cones. These plants are regarded as the most primitive members of the family. They are natives of Japan, Australia, and Madagascar.

Cycas Chamberlainii Brown & Keimholtz (Fig. 76). Grains uniform in size and shape, 26.2 to 26.8 μ in length, almost as broad as long. Surface minutely warty, furrow floor smooth.

A slender tree, reaching a height of about 24 ft., seldom branching; of restricted range in the vicinity of Mount Arayat, Luzon, Philippine Islands (Brown and Keimholtz, 1925).

Cycas circinalis L.   Grains essentially as in *C. Chamberlainii*, 27.4 to 32.5 μ in length.

A low tree, with broad, columnar trunk. Native of Madagascar.

ZAMIA L. Coontie, Comfortroot

Grains similar to those of *Cycas*, 26.2 to 29.1 μ long, outer surface quite smooth or only faintly granular, surface of the furrow floor always smooth.

In unexpanded grains the furrow is deep and with overhanging rim, but as they expand the furrow gapes widely open, in some cases its floor becoming evaginated to such an extent that the grain becomes entirely spherical.   Occasionally under such conditions the floor of the furrow separates from the rest of the exine along the greater part of its rim and rises as a lid (Fig. 76 *c*), almost exactly duplicating the condition which obtained among the Carboniferous dolerophyllums (see page 226).   The grains of the five species of *Zamia* which I have examined are exactly alike in all observable respects.

The coonties are low, perennial, fern-like or palm-like plants with short, stocky, generally unbranched stems, scarcely rising above the surface of the ground, bearing a crown of long pinnate leaves with thick, shining leathery leaflets.   The genus comprises about 35 species in tropical and subtropical America. They are the only representatives of the Cycadales found in the United States.   For a complete study of the genus accompanied by a valuable bibliography, the reader is referred to Webber (1901); and for further studies of their pollen grains, to Schacht (1860) and Juranyi (1872).

The following is a list of the species upon which the above description of the pollen grains was based: *Zamia silvicola* Small, a low, fern-like plant, with short, turnip-like stems scarcely emerging from the ground, bearing a few pinnate leaves about 3 ft. long; native of Florida (Small, 1926); *Z. integrifolia* Ait. (Fig. 76), native of West Indies and Florida; *Z. umbrosa* Small, native of the Bahamas and Cuba; *Z. angustifolia* Britt. & Millsp., native of Bahamas and Cuba; *Z. latifoliolata* Prenb., native of West Indies.

Ceratozamia mexicana Brongn. Grains similar to those of *Cycas* and *Zamia*, about 38.8 μ long; exine smooth.

The plant is a low tree with a broad conical trunk, 3 to 6 ft. high, topped by a crown of glossy, dark-green leaves. It grows in dense forests often associated with *Dioon edule*, of a very restricted range in the neighborhood of the extinct volcano Naolinco in Mexico (Chamberlain, 1919). This species has been exhaustively studied and described with very beautiful illustrations by Chamberlain (1912), and its pollen has been studied in detail by Juranyi (1872).

Dioon spinulosum Dyer. Grains similar to those of *Cycas* and *Zamia*, 27.4 to 29.4 μ in length; exine of the exposed surface conspicuously wrinkled, but that of the part included in the furrow not wrinkled. Upon the expansion of the grain the furrow completely evaginates, causing the grain to assume a spherical shape. In this condition no part of the surface is wrinkled, but the whole is seen to be uniformly finely reticulate-pitted. This latter character serves to distinguish the grains of this species from those of all other members of the Cycadaceae so far examined. But the same sort of pitting is found in the grains of *Agathis* and *Araucaria*, and the wrinkling of its exine it shares, in a more permanent form, with the next species to be described.

Dioon is a palm-like tree with a tall, somewhat conical trunk, 10 to 30 ft. high, topped by a crown of glossy, pinnate leaves among which are borne the large female cones weighing as much as 30 lb. each. The seeds of this tree, when ground, furnish meal for *tortilla*, as do those of the allied species *D. edule*. The species is abundant, almost forming forests in parts of Mexico. For a further discussion see Chamberlain (1909, 1919).

Microcycas calocoma (Miq.) DC. Palma, Corcho. Grains in general form similar to those of *Cycas* and *Zamia*, 28.5 by 20 μ. Texture of the exine smooth, but that of the dorsal surface is thrown into fine wrinkles, as in the grains of *Dioon*. When excessively expanded, the inner part of the furrow becomes completely evaginated, causing the grain to assume a spherical form. In this condition the exine of the dorsal surface remains wrinkled and sharply marked off from the part of the ventral side which was enclosed in the furrow, a condition which seems to foreshadow such grains as those of *Podocarpus* and *Pinus*, in which the dorsal surface is thick and pebbled in appearance, and the ventral thin and smooth.

The genus *Microcycas* includes only the above species, of restricted range in and about the mountains of Pinae del Rio in Cuba. It is among the largest of the cycads, exceeded in size only by *Macrozamia Hopei*, despite its name, which is ill chosen, first applied to a small fragment of the plant. The plants are from 10 to 30 ft. high, with a dense crown of glossy, dark-green leaves (Chamberlain, 1919; Caldwell, 1907).

GINKGOALES

The grains of the Ginkgoales, like those of the cycads, are notable for their single deep and broad unprotected furrow and their lack of prothallial tissue. At maturity they present nothing of the pluricellular tissue which characterized the grains of the extinct Cordaitales and Bennettitales. The male gametophyte is reduced to nominally three cells, *i.e.*, one vegetative, one generative, and one tube cell (Coulter and Chamberlain, 1917, page 206). These are separated only by weakly developed walls and are of very unequal size, the large tube cell occupying the major portion of the interior of the grain, with the other two flattened out and closely appressed against the inner surface of the dorsal side. The furrow, on the other hand, is of practically the same form as that of the grains of the Cordaitales, except that, there being no internal tissue developed within, it remains deeply invaginated until the pollen tube begins to emerge. When the floor of the furrow is just beginning to bulge out beyond the furrow rim, the appearance of the grain strikingly recalls that of *Dolerophyllum* described by Renault. Indeed, a cross section of the grain in this stage of development shows precisely the same outline as the cross section of the *Dolerophyllum* grain in Renault's figure, reproduced here (Fig. 69) but lacking the internal cellular tissue. Such an appearance as this has led Jeffrey (1917, page 339) to make the statement that "in the monotypic *Ginkgo* the pollen is winged as in the more primitive Abietineae." His own figure (Fig. 245) shows that what he regarded as wings are the two protuberances in the outline of his section where it passes through the furrow rim.

In its reduction of prothallial tissue and its acquisition of a pollen tube the pollen grain of *Ginkgo* records a distinct advance over the Cordaitalean form, and the hereditary broad furrow is made use of as a place of emergence for the pollen tube. When we recall that in the pollen grains of the vast majority of the angiosperms the tube may emerge through a relatively tiny hole occupying only a small fraction of the surface of the grain, this enormous furrow of *Ginkgo*, reaching the entire length of the grain and involving nearly a half of its surface, seems out of all proportion to the requirements of a pollen tube. Nevertheless, it was the grain's heritage from the past, and, its function of proliferation chamber for a developing prothallus being no longer required, it was turned to account as a place of emergence for the newly acquired pollen tube. That it served its purpose well in this particular instance is abundantly attested by the enormous age of the species. But that such a furrow was not so serviceable in many other cases is broadly suggested by the fact that only two modern groups, *viz.*, the Cycadales and Ginkgoales, have retained such a furrow in an unmodified form, and these two phyla are now nearly extinct.

The Ginkgoales are a venerable race of tall and stately trees. In many respects they show a marked affinity to the cycads. In fact "*Ginkgo* is much more Cycad-like than Conifer-like" (Coulter 1898), but like the extinct Cycadofilicales they possess both filicinean and cycadean characters (Seward and Gowan, 1900). In all probability they originated from the Cordaitales soon after the latter took their departure from the Cycadofilicales late in the Paleozoic. They reached their culmination in the Jurassic, and their remains are found in every country of the world where rocks of that period have been studied. But from that time on they have steadily declined until now the phylum is represented only by the single species *Ginkgo biloba*.

Ginkgo biloba L. (*Salisburia adiantifolia* Sm.) Ginkgo, Maidenhair tree (Plate II, Fig. 6). Grains uniform in shape and size, boat-shaped with a single longitudinal furrow, elliptical in outline when seen from the ventral side, 27.4 to 32 μ in length. Exine minutely roughened up to the edge of the furrow rim, which is slightly wavy; occasionally the floor of the furrow is marked by slight transverse corrugations. The furrow tends to open when moistened, but the invaginated part seldom becomes evaginated.

This grain is similar in all its major features to that of *Cycas* but may be distinguished from the latter by its more elongate shape, smoother surface, and the slightly wavy margins of its furrow.

A large and handsome tree, occasionally reaching a height of 100 ft. and an age of a thousand years; native of China but now much cultivated throughout the United States and elsewhere. Dioecious; flowers in early spring, wind pollinated. Not known to cause hayfever, though it has occasionally been suspected of doing so.

CONIFERALES

LIST OF GENERA*

Pinaceae
  I. Araucarineae
    Araucaria
    Agathis
  II. Abietineae
    Winged
      Pinus
      Cedrus
      Picea
      Abies
      Pseudolarix
    Wingless
      Pseudotsuga
      Larix
      Tsuga
  III. Taxodineae
    Cryptomeria
    Sequoia

Glyptostrobus
Taxodium
Cunninghamia
  IV. Cupressineae
    Juniperus
    Thuja
    Libocedrus
    Cupressus
    Chamaecyparus
    Callitris
Taxaceae
  V. Taxineae
    Torreya
    Taxus
  VI. Podocarpineae
    Podocarpus
    Dacrydium
    Pherosphaera

* For key to genera see p. 233.

Diversity of Form.—The pollen grains of the Coniferales are notorious for their extraordinary diversity of form. It is, accordingly, without profit to attempt to frame a definition to include them all. A few generalizations, however, can be made. As compared with the grains of the more primitive gymnosperms, we find little trace of the pluricellular gametophytic tissue which was much in evidence among the Cycadofilicales and Cordaitales.

And the elongate deep furrow which had become a fixed and pronounced character of the grains among all the preceding groups of gymnosperms is, among the Coniferales, no longer fixed. In fact in this respect it may be said that the different lines of development of the pollen-grain forms among the Coniferales represent different ways of modifying, suppressing, or protecting the long, deep, and wide-open furrow which was the heritage of the phylum from the earlier gymnosperms. With the suppression of the gametophyte tissue, the furrow appears to have outlasted its usefulness.

Perhaps the most striking character of the grains of the group is the somewhat sporadic appearance of wing-like bladders. These are found only among some of the genera of the tribes Abietineae and Podocarpineae. In the Abietineae the wings when present are nearly always normally two, one on each side of the furrow and forming for it a protective cover when the grain dries; while in the grains of the Podocarpineae there may be two, three, four, five, or six bladders, and in the pollen of one species of *Podocarpus* some grains have a single bladder encircling them completely like a frill. But in both tribes there are genera with grains entirely lacking bladders. Bladdery wings of this character are unknown elsewhere among the pollen grains of living spermatophytes. Similar wings, however, are known to have occurred on the microspores of some Paleozoic Cycadofilicales and Lycopodiales and still occur on the spores of some of the modern ferns and Lycopods, and their presence among the Coniferales suggests the great antiquity of the group. The capacity to develop wings has apparently been inherited from the remote past, but only in these few genera has it been called forth, here, apparently, in response to a need of protection for the broad, open furrow with which such wings are here associated.

In spite of the wide diversity of character among the pollen grains of the Coniferales they offer no evidence that the group is actually polyphyletic. Respecting the origin of the group, the evidence of the pollen grain leads to much the same conclusion as the evidence from other sources. For example, Coulter (1898) states: "The existing gymnosperm groups are so very diverse that one of two things seems evident; either they differentiated into divergent lines from a common gymnosperm stock in very ancient times, or they originated independently from the pteridophyte stock." And they appear to be united to this ancient pteridophyte stock or Cycadofilicales through the Cordaitales. Scott (1905) asserts, "I, at least, find it impossible to believe that the Coniferales are an unnatural group, and that their various tribes can have been derived from totally different sources. The final conclusion to which we are led is that the conifers are monophyletic, having been ultimately derived from the pteridophyte stock." At the same time there is evidence that the different main groups sprang from the ancient pteridophyte stock at different times and at different points.

Diversity of Size.—Some evidence in favor of the theory of separate origins from the ancestral stock is found in the enormous difference in size between the pollen grains of some of the different groups, *e.g.*, between those of the Abietineae and the Podocarpineae, for it is well known that the grains of the Cycadofilicales and Cordaitales, though uniform in shape, differed widely in size (Renault, 1879). Thus it may be that the Abietineae, since they have large grains, originated from a large-grained member of the ancestral stock, while the Podocarpineae, since they have small grains, originated from one of its small-grained members. Whatever their origin, the pollen-grain forms of the Coniferales suggest that their subsequent evolutionary history was one of marked divergences. But from whatever point or points of the ancestral stock they originated they could have inherited only the simple boat-shaped form of grain with its long, deep furrow because, as we have already seen, this type of grain is present, without any important modifications, throughout the Cycadales, the Bennettitales, the Cordaitales, and the Ginkgoales. It was the archaic form and appears to have been universal among the early seed-bearing plants above the Cycadofilicales.

The Ancestral Form.—The outstanding and, I think, the significant character of this ancient form of pollen grain is its unprotected furrow with no adequate mechanism of closure. This type of furrow, as we saw it in the grains of *Cycas* and *Ginkgo*, is just a deep, longitudinal invagination with inturned margins, its very shape making it impossible for it ever to close completely. When a grain provided with such a furrow as this dries, the furrow margins bend in toward each other and may even touch in the middle, but the broad, rounded ends always remain open. When we compare the loose and ineffective closure of this ancient type of furrow with the methods of closure of the more modern forms of furrow and pore found among the grains of the angiosperms, nearly all of which are conspicuous for the effectiveness and mechanical perfection of their closure devices, it seems quite likely that the ancient type of furrow was not, in modern associations, all that could be desired, and it seems to be quite within the realm of possibility that the Coniferales and incidentally, as we shall see later, the angiosperms partly owe their ascendency over their contemporaries the Cycadales and Ginkgoales to the fact that they were able to modify, protect, or abandon the open furrow of the archaic form of pollen grain which was their heritage from the past. As we look over the forms of the pollen grains of the various tribes of the Coniferae we see that each had its own way of dealing with it. Consequently, in the following discussion each of the tribes will be given separate consideration.

The *Araucarineae* are undoubtedly among the most ancient living conifers. Their exact position is not quite understood but has been the subject of much vigorous discussion, with the result that many interesting things have been discovered about them. Seward and Ford (1906) regard the Araucarineae as derived from Paleozoic Lycopodineae, but, though the evidence that they have amassed seems adequate and convincing, they do not get much support from other investigators, most of them finding that the Araucarineae are in some way or another derived from the Cordaitales. Jeffrey (1917, page 353) regards them as relatively young, having originated from the Abietineae. Stiles (1908) believes them to be ancient and regards them as ancestral to the winged-grained Podocarineae, having given rise to that group through the wingless-grained *Saxegothaea*. Since the discussion of this very interesting problem is somewhat outside the scope of the present work, the reader is referred to the works mentioned above, also to Scott (1905) and Thomson (1913), for a complete presentation of the case. During the Mesozoic the Araucarineae were the dominant type of conifers, with almost world-wide distribution; but now they are restricted to South America and the Australasian region. The great antiquity of *Araucaria* is suggested by a beautiful photograph in Wieland's book (1916) of *Araucaria imbricata* growing in the foothills of the Andes in western Argentina, and of which he says, "No more ancient-appearing landscapes than these can be found on the globe today. A very distinct likeness to *Cordaites*, strongest in the young forms, at once comes to mind," and indeed one is impressed with the similarity between this photograph of the living *Araucaria imbricata* and Grand 'Eury's famous restoration of *Dorycordaites* (Scott's "Fossil Botany," page 267, 1923).

Most students of the Coniferales are agreed that the Araucarineae are "very distinct from the other Pinaceae and must have been distinct for a long time" (Coulter and Chamberlain, 1917). In fact so impressed have Seward and Ford (1906) been with the isolation of the Araucarineae that they have proposed a separate phylum for them, the Araucariales.

The grains of both *Araucaria* and *Agathis* are without a true furrow or pore (Fig. 77). In the grains of *Agathis* no vestige of a furrow can be found, but in those of *Araucaria* there is an annular thickening which corresponds in position to the furrow rim in the expanded *Cycad* grains and which appears to be the vestige of the cycadean furrow rim. The grains of *Agathis* and *Araucaria* differ from all other Coniferales in the pitted texture of their exine. This characteristic, however, is almost exactly duplicated in the grain of *Dioon* among the Cycadales. Indeed, from such a form of grain as that of *Dioon* those of the Araucarineae could have been derived by simply assuming the spherical form through the evagination of the furrow floor with a partial retention of the furrow rim in *Araucaria* and its complete obliteration in *Agathis*. There is no evidence that the Araucarian form of grain leads to any other form and certainly none that it could lead to that of the winged grains of the Podocarpineae through *Saxegothaea*, as suggested by Stiles (1908), for the simple reason that the bladders in the Podocarpineae are obviously developed on the two sides of the furrow rim. The suppression of the furrow in the grain of the Araucarineae,* therefore, precludes the possibility of its leading to winged grains such as those of either the Podocarpineae or the Abietineae. From the evidence of the pollen grain the two genera of the Araucarineae appear to represent the end of a

* I have had opportunity to observe the pollen of only two species of the Araucarineae but assume that the grains of all species are without wings; thus Lopriore (1905) states that the grains of *Araucaria Bidwillii* are round and without wings.

very distinct line of development. Its origin appears to have been from some form which had a monocolpate grain, *e.g.*, the Cordaitales of Bennettitales.

The *Abietineae* are regarded by Jeffrey (1917) as the most ancient of the Coniferales derived from the cordaitalean stock in close association with *Ginkgo* and giving rise, in comparatively recent time, to the Taxodineae and Cupressineae. There is much geological evidence that the group is very ancient; fossil wood of Abietineae and winged pollen grains which are undoubtedly those of Abietineae have been found in the Triassic (Seward, 1917, Fig. 790). They are rival claimants with the Auracarineae for antiquity. The Abietineae are all northern species, constituting the major coniferous display throughout the Northern Hemisphere and are generally regarded as a natural group. Nevertheless, within the group are found three distinct types of pollen grain. This suggests that it is not entirely natural or at least shows some very early divergences (Fig. 77). The grains of the five genera *Pinus*, *Cedras*, *Picea*, *Abies*, and *Pseudolarix* resemble each other in their common possession of bladders and in all the major features of their construction, such as the differentiation between the dorsal and ventral side and their possession of a single long furrow. In contrast to these the grains of *Tsuga* have no true furrow or wings but resemble those of the winged-grained Abietineae in the character of their exine, which is similar to that of the dorsal side of the winged-grained Abietineae, with little differentiation between dorsal and ventral surfaces. The grains of *Larix* and *Pseudotsuga* are also entirely without furrow or bladders, but they reveal little or nothing of their phylogenies because their characters are mainly those of reduction; they have a thin and perfectly smooth exine and rather thick intine, which swells upon being moistened, ruptures, and casts off the exine. Though the grains of *Larix* and *Pseudotsuga* are virtually identical, their origins might have been widely different, for in the face of so complete a reduction the similarity between them becomes meaningless.

The *Taxodineae* and *Cupressineae* are generally regarded as much younger than the Abietineae and Araucarineae. Jeffrey (1917) regards both groups as derived from the Abietineae in comparatively recent times. Coulter and Chamberlain (1917) state that "it is clear . . . that the Abietineae are much older than the Taxodineae and Cupressineae," basing this conclusion on the absence of their fossil remains below the Upper Cretaceous (page 305), and they go on to say that that is evidence of the two groups, being derived from Abietineous stock and that "these two branches may be assumed to have arisen during the Mesozoic." On the other hand, the unusually wide distribution in isolated regions which is recorded for the genera of both groups suggests that they are either artificial assemblages or very ancient, the existing genera representing the disappearing remnants of a once more abundant group of plants of world-wide distribution.

The characters of the pollen grains of the Taxodineae and Cupressineae do not suggest that these groups are unnatural but rather that they are closely related to each other and that they are far removed from the ancient pteridophyte stock (Fig. 77). The grains of both the Taxodineae and Cupressineae are entirely without prothallial cells (Coulter and Chamberlain, 1917, page 277), which gives them a decidedly modern aspect among the Coniferales. Considering first the Taxodineae: in the grains of *Taxodium* the furrow appears to be reduced to the vanishing point, represented by only a small protuberance. In those of *Cunninghamia* there is no trace of furrow or pore, but in those of *Cryptomeria*, *Sequoia*, and *Glyptostrobus* the pore is drawn out into a more or less prominent papilla. In other respects the grains of all five genera of the *Taxodineae* are much alike; all are nearly spherical or somewhat angular, as if deformed by pressing against their neighbors in the anther sac; in all the exine is thin and flecked, and the intine very thick, but in the grain of *Cunninghamia*, which has no pore, it is thickest. The forms of these grains are such that they could have been derived from the archaic, open-furrowed type by a reduction of the furrow accompanied by a thinning of the exine and a thickening of the intine, with those of *Cryptomeria*, *Sequoia*, and *Glyptostrobus* retaining a modified vestige of the vanishing furrow (Fig. 77). Continuing on in the direction of the main line of this development would lead to the form of the grains of the Cupressineae, for these differ from those of *Cunninghamia* of the Taxodineae only in the greater thickness of their intine. The remarkable similarity of the grains of the five genera of the Cupressineae which are here shown, amounting almost to identity, constitutes a very strong argument that they are all closely related, and their similarity to those of the Taxodineae likewise argues that the two groups are related to each other.

It is probable that the great thickening of the intine which characterizes the grains of these two groups functionally replaces the lost furrow. The thickened material of the intine is callose, a substance which has the faculty of swelling to such an extent upon the absorption of water that the thin exine is ruptured and thrown completely off as soon as the grain is made wet, the whole surface of such grains thereby functioning as the furrow. This appears to be a rather curious return to the condition which obtained among the Cycadofilicales, where the grain, upon entering the pollen chamber, ruptured its exine, threw it off, and continued development as a naked prothallus. The remarkable persistence and stability of such characters as the thin, flecked exine and greatly thickened intine strongly suggest antiquity of origin and lead me to believe that the Taxodineae and Cupressineae originated from the cordaitalean stock quite independently of the Abietineae. Or if they originated from the Abietineae they must have done so before the grains of the latter had assumed anything like their modern aspect.

The *Taxineae* and *Podocarpineae* are, in taxonomic works, generally associated with each other, constituting the family Taxaceae, brought together because the seeds of both develop a fleshy testa instead of forming the customary ovulate strobili. This association, however, is certainly not well founded, for the two groups are entirely different in most other respects; particularly is this true of their pollen grains. In fact, it seems more likely that the Taxineae are more closely related to the Taxodineae-Cupressineae plexus and that the Podocarpineae are related to the Araucarineae.

The *Taxineae* are, of all conifers, most like *Ginkgo* and are, therefore most closely related to the Cordaitales. Robertson (1907) says that the Taxineae

. . . are a group retaining many relatively primitive characters, though considerably specialized along their own lines. Phylogenetically they may be regarded as an offshoot of the Cordaitalean stock. Their descent is marked by the resemblance of *Cephalotaxus* to *Ginkgo*, and of *Taxus* to *Cordaianthus* . . . The female flower of *Taxus* more closely recalls that of *Cordianthus* than of any known plant.

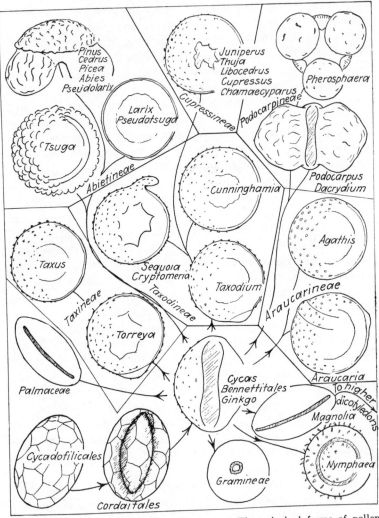

Fig. 77.—Gymnosperm pollen-grain forms. The principal forms of pollen grains are indicated diagrammatically, partly in surface view and partly in optical section. The possible courses and directions of the development of the different forms from each other are indicated by the sinuous lines, but the extent of this development is not intended to be suggested by the varying lengths of the lines, the latter being chosen merely for display.

The arrangement suggests that the form of pollen grain of the Cycadofilicales gave rise to that of the Cordaitales, by a partial suppression of the prothallial tissue and the development of a furrow. This form in turn gave rise to that of the Bennettitales, *Cycas*, and *Ginkgo*, through the further suppression of prothallial tissue. This form of pollen grain was the starting point for all other forms, which achieved further development by the modification, elimination, or pro-

Coulter and Chamberlain (1917) believe that the group is not quite so ancient. They say, "The conclusion seems reasonable that the living Taxineae represent a phylum which was derived early from the Abietineous stock, and which has retained Cordaitean features that have disappeared among existing Abietineae, Taxodineae and Cupressineae." Nevertheless, as these authors point out, there are certain characters which seem to associate them more closely with the Taxodineae and Cupressineae than with the other groups of Coniferales.

The *Podocarpineae* appear to be most closely related to the Araucarineae (Thomson, 1908). They have a similar distribution in the southern hemisphere, standing in this respect in sharp contrast to the Taxineae, which are entirely of the northern hemisphere. It has even been suggested (Tison, 1909) that the podocarps and araucarians should constitute a single group. Perhaps the strongest argument in favor of such an association is found in the extensive development of the prothallial tissue in the pollen grains of both (Coulter and Chamberlain, 1917). In both cases this consists of nuclei, formed either without separating walls or with weakly developed walls which are eventually absorbed, leaving the nuclei free. Their presence, however, obviously represents a partial retention of the prothallial condition of the ancestral Cordaitales and Cycadofilicales and is strongly suggestive of the primitive connections of their modern possessors the Araucarineae and Podocarpineae. In the grains of *Torreya* and *Taxus* among the Taxineae, on the other hand, the first division of the pollen cell results in the formation of the generative and tube cells, omitting entirely any prothallial tissue, thus standing in sharp contrast to the Podocarpineae but resembling the Taxodineae and Cupressineae. In this respect, then, the Podocarpineae appear to be primitive, associated perhaps with the Araucarineae, while the Taxineae appear to be among

---

tection of the wide-open furrow, which owing to the suppression of prothallial tissue, had become useless. In the Taxineae and the Taxodineae and Cupressineae the germinal furrow was pinched up into a papilla and finally disappeared. In the Araucarineae it was floored over. In the Abietineae and Podocarpineae it was provided with lateral bladders. In the Palmaceae and *Magnolia* it was reduced to a narrow slit by the elongation of the grain. In the Nymphaeaceae and Grimineae it was provided with an operculum. The origin of the tricolpate form of the higher Dicotyledons probably took place through the Magnoliaceae, and is discussed under that family.

the most advanced, associated, perhaps, with the Cupressineae and Taxodineae.

The evidence of the external morphology of their pollen grains likewise suggests that the Taxineae are entirely separate from the Podocarpineae (Fig. 77) but probably closely related to the Taxodineae. The grains of *Torreya* and *Taxus*, among the Taxineae, are remarkably similar to those of *Cunninghamia* and *Taxodium* among the Taxodineae. All have a thin exine flecked with granules and a remarkably thick intine which expands excessively upon absorbing moisture. The grains of *Torreya* have a vestige of a furrow similar to that of the grains of Taxodium, though it is somewhat broader and flatter. The grains of *Taxus* differ only in having not even a vestige of a furrow, in this respect resembling those of *Cunninghamia*. The grain of *Taxus* is thus more advanced than that of *Torreya* and bears the same relation to it that the grain of *Cunninghamia* does to that of *Taxodium* (Fig. 77). The evidence of the morphology of the pollen grain, therefore, seems to compel the separation of the Podocarpineae from the Taxineae, and suggests that the latter are probably more closely related to the Taxodineae and Cupressineae.

The Winged Grain of the Podocarps.—The grains of the Podocarpineae are notorious for the possession of bladdery wings in most of their species, causing them to bear a superficial resemblance to the grains of the Abietineae. But in neither the Abietineae nor the Podocarpineae are the grains of all species winged. The podocarps include 6 genera and about 86 species. Of these I have been able to examine material of only the three genera *Podocarpus*, *Dacrydium*, and *Pherosphaera*. The grains of the different species of *Podocarpus* nearly always have two wings, though of some species (*e.g.*, *P. dacrydioides*) they normally have three. In the grains of *Microcachrys* the bladders may be three, four, five, or six (*Thomson*, 1909). In those of *Phyllocladus* there are two bladders (Young, 1910). In fact the presence of these two bladders on their grains is one of the reasons for including this aberrant genus among the Podocarpineae (Kildahl, 1908). But the grains of *Saxegothaea* have no wings (Norén, 1908). The fact that the wings are various, varying in number when present from two to six, makes this character appear to be a recent acquisition, and it has been suggested that, in this respect, *Microcachrys*, with a variable number of wings, is intermediate between the wingless *Saxegothaea* and the winged podocarps (Coulter and Chamberlain, 1917). But I do not feel that this is a valid suggestion, because the wings of the podocarp grains are developed on the rim of the primitive furrow which is a distinctive character of the grains of the podocarps, while in *Saxegothaea* the furrow is absent. Rather does the development of wings on the rim of the furrow in the one case and the obliteration of the furrow in the other suggest an early divergence of the two genera. In fact Stiles (1908) from his studies of wood structure has suggested that *Saxegothaea* is closely related to *Araucaria*, a suggestion which, as far as the morphology of the pollen grains is concerned, seems to be quite possible. Stiles, however, further suggests that *Saxegothaea* may stand as a sort of connecting link between the Podocarpineae and Araucarineae. With this viewpoint the evidence of the pollen grain does not seem to agree, for it is difficult to see how the winged grains of the Podocarpineae could have been derived from the spherical grains of the Araucarineae, as the loss of the furrow of the latter seems to preclude forever the possibility of developing bladders, because these are preeminently organs of the furrow rim.

The presence of wings on the grains of some species of Podocarpineae and some of Abietineae is certainly the most striking thing about the grains of these two groups and has frequently been advanced as an argument in favor of a relationship between them. The fact that the grains of only some of the members of each group are provided with wings, while casting some suspicion on such a claim, cannot be said to invalidate it entirely, particularly since the evolution of the pollen grains of the conifers is marked throughout its course by reductions. Are the bladders recent developments within the group; or are they survivals from the past, from a time when the Abietineae and the Podocarpineae were just beginning to diverge? In the Abietineae and Podocarpineae wherever bladders are found they are always associated with the ancestral type of furrow—one does not exist without the other—and, judging by the way that the bladders close over the furrow forming a protection for it when the grain dries, it seems reasonable to suppose that in these grains the survival of the furrow was made possible only by the presence of the bladders. The furrow is obviously a survival from the past on account of its presence in the grains of the Cordaitales and Bennettitales and all other primitive groups above the Cycadofilicales. But we seek in vain for bladders of any description among these, so the bladders appear not to have been inherited in association with the furrow.   Nevertheless, these organs are not the special property of the grains of the Podocarpineae and Abietineae.   In fact, there is evidence that they are very ancient, having occurred sporadically among the Cycadofilicales and Lycopodiales of the Paleozoic period.   As we have seen, the pollen grain of *Stephanospermum caryoides*, of the former group, was provided with a single large, bladdery wing completely encircling it.   The grains of *Spencerites insignis*, among the Lycopodiales (Scott, 1907), were likewise provided with a bladdery membrane encircling them like a frill.   But neither of these grains had a furrow. Thus the bladdery wings constitute a character that was originally quite separate from and far more ancient than the ancient furrow with which it is always associated among the modern spermatophytes.   Therefore, it seems clear that any relationship that can be claimed between the Podocarpineae and Abietineae on the basis of their both possessing bladders points only to the remote connection through the Cycadofilicales which they share with all living gymnosperms.

Bladdery Wings as Organs of Flight.—The wings of the grains of Podocarpineae and Abietineae are generally regarded as organs of flight.   Unquestionably they do actually give the pollen grains a greater range of flight, but whether or not this is of value to their possessors is doubtful, and that they were developed in these grains to meet such a need is still more doubtful.   On the other hand, the construction of the winged grains of both the Abietineae and the Podocarpineae is such that the wings close together, in some cases very tightly, as the grain dries.   So that if the bladders are organs of flight, pollen grains are possibly the only flying organisms of which it can be said that they fold up their wings and fly away.   If wings were necessary to pollen grains in flight, we should expect to find the largest and heaviest grains the best provided with wings, but a glance at the sizes of the winged and wingless grains of the Coniferae shows that no such correlation exists.   Among the winged Abietineae the diameter of the grains of *Pinus austriaca* is 51 to 55 μ; that of *Picea concolor* is 85 to 97 μ; and that of *Pseudolarix amabilis* is 51 to 57 μ, while among the wingless Abietineae that of *Pseu-*

dotsuga mucronata is 90 to 100 μ; *Larix Lyallii* is 85 to 102 μ; and *Tsuga* is 62 to 70 μ. The grains of the podocarps are much smaller, their diameter ranging from 23 to 45 μ, yet they generally have wings larger in proportion to the size of the grain than do the winged Abietineae. The smallest grain that I have encountered among the Coniferales is that of *Pherosphaera Fitzgeraldi*, with a diameter of 23.9 μ, and it is provided with three wings. These grains are smaller than those of most of the grasses, the chenopods and plantain, which are quite successful in flight without the aid of wings. On the other hand, there is no doubt that the bladders of both the Podocarpineae and the Abietineae form a very effective closure for the type of furrow which the bladders accompany and which is mechanically so constructed that complete closure is otherwise impossible. Why it should be so necessary for pollen grains to have an effective furrow closure I cannot say but suspect that it is to prevent excessive desiccation. But that an effective furrow closure is a vital necessity to most pollen grains will become quite apparent as we pass in review the different forms and observe the many different mechanisms that have been devised to accomplish this end.

Araucaria imbricata Pav. (Fig. 77). Grains when expanded approximately spheroidal but generally more or less flattened on one side, 63 to 74 μ in diameter. Exine thin but considerably thickened in a rim surrounding the flattened area; texture finely pitted throughout, resembling that of the grains of *Dioon* but with the pits more scattered and more rounded in shape. Intine thick, about three times as thick as the exine, much less thick than in the grains of *Juniperus* and other Cupressineae.

When the grains break from overexpansion the rupture of the exine always takes place in the flattened area within the thickened rim. Clearly, this area corresponds morphologically to the furrow of the grains of the more primitive gymnosperms, and the thickened rim corresponds to the furrow rim.

The genus includes about 10 species of tall trees, native of Australia and neighboring islands and of South America. Perhaps the best known representative of the genus is the Norfolk Island pine (*A. excelsa* R. Br.), which is much cultivated on account of the beauty and symmetry of its form.

Agathis philippinensis Warb. (*Dammara Rumphii* Presl.). Grains uniform in size, about 43 μ in diameter, approximately spheroidal, with no trace of furrow or thickened rim. Exine thick, marked with pits of various size, similar to, but somewhat coarser than in, the grains of *Araucaria*.

The tree is a broad-leaved conifer of the Philippine Islands and is there the source of Manila copal. About four species of this genus are found in the Malay Islands, the Philippines, Fiji, New Zealand, and northern Australia.

PINUS L. Pine

Grains characterized by the possession of two large, conspicuous, air-filled bladders (Plate II, Fig. 9). The body of the grain, in the moistened condition, is something the shape of a double convex lens, round or slightly elliptical when seen from the dorsal or ventral side. The dorsal side is covered with a thick, rugged exine marked by a heavy, coarse, reticulate-granular structure. The ventral side is mainly occupied by the two bladders which diverge sharply from each other, strongly suggesting, in appearance, wings to be used in flight (Fig. 78). Between the bladders is a single long but poorly defined furrow reaching almost completely from end to end of the grain. At the margin of the grain, where the dorsal surface merges with the ventral or into the bladders, there is often developed a slight ridge or frill-like projection, and there is much variation in the appearance and extent to which this *marginal ridge* is developed in the different species. It cannot, however, be used as a reliable guide to identification on account of its variousness within the species. The reticulate appearance of the exine of the cap, or dorsal surface, is not due to surface roughenings so much as to reticulately arranged material of denser nature and darker color embedded in a matrix of less dense material and of a lighter color. Where the exine of the cap merges into that of the bladders at their dorsal roots the reticulum is heavier, of a more open structure, and, in the bladders, is seen to take the form of prominent ridges on their inner surface. These serve to stiffen the structure of the bladders and prevent them from collapsing, in the same way that, in buildings floor beams serve to prevent the collapsing of the floors.

At the ventral roots of the bladders, where they make contact with the lower surface of the body of the grain, the reticulum comes abruptly to an end. The intervening space between the bladders, which is morphologically the furrow, is covered by an exceedingly thin and flexible membrane, smooth and devoid of markings of any kind. The furrow is not bounded by a thickened rim, and its limits are not sharply defined.

The mechanical effect of this thin, flexible membrane on the ventral side of the grain opposed to the thick, inflexible dorsal surface is such that when the grain dries and shrinks the dorsal surface remains convex while the flexible ventral surface becomes flattened or even invaginated, and the furrow drawn in; this causes the two bladders to press tightly together, effectually closing the furrow (Fig. 78 *A*). The bladders, however, are not

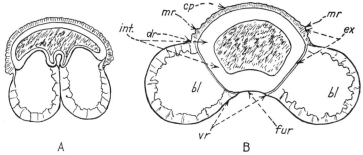

Fig. 78.—Pollen grains of *Pinus scopulorum*, diagrammatic transverse optical sections: *A*, dry and contracted; *B*, moist and expanded: *ex*, exine; *int*, intine; *cp*, cap; *mr*, marginal ridge; *fur*, furrow; *bl*, bladders; *dr*, dorsal root of the bladders; *vr*, ventral root of the bladders.

noticeably deformed by the process, differing in this respect from those of the grains of *Picea* and *Cedrus*.

The grains of *Pinus* are rather large, ranging in the different species, here observed, from about 45.5 to 65 μ in diameter, the bladders measuring about two-thirds of the diameter of the body of the grain. The grains of the different species are scarcely to be distinguished from each other, though Hörmann (1929) has shown that there are slight differences in the pattern of the reticulum, both of the dorsal surface of the grain and of the bladders. The differences in size, though often slight and showing much overlapping in the different species, give greater promise as a means of distinguishing the different species. Hörmann (1929) has shown that, by applying the statistical method, measurements can be used to distinguish *P. cembra, P. montana,* and *P. silvestris.*

The pines are all wind pollinated and are notable for the enormous quantities of pollen that they shed and the great distances it may be carried by air currents, but it is not known to cause hayfever. Pine pollen is, however, one of the most abundant and easily recognized grains found in postglacial silts, and it is of the utmost importance in the studies of such deposits that the different species should be distinguished, though this is at present extremely difficult. The genus includes about 66 species widely distributed throughout the northern hemisphere.

Pinus nigra var. **austriaca** Asch. & Graeb. Austrian pine (Plate II, Fig. 9) type. Grains uniform in shape and size, circular in outline or nearly so when seen in dorsal view, about 51.3 μ in diameter. Marginal ridge only slightly developed or entirely absent but uniform all around the grain.

A large tree introduced from Europe but now much planted in the northeastern U.S. Flowers in May.

Pinus scopulorum (Engelm.) Lem. Rock pine, Yellow pine. Grains uniform in size and shape, 57 to 58 μ in diameter, essentially as in the type but with the marginal ridge somewhat better developed and more pronounced in the region of the bladders.

A large tree. South Dakota to Nebraska to Texas to Utah, and Arizona. April and May.

Pinus tuberculata Gord. (*P. attenuata* Lem.) Knobcone pine. Grains approximately circular in outline when seen in dorsal view, 52.3 to 64 μ in diameter. A few grains have three or four bladders. Marginal ridge prominent in the region of the bladders, absent between them. Otherwise as in the type.

Grains with supernumerary bladders, though not constituting any considerable proportion of the pollen, are of great interest. They are always larger than normal. They may be perfectly regular in shape, with the bladders all of the same size; or they may be extremely irregular, with the bladders of different sizes. When there are three bladders the exine between them is quite smooth, as in normal grains, suggesting that the space between the bladders represents a single furrow of triangular form. But when there are four bladders, there is a quadrangular area between them which is largely granular-reticulate like the surface of the cap, suggesting that the presence of four bladders arises from the presence of four furrows, each giving rise to a bladder only on its outer side.

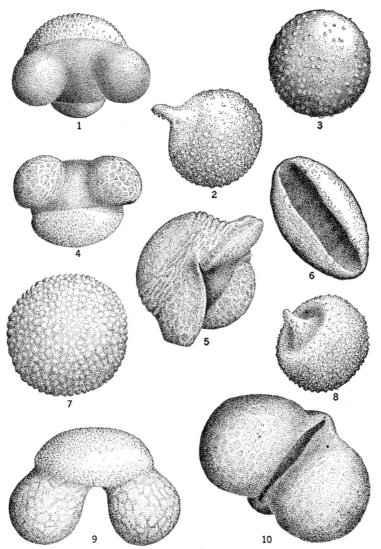

PLATE II.—Pollen grains of gymnosperms. 1, *Pherosphaera Fitzgeraldii* (Podocarpineae), expanded, 23.9 μ in diameter. 2, *Cryptomeria japonica* (Taxodineae), expanded, 28.5 μ in diameter, *cf.* 8. 3, *Juniperus mexicana* (Cupressineae), 21 μ in diameter. 4, *Abies concolor*, end view with ventral surface uppermost, 100 μ broad. 5, *Podocarpus dacrydioides*, 45 μ broad. 6, *Ginkgo biloba* (Ginkgoales) ventral view, 28 μ long. 7, *Tsuga canadensis* (Abietineae), 70 μ in diameter. 8, *Cryptomeria japonica*, contracted, *cf.* 2. 9, *Pinus nigra* (Abietineae), end view expanded, 54 μ broad. 10, *Podocarpus elongatus* (Podocarpineae), ventral view, 33 μ broad.

A large tree, California and Oregon.

Pinus inops Ait. (*P. virginiana* Mill.) Jersey pine, Scrub pine. Grains generally broadly elliptical when seen from the dorsal side, the marginal crest prominent over each of the bladders or sometimes more so at four points on the periphery, one on either side of each of the bladders, absent between them; 53.6 μ in diameter. Otherwise as in the type.

A small tree, 30 to 40 ft. high, though occasionally reaching a greater height. New York, Georgia, Alabama, Indiana, and Tennessee. April and May.

Pinus Mugo var. **Mughus** Zenari Swiss mountain pine, Mugho or Knee pine. Grains rather various in size, 45.2 to 51.3 μ in diameter. In dorsal view circular or more or less elongate in outline; marginal ridge most prominent over the bladders, absent between them or sometimes entirely absent. Bladders smaller in proportion to the size of the grain, 26.2 to 28.5 μ. Otherwise as in the type.

A low shrub introduced from Central and Southern Europe but now much cultivated in America. Flowers in May.

Pinus rigida Mill. Pitch pine. Grains uniform in size, 57 to 65 μ in diameter. Cap nearly circular in outline, generally with a marginal crest all around. Bladders with conspicuous bead-like thickenings inside on their proximal walls.

A tree 50 to 60 ft. or occasionally higher. Sandy plains and dry, gravelly uplands. New Brunswick to Georgia, west to southern Ontario, Ohio, West Virginia, Tennessee, and Alabama, the common tree of the pine barrens of Long Island and New Jersey.

Pinus Strobus L. White pine, Weymouth pine (Plate III, Figs. 3, 9 to 11). Grains somewhat various in size and shape, 36.4 to 52 μ in diameter. Cap circular or more often elliptical, elongate transversely. Marginal crests generally best developed over the dorsal roots of the bladders.

A large tree occasionally over 200 ft. in height, Newfoundland to Manitoba, south to Delaware, along the Alleghenies to Georgia and to Illinois and Iowa. Flowers in June.

Pinus sylvestris L. Scotch pine. Grains somewhat various in size, 44.2 to 52 μ in diameter, occasional grains as small as 32 μ in diameter. Cap circular to broadly elliptical, elongate transversely. Marginal crest best developed above the dorsal roots of the bladders.

A large tree, often over 100 ft. in height. Native of Europe and western Asia, frequently cultivated in America.

Pinus excelsa Wall. Himalaya pine. Grains somewhat various, about 54.5 μ in diameter. Bladders proportionately small and somewhat various. Marginal crest present all around but best developed over the dorsal roots of the bladders.

A large tree reaching a height of 150 ft. Native of the Himalayas.

Pinus longifolia Roxb. (*P. Roxburghii* Sarg.) Chir pine. Grains uniform, 52 to 57.2 μ in diameter, mostly about 54.5 μ. Bladders large in proportion to the size of the grain. Marginal crest developed above the dorsal roots of the bladders.

A forest tree reaching 100 ft. in height. Native of the Himalayas. Cultivated in California.

CEDRUS Link CEDAR

Grains rather uniform in size, generally about 65 μ in diameter (62 to 78 μ). Bladders various but generally proportionately much smaller than those of the grains of *Pinus* and always more laterally placed, leaving a broader and longer furrow area between them. Cap circular or slightly elongate transversely, its texture merging gradually with that of the bladders. Marginal crest scarcely or not at all developed.

The grains of *Cedrus* are intermediate in size between those of *Pinus* and *Picea*, and since there is considerable overlapping from both groups it is often difficult to distinguish them when they occur together. When seen in end view, however, the grains of *Cedrus* may generally be recognized by the sweeping curve of the dorsal surface, which is continuous from bladder to bladder over the surface of the cap with little or no interruption at the roots of the bladders.

The genus comprises four very similar evergreen trees of the Mediterranean region and western Himalayas, "perhaps to be regarded as geographical forms of a single species."

Cedrus Deodara Loud. Deodar cedar (Plate III, Fig. 12). Grains as in the generic description and indistinguishable from those of *C. libanitica.*

A tall tree reaching 150 ft. or more. Native of Himalaya. Introduced into California and sparingly elsewhere in the United States.

Cedrus libanitica Link Cedar of Lebanon. Grains as in the generic description and indistinguishable from the preceding species.

A large tree, native of Asia Minor, occasionally planted in America.

PICEA Diets. SPRUCE

Grains similar to those of *Pinus* but larger, 68 to 91 μ in diameter, mostly less than 85 μ. Bladders small in proportion to the size of the grain, concave on their proximal sides unless fully expanded, becoming more and more concave as the grain dries and finally closing over its broad ventral surface. Furrow generally clearly defined as a shallow groove between the bladders. Cap circular in outline, with no trace of marginal crest. Texture of the exine of the cap very fine—finer than that of the grains of *Pinus*, though of similar character.

The spruces include about 37 species of tall, pyramidal trees with thin, scaly bark and sessile, four-sided leaves. Of wide distribution, forming great forests throughout the cooler and temperate regions of the northern hemisphere. Many of them are valuable timber trees.

Picea sitchensis (Bong.) Carr. Sitka spruce. Grains as in the generic description, 70 to 78 μ in diameter.

A large tree reaching a height of over 100 ft. Moist and swampy soils, Alaska to Mendocino County, California.

Picea asperata Mart. (Plate III, Fig. 7). Grains as in the generic description, 83 to 91 μ in diameter. Cap broadly elliptical, elongate transversely.

A rapidly growing tree, reaching a height of 100 ft. Mountains of western China.

Picea canadensis (Mill.) B. S. P. White spruce (Plate III Fig. 4). Grains as in the generic description, 68 to 85 μ in diameter.

A large tree. Newfoundland to Hudson Bay to Alaska to South Dakota to Michigan to northern New York to Maine. April and May.

Picea rubens Sarg. Red spruce (Plate III, Fig. 6). Grains as in the generic description, about 80 μ in diameter.

Newfoundland, northern New York, Minneapolis, and along the higher Alleghenies to Virginia and Georgia. May and June.

Picea Engelmanni (Parry) Englm. Engelmann's spruce. Grains as in the generic description, about 85 μ in diameter.

A large tree. British Columbia southward through the Rocky Mountains to Arizona and on the eastern slopes of the Cascades to Oregon.

ABIES Hill Fir

Grains 78 to 111 μ in diameter, mostly over 90 μ. Exine of the cap very thick and coarsely granular, generally faintly marked with three streaks radiating from a point near its center. Marginal crest absent or only faintly suggested by a few slight undulations near the dorsal roots of the bladders. Boundary of cap generally sharply defined. Exine of the ventral surface smooth or slightly warty. Bladders various but generally small in proportion to the size of the grain and always forming a sharp re-entrant angle with the cap at their dorsal roots.

These grains are generally easily distinguished from all others of the winged-grained Abietineae by their large size; the thick and coarse texture of the cap; and the bladders, which are generally small and frequently globular, having the appearance of being stuck on to the grain. The triradiate streak is a reliable diagnostic character when found, but it is generally very faint and difficult to see and often entirely absent. In all probability the triradiate streak is homologous with the triradiate crest of the fern spores of which it probably represents a vanishing remnant. Among the fern spores it generally consists of three prominent convergent ridges bearing grooves in their crests which serve as lines of dehiscence. In the grains of *Abies* it is merely a streak on the cap, marked by the texture's being a little finer and firmer. As far as I am aware not even a trace of the triradiate crest is found elsewhere among the grains of the conifers, though it does occur well developed among the Magnoliaceae.

The genus comprises nearly 40 species of beautiful evergreen trees in the northern hemisphere as far south as Guatemala, northern Africa, and the Himalayas, but, for the most part, the firs are restricted to cool, humid climates.

Abies concolor Lindl. & Gord. White fir (Plate II, Fig. 4). Grains 85.5 to 97 μ in diameter. Bladders rather small, bulbous, generally about 57 μ in diameter but various in size. Marginal crest slightly developed.   Triradiate crest poorly developed or absent.

A large tree, occasionally reaching a height of 250 ft.   Mountain slopes.   Colorado to New Mexico to Lower California to Oregon.   Common in the great forest belt of the Sierra Nevada where it reaches its best development.

Abies lasiocarpa (Hook.) Nutt. Alpine or Balsam fir.   Grains uniform, 78 to 91 μ in diameter, mostly about 90 μ.   Bladders rather large.   Exine of cap very thick and rough, its texture merging gradually into the thin, smooth exine of the ventral side. Triradiate streak and marginal crests absent.

A tree 75 to 120 ft. high.   Alpine valleys and mountain slopes, southeastern Alaska, British Columbia, and western Alberta, southward to southern Arizona and New Mexico.

Abies magnifica Murr. Red fir (Plate III, Fig. 14).   Grains uniform, 90 to 104 μ in diameter.   Cap smooth except for slight undulations just above the dorsal roots of the bladders, its boundary generally sharply defined.   Triradiate streak faint but present on most grains.   Bladders generally bulbous.

A superb tree 180 to 200 ft. high.   Sierra Nevada, north to Mount Shasta and south to southern Oregon.

Abies grandis Lindl. Lowland fir (Plate III, Fig. 1).   Grains uniform, 78 to 91 μ in diameter, generally about 90 μ.   Exine of cap excessively thick and bumpy, its boundary sharply defined but with no trace of marginal crest.   Triradiate streak generally expressed as a shallow groove.   Bladders generally bulbous.

A forest tree, 40 to 160 feet high.   Low hills or valleys near the sea, Vancouver Island to northern California.

Abies balsamifera (L.) Mill. Balsam fir.   Grains various, some with three and some with four bladders, and in size ranging from 50 to 104 μ in diameter but averaging about 90 μ.   Exine of cap smooth, its boundary sharply defined, and marginal crest absent. Triradiate streak faint or absent.   Bladders generally bulbous.

A small tree attaining a maximum height of 100 ft.   Newfoundland and Labrador to Hudson Bay and Alberta, southward to Massachussetts and Pennsylvania and southward along the Alleghenies; flowers May, June.

Abies venusta (Dougl.) K. Koch   Santa Lucia or Bristlecone fir.   Grains uniform, 83 to 88 μ in diameter.   Exine of cap thick and undulating, its boundary sharply defined, marginal crest

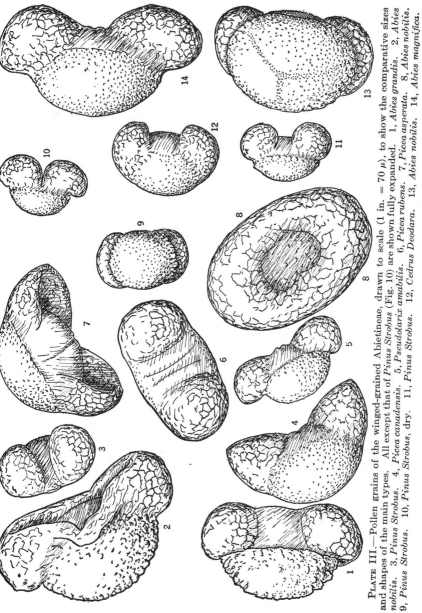

PLATE III.—Pollen grains of the winged-grained Abietineae, drawn to scale (1 in. = 70 μ), to show the comparative sizes and shapes of the main types. All except that of *Pinus Strobus* (Fig. 10) are shown fully expanded. 1, *Abies grandis*. 2, *Abies nobilis*. 3, *Pinus Strobus*. 4, *Picea canadensis*. 5, *Pseudolarix amabilis*. 6, *Picea rubens*. 7, *Picea asperata*. 8, *Abies nobilis*. 9, *Pinus Strobus*. 10, *Pinus Strobus*, dry. 11, *Pinus Strobus*. 12, *Cedrus Deodara*. 13, *Abies nobilis*. 14, *Abies magnifica*.

absent. Triradiate streak generally faint. Bladders small and bulbous.

A tree 30 to 75 ft. high. Found only in the Santa Lucia Mountains, California.

Abies nobilis Lindl. Red fir (Plate III, Figs. 2, 13). Grains uniform, 96 to 109 μ in diameter, generally about 100 μ. Exine of cap thick and rough, its boundary not sharply defined; marginal crests absent. Triradiate streak generally very distinct. Bladders generally more or less fused and often encircling the grain as a single bladder (Plate III, Fig. 8).

A forest tree reaching a height of 150 ft. Washington, Oregon, and northern California, forming extensive forests in the Cascade Mountains.

Pseudolarix amabilis Rehder (*Abies Kaempferi* Lind., *Laricopsis Kaempferi* Kent.) Golden larch, Chinese larch. Grains essentially as in *Pinus*. Cap circular in outline, 51.3 to 57 μ in diameter, marginal ridge absent, texture extremely finely reticulate-granular. Bladders widely divergent, rounded at their extremities, not flattened dorsoventrally.

A tree 120 to 130 ft. high presenting an appearance between the cedar and the larch. Leaves deciduous. Native of China, extensively cultivated in England, United States, and elsewhere. This is the only species of the genus.

Pseudotsuga mucronata (Raf.) Sudw. Douglas fir. Grains approximately spheroidal, without trace of bladders, pore, or furrow, rather uniform in size, 90 to 100 μ in diameter, closely resembling those of *Larix*. Exine thin and quite smooth. When the grain is moistened it swells; the exine generally splits wide open and is frequently thrown completely off. The castoff exines have a tendency to curl tightly inward, showing that they are of an elastic nature. The intine is thick and uniform throughout, of hyaline appearance.

A large tree. Hills and mountains of western United States and Canada, most abundant in western Washington and Oregon.

The genus includes four species of tall, pyramidal trees with thick, deeply furrowed bark and scattered, petiolate leaves. In distribution confined to western North America, southern Japan, southwestern China, and Formosa.

Tsuga canadensis (L.) Carr. Canada hemlock (Plate II, Fig. 7). Grains rather uniform, 62 to 85 (mostly about 64) μ in diameter, thick-lens shaped to almost spheroidal when fully expanded. Exine of one side, presumably the dorsal, thick and heavily reticulate-corrugated, resembling the dorsal surface of *Pinus* and other winged-grained Abietineae. Exine of the ventral side thinner but of similar, though somewhat less coarse, texture, not rupturing easily. Bladders absent. Intine thin, approximately uniform throughout.

As the grain dries the ventral side becomes concave while the dorsal remains convex, the whole grain becoming thereby bowl-shaped. The exine along the margin of the depressed ventral area is occasionally thrown into convolutions larger and somewhat more puffy than elsewhere, suggesting a rudimentary bladder encircling the grain. Morphologically the concavity of the ventral surface corresponds to the furrow of the winged-grained Abietineae, which here, in the absence of protecting bladders, is completely covered with an exine almost as thick and resistant as that of the dorsal surface. Superficially these grains do not resemble those of the winged-grained Abietineae. Yet, in reality, the only difference between them is the absence of bladders in those of *Tsuga* and the necessary corollary, the thickened exine of the ventral surface. Apparently there is in existence today no intermediate form between that of the wingless *Tsuga* grain and the winged form of the Abietineae, but I (Wodehouse, 1933) have described a fossil species (*Tsuga viridiflumi-nipites*) from the Eocene, which has rudimentary bladders encircling the whole grain and a fairly well-developed furrow, thus presenting a form which seems to me to stand intermediate between that of the present species and those of the other Abietineae. Also, Kirchheimer (1934) has shown many fossil *Tsuga* pollen grains from the Tertiary which seem to bear rudimentary bladders. The fossil evidence is, therefore, at least suggestive that the present form of *Tsuga* pollen grain is derived from a winged ancestral form through the suppression of the bladders.

A large forest tree. Nova Scotia to Minnesota to Delaware to Alabama to Michigan to Wisconsin. Flowers April and May. The genus includes 14 species and many horticultural varieties, native in temperate regions of North America and the eastern Himalayas to Japan and Formosa. Not known to cause hayfever.

LARIX Adans. LARCH

Grains spheroidal, various in size, ranging in the different species from 62.5 to 102 μ in diameter, closely resembling those of *Pseudotsuga mucronata*. Exine thin, generally rupturing and frequently cast off completely when the grains are moistened; texture smooth, with no trace of the flecks. Intine thick and hyaline but less thick than in the grains of *Juniperus*. Furrow, pores, and bladders entirely absent.

About 10 species of tall, pyramidal trees with deciduous leaves. Of wide distribution over northern and mountainous regions of the Northern Hemisphere.

Larix laricina (Du Roi) K. Koch. (*L. americana* Michx.) Tamarack, American larch. Grains spheroidal, rather uniform in size, 62.7 to 80 μ in diameter. Otherwise as in the generic description.

A large forest tree. Swamps. Labrador, to Massachusetts, to Pennsylvania, to Illinois, Saskatchewan to Alaska. March and April.

Larix Lyallii Parl. Lyall's larch. Grains spheroidal, somewhat various in size, 85.5 to 102 μ in diameter, otherwise as in the generic description. A small tree.

Taxodium distichum (L.) L. C. Rich. Bald cypress. Grains more or less spheroidal or somewhat irregular in shape when moistened, rather uniform in size, 27.4 to 31.4 μ in diameter, similar to those of *Juniperus* except that the exine is slightly rougher, and it is provided with a single germ pore. This consists of a conical papilla similar to but much less prominent than that of *Cryptomeria* and not bent at the tip. Intine hyaline and thick, though less so than in the grains of *Juniperus*, its inner boundary less angular in optical section.

A large tree in swamps and along rivers. Southeastern United States. March and April.

The genus includes only three species, large spreading trees of swampy places of the southeastern United States and Mexico. In Miocene and Pliocene times the taxodiums were widely distributed throughout North America and Europe. For a discussion of this "remnant of a northern fossil type" see Small (1931).

Cryptomeria japonica D. Don Japanese cedar, Sugi (Plate II, Figs. 2, 8) type. Grains spheroidal, somewhat various in size,

23.9 to 31.9 μ in diameter, provided with a single germ pore, consisting of a finger-like projection standing straight up off its surface and slightly bent at the top. Exine thin and flecked with rather closely packed granules of darkly staining material. Intine thick, as in the grains of *Juniperus*.

This grain resembles that of *Sequoia* but may be distinguished from it by its longer and less bent finger-like germinal papilla and its smaller size.

A large tree native of Japan and possibly southwest China. Frequently cultivated, particularly in its smaller varieties. This is the only species of the genus living at the present time, though the genus is known to have had a number of different species of wide distribution in Permian and Triassic times. *Cryptomeria* is one of the finest trees in Japan, and that country owes much of the beauty of its groves and gardens to it.

SEQUOIA Endl. Redwood

Grains approximately spheroidal in shape, somewhat various in size, 28.5 to 41 μ in diameter. The exine is thin and flecked and the intine thick and hyaline, as in the grain *Juniperus*, but unlike the latter it is provided with a single conspicuous germ pore. This consists of a conical projection rising abruptly from the surface and bent sharply to one side, suggesting in appearance the handle of a curling stone. This grain differs from that of *Cryptomeria* (q.v.) only in its slightly larger size and the bent shape of its germinal papilla.

The Sequoias are among the tallest, if not the tallest, trees in existence. The genus contains only the two following living species, confined in distribution to the coast of California and Oregon and the mountains of California; but it is known to have had a distribution with several species over most of the Northern Hemisphere in Cretaceous and Tertiary times.

Sequoia sempervirens (Lamb.) Endl. Redwood. Grains as in the generic description.

A large tree attaining a height of 340 ft., of limited distribution in California and southern Oregon.

Sequoia gigantea Torr. California bigtree. Grains as in the generic description. Indistinguishable from those of *S. sempervirens*.

A large tree, perhaps the largest in the world, exists naturally only in restricted areas of California but now cultivated in southern and western Europe.

Glyptostrobus heterophyllus Endl. Canton water pine, Chinese deciduous cypress. Grains similar to those of *Cryptomeria* and *Sequoia* but with a much smaller germinal papilla, which is pointed and curved sharply to one side, suggesting a small rose thorn; uniform in size, 29.6 to 30.8 μ in diameter, spheroidal when moist and expanded. When the grains dry the region surrounding the papilla becomes dipped in, the papilla remaining erect in the middle of the bowl-like depression. The exine is thin, uniform in thickness throughout, and lightly flecked with a few scattered granules. Intine thick, swelling enormously when made wet and completely throwing off the exine after the fashion of the grains of *Juniperus*, which suggests that the papilla is a nonfunctional vestige of the germ pore.

Many of the grains (about 20 per cent) are firmly united in tetrads in the tetrahedral arrangement. I am not prepared to say whether or not this is a characteristic inherent in the species or only of the specimen under observation, but it is of the utmost interest. The grains so united are in no way modified by their union, each one behaving quite independently of its associates. They are always joined by their dorsal surfaces, that is to say, each with its papilla facing outward, and when they dry each becomes cupped on its outer or ventral surface, a condition strikingly similar to that of the grains of *Drimys* (q.v.). This is a primitive type of tetrad, even more so than that of *Drimys*, for the association is looser and does not involve all the pollen. It stands in sharp contrast to the tetrads of the Droseraceae pollen, for example, in which the members of the group are profoundly modified by their association with each other, the four grains functioning together in some ways as an individual.

Glyptostrobus is a small shrub, 8 to 10 ft. high, native of China, growing in moist places in the neighborhood of Canton and along the banks of the river Whampo; occasionally cultivated in Europe. There is but a single species of the genus. Though now of restricted distribution, the fossil record shows that it once had a wider distribution similar to that of *Taxodium* and *Sequoia*. *Glyptostrobus* is closely related to *Taxodium*, with which it is often confused and sometimes called *Taxodium heterophyllum* Brong., *T. Distichum imbricarium* Sarg., and *T. sinense* Forbes, but it may easily be distinguished from *Taxodium* by its pear-shaped, staminate cones borne on long stalks. (Dallimore and Jackson, 1923, page 230; Veitch, 1881, page 217; and Masters, 1900.)

Cunninghamia sinensis R. Br. China fir. Grains approximately spheroidal, somewhat various in size, ranging from 34.2 to 40 μ in diameter. Exine thin and loosely flecked with deeply staining granules. Germ pore a minute papilla, frequently not apparent. Intine thick.

The China fir is a large evergreen tree native of China, frequently cultivated in the United States and elsewhere. The genus includes but a single other species, the Formosa fir (*C. Konishii*), occasionally cultivated in California and Florida.

Thuja occidentalis L. White cedar, Arborvitae. Grains spheroidal, 25 to 28.5 μ in diameter. Exine thin, intine thick. Germ pore entirely absent. These grains are essentially the same as those of *Juniperus* except that the exine is less flecked with surface granules.

A conical tree of medium size with fragrant foliage. Native of northeastern United States and Canada. Much cultivated elsewhere. Flowers March and April. Not believed to cause hayfever.

The genus includes about five species of resinous aromatic trees with pyramidal heads. In northeastern and northwestern America, Japan, Korea, and northern China. The Chinese arborvitae, *T. orientalis*, in many varieties is much cultivated in America together with several native species.

Libocedrus decurrens Torr. Incense cedar. Grains spheroidal, rather uniform in size, 29.6 to 36.5 μ in diameter. Exine thin and flecked as in the grains of *Juniperus*. Pore entirely absent. Intine thick.

A large tree 100 to 200 ft. high. Mountains and canyons, Oregon to Lower California, western Nevada. Cultivated elsewhere.

The genus includes about eight species of tall, resinous, aromatic trees with scaly bark. In western North America and western South America from Chile to Patagonia, New Zealand, New Caledonia, New Guinea, Formosa, and southwestern China.

Cupressus macrocarpa Hartw. Monterey cypress. Grains spherical, various in size, 23.1 to 27.4 μ in diameter. Exine thin, flecked with a few irregularly arranged surface granules. Furrow entirely absent. Intine thick and hyaline. This grain is essentially the same as that of *Juniperus,* except that the surface of the exine is less granular, and the intine less thick.

A medium-sized tree of restricted distribution, occupying a narrow belt on the two promontories Cypress Point and Point Lobos, a few miles south of Monterey, California.

The genus includes about 12 species of trees and shrubs with shreddy bark and aromatic foliage, widely distributed in the warmer parts of the world. About nine species are cultivated in the United States.

Chamaecyparis thyoides (L.) B. S. P. Southern white cedar, Swamp juniper. Grains with surface prominently flecked with granules, otherwise indistinguishable from the preceding species.

A large tree in swamps, southern Maine to Florida, westward to Mississippi. April and May. Occasionally planted as an ornamental tree in the eastern United States and Europe.

The genus comprises about six species of tall, resinous, pyramidal trees, in distribution confined to the Atlantic and Pacific coastal regions of North America and in Japan and Formosa. The Japanese retinosporas, *Chamaecyparis obtusa* Endl. and *C. pisifera* Endl. are familiar in cultivation in all temperate regions.

JUNIPERUS (Tourn.) L. JUNIPER

Grains almost perfectly spheroidal when moist and rather uniform in size, 20.5 to 32 μ in diameter. The exine is always exceedingly thin and transparent, easily ruptured, and generally cast off completely when the grains expand upon being made wet. The entire surface of the exine is covered evenly with minute, deeply staining flecks. These show no recognizable pattern in their arrangement. The intine is extremely thick, constituting more than half of the bulk of the grain, its inner boundary more or less angular, sometimes appearing star-shaped in optical section. Furrows, pores, and bladders entirely absent. When the grains dry and shrink they collapse irregularly without the formation of a predetermined furrow.

The genus comprises about 35 species widely scattered over the northern hemisphere. About eight are native of North America; and several others, *e.g.*, *J. Sabina* L., and *J. chinensis*, have been introduced from the Old World.

Juniperus mexicana Spreng. (*J. sabinoides* Nee.) Mountain cedar, Mexican cedar, Rock cedar (Plate II, Fig. 3) type. Grains when moist, but with the intine still intact, spheroidal, 20.5 to 22.8 μ in diameter. When dry somewhat crumpled and 18.2 to 21.6 μ in diameter.

A small to medium-sized tree; on the limestone hills of western and southern Texas and southward along mountain ranges into Mexico. Flowers in January, producing enormous quantities of pollen, which is known to cause much winter hayfever in and about Austin, Texas (Key, 1918).

Juniperus virginiana L. Red cedar, Savin. Grains as in the type. 21.6 to 25.1 μ in diameter when moist.

A shrub or tree 50 ft. or more high with a pyramidal head. Dry hills or deep swamps, eastern United States. Flowers in March and April shedding relatively little pollen. Not known to cause hayfever.

Juniperus communis L. Common juniper. Grains as in the type, rather uniform in size. In the moistened condition measuring 26.2 to 31.9 μ in diameter. Can be distinguished from those of the two preceding species by their slightly larger size.

A low shrub widely distributed almost throughout North America and in Europe. Flowers in March and April shedding relatively little pollen, not known to cause hayfever. The grains of this species are figured by Meinke (1927, page 394) and stated to be 25 to 35 μ in diameter.

Callitris Endlecherii Parlat. Grains essentially as in *Juniperus*, 18.2 to 21.6 μ in diameter. The flecks on the surface irregularly distributed and inclined to be clumped, numerous or few.

A large tree native of Australia. The genus contains about 15 species of valuable timber trees, the cypress pines, native of Australia and Africa.

PODOCARPUS L'Hér.

Grains lens-shaped or more or less spheroidal when expanded but with sharply differentiated dorsal and ventral surfaces; provided with two or three well-defined bladders or with bladdery

projections.   In size they range from 23.1 to 45.6 μ in diameter.
The upper limit is attained only in *P. dacrydioides*, which is also
aberrant in many other characters and decidedly exceptional
in the genus.   For this reason it is not included in the present
definition but will be treated separately (see page 279).   Apart
from this species, their range in size does not exceed 38.8 μ in
diameter.

Viewed from the dorsal surface the cap is more or less circular,
slightly quadrangular or ellipsoidal.   The exine of the central
region of the cap is nearly smooth or slightly granular but toward
the margin becomes more granular and at the dorsal roots of the
bladders is thrown into more or less pronounced convolutions.

The furrow is generally long, reaching almost, or quite, from
end to end of the grain, and its boundaries are always sharply
delineated by an abrupt change in texture and a more or less
pronounced thickening along its rim.   Occasionally, however, the
furrow may be short-elliptical or almost circular, but even under
these conditions its margin is sharply defined.

The bladders are various in the different species.   They are
usually large and spreading, but tend to be weak and flaccid.
They are smooth of texture on their outer surface but are conspicuously marked inside by reticulate thickenings.   At their
dorsal roots their texture merges with that of the cap at its
margin.   At their ventral roots they are attached to the rim
of the furrow on either side throughout its entire length, and
sometimes they arch out, frill-like, beyond the furrow at both its
ends.   A definite correlation appears to exist between the shape
of the furrow and the form of the bladders.   When the furrow
is long and narrow there are always two bladders, one on each
side, but when it is broad and short the bladders may be more or
less fused; occasionally this is carried to such an extent that they
encircle the grain as a single, continuous frill, recalling, in striking
fashion, the grains of *Stephanospermum caryoides* (q.v.).

The grains of *Podocarpus* differ from the winged grains of the
Abietineae in their smaller size, their sharply delineated germinal
furrow, the flaccid nature and extreme variability of the bladders
among the different species.

From the above discussion have been omitted the grains of
P. dacrydioides which have always three bladders, because
inclusion would require an undue extension of the limits of the

generic description. According to the classification of R. Pilger (1903) the species of *Podocarpus* fall naturally into the five sections (1) Dacrycarpus, with 3 species, one of which is *P. dacrydioides;* (2) Microcarpus, with but a single species; (3) Nageia, with 5 species, of which *P. nagi* is here included; (4) Stachycarpus, with 10 species, of which *P. gracilior* is here included; and (5) Eupodocarpus, including the remaining 41 species, all the more typical members of the genus. It therefore seems possible that the marked differences exhibited by *P. dacrydioides*, including the possession of three bladders, may be of sectional value.

A genus of about 62 species of trees and shrubs of wide distribution, particularly in the southern hemisphere, and comprising some of the most valuable timber trees in Australia, New Zealand, Tasmania, East Indies, Japan, South Africa, West Indies, and tropical and subtropical America.

Podocarpus elongatus L'Hér. (*Taxus elongata* Ait.) Common or Outeniqua yellowwood (Plate II, Fig. 10) type. Grains somewhat various in size, but the smaller are apparently abortive; provided with two bladders; normal grains 29.6 to 33.1 μ in diameter. When seen in end view in the moist condition, the optical section of the grain is four-sided, presenting a long, arched dorsal side, two sharply convergent lateral sides which bear the bladders, and a short ventral side which is generally more or less concave, representing a transverse section of the furrow. The bladders are nearly as large as the body of the grain, generally appearing fully expanded, rounded, and directed as much ventrally as laterally. When seen in dorsal view the cap is more or less circular or squarish in outline, with one of its diagonals directed lengthwise or furrow-wise and the other crosswise. The texture of the cap is quite smooth in the central region, becoming granular toward its margin and thrown into slight convolutions at the dorsal roots of the bladders. These convolutions merge into the more open formation of the texture of the bladders, forming the characteristic internal reticulate thickenings.

The furrow is long, extending from end to end of the grain, quite smooth and without markings of any kind. Its two margins are sharply defined by slight thickenings which bound the furrow as its rim and also serve as the ventral roots of the bladders. These extend the full length of the furrow but do not project beyond its ends.

A fairly tall tree of South Africa, sometimes attaining a height of 75 ft. It is the largest, most abundant, and most useful timber tree of Cape Colony.

Podocarpus gracilior Pilger. Grains uniform in size and shape, provided with two large bladders, each nearly as large as the body of the grain; about 27.4 μ in diameter exclusive of the bladders. When seen in dorsal view the cap is inclined to be rhomboidal in outline, elongate transversely to the furrow, *i.e.*, broader than long. The central part of the cap is rather coarsely granular, but it is more coarsely and more reticulate-granular toward its margin and is here thrown into slight convolutions where it merges into the dorsal roots of the bladders. Furrow long, reaching almost completely from end to end of the grain, usually rather deep, and flanked on either side by slight ridges which serve as the ventral roots of the bladders. The latter are generally more or less collapsed and variously folded when the grains are mounted for examination.

A tree 45 to 60 ft. high, of rather wide distribution in African forests and steppes. Flowers in August.

Podocarpus montanus (Willd.) Lodd. (*P. taxifolius* H. B. & K., *Taxus montana* Willd.). Grains rather uniform in size and shape, 29.6 to 33.1 μ in diameter, provided with two large bladders. As seen in side view the grains are approximately lens-shaped, with the bladders on the ventral surface directed as much ventrally as laterally. Seen in dorsal view the cap is round or somewhat ellipsoidal, with its major axis transverse. The texture of the cap is finely but distinctly granular, except toward the roots of the bladders, where it is thrown into very slight convolutions which merge into the internal thickenings of the bladder membranes. The furrow is long and broad, reaching from end to end of the grain and, in the moistened condition, gapes widely open. Its rim is marked on either side by slightly thickened ridges to which the ventral roots of the bladders are attached. From the two ends of the furrow the bladders arch out a little beyond the body of the grain.

A small tree or spreading shrub resembling *Taxus baccata.* Andes of Peru, Colombia, Venezuela, Costa Rica.

Podocarpus macrophyllus D. Don. (*Taxus macrophylla* Thunb.) Kämpfer, Kusamaki. Grains generally uniform in size, 27.5 to 32 μ in diameter, similar to the type. Bladders two, each about the size of the body of the grain or a little smaller. The cap is approximately circular in outline. Its texture is coarsely granular, more so toward its rim and thrown into marked convolutions at the dorsal roots of the bladders. The furrow is well defined, with a slightly thickened rim to which the ventral roots of the bladders are attached, and they project out in sweeping arches considerably beyond the ends of the furrow.

The above description serves for the pollen of most trees of this species. Occasionally, however, specimens are found *e.g.*, one collected in the gardens of Cambridge University in 1841, now in the herbarium of the New York Botanical Garden ('*ex Herb. Gray*'), in which the grains are various in size and shape, with by far the majority obviously abortive and empty. The bladders show an enormous variation in their size and shape, and this is definitely related to the shape of the furrow, which is also extremely various. The furrow may be long, reaching from end to end of the grain, in which case the grain may be regarded as normal and resembles the type. In such cases it is flanked by two bladders, one on either side. Or the furrow may be broadly elliptical, in which case the bladders are more or less fused at one or both of their ends (Fig. 79*a*). Or the furrow may be circular, in which case the bladders are completely fused and encircle the grain as an unbroken frill. Always the furrow presents a slightly thickened margin to which the ventral roots of the bladders are attached.

The abortive grains, having no cell contents, are greatly contracted, and the furrow generally drawn up into a short spout with a funnel-like orifice (Fig. 79*b*), as if its thickened rim behaved like a stretched elastic band and, in the absence of turgor to keep it open, contracted, drawing the rim of the furrow tightly together like the neck of a bag with a string passed around it.

A small tree, 25 to 50 ft. high, native of Japan. It occurs in several varieties some of which are cultivated. The numerous abnormal and abortive grains found in some of the forms, such as the Cambridge University specimen, suggest that the trees are of hybrid origin.

Podocarpus Nakii Hayota.   Grains similar to the type, uniform in size, about 34.2 μ long and 28.5 broad, exclusive of the bladders.   Bladders always two, appearing to be inflated and more or less globular, directed as much ventrally as laterally, about 50 per cent larger than the body of the grain but not extending beyond the ends of the furrow.   Cap rhomboidal, with its long diagonal directed furrow-wise; nearly flat, texture quite smooth but thrown into slight convolutions at the dorsal roots of the bladders.   In side view the grain simulates the appearance of a bivalved mollusk.

A small tree in the island of Formosa.

Podocarpus Nagi (Thunb.) Pilger.   Grains essentially as in *P. Nakii*, except that the surface of the cap is finely pitted all over, 34.2 by 28.5 μ.

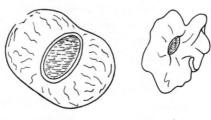

a   b

Fig. 79.—Pollen grains of *Podocarpus macrophyllus; a*, normal, *b*, abortive.

A tall tree reaching a height of 75 ft. with broad-leaved foliage on pendant branches.   Native of northern Japan, frequently cultivated elsewhere.

Podocarpus neriifolius D. Don Oleander-leaved podocarp, Kinarch or Kiputri.   Grains uniform, 27.5 to 32 μ in diameter. Similar to the type.   Bladders always two, large and globular, about equal in size to the body of the grain, the ventral roots of the bladders attached along the rim of the furrow and extending in sweeping curves beyond it at both ends.   Cap circular or slightly elongate transversely; texture coarsely reticulate-granular especially toward the margin, and thrown into conspicuous convolutions at the dorsal roots of the bladders.   Furrows sharply defined and with a thickened rim.

A medium-sized tree, native of the East Indies, China, and Japan, occasionally cultivated elsewhere.

Podocarpus coriaceus Rich.   Grains rather uniform in size and shape, 30 to 33 μ in diameter.   The body of the grain is more or less lens-shaped when moist. As seen in dorsal view the cap is elliptical, nearly smooth in its central region but toward the margin thrown into deep convolutions which reach their greatest development at the dorsal roots of the bladders. Furrow long, reaching almost the entire length of the grain, sharply defined, with a thickened rim. The bladders are thin and filmy, variously collapsed and folded. When fully expanded each extends laterally a distance equal to or greater than the diameter of the grain proper; they also extend in frill-like folds beyond the length of the furrow at both of its ends.

A small tree with spreading branches. Native of the West Indies, Venezuela, and Colombia.

Podocarpus dacrydioides Rich. Kahika, Kahikatea, White pine (Plate II, Fig. 5). Grains approximately spheroidal or deeply double convex, uniform in size, 44.5 to 45.6 μ in diameter, provided with *three* well-developed bladders originating mostly on the ventral surface. The exine of the dorsal side or cap is coarsely granular especially toward its margin, and where it merges into the dorsal roots of the bladders it is coarsely reticulate-granular and thrown into small ridges or folds. Bladders smooth and thin, with reticulate thickenings on the inner surface, as in the grains of *Pinus* but less developed; consequently, the bladders are less rigid. They are quite small and flattened dorsoventrally, often crumpled or partly collapsed, rounded at their extremities.

When the grains are unexpanded the ventral surface tends to be invaginated and the three bladders pressed together, leaving only a small triangular opening between them; but when they are expanded the ventral surface becomes evaginated and the three bladders diverge, leaving exposed a large triangular area of the ventral surface between them. This is morphologically the furrow and is seen to be covered by an exceedingly thin membrane devoid of markings of any kind. This grain differs from those of the other members of the genus in the lack of definition and triangular shape of its germinal furrow, its large size, and its possession of three bladders.

A tall timber tree, reaching 150 ft. in height, with fine, drooping branchlets and foliage resembling that of *Cupressus*. New Zealand.

Dacrydium laxifolium Hook. Loose-leaved Dacrydium, Pigmy pine. Grains similar to the *Podocarpus* type, various in

size, many dwarfs.   Normal grains 44 to 48 μ in diameter, provided with two large bladders.   As seen in end view, when the
grains are moist, their optical section is more or less lens-shaped
in outline, with the two bladders borne on the ventral surface and
projecting ventrally and laterally from it.   The bladders are
fully as large as the body of the grains, generally flaccid or
scarcely inflated; their membranes are thin but provided with
internal reticulate thickenings, as in the grains of *Podocarpus*.

As seen in dorsal view the cap is uniformly reticulate-granular.
At the dorsal roots of the bladders its texture merges rather
abruptly into that of the bladders.   The furrow is long, extending
the whole length of the grain and gaping widely open.   Its rim

FIG. 80.—Pollen
grain of *Dacrydium
Gibbsiae*,   transverse
optical section, fully
expanded.

is distinctly thickened and serves for the
attachment of the ventral roots of the bladders, the latter arching out considerably
beyond the ends of the furrow.

A small, prostrate shrub, abundant in New
Zealand.

Dacrydium Gibbsiae Stapf. (Fig. 80).
Grains uniform in size and shape; when moist
and expanded 36.5 μ in diameter, spheroidal
or more or less lens-shaped, more flattened
on the dorsal than on the ventral surface.

Bladders always two but almost rudi-
mentary, scarcely or not at all inflated.   Cap circular in
outline, coarsely reticulate-granular, and at the two sides
thrown into conspicuous convolutions which merge into the two
little puffs which represent the bladders.   Furrow short, not
clearly defined and not surrounded by a thickened rim.

A tree reaching a height of 60 ft. characteristic of the forest
and scrub areas of Mount Kinabalu, British North Borneo.

Pherosphaera Fitzgeraldi, F. Muell.   (*Dacrydium Fitzgeraldi*,
F. Muell.)   (Plate II, Fig. 1).   Grains uniform in size and shape,
23.4 to 23.9 μ in diameter; provided with three bladders, except
for some irregular grains which may exhibit various degrees of
fusion between two or all of the bladders and some giants which
have four or five bladders; but these are relatively few and must
be regarded as abnormal.

Normal grains are deeply lens-shaped, with the bladders
originating almost wholly from the ventral surface and directed

more ventrally than laterally. As seen in dorsal view the cap is circular. The exine is thick and finely but distinctly granular throughout. Toward the margin of the disk between the roots of the bladders it is slightly thicker and slightly more granular. Unlike the grain of *Podocarpus* the texture of the cap does not merge gradually into that of the bladders; the transition is abrupt, as it also is from the dorsal to the ventral surface in the regions between the bladders. There is no marginal ridge. The bladders are smooth on the outside and lack the internal reticulate thickenings characteristic of the grains of *Podocarpus* but possess instead a few disconnected, speck-like internal thickenings. In shape the bladders are globular, flattened only on the side, by which they are joined to the body of the grain.

These grains differ from those of *Podocarpus dacrydioides*, which also consistently have three bladders, and from *Dacrydium laxifolium*, in their much smaller size; in their globular form and the exclusively ventral origin of their bladders, which lack internal reticulate thickenings; and in the abrupt transition of the texture of the disk to that of the bladders.

A fairly large number of atypical grains are found. These are of three kinds: (*a*) normal except for what appears to be an additional bladder, rudimentary in character, centrally placed on the ventral surface between the three normal bladders; (*b*) with four marginal bladders in place of the usual three and with a fifth rudimentary bladder centrally placed between them; (*c*) with a single ring-like bladder—as if the three marginal ones had completely fused—surrounding a central rudimentary bladder.

A low prostrate shrub of limited distribution in the Blue Mountains of New South Wales, where it is said to occur at the base of most of the chief waterfalls. An interesting photograph of a plant in such a habitat is shown by Baker and Smith (1910).

Besides the present species there is one other, *P. Hookeriana*, restricted to alpine moors in Tasmania. Some doubt has existed as to the proper relationship of *Pherosphaera* to the other Podocarpineae. It was originally associated with *Dacrydium* but was separated by Archer (Groom, 1916). Pilger (1903), in his monograph on the Taxales, regards it as a separate subfamily. According to Saxton (1930), the pollen grains of *Pherosphaera* do not have the prothallial cells which characterize the Podocarpineae, and this is regarded as a strong argument in favor of removing it from the Podocarpineae altogether; but he goes on to say, "On the other hand, the winged pollen is precisely like that of *Microcachrys* and the solitary ovule per scale is also characteristic of the Podocarpaceae." Moreover, he shows that the roots of both species of *Pherosphaera* possess root tubercles apparently caused by some nitrogen-fixing symbiont, and the fact that this character is shared by all other Podocarpineae and is absent elsewhere among the Coniferales "strongly supports the view that *Pherosphaera* should remain in the Podocarpineae," but in consideration of its other peculiarities "the retention of Pilger's subfamily Pherosphaeroideae within the Podocarpaceae to include *Pherosphaera* alone seems justified." I feel that the striking difference between the pollen grains of *Pherosphaera* and those of *Dacrydium* and all the other Podocarpineae, which I have seen, is likewise a strong argument in favor of the isolated position of this genus within the Podocarpineae.

TORREYA Arn. TORREYA

Grains similar to those of *Taxodium* (Fig. 77); somewhat irregular in shape, tending to be angular as if deformed by pressure against their neighbors in the anther, 28.5 to 30 μ in diameter, without bladders but provided with an evident, though greatly reduced germinal furrow, pore-like in form. Exine thin, marked with closely packed flecks over its entire surface including the furrow. Intine thick with its inner boundary angular in optical section.

This form of grain resembles that of *Juniperus*, except in its possession of a rudimentary furrow. This is merely a slight promontory covered by extremely thin exine, slightly more prominent than in the grains of *Taxodium distichum* but much less so than in those of *Sequoia* and *Cryptomeria*.

The genus comprises four species of medium- or small-sized trees, with drupaceous fruits. In distribution they are now confined to Florida, Georgia, western California, Japan, and central and northern China.

Torreya nucifera Sieb. & Zucc. (*Tumion nuciferum* Greene) Kaja. Grains as in the generic description.

A small tree, 20 to 30 ft high. Native of Japan and, in its variety *grandis*, of southeastern China. Occasionally cultivated in the eastern United States.

Torreya taxifolia Arn. (*Tumion taxifolium* Greene) Stinking cedar, Torreya. Grains as in the generic description.

A medium-sized tree of local distribution in Florida and Georgia but occasionally planted elsewhere.

Taxus brevifolia Nutt. Western yew. Grains of the *Juniperus* type. More or less spheroidal or somewhat angular in outline, 23.9 to 26.8 μ in diameter. Exine thin and flecked throughout with closely packed granules. Intine thick but less so—and its internal boundary less angular—than in the grains of *Juniperus*.

There is no well marked germinal pore or furrow, but generally there may be found a slightly bulging area where the exine is visibly thinner than over the rest of the grain. It is probable that this should be regarded as a vestige of the furrow. This grain differs from that of *Torreya* only in the weaker development of its germinal furrow.

A medium-sized tree of moist places, southern Alaska to western Montana to California. The genus includes about seven species of trees and shrubs of wide distribution throughout the Northern Hemisphere. *Taxus baccata* L., *T. cuspidata* Sieb. & Zucc. and *T. canadensis* Marsh. are much cultivated.

GNETALES

The order Gnetales includes only the three genera *Welwitschia*, *Ephedra*, and *Gnetum*. Until more evidence is brought to bear on the subject of their relationships it is perhaps better to regard the group only as one of convenience. All three genera combine certain characters of both angiosperms and gymnosperms, and they were at one time regarded as a transition group between the Coniferales and the angiosperms. Such a view, however, has been discredited, and the Gnetales are now, at best, cited only as indicating the sort of path that the angiosperms might have traversed in emerging from the gymnosperms.

Relationships Uncertain.—After making the examinations of the pollen of the Gnetales which are presented here, the conditions found seemed so perplexing yet so suggestive that I was curious to see to what conclusion great thinkers in the phylogeny of the gymnosperms had come regarding the Gnetales, so I turned to the memorable discussion, "The Origin of the Gymnosperms and the Seed Habit," by John M. Coulter (1898). Here he says:

From this discussion I wish to exclude the Gnetales . . . They are
such dissimilar fragments, living in such extreme conditions, that their
origin is totally obscure. In some respects they are more like cycads
than conifer-like, but in most respects they are so unlike both that a
separate origin seems possible. It may even be that the three genera
belong to groups of independent origin.

This passage, in denying any conviction, suggests a great deal
regarding the relationships of the Gnetales. In his later works
Coulter tended a little more toward a conviction of the existence
of some relationship between the three genera but, as far as I am
aware, did not greatly modify his original viewpoint. For a
more complete discussion of the Gnetales see Pearson (1929).
The evidence of the morphology of their pollen grains leaves us
in much the same quandary as the evidence from other sources
regarding their origin but suggests a strong probability of a
relationship between *Welwitschia* and *Ephedra*. On the other
hand, it militates decidedly against any connection between
these two genera and *Gnetum*. The monocolpate grain of
Welwitschia with its vanishing furrow might easily have been
derived from the progenitors of the cycads but, in its acquisition
of a number of longitudinal grooves, while pointing toward the
grain of *Ephedra*, offers no possibility of leading on toward any
known angiospermous form of grain. It might with propriety
be argued that such a grain as that of *Welwitschia* could have
been derived from any one-furrowed form, for example, those
found among the monocotyledons and primitive dicotyledons—
and indeed such a possibility must not be overlooked. We have
seen, however, that there has been an almost universal tendency
among the pollen grains of all the races of plants which have
presumably arisen from the pteridosperms to modify, protect, or
eliminate the wide-open furrow which they inherited from their
remote ancestors, each in its own way; and the forms of the grains
of *Welwitschia* and of *Ephedra* seem to present just another way
in which this is done, that of *Ephedra* having proceeded a little
farther along the same path as that of *Welwitschia*. The
spheroidal echinate grain of *Gnetum*, on the other hand, stands
quite apart from these two and appears to have no connection
with the gymnosperms. It is obviously reduced. In its thin
exine and thick intine it finds a parallel in the form of the grain of
Juniperus, among the Coniferales. But this means little, because

the same condition occurs again in the grains of both dicotyledons and monocotyledons. Moreover, the possession of spines on pollen grains is rare among the gymnosperms but is a character that is pre-eminently associated with insect pollination among the angiosperms. The possession of spines in the reduced form in which they occur in the grains of *Gnetum* makes it seem improbable that this grain is derived from a gymnospermous ancestor, unless by a most indirect route, but suggests, instead, that *Gnetum* may be a reduced angiosperm.

Since the relationships of the Gnetales, both with other plant phyla and with each other, are so poorly established, any group description of their pollen-grain forms might be more misleading than valuable. Accordingly, the grains of the three genera are here treated separately. The following key, however, serves to bring out the similarities and differences between them:

KEY TO THE SPECIES

I. Grains ellipsoidal in shape, marked by 5 to 25 longitudinal ridges. Spines absent.
    A. With a single germinal furrow with slight harmomegathic function. Ridges 19 to 20, low, not sharp-crested. 51 to 57 μ long.   Welwitschia mirabilis
    B. Without a permanent germinal furrow. Ridges 5 to 15.
        1. Ridges 11 to 15, low; hyaline lines in the grooves nearly straight and unbranched or absent. 35 to 40 μ long.
        Ridges about 15; hyaline lines present.   Ephedra foliata
        Ridges about 11; hyaline lines faint or absent.   Ephedra altissima var. algerica
        2. Ridges 5 to 8, high and sharp-crested, the grooves between them marked by zigzag, branching, hyaline lines. 44.5 to 54.7 μ long.   Ephedra glauca
                                         Ephedra intermedia
                                       Ephedra equisetina
                                       Ephedra viridis

II. Grains tending to be spheroidal but generally more or less irregular. Furrows, pores, and grooves absent. Exine provided with small or vestigial spines.
    A. Spines conical and sharp-pointed. 16 to 18 μ in diameter.   Gnetum leptostachyum
                                         Gnetum neglectum

B. Spines vestigial—too small to exhibit recognizable shape. 11.5 to 18.7 μ in diameter.

   1. 14 to 18 μ in diameter.   Gnetum scandens
                                        Gnetum indicum
                                        Gnetum Gnemon

   2. 11.9 to 13.7 μ in diameter, spine vestiges
      scarcely visible.   Gnetum Rumphianum

Welwitschia mirabilis Hook. f, Tumbo, Kharoub, Chories (Fig. 82; Plate IV, Fig. 2). Grains ellipsoidal, monocolpate, uniform in size, when moist measuring about 51 to 57 μ in length and 29.5 to 32 μ in width. Exine of perfectly smooth texture, thick and rigid, but marked by 19 to 20 longitudinal ridges and grooves, the former low, rounded on top, and uniform, and the latter without the hyaline streaks which characterize the grains of most species of *Ephedra*.

When the grains dry they contract in width, the lateral contraction inducing an increase in length, so that in this condition they measure about 63 by 27 μ. The single germinal furrow is long, reaching from end to end of the grain; when expanded it is broad and shallow, with its floor only slightly depressed below the general surface, and with rounded ends and nearly parallel sides. The closure that takes place is not at all complete, much less so than in the grains of *Cycas* and *Ginkgo*. Correlated with the perpetually open condition of the furrow, its floor is covered by the same sort of thick and resistant exine as the general surface of the grain. Changes in volume appear to be accommodated only in part by the movements of the furrow, this function being shared to a larger extent by the smaller longitudinal grooves. The thick resistant floor of this furrow, with its resultant ineffectiveness in accommodating changes in volume, suggests that it is a vanishing structure, its harmomegathic function being largely taken over by the 19 or 20 smaller grooves. It still serves, however, as a place of emergence for the pollen tube, according to Strasburger (1892) who shows a figure of a grain with a broad tube emerging through a region occupying the whole length of one side of the grain.

The presence of the single broad furrow in this grain suggests that *Welwitschia* is derived from the primitive gymnosperm stock, not from the Coniferales but coincidently with or possibly earlier than they, because, as we have already seen, the grains of the Coniferales are all highly specialized, with their furrow either already modified in some other way or completely obliterated. *Welwitschia* has apparently diverged widely from the Coniferales, and in its grain we see still another way of getting rid of the wide-open furrow. The method adopted by *Welwitschia* of dealing with it is perhaps simpler and more direct than that of any of the tribes of the Coniferales.

There is no known pollen grain which even remotely resembles this, except that of *Ephedra*. The grains of some species of *Ephedra* present a form which is just what we should expect the line of development, which gave rise to that of *Welwitschia*, to lead to if continued on in the same direction; for these differ in outward appearance from those of *Welwitschia* only in the total absence of a germinal furrow and the greater prominence of the substituted longitudinal grooves and ridges. From the evidence of their pollen grains it thus appears that *Welwitschia* and *Ephedra* may represent a group co-ordinate with the conifers.

Welwitschia is a plant of remarkable habit. The very tough body has the shape of a "gigantic radish," growing with its top nearly flush with the ground and with a broad, generally two-lobed, concave crown bearing two large opposite leaves. These persist throughout the life of the plant, which may be several hundred years, growing all the while at the base and splitting from the ends into ribbons which are blown about by the wind giving the plant the appearance of a living giant octopus.

Welwitschia is thought by some to have been derived from the gymnosperms, possibly from the conifers, but, on account of its floral structure, which is decidedly angiospermous in appearance, it is thought to be farther removed from them than *Ephedra* (Coulter and Chamberlain, 1917). The morphology of its pollen grains described above, however, suggests that it is a highly advanced gymnosperm divergent from the modern Coniferales and angiosperms but less advanced than *Ephedra*.

Welwitschia mirabilis is the only species of the genus and has no known relatives. It exists only in extremely isolated and restricted regions in southeast Africa. The plant was discovered in 1860 by Frederic Welwitsch and sent to J. D. Hooker (1863), who named it in honor of its discoverer. Hooker believed it to be most nearly related to *Ephedra* on account of the many resemblances which their cones bear to each other, but admits that its relationships are difficult to explain. He described the pollen grains as very minute and having a delicate hyaline exine with longitudinal wrinkles, but he failed to mention the single longitudinal furrow. The pollen grains are also described by Pearson (1906), who points out that "in form and sculpturing they are very like those of *Ephedra*."

Welwitschia occurs, as far as known, in only two localities, that of its original discovery, between the Mossamides and the Cuene rivers, and about 400 miles to the south, on the Namib in the vicinity of the Swakop River. Both localities offer the most extreme desert conditions, with rain falling only at intervals of about once in 10 years.

According to most observers the plant is largely, if not entirely, insect pollinated, but Strasburger believes it to be anemophilous but derived from an entomophilous progenitor. The character of the pollen grain suggests that it is wind pollinated and shows no indication of its ever having been otherwise.

For a complete discussion of this extraordinary plant the reader is referred to the two monographs, already mentioned, of Hooker and of Pearson, the former profusely illustrated with some of the pictures of the plant in its natural habitat, in colors, and the latter accompanied by a complete review of the literature.

EPHEDRA Tourn. EPHEDRA, JOINT FIR

Grains ellipsoidal in shape, 35.3 to 54.7 μ long and 18.2 to 28.5 μ broad, subject to wide changes, with variation of moisture content. Exine thick, rigid, opaque, and of perfectly smooth texture but provided with 5 to 15 longitudinal ridges.

When the ridges are few (5 to 8) they are high, with their crests blade-like and arching from end to end of the grain, and in each of the grooves between the ridges is a hyaline line which follows a serpentine course its full length, giving off at each bend a short lateral branch which extends outward toward the crest of the ridge and occasionally forking once. When the ridges are more numerous (11 to 15) they are not so high, and the hyaline lines in the grooves are absent or only represented by a faint streak, which is unbranched and straight or only slightly wavy. When these grains dry, they shrink by a lateral contraction which is permitted by a deepening of the grooves which at the same time induces a lengthening of the grain, thus causing it to assume a more slender form, with the vertical ridges less arched thinner and closer together. But when the grains are moistened and expand the ridges flatten out, and the grains occasionally split open along the grooves. Those grains which have few ridges entirely lack the germinal furrow, harmomegathy being accomplished by the hyaline lines at the bottoms of the grooves which impart a sort of flexibility to the otherwise rigid exine, through a hinge-like action, permitting the grooves to become deeper and narrower as the grain shrinks, and the branches of the hyaline lines permitting the slight straightening that takes place in the arched curvature of the ridges. But those grains which have a larger number of grooves and lack the hyaline lines appear to possess at least a temporary longitudinal furrow. Thus Strasburger (1872) describes the pollen grain of *Ephedra campylopoda*, which has about 15 ridges, as dipping in on one side throughout its entire length, in this condition presenting an appearance strikingly like the grain of *Welwitschia*. Nevertheless, this condition appears to be only transitory, and it is questionable whether such a longitudinal concavity should be regarded as even the vanishing remnant of the archaic furrow.

When *Ephedra* pollen grains germinate the exine dehisces, splitting into two or more parts through the grooves. I have observed such dehiscence in the grains of *E. intermedia*, and the same is recorded by Stapf (1889) for those of other species, his figures showing a grain so split and with the pollen protoplast emerging from the split end.

With the obliteration of its hereditary archaic furrow and the transferring of its functions of harmomegathy and provision for the pollen tube emergence to the longitudinal grooves, *Ephedra* records a distinct advance beyond *Welwitschia* but of the same direction away from the primitive gymnosperms. Respecting their pollen grains, these two genera appear to form a group coordinate with, but divergent from, the higher gymnosperms, the monocotyledons, and primitive dicotyledons.

The genus includes about 30 species of low, straggling shrubs with long, jointed and fluted green stems lacking true foliage and bearing a strong resemblance to a shrubby *Equisetum*. The species are widely distributed in arid and desert regions, of southwestern United States, western South America and Patagonia, north Africa and central Asia. They are wind pollinated but are not known to cause hayfever. Several of the Chinese species are the source of ma huang, from which the drug ephedrin is obtained (Small, 1928). For a complete discussion of the genus together with a review of the literature the reader is referred to Stapf's monograph (1889) and Pearson (1929).

Ephedra glauca Regl. (Plate IV, Fig. 3) type. Grains uniform, when moist and expanded 44.5 to 49 μ long and 21.5 to 25.1 μ broad. Ridges 7 or 8. Hyaline lines in the grooves conspicuous and branching.

A low, spreading shrub, about 1½ ft. high. Steppes and desert regions from the Caspian Sea through Turkestan and Central Asia to eastern Mongolia and southward to Cashmere.

Ephedra intermedia Schrenk & C. A. Mey Aldschanek. Grains uniform, about 46.7 by 22.8 μ. Ridges 6 to 7; indistinguishable from the type.

A plant similar in both appearance and distribution to the preceding, and according to the classification of Stapf (1889) *E. glauca* is regarded as a variety of *E. intermedia*.

Ephedra equisetina Bunge. Grains rather various in size 48 to 54.7 μ long and 19.4 to 20.5 μ broad; ridges generally 6. Otherwise as in the type.

An erect bush, rarely prostrate at the base, 3 to 6 ft. high, in arid regions. Balkans, Turkestan, Central Asia, and Mongolia.

Ephedra viridis Cov. (*E. nevadensis* S. Wats.). Grains uniform, 51.3 to 54.7 μ long and 27.4 to 28.5 μ broad. Ridges generally 6, occasionally 5, hyaline lines very faint. Otherwise as in the type.

Erect, green shrub 1½ to 3 ft. high. Mojave Desert, southeastern California, eastward to Arizona and Utah.

Ephedra foliata Boiss. & Kotschy Bratta, Nangarwal, Tandala. Grains uniform in size, and about 37.5 to 40 μ long and 18.2 to 22.1 μ broad. Ridges about 15 in number and much less prominent than in the foregoing species. Hyaline lines straight or slightly wavy and without branches, extremely faint; they are seen only with difficulty and may not always be present, in these respects differing rather widely from the type but possessing the same general shape and smooth, rigid type of exine. In the large number and low form of their ridges these grains bear a rather close resemblance to those of *Welwitschia* but differ from them in the absence of a permanent germinal furrow.

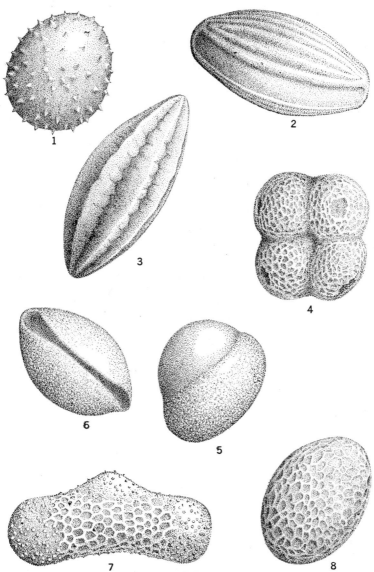

PLATE IV.—Pollen grains of Gnetaceae, Typhaceae, Palmaceae and Naiadaceae. 1. *Gnetum leptostachyum*, 17 in diameter. 2, *Welwitschia mirabilis*, 55 × 30 μ, showing its single broad furrow on the ventral side. 3, *Ephedra glauca*, 47 × 24 μ. 4, *Typha latifolia*, each of the four grains about 21 μ in diameter. 5, *Phoenix dactylifera*, side view, expanded, *cf.* Fig. 6. 6, *Phoenix dactylifera*, ventral view, contracted, 24 μ long. 7, *Ruppia maritima*, 61 μ long. 8, *Potamogeton natans*, 26 μ in diameter.

Dioecious or monoecious shrubby climber, reaching a height of 15 ft. or more in the arid regions of Persia, Afghanistan, and Turkestan.

Ephedra altissima var. **algerica** Stapf Alenda, Belbal. Grains uniform, 35 to 37.6 μ long and 18.2 to 21 μ broad. Ridges about 11, rather low; hyaline line extremely faint and unbranched or entirely absent. Similar to that of *E. foliata*, differing principally in the smaller number of its grooves.

Ephedra altissima is a woody climber reaching a height of about 24 ft., an inhabitant of north Africa from Morocco to Tunisia and in mountainous regions on both sides of the Atlas. The variety *algerica* has a somewhat more restricted range in Algeria and Tunisia.

Both this and the preceding species belong to the "tribe" Scandentes (Stapf). It therefore seems probable that the large number of low ridges which characterize the grain of both species may prove to be of tribal value.

GNETUM L. GNETUM

Grains spheroidal or variously irregular in shape, 11.9 to 18.2 μ in diameter. Exine thin, uniform throughout, provided with spines which are always small but vary considerably in size in the different species; in some they are conical and sharp, resembling those of the grains of *Ambrosia*, but more often they are represented only by the merest vestiges, more like those of the grains of *Xanthium*, and scarcely recognizable as spines. They are never uniform in distribution over the surface, tending to be more or less clumped. The texture of the exine is smooth. The intine is thick and hyaline (Fig. 81), and when moistened it expands visibly, stretching but not rupturing the exine; when dry it contracts, causing the exine to crumple irregularly. There is no trace of pore or furrow and no permanent mechanism for accommodating changes in volume.

This form of grain is clearly reduced and exhibits the kind of reduction which is brought about by wind pollination, calling to mind the pollen grains of the wind-pollinated *Xanthium* which is provided with only minute vestiges of spines irregularly arranged, while that of its near relative the insect-pollinated *Parthenium* is provided with prominent spines regularly arranged.

The *Gnetum* pollen grain is certainly not primitive, whether regarded as a gymnosperm or as an angiosperm, for in either case it shows no trace of the primitive germinal furrow. In its lack of furrow and possession of reduced spines this grain appears to have been derived either from the monocolpate form of grain of the gymnosperms or from the tricolpate form of the dicotyledons. But it is so far reduced that it is difficult even to guess the appearance of its ancestral form. Nevertheless, it can be said with certainty that its advance along the evolutionary line carried it far enough to rid it entirely of the ancestral single furrow, but whether or not it had proceeded still farther before entering the phase of reduction and acquired furrows in the trischistoclasic

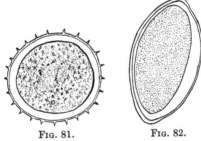

FIG. 81.   FIG. 82.

FIG. 81.—Pollen grain of *Gnetum leptostachyum*, optical section.
FIG. 82.—Pollen grain of *Welwitschia mirabilis*, sagittal section showing the thin exine and thick intine underlying the germinal furrow on the right.

system of the dicotyledons we have no way of telling. But the evidence that we have before us strongly suggests that *Gnetum* is derived from a form that was insect pollinated and with its grains provided with well-developed conical sharp spines. The evidence of the pollen grain, therefore, suggests that *Gnetum* may have been derived either from a primitive dicotyledon or monocotyledon or from a highly advanced dicotyledon and at present represents a reduction no greater in extent that that of *Xanthium* from *Parthenium*. The examination of the pollen from more species of *Gnetum* may reveal one of which the grains exhibit some trace of pore or furrows which would show the natural affiliations of *Gnetum*.

The only recognizable differences among the grains of the six species that I have examined are in their size and in the size of their spines. Accordingly I have arranged them in order of

294 POLLEN GRAINS

their spine size, taking as the type the grain of *G. leptostachyum*, the one in which the spines are most prominent.

"The species of *Gnetum* are either small trees or woody climbers, being among the lianas of tropical forests. The leaves are leathery in texture and are suggestive of those of dicotyledons, the well-developed opposite leaves being lanceolate to ovate in outline and pinnately net veined" (Coulter and Chamberlain, 1917). There are, according to the classification of Markgraf (1929), 28 species distributed in scattered regions in tropical South America, tropical Africa, India, the East Indies, and the Philippines.

Their relationship to the other groups of plants has long been a matter of controversy. Most investigators regard them as highly developed gymnosperms: "So far as the feature of the embryo sac can determine advancement—*Gnetum* is more advanced than any other gymnosperm." Among the Gnetales they are regarded as perhaps most closely related to *Welwitschia*, though the connection is considered a distant one. For a discussion of this interesting genus and a complete review of the literature the reader is referred to Markgraf's monograph (1929).

Gnetum leptostachyum Bl. (Plate IV, Fig. 1) type. Grains rather irregular in shape; about 16 to 18 μ in diameter. They may be ellipsoidal, ovoidal, pear-shaped, or variously irregular but tend to be spheroidal more than any other form. Spines sharp-conical, about as high as those of *Ambrosia* but less broad, irregularly arranged and of uneven size; in this they are similar to the reduced spines of *Xanthium* and of most of the Mutisieae. A woody climber with leathery leaves about 12 in. long and 7 in. broad. Native of northeast Borneo and in variety *robustum* in the Andaman Islands.

Gnetum neglectum Bl. Grains uniform in size but somewhat various in shape, about 16.0 μ in diameter. Otherwise as in the type. A low shrub with slender climbing branches, known only in northeast Borneo.

Gnetum scandens Roxb. Grains 14.8 to 17.1 μ in diameter, as in the type, except that the spines are much less prominent. A robust or slender woody climber. Burma, Siam, Indo-China and southeastern China.

Gnetum indicum (Lour.) Merr. (*G. latifolium* Bl.) Trangkil. Grains 14.3 to 17.1 μ in diameter, as in the type, except that the spines are much smaller—slightly smaller even than in the preceding species.

A climbing shrub represented by several varieties, distributed nearly throughout the East Indies and Malaya.

Gnetum Gnemon L. Grains somewhat various in size, 16 to 18.2 μ in diameter; similar to the type, except that the spines are much smaller—about the same as in *G. indicum*.

A small tree or erect shrub with oblong, leathery leaves, rarely partly climbing. Represented by six rather distinct varieties. Almost throughout the East Indies, Borneo, and Malaya.

Gnetum Rumphianum Becc. (*G. gnemonoides* Brong.). Grains rather uniform in shape and size, tending to be spheroidal, 11.9 to 13.7 μ in diameter. As in the type, except that the spines are smaller, so far reduced that they appear only as flecks.

Malaya and the East Indies.

ANGIOSPERMAE

MONOCOTYLEDONS

TYPHACEAE Cattail Family

TYPHA (Tourn.) L. Cattail, Cattail flag

Grains irregularly spheroidal or, if united in tetrads, variously modified in shape by their mutual contacts, 18.2 to 26.2 μ in diameter. Germ pore single, various in size and shape, appearing as a jagged hole broken through the exine. Exine thin, covered with delicate, reticulate thickenings resembling a fine foam pattern.

In spite of their weak development the ridges of the reticulum show some trace of buttressing at their bases, a feature which is generally associated with reticula of a more robust development. The mesh of the reticulum is always fine but is various, finer in some grains than in others and in most grains not uniform throughout. The distribution of fine and coarse mesh is quite fortuitous and bears no relation to the orientation of the grain in its tetrad or to the position of the germ pore. The reticulum ends at the margins of the pore with open lacunae, and occasionally the pore membrane bears a few scattered flecks which appear to be fragments of the ridges.

The germ pore of the grains of *Typha* is in many ways anomalous. It plays no part in volume-change accommodation, for its membrane does not bulge when the grains are moistened; when the grains dry they collapse irregularly without reference to the pore. Furthermore, the position of the germ pore on the surface of those grains which are shed united in tetrads may be anywhere on their exposed surface, not necessarily on the distal side, which we have seen is the usual position of the pore or furrow in ordinary monocolpate grains. On the contrary, in the grains of *Typha*, there seems to be a tendency among the grains of those tetrads which are flat for the pores of all four grains to be on the same side of the tetrad.

The characters of the grains of *Typha* are of the kind that suggest that they are modifications in response to anemophily. For example, in the grains of *Fraxinus*, which is anemophilous, as compared with those of its close relative *Ligustrum*, which is entomophilous, we find that the change from entomophily to anemophily was accompanied by a flattening out of the reticulum and a loss of the definition of the furrows which in their shape and jagged outline are strongly suggestive of the pore of the grains of *Typha*. It is unfortunate that there is available no closely related entomophilous form for comparison with *Typha*. Nevertheless, by analogy it seems likely that the weakly developed reticulum and poorly defined germ pore of the grains of *Typha* are likewise correlated with its mode of pollination by wind and denote that *Typha*, though now entirely wind pollinated, is derived from some insect-pollinated ancestor which probably had pollen grains provided with heavy reticulate thickenings buttressed at their bases and, owing to the stiffening effect imparted by these ridges to the exine, also possessed a well-developed furrow with complete harmomegathic function.

The genus includes about 10 species of marsh or aquatic herbs, of wide distribution in temperate or tropical regions. The family Typhaceae, of which *Typha* is the only genus, is regarded as the most primitive of the Monocotyledons on account of the extreme simplicity of its floral structures. It seems quite possible, however, that the simplicity of their flowers has been brought about by reduction in response to wind pollination and that therefore, the Typhaceae really belong much higher up in the scale. Certainly it seems that they should be regarded as more highly advanced in the evolutionary scale than the Palmaceae, which retain the primitive monocolpate form of pollen grain, only slightly modified from that of the Bennettitales.

Typha latifolia L. Broad-leaved or Common cattail (Plate IV, Fig. 4) type. Grains always united in tetrads. Occasionally groups of fewer are found, but these show evidences of having been broken apart. The four grains occur in all possible arrangements (Fig. 83), but the square and rhomboidal predominate. Cells uniform in size, 18.2 to 22.8 μ in diameter. Their shape is largely determined by their arrangements in the tetrad. The surface reticulum is continuous throughout the tetrad, passing from cell to cell apparently uninfluenced by the sutures between them.

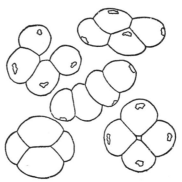

Fig. 83.—Diagram of some of the arrangements of the four pollen cells encountered in the tetrads of *Typha latifolia.*

Marsh and shallow water herbs of cosmopolitan distribution. Wind pollinated, shedding enormous quantities of pollen in June, but not known to cause hayfever.

Typha angustifolia L. Narrow-leaved cattail. Grains single, never united in tetrads, uniform in size, 19.4 to 26.2 μ in diameter, irregular and various in shape but tending to be spheroidal. The surface reticulum, as in the type, or slightly finer.

Tall herbs with narrow, sword-shaped leaves, in marshes and shallow water. Wind pollinated, flowering in June, but not a cause of hayfever. Southern Maine to North Carolina, and westward but less abundant than *T. latifolia.*

NAIADACEAE NAIAS FAMILY

Grains various. Exine thin, reticulate (*Potamogeton, Ruppia*) or absent (*Zannichellia, Zostera, Naias*). Intine not excessively thickened, only slightly thickened in the grains of *Ruppia.*

The forms of pollen grain encountered in this family all suggest various stages of reduction—loss of exine. In those of *Potamogeton* the reduction in the thickness of the exine has progressed about as far as in the grains of *Typha;* the walls are thin and flexible enough to accommodate changes in volume without any special organs of harmomegathy. In those of *Ruppia* the exine is represented by a delicate network, continuous over little more than half of the surface of the grain, broken up and represented only by detached fragments over the two ends and part of the middle. The way that the detached fragments carry on the rhythm or symmetry of the pattern of the net presents an appearance suggesting the dissolving away of an original net in these areas, arrested just before the last fragments disappear. In the pollen of the other members of the family there is almost no trace of the exine, certainly not enough to exhibit any organization. Associated with this reduction in thickness and loss of the exine there occurs no compensating increase in thickness of the intine, which we have seen was invariably the case among the gymnosperms and, I might add, is likewise the case among those angiosperms in which the reduction of the exine is due to anemophily. On the contrary, among the Naiadaceae, in the grains of *Zostera* and *Naias*, which have no exine, the intine is thinner even than in those of *Potamogeton* and *Ruppia*, where the exine still persists.

All the plants of this family are aquatic but exhibit varying degrees of completeness of adaptation to the aquatic environment; *Potamogeton* and *Ruppia* emerse their flowers for pollination, while *Zannichellia*, *Zostera*, and *Naias* are pollinated entirely under water. It is something more than a coincidence that the grains of those which are pollinated under water should be without exine, while the grains of those which are pollinated just above the water should possess an exine only in a reduced form. In this connection it is interesting to compare the pollen of the Naiadaceae with that of *Vallisneria*. *Vallisneria*, though unrelated, is aquatic. The female flowers just emerge above the surface of the water at maturity, while the male flowers mature and are released near the root of the plant, often several feet below. They rise to the surface where they must be wafted against the female flowers to effect pollination. Though *Vallisneria* is entirely unrelated to the Naiadaceae, its pollen, like theirs, possesses only a vanishing trace of exine, and at the same time the intine is only a thin, delicate membrane so easily broken that it is difficult to keep it intact while preparing the grains for microscopic examination. According to Strasburger (1902), the same condition obtains in the pollen grains of *Ceratophyllum demersum*, which is pollinated under water, though it is unrelated to both the Naiadaceae and *Vallisneria*. The evidence from these sources, therefore, suggests that thinness and total absence of exine, without a compensating increase in thickness of the intine, are correlated with the aquatic habit. Upon reflection this is not surprising, for the exine, as it occurs in the pollen of most terrestrial angiosperms, appears to serve primarily the purpose of preventing desiccation; moreover, it is generally ruptured by exposure to excessive moisture. It is therefore unnecessary to the pollen of aquatic plants if, indeed, not entirely incompatible with pollination on or under water.

The Naiadaceae are counted among the most primitive of the monocotyledons on account of the extreme simplicity of their floral structures, a simplicity which we see also extends to their pollen grains; but if this is a sign of primitiveness one would expect to find among these families the primitive monocolpate form of grain well represented. This is not the case. The weak development of the reticulum in the grains of *Potamogeton* and *Ruppia* and the entire absence of both in the grains of the other genera of the family suggest that the simplicity of these grains is one of reduction and advance rather than of primitiveness and that these plants belong much higher up in the evolutionary scale. At any rate it seems certain that they should be regarded as higher than the Palmaceae, which also have a simple form of grain, which, however, is monocolpate and therefore of a simplicity that denotes primitiveness.

POTAMOGETON L. Pondweed

Grains, when moist and expanded, ellipsoidal or approximately spheroidal, 23 to 31 μ in diameter. Exine covered with delicate reticulate thickenings throughout, resembling a foam pattern of varying mesh and similar to that of *Typha*. Intine of most of the grain thin but greatly thickened in a longitudinal strip on one side.

When the grain dries it shrinks with the formation of a single longitudinal depression induced primarily by the contraction of the elongate thickening of the intine; therefore this should probably be regarded as corresponding to the single furrow; the exine, however, is not modified in any way in this region, so, in the ordinary sense of the word, it is not a true furrow (Fig. 84).

The reticulum of the exine, though extremely thin and delicate, presents a beaded appearance, which suggests that this form of grain may have been derived from one in which the reticulate thickenings were very much more highly developed and buttressed, for, as we shall see in the following pages, reticulate patterns are common and found in many different families; and where such a reticulum reaches its highest development the ridges are generally conspicuously buttressed at their bases. The problem of the origin of this type of grain deserves further study, for it is likely that it will be found to represent a connecting link between the terrestrial forms with a fully reticulate exine and the aquatic forms which entirely lack exine.

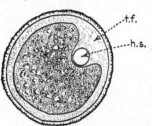

Fig. 84.—Pollen grain of *Potamogeton natans*, transverse optical section passing through the thickened intine of the temporal furrow (*tf*). There is also shown imbedded in the intine a globular mass of hyaline substance (*hs*).

The genus includes 65 species of aquatic herbs of wide distribution in temperate regions. Fossilized grains of *Potamogeton* pollen are to be expected in peats and postglacial silts. In this connection Meinke (1927) has figured *Potamogeton lucens, P. praelongus, P. alpinus, P. mucronatus,* and *P. obtusifolius.* They are all essentially alike, and he says of them (page 395), "form spherical, exine continuous throughout, no folds, no pores."

Potamogeton natans L. Common floating pondweed (Plate IV, Fig. 8) type. Grains as in the generic description, various in shape but tending to be ellipsoidal or globular, 21 to 31 μ in diameter.

A common weed in nearly all ponds and streams in northeastern United States, also in Europe and Asia. July to September.

Potamogeton amplifolius Tuckerm. Grains essentially as in the type, except that they are more nearly spheroidal and more uniform in size and shape, 23.9 to 30.2 μ in diameter.

A common weed in ponds and streams, throughout the northeastern United States. July to September.

Ruppia maritima L. Ditch grass (Plate IV, Fig. 7). Grains uniform, about 61 μ long and about one-fourth as broad, arcuate, swollen at the ends, and at the center on the convex side. Exine exceedingly thin, consisting of a delicate reticulum covering the surface, in an unbroken, coarse mesh, except over the three swellings, where it is discontinuous. Intine rather thick and slightly further thickened in the swollen regions where the exine is defective (Fig. 85).

A slender aquatic herb, of salt or brackish water, entirely submerged, but the flowers are raised to the surface at time of anthesis. Cosmopolitan in distribution.

The genus comprises only three or four species of similar character. The grains of *R. maritima* have been described and beautifully illustrated by Fritzsche (1837).

Zannichellia palustris L. Horned pondweed. "The pollen spores are small globular cells, which contain two nuclei at

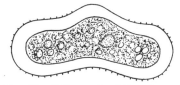

Fig. 85.—Pollen grain of *Ruppia maritima*, longitudinal optical section.

Fig. 86.—The tip of the filamentous pollen grain of *Zostera marina*, 2500 μ long and 3.7 μ thick.

maturity, a large vegetative and a small germinal one contained in a separate antheridial cell. No exospore [exine] is developed, and the ripe spore contains numerous starch granules" (Campbell 1897).

A slender aquatic herb of fresh or brackish water, entirely submerged and pollinated under water. Cosmopolitan in distribution. The genus contains only two or three species.

Zostera marina L. Eelgrass (Fig. 86). Grains elongate, about 2,550 by 3.7 μ. Exine apparently entirely absent. Intine thin and membranous.

These grains have been described and illustrated by Fritzsche (1837), who likens them to pollen tubes. They are, in fact, slender, membranous tubes filled with granular protoplasm. On their surface scattered at irregular intervals are slight thickenings which suggest by their appearance that they might be vestiges of a vanished exine.

In the ripe anther the grains—apparently several thousand of them—occur in a sheaf closely packed together and parallel. If the anther is touched with a needle under water, some of the pollen is forcibly discharged with the filamentous grains all completely separated, but if the grains are touched with the needle, they immediately stick to it and clump together in tangled masses from which they can never again be separated.

Grass-like marine plants entirely submerged and pollinated under water; in bays and estuaries usually on muddy bottoms. At time of anthesis the leaves break off just above the inflorescence so that the flowering plants look like new-mown stubble. Generally of cosmopolitan distribution but recently almost exterminated throughout most of its range.

Naias flexilis (Willd.) Rost. & Schmidt Slender naias. Grains ellipsoidal, 56.6 by 33.3 μ. Exine none. Intine thin.

These grains consist of one-layered sacs packed with starch grains and granular protoplasm. There is no trace of germinal pore or furrow, and the pollen tube emerges indifferently from the side or end of the grain. It has been described and illustrated by Fritzsche (1837) and Campbell (1897), the latter showing the grains germinating.

A slender aquatic herb, entirely submerged and pollinated entirely under water; in ponds and streams nearly throughout North America and Europe. The genus includes about 10 species of world-wide distribution.

PALMACEAE PALM FAMILY

Phoenix dactylifera L. Date palm (Plate IV, Fig. 5, 6) type. Grains uniform in shape and size; when dry about 24 by 12.5 μ, expanding in width when moistened; ellipsoidal in form and provided with a single furrow, deeply invaginated and reaching from end to end of the grain. Exine thin, finely and faintly reticulate-pitted. Intine thin but greatly thickened beneath the furrow.

The furrow is similar to those of the grains of *Cycas* and *Ginkgo*, except that it closes tightly almost or quite throughout its entire length. The more effective closure is rendered possible by the more elongate form of the grain and the tapering of its ends; these grains are a little more than twice as long as broad, as compared with those of *Ginkgo*, which are only a little more than one-third longer than broad, and those of *Cycas*, which are scarcely or not at all elongate. When moistened the furrow becomes completely evaginated, causing the grain to assume an irregular globular form (Plate IV, Fig. 5). But in this condition the part that was inside the furrow can easily be distinguished from the rest of the grain by the extreme thinness of its exine and its perfectly smooth texture.

This form of grain is unquestionably primitive. The only advance that it shows over those of the lower gymnosperms is in its more elongate shape, permitting more complete closure of the furrow. The remarkable similarity of this form of grain to those of the Cycadales and Bennettitales suggests that the palms may not be very far removed from their gymnospermous ancestors, bearing to them among the monocotyledons perhaps about the same relationship that the Magnolieae do among the dicotyledons. Certainly this form of grain appears to be more primitive than those of the Typhaceae or Zannichelliaceae, both of which are generally regarded as lower in the scale than the Palmaceae.

The date palm is a tall tree about 100 ft. high, with a slender, unbranched trunk and a crown of long, stiff, pinnate leaves arching upward. The flowers are dioecious, in branching spadices borne among the foliage, and shedding large quantities of light pollen which may be air-borne, though primarily the tree is insect pollinated. It is not known to cause hayfever. The date is native of Africa but is now cultivated in California and the warmer parts of the United States.

The genus includes about 12 species, native of Africa and Asia; of these, 4 others besides the present species are cultivated in tropical and subtropical countries.

The Palm family (Palmaceae or Arecaceae) includes about 130 genera and probably over 1,200 species of wide distribution in tropical and subtropical countries. Its relationships are not fully understood, but its isolated position among the monocotyledons—it is regarded as the only family of the order Arecales —suggests that it has no living relatives. The primitive monocolpate pollen grain of the palms suggests that their nearest relatives may be found only among the lower gymnosperms.

GRAMINEAE GRASS FAMILY

The pollen grains of the grasses are remarkably uniform throughout the family. When fully expanded they are generally

spheroidal or, in some species, tend to be ovoidal or ellipsoidal.
In size they range from about 22 to a little over 100 μ in diameter.
In keeping with their mode of pollination by wind their exine is
thin and lacks entirely sculpturing and adornments of any kind,
except a slight but characteristically granular texture, and their
intine is thick and hyaline (Fig. 87).   The interior of the grain
is generally tightly packed with small starch grains and possesses
a small hyaline body diametrically opposite the pore; and it is
to the expansion of these materials and the thick intine, upon
the absorption of water, that the grains owe their roundish
contour when moist.   When the grains dry they shrink and

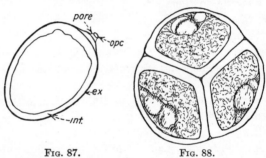

FIG. 87.   FIG. 88.

FIG. 87.—Pollen grain of grass, *Triticum aestivum*, transverse optical section:
int, intine; *ex*, exine; *opc*, operculum.

FIG. 88.—Pollen tetrad of rush, *Juncoides campestris*, optical section traversing
the three grains shown in Plate V, Fig. 1.

assume a somewhat angular form owing to the collapse of their
thin walls (Plate V, Fig. 5).   They always have one and only one
germ pore, and it does not participate in harmomegathic function.

In the expanded form the shape of the grain occasionally
deviates from the spheroidal enough to be of some diagnostic
or phylogenetic value.   In some, as, for example those of *Avena*
and *Arrhenatherum*, the form is consistently ovoidal, with the
germ pore at the large end, while in those of *Secale cereale* the
form is generally ellipsoidal, with the germ pore on one side
toward one end.   In the pollen of some species, regardless of
what the prevailing shape may be, are frequently found varying
proportions of the grains, which are ovoidal, and when this is
the case the germ pores tend to be at the large end.

Single Germ Pore.—The most outstanding and distinctive
character of the grains of the grasses is that of their single germ

pore (Plate V, Fig. 3). This consists of a small aperture surrounded by a thickened rim of the exine and crossed by a delicate transparent membrane bearing a rather conspicuous thickening, the operculum, at or near its center. The thickened rim causes the orifice to be slightly raised above the general surface of the exine and gives the pore a dome-shaped appearance, with the aperture at the top of the dome and more or less closed by the operculum. The diameter of the aperture ranges in the different species from about 2.3 to 9.1 μ. In general, the larger grains have the larger apertures, but there is not a consistent correlation between these two dimensions. The shape of the pore is nearly always circular or approximately so. Sometimes its margin follows a smooth, even curve; sometimes it is wavy; and sometimes it is quite irregular; but never does it tend to be elliptical or slit-shaped, as so often are the germinal apertures of the grains of other plant families.

The *operculum* is generally a more or less hemispherical or dome-shaped thickening in the pore membrane (Plate V, Fig. 3). It is composed of material having the same staining properties as the exine. The pore membrane is transparent and does not take the stain. It is very elastic and bulges out like a little bubble when the grain is moistened, causing the operculum to appear to be floating unsupported above the germinal aperture; but if the grain is partly dry the operculum is drawn into the throat of the aperture, which it rather effectually closes. As a general rule, the operculum is rather well defined and of measurable bulk, ranging in size in the grains of the different species from 1.1 to 3.4 μ in diameter. It is much less regular in outline than the aperture in which it lies, but when the latter is irregular in shape the operculum generally partakes to a certain extent of the same irregularity, its outline paralleling the contours of the aperture. In the grains of some species, however, its outline exhibits an irregularity quite independent of the surrounding rim, and on rare occasions the operculum may even be represented by a number of more or less separate thickenings in the pore membrane.

The *texture* of the exine is always slightly rough. This roughening is of a peculiar type and not exactly duplicated in pollen grains outside the Gramineae. Its appearance is perhaps best, though inadequately, described by likening it to the stippled

surface of an ordinary stucco wall. In the grains of some
species the stippling is coarse and conspicuous, while in others
it is very fine and scarcely visible with any but the highest
power of the microscope. In such cases it can best be seen in
empty grains or in fragments of the exine through which trans-
mitted light may pass without interference from the cell contents.
The degree to which the roughness is developed often affords a
useful diagnostic character. Though the texture ordinarily
presents a granular appearance, when examined with the highest
resolving power of the microscope it is sometimes seen to possess
a minutely reticulate structure which suggests that it may represent a vanishing reticulum.

It may be said that the *differentiating characters* of the grains
of the grasses have to do with the relatively slight and inconstant
differences in their shape and size, the shape and size of the
germinal aperture and its operculum, and the texture of their
exine. On the whole the grains of the different grasses are much
more notable for their similarity than for their differences, and
it is only in relatively few cases, where such characters as those
mentioned above reach their most extreme development, that
specific or even generic identification of the grains can be made
with any degree of certainty.

The thin and almost smooth character of the exine, the thick
intine, and the small size of the germ pore of the grass pollen
grains are characters of reduction, obviously associated with
their mode of pollination by wind. The single minute germ pore
with its tiny operculum is unique, having been recorded in the
grains of no other plants. Nevertheless, the pollen grain of the
grasses must have inherited their single germ pore, as have those
of other monocotyledons, from the archaic one-furrowed pollen
grain of the ancient gymnosperms. We have already seen that
most of the other groups of plants that inherited this one-pored
type of grain protected, modified, or eliminated its wide open
furrow—each accomplishing this in its own way. Apparently
in the grains of the grasses we see still another way of accomplishing the same end; but here the reduction of the furrow has been
arrested in its final state of elimination, retained in its reduced
form because it is still useful in permitting the emergence of the
pollen tube. The exine of the grass pollen grain is thin enough
to permit harmomegathy freely without the aid of a furrow, but

it is still apparently thick enough to hinder the exit of the pollen tube, hence the persistence of the pore.

Comparative Morphology.—The Gramineae are generally believed to have been derived from some insect-pollinated ancestor. The pollen-grain form suggests that this may be so; but, since nearly all its characters are those of reduction, it could likewise have arrived at its present condition directly from the archaic monocolpate form of grain in the same way as such reduced forms as those of *Juniperus*, *Sequoia*, and others of the Coniferales. In either event the single pore of the grass grain must be homologous with the single furrow of the primitive monocolpate grain. The annular thickening around the aperture then corresponds to the furrow rim, and the operculum to the furrow floor. The thin, flexible membrane surrounding the operculum is then homologous with the hinge line, or line of dehiscence, in the grains of *Zamia*. Though the type of germ pore of the grasses is unique, it finds its counterpart in the grains of *Castalia*. In these the furrow floor is scarcely reduced at all, occupying about one-third of its surface, but differs from the archaic form in being surrounded by a narrow strip of flexible membrane, intervening between it and the furrow rim. The form of the grass pollen grain apparently traversed in its evolution the same path as that of *Castalia*, but, having abandoned insect pollination in favor of wind pollination, the exine became thinner, losing its decorations, which probably consisted of a marked reticulum, permitting it to expand and contract with the changes in volume of the grain and so doing away with the necessity of any special harmomegathic mechanism. Consequently, the furrow became reduced to its present minute size, which is just sufficient to permit the emergence of the pollen tube.

The Plants.—The grasses shed light pollen, sometimes in enormous quantities, which is the cause of much hayfever. Next to the ragweeds and their allies, they are probably responsible for more hayfever than are the plants of any other group. Most of the species that produce the largest quantities of pollen flower in late spring and early summer throughout the greater part of North America; and thus it is that the responsibility for the greater part of the late spring and early summer hayfever may be laid almost entirely at the door of the grasses. However, there are some grasses that have a more extended flowering period, for example, Bermuda grass, which flowers almost throughout the year in the southern United States, and Johnson grass, which flowers principally during the latter part of summer, both causing much hayfever.

In the family are about 4,500 species in about 500 genera distributed almost throughout the world wherever conditions are suitable for plant growth. They are classified into 14 tribes of which representatives of the following 10 are here considered. These are the Bambosidae, Festuceae, Hordeae, Aveneae, Agrostideae, Chlorideae, Phalarideae, Zizaneae, Andropogoneae, and Tripsicaceae.

BAMBOSIDAE.—The bamboos are for the most part confined to the tropics and subtropics, only the genus *Bambusa* extending into the southern United States.

FESTUCEAE.—A large and important tribe, containing some of our worst hayfever plants, as, for example, *Dactylis, Poa*, and *Festuca*, and others of lesser importance, as *Distichlis* and *Bromus*. The pollen grains of all members of this tribe are spheroidal, but further than this is cannot be said that they resemble each other more than they do the members of some of the other tribes. In size the grains range from 22 to 48.5 μ in diameter, with a proportionately wide range in the size of the germinal aperture and operculum.

HORDEAE.—This small but important tribe is widely distributed in the temperate regions of both hemispheres and includes our most important cereals—wheat, barley, and rye. Besides these it contains such notable hayfever genera as *Lolium, Agropyron*, and *Elymus*. There is considerable divergence in their form, suggesting that the tribe may not be entirely natural. The grains of *Lolium* tend to be spherical, those of *Agropyron* and *Triticum* tend to be ovoidal, while those of *Secale* are nearly always ellipsoidal. The grains of all except those of *Lolium* are large, ranging from 47 to 62 μ in diameter, while those of *Lolium* are only 28 to 33 μ in diameter.

AVENEAE.—A rather small tribe but widely distributed in both warm and cool regions. About nine genera are represented in North America, and of these we consider here the pollen of representatives of four—*Koeleria, Arrhenatherum, Nothoholcus*, and *Avena*. Here, again, there is considerable divergence of form; the grains of *Koeleria* and *Nothoholcus* tend to be spheroidal and small (27 to 34 μ in diameter), while those of *Avena* and *Arrhenatherum* tend to be ovoidal and large (34 to 68 μ). All these plants are important causes of hayfever.

AGROSTIDEAE.—A large and important tribe, inhabiting cool regions, represented in North America by about 25 genera and including such notable hayfever plants as *Agrostis* and *Phleum*. Their grains are spheroidal and rather small—25 to 32 μ in diameter—and their texture is conspicuously but finely granular.

CHLORIDEAE.—A large and rather important tribe confined mostly to the warmer regions. It comprises three genera of rather notable hayfever plants—*Cynodon*, *Bouteloua*, and *Beckmannia*. *Cynodon* (Bermuda grass) is probably the most important hayfever grass in the United States, while several species of *Bouteloua*, which are abundant and valuable agricultural grasses in the arid regions of the southwestern states, are also rather important. The grains of all are spherical and small, ranging in the different species from 34 to 38 μ in diameter.

PHALARIDEAE.—A small tribe of about six genera, represented by only three in North America, and of these we consider here the pollen of only *Anthoxanthum* and *Phalaris*. The grains of both are almost identical; they are spherical and about 34 to 45 μ in diameter, with a faintly granular texture. The germinal apertures of both are circular but wavy in outline and provided with an operculum of irregular shape. *Anthoxanthum* ranks among the grasses of first importance as a cause of hayfever, but *Phalaris* is of relatively little importance in this respect.

ZIZANEAE.—A small tribe of aquatics represented in North America by four genera of which only *Zizania* is here considered.

ANDROPOGONIEAE.—A large tribe confined mostly to warm regions, represented in North America by 13 genera of which we consider here only *Holcus*, a genus of rather large grasses, including such important hayfever plants of the central and southern states as Johnson grass, sorghum, and Sudan grass.

TRIPSICACEAE (Maydeae).—A small tribe represented in North America by only four genera, closely affiliated with the Andropogonieae. We consider here only *Zea*, the Indian corn, which is a hayfever plant of minor importance.

For a systematic study of the Gramineae the reader is referred to Hitchcock (1920 and 1935).

Bambusa vulgaris Schrad. (*B. arundinacea* Ait.) Bamboo. Grains spheroidal, uniform in size, 46 to 48 μ in diameter. Germinal aperture approximately circular, 5.1 to 6.3 μ in diameter; operculum irregular in outline, about 2.3 μ in diameter. Texture smooth.

Phyllostachys Sp. Grains as in *Bambusa vulgaris*, except for size, 35 to 36.5 μ in diameter, with germinal aperture 3.4 to 4 μ and operculum about 2 μ in diameter. Plants similar to bamboo. Native of Asia.

Bromus inermis Leyess. Hungarian brome grass, Smooth brome grass. Grains uniform in size but various in shape from spherical to ovoidal, about 48.5 μ in diameter. Germinal aperture circular, with smooth margin, 6.3 μ in diameter. Operculum somewhat irregular, about 3.3 μ in diameter.

Hungarian brome is a European grass extensively cultivated for hay in North America in the northern portions of the Great Plains region from northern Kansas to Minnesota and Montana. Now escaped from cultivation and widely distributed in fields and waste places, especially in South Dakota, Ohio, and Colorado. Flowers in June and July shedding relatively little pollen, probably of no importance in hayfever.

The genus comprises about 60 species in the north temperate zone, with 32 species in North America. None is regarded as a serious cause of hayfever. *B. secalinus* L. (cheat) is stated (Balyeat, 1920) to be unimportant in hayfever.

FESTUCA L. Fescue grass

Grains spheroidal or somewhat ovoidal, with the germ pore at the large end, rather various, 31 to 36.5 μ in diameter. Pore approximately circular but with wavy margin, 2.5 to 4.5 μ in diameter. Operculum irregular in outline, 1.5 to 2 μ in diameter. Texture finely but distinctly granular. A genus of about 14 species in all temperate regions. Flowering in summer, they produce large quantities of pollen, some species undoubtedly causing some hayfever, though *F. octoflora* Walt. is said to be unimportant in this respect (Balyeat, 1926).

Festuca rubra L. Red fescue grass. Grains as in the generic description, about 31.9 μ in diameter, aperture 2.5 μ, and operculum 1.7 μ in diameter.

A common grass of dry and acid soils from Labrador to Alaska and Virginia. Flowers in early summer shedding much pollen which is unquestionably an important cause of hayfever in regions where abundant.

Festuca elatior L. Meadow fescue grass (Plate V, Fig. 1). Grains indistinguishable from those of *F. rubra.*

A common grass native of Eurasia, much cultivated for hay and pasture in humid regions and naturalized in fields and waste places almost throughout North America. Flowers in early summer shedding much pollen, which is an important cause of hayfever.

POA L. Bluegrass

Grains approximately spheroidal, though often tending to be somewhat irregular in outline, rather uniform in size, 22.8 to 32 μ in diameter. Germinal apertures nearly circular but with a decidedly wavy outline, 2.3 to 5.1 μ in diameter. Texture finely but distinctly granular. In all observable characters the grains of the three species which have been examined are alike.

The genus includes probably 200 species in temperate and cool regions. Of these about 90 are found in the United States. Most of them flower in late spring or early summer, and many produce large amounts of pollen, which, being of rather smaller grains than that of most grasses, is carried greater distances in the air, and, for that reason and because of the great toxicity which their pollen is known to possess, the bluegrasses are counted among the most important causes of hayfever. Besides the species mentioned below, others that are potent causes of hayfever are *P. scabrella* Benth. of California, *P. Fendleriana* Vasey of California, Wyoming, and New Mexico, and *P. compressa* L. (Canada bluegrass) more or less abundant throughout the United States and Canada.

Poa pratensis L. June Grass, Kentucky bluegrass. Grains as in the generic description, 28.5 to 32 μ in diameter. Germinal aperture 3.4 to 5.1 μ in diameter; operculum usually very irregular in shape, about 1.7 μ in diameter.

June grass flowers in late May and early June, shedding enormous quantities of pollen. It is ubiquitous throughout North America, and since it is much used in lawns it is abundant in cities and suburbs and is unquestionably one of the most important causes of early summer hayfever.   It has been stated by Duke and Durham (1928) that in the region of Kansas City the pollen count for June grass at its peak reaches a greater number of grains per unit volume of air than any other grass. This, together with the extreme toxicity of its pollen and the fact that it is a plant preeminently associated with dwellings, gives it a foremost place among the hayfever grasses of North America, outranking timothy and other crop grasses, which are primarily plants of the farm and country.

Poa trivialis L. Rough-stalked June grass.   Grains as in the generic description, 22.8 to 25.1 μ in diameter.   Germinal apertures 2.3 to 3.4 μ in diameter; operculum 0.85 to 1.1 μ in diameter. The grains of this species can be distinguished by the size of their operculum, which is the smallest that I have observed in the pollen of any grasses.

In meadows and waste, generally moist, places.   Newfoundland to Ontario, South Carolina, and Louisiana.   June to August. Its pollen occurs in much smaller quantities than that of June grass but is fully as toxic to hayfever sufferers.

Poa annua L. Low spear grass, Annual bluegrass.   Grains as in the generic description but with texture slightly more coarsely granular, 25 to 27 μ in diameter.   Pore about 3.4, and operculum 2.0 μ in diameter.

A low, sprawling grass of waste places almost throughout North America.   It can be found in flower throughout the year except in the coldest winter months, but the bulk of its flowering takes place very early in spring.   It is obviously of negligible importance in hayfever on account of the small size of the plants and the small amount of pollen produced by them.   Nevertheless, it is regarded by Scheppegrell (1917) and Rowe (1928) as important in California but is said by Selfridge (1920) to be of only secondary importance in California.

Digitaria sanguinalis (L.) Scop. (*Syntherisma sanguinale* (L.) Dulac., *S. fimbriata* Nash), Crab grass.   Grains uniform, except a few that are abortive, almost exactly spherical in form, 36.5 to 40.3 μ in diameter.   Pore 4.6 to 6.3 and operculum 2.3 to 3.4 μ in diameter.   Exine rather coarsely and distinctly granular.

Crab grass is a weed of cultivated and waste ground and is cosmopolitan in distribution, introduced into America from Europe.   It flowers in August and September.   It is of relatively little importance in hayfever but occasionally causes a late flare-up of early summer cases.

Dactylis glomerata L. Orchard grass. Grains somewhat various in shape, spheroidal, ovoidal, or ellipsoidal, 28.5 to 36 μ in diameter. Germinal aperture irregular and various in outline, sometimes tending to be elliptical, 4.6 μ in diameter; operculum also irregular, tending to correspond in outline to that of the aperture, 2.3 to 3.4 μ in diameter. Texture distinctly and rather coarsely granular.

A tall, robust grass forming tussocks in fields and waste places, extremely common and widely distributed almost throughout the United States and Canada. Flowers in June, shedding enormous quantities of pollen which, in the experience of the author, has been found to give generally larger reactions by means of the skin test on hayfever patients than that of any other grass. The abundance of this grass, together with the extreme toxicity of its pollen and its habit of growing near dwellings in and about cities, makes it one of the worst, if not the worst, of the hayfever grasses in the eastern United States.

Phleum pratense L. Timothy, Herd's-grass (Plate V, Fig. 2). Grains uniformly spherical but somewhat various in size, 31.9 to 36.5 μ in diameter. Germinal aperture circular with a slightly wavy margin, 2.8 to 4.6 μ in diameter, with operculum irregular in outline. Texture distinctly granular.

Timothy is a common grass much cultivated for hay and wild in fields and meadows almost throughout North America. Flowers in June and July, shedding large quantities of pollen which is an important factor in hayfever. Its pollen is second in toxicity only to that of orchard grass. It is primarily a grass of the country and is a much less successful invader of city lots than some of its cousins, *e.g.*, *Dactylis*, *Poa*, and *Agrostis*. Consequently, in point of the number of its victims, it is a less important factor in hayfever than they.

Agrostis palustris Huds. (*A. alba* L.) Redtop (Plate V, Fig. 4). Grains rather various in shape and size but tending to be spheroidal, 25 to 31 μ in diameter. Pore circular but with wavy margin, 2.3 to 4.6 μ in diameter; operculum irregular in outline, 1.7 to 2.3 μ in diameter. Texture finely but distinctly granular, though less so than in the grains of timothy.

Redtop is a common grass in fields and meadows nearly throughout North America and extensively cultivated for fodder. Flowers in July shedding quantities of light pollen which is the cause of much hayfever.

The genus *Agrostis* includes about 100 species of which about 25 are found in the United States of America. *Agrostis capillaris* L., Rhode Island bent, and *A. stolonifera* L., carpet bent, are much used in lawns and are among the favorite grasses for golf courses. They are smaller and finer than redtop but otherwise of similar appearance. There are several other species, as, for example, *A. spica-venti* L. in the eastern United States and *A. perennans* (Walt.) Turkerm. in the western states, which deserve consideration. The different species are apparently not distinguishable from each other in hayfever studies; nevertheless, it is likely that much of the hayfever credited to redtop is due to some of the bent grasses. For a taxonomic discussion of this rather complicated genus the reader is referred to Hitchcock (1920, 1905) and Piper (1918).

HOLCUS L.

Grains larger than those of most grasses, 40 to 55 μ in diameter, and generally spheroidal or nearly so. Pore circular or occasionally slightly irregular, 3.4 to 5.1 μ in diameter; operculum 2.3 to 3.4 μ in diameter. Texture more or less granular.

The genus comprises about six species of tall, robust grasses, native of Europe, and one of Mexico, valuable for fodder and in some cases their grain and extensively cultivated in the warm and arid regions of North America. For a complete taxonomic discussion of the group the reader is referred to Ball (1910), Bailey (1924), and Hitchcock (1920, 1935).

Holcus halepensis L. (*Andropogon halepense* Brot., *Sorghum halepense* Pers.) Johnson grass. Grains as in generic description. Texture faintly granular.

A common perennial weed, escaped from cultivation in the southern states. It flowers throughout most of the summer but sheds pollen rather sparingly, and its pollen has only a limited range of flight on account of the large size of the grains. Nevertheless, on account of the great abundance and large size of the plants, which often reach a height of 6 ft., and the extreme toxicity of its pollen, it is an important cause of hayfever in Oklahoma

(Balyeat, 1926), Oregon (Chamberlain, 1927), and southern Arizona (Phillips, 1932) and elsewhere.

Holcus Sorghum L. (*Andropogon Sorghum* Brot., *Sorghum vulgare* Pers.) Sorghum, Milo maize, Broom corn. Grains as in generic description.

Extensively cultivated and existing in many varieties. Sometimes regarded as a minor cause of hayfever in regions where abundant—Kansas, North Carolina, and Texas.

Holcus Sorghum var. **sudanensis** (Piper) Hitchcock, (*Andropogon Sorghum sudanensis* Piper, *Holcus sudanensis* Bailey) Sudan grass. Grains as in the generic description but more coarsely and conspicuously granular than those of the two preceding species, 43 to 55 μ in diameter.

Sudan grass is a tall annual, 6 to 10 ft. high, extensively cultivated for hay in semiarid regions of the United States. It flowers throughout most of the summer but produces relatively little pollen, which is rather poorly adapted to dispersal; hence it is unimportant in hayfever, though it has occasionally been reported as a minor cause.

Zizania palustris L. (*Z. aquatica* L.) Indian rice, Water oats. Grains various in shape and size but tending to be spheroidal, about 34.4 μ in diameter; operculum irregular in outline, about 2.3 μ in diameter.

A large aquatic or semiaquatic annual, common in the northeastern states along swampy borders of streams and in shallow water. Flowers in June and July, shedding large quantities of light pollen well adapted to dispersal, but apparently not a factor in hayfever on account of its lack of toxicity to most hayfever patients.

Nothoholcus lanatus (L.). Nash (*Holcus lanatus* L.) Velvet grass, Meadow or Woolly soft grass. Grains spheroidal, 27.6 to 34.2 μ in diameter. Germinal aperture circular to extremely irregular, about 3.4 μ in diameter; operculum circular to irregular, its outline following the contours of the aperture 1.7 to 2.3 μ in diameter.

A low grass in fields, meadows, and waste places but only locally abundant. Nova Scotia to Ontario and Illinois, North Carolina and Tennessee, also in the Pacific states. Flowers in June and July, shedding large amounts of buoyant pollen which, in the author's experience, is toxic to hayfever patients. It is said to be an important cause of hayfever in California (Rowe, 1928), Oregon (Chamberlain, 1927), and Washington (Scheppegrell, 1917).

AVENA L. Oat

Grains generally ovoidal or, occasionally, irregular in shape, 56 to 68 μ in diameter. Germ pore with its aperture circular or nearly so, 4.3 to 8.5 μ in diameter, generally at the large end of the grain; operculum circular or irregular in outline, 3.4 to 4.6 μ in diameter (Plate V, Fig. 3). Texture finely but sharply and conspicuously granular. The grains of the three species described below show scarcely any observable differences.

Species about 55 in temperate regions.

Avena fatua L. Wild oat. Grains as in the generic description, differing from those of the two following species only in their slightly larger size, about 68 μ in diameter.

Abundant in the Pacific coast states, where it is said to be an important cause of hayfever (Rowe, 1928; Selfridge, 1920). Flowers in April, May, and June.

Avena barbata Brot. Slender wild oat. Grains as in the generic description, 51.3 to 62.7 μ in diameter.

Abundant in the Pacific coast states, where it is said to be an important cause of hayfever (Selfridge, 1920). Flowers March to June.

Avena sativa L. Oat. Grains as in the generic description, 56 to 59 μ in diameter.

Cultivated throughout. Flowers in May and June, shedding relatively little pollen which is not a factor in hayfever.

Arrhenatherum elatius (L.) Beauv. (*A. avenaceum* Beauv.) Tall oat grass. Grains spheroidal, ovoidal, or occasionally ellipsoidal in shape, 34 to 39 μ in diameter. Germinal aperture circular but with wavy margin, 4.0 to 4.6 μ in diameter. Texture fine granular.

A tall, slender grass introduced from Europe; sometimes cultivated as a meadow grass but more often a weed along roadsides. Newfoundland to Ontario and Minnesota, south to Georgia, Tennessee, and Nebraska. Also in the Pacific coast states. Flowers June and July, shedding relatively little pollen which is only a minor factor in hayfever.

Koeleria gracilis Pers. (*K. cristata* (L.) Pers. in part) Crested hair grass. Grains somewhat various in shape but tending to be spheroidal, 27.4 to 28.5 μ in diameter. Germinal aperture circular but with a wavy margin, or irregular, about 3.4 μ in diameter. Texture conspicuously and rather coarsely granular.

A common forage grass throughout the western states. Flowers in June and July, shedding much pollen which is the cause of some hayfever and is said to be important in Oregon (Chamberlain, 1927) and Wyoming (Scheppegrell, 1917).

Cynodon Dactylon Pers. (*Capriola Dactylon* (L.) Ktze.) Bermuda or Scutch grass. Grains somewhat various in shape but tending to be spheroidal, 34 to 35.5 μ in diameter. Germinal aperture circular but with wavy margin, 3.4 μ in diameter; operculum nearly circular or slightly irregular, 1.7 to 2.3 μ in diameter. Texture finely but distinctly granular.

A creeping perennial extremely abundant throughout the southern United States. Flowering almost throughout the year, shedding large quantities of pollen which is excellently adapted to wind dispersal, it is known to be one of the worst hayfever grasses and is said to be the most important in this respect of all grasses in Oklahoma, where it flowers from May 15 to frost (Balyeat, 1926). It is also stated to be important in California (Rowe, 1928), particularly in the lowlands (Selfridge, 1920), and in southern Arizona (Phillips, 1922, 1923).

Bouteloua gracilis Steud. (*B. oligostachya* Torr.) Blue grama grass, Mesquite grass. Grains somewhat various but tending to be spheroidal, 34.2 to 38 μ in diameter. Germinal aperture circular, 3.4 to 3.7 μ in diameter; operculum decidedly irregular, 2.3 to 2.8 μ in diameter. Texture finely granular.

Plains and hills, Manitoba to Mexico and southern California. Flowers almost throughout the summer but shedding relatively little pollen which is only a secondary cause of hayfever.

The genus *Bouteloua* comprises about 30 species of which many are our most valuable and abundant range grasses in that region, extending from Saskatchewan and Manitoba southward between the Mississippi River and the continental divide. Where abundant they are known generally to cause some hayfever. For example, *B. Rothrockii* and *B. gracilis* are stated by Scheppegrell to be important hayfever plants. For a taxonomic discussion of the genus the reader is referred to Griffiths (1912).

AGROPYRON Gaertn.

Grains spheroidal or ovoidal, with the pore at the large end, 47 to 52 μ in diameter. Germinal aperture circular, 5.7 to 6.4 μ in diameter; operculum irregular, 2.8 to 4.6 μ in diameter.

The genus comprises about 60 species in temperate regions of both hemispheres; about 25 species in the United States.

Agropyron Smithii Rydb. Western wheat grass, Bluejoint, or Bluestem grass. Grains as in the generic description.

Manitoba and Minnesota to British Columbia, south to Missouri and Texas. Flowers in early summer, causing some hayfever. Said to be important in this respect in Wyoming (Scheppegrell, 1917).

Agropyron repens (L.) Beauv. Quick, Quitch, or Quack grass. Grains as in the generic description.

A common weed introduced from Europe in fields and waste places almost throughout North America. Flowers in June and July but sheds relatively little pollen, of only secondary importance in hayfever.

Lolium perenne L. Ray grass, Rye grass. Grains somewhat various, tending to be spheroidal or ovoidal, 28.5 to 33.1 μ in diameter. Germinal aperture circular, 2.8 to 4.0 μ in diameter; operculum irregular, 1.1 to 1.7 μ in diameter. Texture faintly granular.

A common weed in cultivated ground and waste places almost throughout the United States and Canada. Flowers in June and July, shedding much pollen, which is admirably adapted to wind pollination and is always an important factor in hayfever in regions where abundant. It is stated to be "the most important hayfever producer of all the grass family on the Pacific coast" (Selfridge, 1920).

Secale cereale L. Rye. Grains ellipsoidal, with the germ pore on the side near one end. This character is rather unique among the grasses and serves to distinguish this species from all others that I have examined. The grains are also rather large, 62 by 40 μ. Germinal aperture approximately circular but with wavy margin, 5.1 to 5.7 μ in diameter; operculum irregular in outline, about 2.3 μ in diameter. Texture distinctly granular.

Cultivated. Flowers in spring or early summer. Known to be a cause of hayfever but has a short effective range owing to the large size of its pollen grains.

Triticum aestivum L. (*T. sativum* Lam., *T. vulgare* Vill.) Wheat (Fig. 87). Grains rather irregular in shape but tending to be ovoid, 48 to 57 μ in diameter. Germinal aperture irregular in shape, 6.3 to 9 μ in diameter; operculum irregular, 4.5 to 6.3 μ in diameter. Texture finely but distinctly granular.

Cultivated throughout North America. Flowers in early summer shedding little pollen and on this account of little or no importance in hayfever.

Phalaris minor Retz. Mediterranean canary grass. Grains somewhat various in shape but tending to be spheroidal, 40 to 45.6 μ in diameter. Germinal aperture circular but with slightly wavy margin, 3.7 to 5.7 μ in diameter; operculum irregular in outline, 2 to 2.3 μ in diameter. Texture faintly granular.

Introduced from Europe and cultivated in California, Oregon, and elsewhere. Not regarded as a cause of hayfever.

Anthoxanthum odoratum L. Sweet vernal grass. Grains always spheroidal or nearly so, 37.6 to 45.6 μ in diameter. Germinal aperture generally circular but with wavy margin, 4 to 6.3 μ in diameter; operculum irregular, 1.7 to 2.3 μ in diameter. Texture nearly smooth, presenting only the faintest possible granular appearance.

A common grass of fields and meadows nearly throughout North America. Flowers in April and May, shedding enormous quantities of pollen which is admirably adapted to wind dispersal and is extremely toxic to hayfever patients. In the northeastern United States and Canada sweet vernal grass is the first of the hayfever grasses to flower and is the undisputed cause of much hayfever, generally serving to start the season.

Zea Mays L. Indian corn, Maize. Grains spheroidal or nearly so, 90 to 100 μ in diameter. Germinal aperture generally almost exactly circular, 6.8 to 9.1 μ in diameter; operculum very irregular, 2.3 to 3.4 μ in diameter, frequently represented by an aggregation of more or less distinct fragments on the pore membrane, and the latter itself is frequently visibly streaked. Texture finely but distinctly granular. This grain may be distinguished with certainty from those of all other grasses by its large size and large germinal aperture, in which characters it greatly exceeds those of all other species that I have observed in these studies.

Native of America but known only in cultivation. Flowers throughout most of the summer, shedding large quantities of pollen which is extremely toxic to some types of hayfever cases, but owing to its short range which is restricted by the large size of its grains, it is rarely an important cause of hayfever.

CYPERACEAE Sedge Family
CAREX L. SEDGE

Grains when moist and expanded ovoid or pear-shaped, with a single irregularly shaped germ pore (Plate V, Fig. 6). Exine thin and more or less rough-granular in appearance. Over the area of the germ pore, which is symmetrically placed at the large end of the grain, the exine is fragmented; the germ pore is thus poorly defined. Intine thick, especially on the sides of the grain, where it dips deeply into the protoplast. When the grain dries and shrinks, it generally does so with the formation of three or four large concavities on its sides and a smaller one at the large end, causing it to become polyhedral, sometimes more or less tetrahedral—though there is much variation in this. In the expanded condition, while the grain as a whole assumes a symmetrically ovoid form, the contained protoplast does not expand much, retaining its angular form. This curious and distinctive appearance has been variously misinterpreted, and the grain described as having four or five furrows, which indeed it appears to have when observed in its collapsed or partially collapsed condition.

The thin, almost fragmentary condition of the exine and the thick intine and poorly defined germinal furrow without harmomegathic function are characters encountered again and again among wind-pollinated plants that were derived from insect-pollinated ancestors, *e.g.*, those of *Populus* and *Fraxinus*, and suggest that the grains of *Carex* are likewise so modified in response to wind pollination and that *Carex* is probably derived from some ancestral form which was insect-pollinated.

Carex is a genus of about 1,000 species of grass-like herbs, widely distributed throughout the temperate regions of the world. All are entirely wind-pollinated and *Carex* pollen is frequently caught on pollen slides but it is not known to cause hayfever.

Carex stricta Lam. Tussock sedge (Plate V, Fig. 6) type. Grains when fully expanded 38.8 to 46.7 μ long and 32 to 38 μ broad. Texture sharply granular and fragmented, suggesting the appearance of the exine of the grain of *Populus*.

A tall, slender herb in swamps; of wide distribution throughout most of North America. Flowers in April and May, shedding rather large amounts of pollen.

Carex pennsylvanica Lam. Pennsylvania sedge. Grains as in the type, about 37.4 μ long.

A low, grass-like herb in dry fields and woods. New Brunswick to North Dakota to Tennessee to North Carolina. Flowers in May and June.

Eleocharis spi. Spear rush. Grains similar to those of *Carex* but with no vestige of a germ pore and a more coarsely granular texture. Various in shape and size but tending to be long pear-shaped and about 34 by 48 μ.

Rush-like herbs in wet meadows and marshes.

JUNCACEAE Rush Family

Juncoides campestre (L.) Ktze. (*Juncus campestris* L., *Luzula campestris* DC., *L. comosa* Meyer) Common wood rush (Plate V, Fig. 7). Grains uniform in shape and size, always united in tetrahedral tetrads, the four grains so closely appressed that the tetrad is almost spherical. Individual cells 25.1 to 29.6 μ in diameter. Exine thin, flecked with small granules, continuous from grain to grain over the whole tetrad, but the sutures between the adjoining grains plainly visible through the exine. Intine thick and hyaline, thicker on the walls of the dissepiments than on the outside walls (Fig. 88).

The germinal furrow is not sharply defined but is represented by a thin area of the exine on the outer face of each grain. This area is further distinguished from the rest of the grain by the elastic nature of its exine and the more open distribution of its granular flecks. Underlying each are a number of large, globular bodies of hyaline material which swell upon being moistened, causing the overlying areas of the exine to bulge outward and contract upon drying so that it becomes invaginated. Though these thin elastic areas are generally overlooked, they are undoubtedly true furrows, as proclaimed by their position on the outer face of each grain and by their harmomegathic function. Moreover, it is through them that the pollen tube emerges at time of germination. At best, however, the germinal furrow of these grains is vestigial. Its reduction is obviously correlated with the extreme thinness of their exine which, in turn, is correlated with their mode of pollination by wind.

The grains of *Juncoides* are so far reduced that they suggest little of their relationships with those of other plant families. It is not possible in the present state of our knowledge to say even whether or not they are derived from some insect-pollinated ancestor—though the floral structure of the Juncaceae is generally believed to indicate that such is the case. Nevertheless, the thinness of the exine, almost complete loss of the furrow, and persistent and complete union of the grains in tetrahedral tetrads stamp them as actually advanced.

The common wood rush is a grass-like perennial, of almost universal distribution throughout the United States, Canada, and the cooler parts of the rest of the world. It flowers very early in spring, shedding much pollen which is often caught in abundance on atmospheric-pollen slides, but it is not known to cause hayfever.

The genus includes about 65 species of low, grass-like herbs, widely distributed, flowering in spring. The family Juncaceae includes about eight genera and 300 species, mostly aquatic or semiaquatic. Their pollen grains have not been much investigated, but Fischer (1890) describes the grains of six species of *Juncus* and six of *Luzula*, "alle mit glatter Exine und zu vier nach den Ecken einer Teträders verwachsen." It therefore seems probable that the grains of the great majority, if not all, of the Juncaceae will be found to be united in tetrahedral tetrads.

DICOTYLEDONS

MAGNOLIACEAE Magnolia Family

The grains of the Magnoliaceae are so different in the three tribes of the family that it is more satisfactory to describe them by their tribes than to attempt a family description. The classification here employed is that of Prantl (1891).

Magnolieae
Magnolia
Svenhedinia
Michelia
Liriodendron
Illicieae
Drimys

Illicium
Zygogynum
SCHIZANDREAE
Schizandra
Kadsura

In more recent treatments the tribes Illicieae and Schizandreae are separated entirely from the Magnoliaceae and constitute the related family Schizandraceae. The evidence of the pollen-grain forms of these plants is decidedly in favor of such a separation. Nevertheless, there is an obvious connection between the different forms. And because this is highly illuminating and suggestive of phylogenetic trends, I have chosen to retain the older classification.

MAGNOLIEAE. Grains elongate, boat-shaped. 41 to 63 μ in length and about one-third to one-half as broad, with a single furrow. Exine smooth, granular, or warty but not reticulate.

Trees and shrubs of widespread distribution. Insect pollinated and frequently with showy flowers.

ILLICIEAE. Grains not elongate, 18 to 34.3 μ in diameter; either with a single furrow and united in tetrads (*Drimys*) or with three furrows and not united in tetrads (*Illicium*). Exine always reticulate.

Shrubs or small trees, native of Asia, Australia, and adjoining islands.

SCHIZANDREAE. Grains oblate spheroidal, 22 to 28 μ in diameter, not united in tetrads, with six furrows meridionally arranged, three long and meeting at one pole and three short and not meeting at either pole.

Woody climbers, native of tropical Asia and Himalaya.

"The Magnoliaceae must be among if not the most primitive of all the angiosperms" (Wieland, 1909). The author of this statement regards them as most closely allied to the Mesozoic Bennettitales. Indeed, as he points out, their likeness to *Williamsonia* and to *Wielandiella* of that group leaves little doubt of their common genetic origin with them. This conclusion is abundantly sustained by the forms of the pollen grains of at least the tribe Magnolieae, for the grains of the four genera of that tribe are virtually indistinguishable in outward appearance from those of the Bennettitales and are of the most primitive type found among the dicotyledons. In these grains, however, we do not find any trace of the prothallial tissue which appears to have characterized the grains of the Bennettitales; but this is in line with the progressive reduction of prothallial tissue which was initiated among the pteridosperms.

The grains of the two remaining tribes of the family, Illicieae and Schizandreae, are very different, and they are of the utmost interest, because we can learn from them much regarding the organization of the grains not only of this group but of the dicotyledons in general. The grains of these two tribes, like those of the Magnolieae, are primitive, but, besides pointing backward toward the ancestral gymnosperms, those of some species show characters pointing unmistakably forward toward the higher angiosperms.

The grains of *Drimys* are of particular interest, because in them we see demonstrated two of the most important laws of pollen morphology. The grains happen to occur united in tetrads, a condition which is exceedingly rare among the lower angiosperms and gymnosperms. They are of the monocolpate or single-furrowed type, as would be expected in the Magnoliaceae, and, still more important, their furrows always face outward; that is to say, the furrow of each grain is on the distal side, the side remote from contact with its neighbors of the tetrad, as we have seen was the case among the gymnosperms. The grains of *Glyptostrobus*, for example, which are sometimes united in tetrads, are joined together by their dorsal surfaces, each with its pore facing outward; this is according to Fischer's law which appears to be universal for monocolpate grains. Thus Fischer (1890) says, "Wo jedes Körn eine Austrittsstelle besitzt, liegt diese stets nach aussen, dem Berührungspunkt der vier Körner gegenüber." Also Fritzsche points out (1837, page 711) that the four grains of the tetrads of *Philydrum lanuginosum* are grown together back to back with their furrows facing outward. It is therefore reasonable to assume that the same relation holds with other monocolpate grains, even though they are separated from each other before they reach maturity, and, conversely, the side upon which the pore or furrow occurs in all monocolpate grains is the distal side, and the opposite the proximal, in relation to its former position in its tetrad. This gives us points of orientation which are essential in making comparisons between the pollen grains of different species, families, and orders.

The most important difference between the grains of *Drimys* and those of the Magnolieae, apart from the union of the former in tetrads, is their shape, which tends to be isodiametric instead of elongate. The reason for this is probably entirely due to the fact that the tetrads are tetrahedral, with which arrangement an elongate shape is obviously incompatible. On the other hand, when grains are arranged in tetrads which are in a single plane they may become elongate in a direction at right angles to the plane of their union. For example, Fritzsche (1837) has pointed out that the pollen grains of *Annona tripetala* are united in one plane, and his figure (Plate IV, Fig. 7) shows that they are distinctly elongate transversely to the plane of the tetrad. A similar example is found in the grains of *Philydrum lanuginosum*, which in many ways are similar to those of *Drimys*. They have a single broad furrow and are joined back to back in the tetrad, but this special arrangement is not always the same; it may be square, rhomboidal, or tetrahedral, with the result that those grains which are associated in a single plane tend to be ellipsoidal and have an elliptical furrow, while those that are associated in the tetrahedral arrangement tend to be more nearly isodiametric, with the furrow circular or somewhat triangular in outline. It can therefore be stated as our second law that the association of pollen grains in tetrahedral tetrads tends to impose upon them an isodiametric form, while association in flat tetrads permits an elongate form.

According to the position at the beginning of the dicotyledonous series assigned by taxonomists to the Magnoliaceae, their pollen grains would be expected to be of a form standing somewhere between that of a pteridophyte spore and that of a higher angiosperm pollen grain. In most ways this is true. Particularly is this brought out when we compare the mechanisms whereby these pollen grains discharge their principal functions with those of the Pteridophyte spores, which come before, and those of the higher Angiosperms, which come after in the evolutionary scale. Two important functions which both spores and pollen grains have to perform are to provide a place of exit for the growing prothallus or for the emerging pollen tube, as the case may be, and, if the spore walls are thick and rigid, to provide an expanding mechanism to accommodate changes in volume due to changes in moisture. The means whereby these two functions are performed is clearly reflected in the morphology of the grain and, in a way, is a sign of the stage to which the pollen grain has attained in its advance up the evolutionary scale.

Among the pteridophyte spores there frequently occurs a triradiate crest with the radii reaching almost halfway round the grain (Fig. 89). Such spores originate in tetrahedral tetrads, and the radii of the triradiate crest mark the boundaries of the three faces of contact that each spore made with its three neighbors of the tetrad during its formative period; therefore the triradiate crest marks the proximal side of the grain. Germination of such spores commonly takes place by the dehiscence of the spore wall

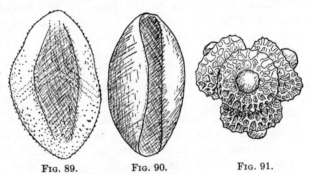

Fig. 89.   Fig. 90.   Fig. 91.

Fig. 89.—Spore of *Osmunda regalis*, 80 μ long, ventral view, drawn as if transparent in order to show the triradiate crest on the dorsal side.

Fig. 90.—Pollen grain of *Magnolia Soulangeana*, 35 by 40 μ, ventral view, partly expanded.

Fig. 91.—Tetrad of *Drimys Winteri*.

along the three ridges, forming a triradiate cleft through which the developing prothallus emerges. The pteridophyte spores appear to have no well-defined mechanism for accommodating changes in volume. In some, particularly those in which the surface is rendered inflexible by the presence of prominent reticulate thickenings, the spores shrink by a cupping in of the three flattened areas alternating with the three radii, probably because in these areas the reticulate thickenings are much less developed or absent, e.g., in the spores of *Lycopodium*. In others of which the distal surface is not stiffened by reticulate thickenings, e.g., the spores of *Osmunda* (Fig. 89), a cup-like depression forms on the distal side, opposite to the triradiate crest. This type of spore is the more interesting to us because the concavity resulting from this method of contraction often closely simulates the furrow of the monocolpate pollen grain, usually slightly distorted, it is true, by the presence of the triradiate crest on the opposite side of the grain. Nevertheless, its appearance suggests that, were it not for the asymmetrical stiffening effect of the triradiate crest, this false furrow of the pteridophyte spore would be essentially the same as the single furrow of the monocolpate pollen grain.

In the monocolpate grains of the Magnolieae and primitive gymnosperms the three lines of dehiscence are ordinarily absent, and both the function of volume-change accommodation and pollen-tube emergence are fulfilled by the single furrow which, in these grains, is a permanent organ. It is long, deep, and much more sharply defined than is the false furrow of the pteridophyte spores. The pollen-grain furrow also tapers similarly at both ends because of the absence of the disturbing effect of the triradiate crest, and it tends to give the grain the shape of a boat, unless, like the grain of *Drimys*, it happens to be formed and remain at maturity in a tetrahedral tetrad which mechanically prevents it from becoming elongate. This furrow is probably strictly homologous with the false furrow of the spores of pteridophytes but has here become a permanent organ. It has become hereditarily fixed in its position on the distal side of the grain, forced into that position by the presence of the triradiate crest on the proximal side. There it remains, though in pollen grains the triradiate crest has since become lost. The origin of this structure is in the same category as the origin of the four-lobed shape of the cells of a *Pediastrum* colony, as described by Harper (1919). The four-lobed shape of these cells was called forth by contact stimuli that each cell sustained from its neighbors of the colony; nevertheless, these cells are now

. . . able to attain their characteristic forms—, when almost entirely free from their normal environmental relations with the other cells of the colony. . . . We have here evidence that a cell form which may well have arisen first simply as a response to environmental stimuli has become fixed in heredity until now the series of growth processes by which it develops can go on quite independently of the stimulative conditions which originally called it forth.

That is to say, both in the cells of *Pediastrum* and in monocolpate pollen grains their basic form is an acquired character—acquired from contact stimuli, but permanently inherited even in the absence of the stimuli.

Among the higher dicotyledons the basic form of grain has three or more furrows arranged in the trischistoclasic system or system of equal linear stresses, as already described, and we know that these furrows occur at the points of contact that the grain made with its neighbors during its formation in the tetrad or elsewhere on its surface through stresses set up by these points of contact. These furrows are entirely different in origin and in form from the single furrow of the monocolpate grain, but their functions are the same, serving to allow both pollen-tube emergence and volume-change accommodation. In some respects, therefore, the trischistoclasic dicotyledonous type of grain is the direct antithesis of the monocolpate form of grain, for in the former the several furrows are initiated either at, or as a consequence of, its points of contact in the tetrad during its formative period, while in the latter the single furrow is initiated at the point on the grain most remote from contacts, originally so placed on account of the absence in this part of the grain of stiffening structures tending to prevent its formation.

The gap between these two types of grain is really very great, truly an expression of the enormous genetic difference that in general exists between the gymnosperms and the higher dicotyledons, and, were it not for the remarkable condition found among the grains of *Schizandra* (Plate V, Fig. 10) and *Kadsura*—the next genera of the Magnoliaceae that we have to consider—a connection between the two types of pollen grain might never be explained. But in the grains of these two genera, we find, existing side by side, the principal features of the triradiate pteridophyte spore, the monocolpate gymnosperm pollen grain, and the trischistoclasic dicotyledonous pollen grain. The grains of *Schizandra* are always shed singly, but the orientation of their parts in relation to their tetrad is clear from what we have learned from the grains of *Drimys* and *Glyptostrobus*, which are shed in tetrads, and from the Pteridophyte spore. The grains of *Schizandra* and *Kadsura* possess a triradiate crest which must have been proximal in the tetrad, marking the boundaries of the contact faces. Opposite the triradiate crest is a flexible area which cups in as the grain dries and bulges outward when it is moistened, homologous with the single furrow in the grains of

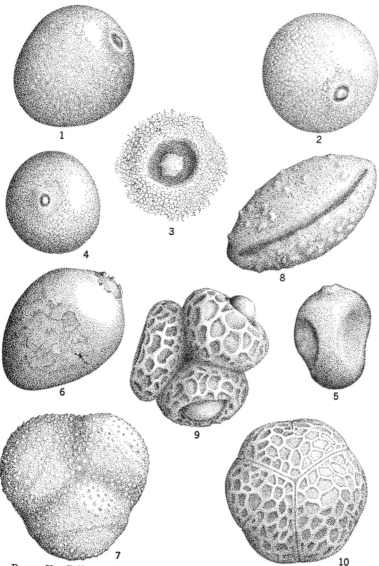

PLATE V.—Pollen grains of Gramineae, Cyperaceae, Juncaceae, and Magnoliaceae. 1, *Festuca elatior*, side view, 32 μ in diameter. 2, *Phleum pratense*, ventral view, 35 μ in diameter. 3, Germ pore and surrounding exine of a pollen grain of *Avena fatua*, diameter of the aperture 7.5 μ. 4, *Agrostis palustris*, ventral view, expanded, 28 μ in diameter. 5, The same contracted. 6, *Carex stricta*, side view, 44 μ long. 7, *Juncoides campestris*, whole tetrad, 38 μ in diameter. 8, *Liriodendron Tulipifera*, ventral view, 40 by 62 μ. 9, *Drimys Winteri*, each grain of the tetrad 34.2 μ in diameter, *cf.* Fig. 91. 10, *Schizandra chinensis*, dorsal view, 21.6 μ in diameter, *cf.* Fig. 93.

Drimys, and must have been distal in the tetrad. Alternating with the radii of the triradiate crest and on the equator of the grain, there are three short furrows which must have traversed in a meridional direction the three contact faces in the tetrad and are therefore homologous with the three furrows which commonly characterize the trischistoclasic grains of the dicotyledons. Thus in many ways this form of grain marks the bridging of the gap between the form of the gymnosperm grain and that of the higher dicotyledons (Fig. 93).

It is interesting to note that the three short furrows of the grains of *Schizandra* and *Kadsura* accommodate neither the pollen-tube emergence nor volume changes, as their homologues do in the pollen grains of the higher dicotyledons. In the grains of *Schizandra* and *Kadsura* the three long furrows which are homologous with the radii of the triradiate crest of fern spores perform the former function, and the flexible area on the distal side of the grain performs the latter. Nevertheless, the structure of the short furrows is exactly the same as that of the long furrows, so it seems reasonable to suppose that, with the loss of the triradiate crest, which appears to be entirely absent from the grains of all the higher dicotyledons, these three short furrows could easily take over their function, by simply splitting longitudinally, just as do the long furrows of this grain and the radii of the triradiate crest of the pteridophyte spores; and, having once acquired a longitudinal split, they could likewise take over the function of volume-change accommodation. Such, I believe, is the origin of the three furrows which characterize the basic form of pollen grains of the higher dicotyledons. In the grains of *Schizandra* and *Kadsura* they appear to function only as structural stiffenings of the walls of the grain, serving with the three long furrows to limit the invaginating area to the ventral side. In the grains of the higher dicotyledons they represent the taking over of two additional functions coincidently with the elimination of the organs that formerly performed them.

The development of these furrows was the great achievement of the dicotyledonous pollen grain. With it the grain was released from the limitations imposed upon it by the single long, deep furrow of the monocolpate form of grain which had been its heritage from the pteridosperms of the remotest antiquity. With this release came the most surprising diversity of form, through the relatively short succeeding span in the evolutionary scale, standing in remarkable contrast to the continuous monotony of the preceding development of the one-furrowed grain which we have traced step by step from the pteridosperms to the Magnoliaceae.   In such a form as this of *Schizandra* and *Kadsura* the grain was freed through the acquisition of a new set of organs allowing it a new way of doing things.   And in the following pages will be shown some of the multifarious forms of pollen grain which arose from its liberation.

KEY TO THE SPECIES

I. Furrow one
    A. Grains not in tetrads, boat-shaped; exine not reticulate; 41 to 63 μ long.
        1. Exine smooth.
            About 41 μ long.   Svenhedinia minor
            About 51 μ long.   Michelia champaca
        2. Exine granular, not warty.
            About 60 by 31 μ.   Magnolia acuminata
            About 54 by 22 μ.   Magnolia Soulangeana
        3. Exine granular and covered with conspicuous warts, 62 by 40 μ.   Liriodendron Tulipifera
    B. Grains in tetrads, exine reticulate.
        1. About 34.2 μ in diameter, tetrads rather loose.   Drimys Winteri
        2. About 18 to 19.5 μ in diameter, tetrads compact.   Drimys piperita
II. Furrows more than one, meridional; exine reticulate.
    A. Furrows three, meeting at both poles, grains 27.5 to 28.5 μ in diameter.   Illicium floridanum
                Illicium religiosum
    B. Furrows three, not meeting at either pole, 28.5 to 31 μ in diameter.   Illicium yunnanense
                Illicium sp. Maire 3327
    C. Furrows six, meridional, three of them long and meeting at one pole but free at the other; and three of them short, not meeting at either pole.   Grains oblate-spheroidal.   22 to 28 μ in diameter.   Area of the exine around the blank pole flexible and dipping in as the grain dries.   Schizandra spp.
                Kadsura spp.

MAGNOLIA L. MAGNOLIA

Grains boat-shaped, with a single deep, longitudinal furrow, essentially like that of the grains of *Cycas* and *Ginkgo*, capable of

gaping widely open (expanded) or becoming completely evaginated (over expanded); 50 to 60 μ long and about one-third as
broad when moist but with the furrow still invaginated.

They are a little more elongate than those of the cycads and
taper more toward their ends than those of *Ginkgo*. The furrow is
slightly pointed and appears to effect a rather complete closure
when the grains dry, differing in this respect from those of
gymnosperms with the same type of furrow. Exine rough-granular
on the outside but less so than in the grains of *Liriodendron*
(Plate V, Fig. 8), which they otherwise resemble closely; inside
the furrow, however, the exine is nearly or quite smooth. When
the grains are moistened they may, but do not always, swell
enormously, the floor of the furrow bulging out and causing the
grain to assume a spherical form. In this condition the part
that was inside the furrow can always be recognized by its
smoother texture and thinner exine, showing that the furrow is a
permanent organ.

About 30 species of trees and tall shrubs in Asia, eastern North
America, and southern Mexico. Commonly with large, showy
white, rose, purple, or yellow flowers, appearing in spring with or
before the leaves. Many species are cultivated. Insect pollinated and not a cause of hayfever.

Magnolia acuminata L. Cucumber-tree type. Grains as in
the generic description, 60 to 65 μ long; texture minutely and
uniformly rough-granular, by which character they can easily
be distinguished from those of the next species.

A large forest tree, reaching nearly 100 ft. in height. Flowers
appearing with the leaves, not showy, Ontario to Alberta and
southward. Often planted.

Magnolia Soulangeana Soul. Magnolia (Fig. 90). Grains as in
the generic description; texture conspicuously granular and
blotchy in appearance, suggesting to a certain extent that of the
grains of *Liriodendron* (Plate V, Fig. 8); 49 by 35 μ when moist but
not overexpanded, 54 by 23 μ when dry, showing that expansion
in width is accompanied by a shortening in length.

A common garden shrub or small tree of hybrid origin, with
large white flowers tinged with purple, appearing before the
leaves. Insect pollinated and not a cause of hayfever.

Svenhedinia minor Urb. (*Talauma minor* Urb.). Grains
essentially as in *Magnolia* but a little narrower in shape and a

little more tapering at their ends, 51 by 27.4 μ. Exine smooth inside and out. When the furrow evaginates the grain becomes ellipsoidal or nearly spheroidal, the exine appearing to be uniform throughout in texture and thickness.

A small tree, native of Cuba.

Michelia champaca L. Champaca. Grains essentially the same as those of *Magnolia*, uniform in size, about 41 μ long and 24 μ broad when moist but not overexpanded; texture smooth throughout. Apparently these grains expand easily, the floor of the furrow bulging so far out that the grain becomes more convex on its ventral than on its dorsal side. The part which was inside the furrow can be distinguished by its much thinner exine. In the expanded condition the grain is the same length as when unexpanded but increases in width to about 28.5 μ.

A medium-sized tree, similar in most respects to *Magnolia*, native of tropical Asia and cultivated elsewhere in tropical countries. The genus includes about 13 species of shrubs and small trees in tropical Asia, Himalaya, and China.

Liriodendron Tulipifera L. Tulip tree (Plate V, Fig. 8). Grains boat-shaped, and, in general form, essentially the same as those of *Magnolia*, about 62 μ long and 40 μ broad when moist but not overexpanded. Texture of the outside is extremely finely pitted, with large, wart-like nodules superimposed in irregular fashion. The rugged, coarse appearance that these grains present is unique and serves to distinguish them from all other monocolpate grains that I have seen.

A tall and beautiful forest tree, attaining a height of over 100 ft., with large, showy flowers which bear a superficial resemblance to yellow tulips. Throughout most of the eastern United States. Flowers in May and June after the leaves are fully developed. Insect pollinated and not a cause of hayfever.

Liriodendron was widely distributed in North America and Europe during the Cretaceous period but is now represented only by the present species and *L. chinensis* Sarg. in central China.

DRIMYS Forst.

Grains always in tetrads, which are nearly always tetrahedral, though occasionally, in *D. Winteri*, groups in other arrangements are found. Individual grains circular or somewhat triangular in outline, about 18 to 34.2 μ in diameter, each with a single furrow occurring as a large, roundish or irregularly shaped depression in the center of its distal (outer) side, with three flattened faces on its proximal (inner) side where pressed against its three neighbors of the tetrad.   All of the exposed surface of the grain, except the furrow, is covered by a reticulate system of high ridges enclosing angular lacunae, similar to but much coarser than those of the grains of *Illicium* and *Schizandra*.   The pattern of the reticulum is not continuous from grain to grain throughout the tetrad.   In each grain its mesh becomes finer toward the junctures with the other grains; at the angles where the surfaces of three grains come together it may even be quite smoothed out; along the edge of the furrow it ends abruptly with closed lacunae.   The floor of the furrow is deeply depressed and smooth and when the grain is moistened bulges out like a bubble, accommodating its expansion.

This tetrad is similar to that of *Glyptostrobus*, except that here the grains are constantly and firmly united.   The four grains function as individuals, each expanding and contracting, through a distention and retraction of its furrow floor, quite independently of its neighbors to which it is joined.   The only effect that the union of the four grains appears to have had upon them is to give them a roundish shape, and even this is due not so much to the fact that the grains remain united in a tetrad as to the fact that the tetrad is tetrahedral.   It is interesting to compare the effect of the grouping of this pollen tetrad with that of the Droseraceae or with the 16-celled compound grain of the Mimosaceae (q.v.), in both of which the whole group functions, in part at least, as a unit, the individual grains becoming profoundly modified as a consequence of their union, with a great reduction or total loss of both the pores and furrows which are conspicuous features of the grains of their nearest relatives.   Certainly the tetrads of *Drimys* and *Glyptostrobus*, in which the union has produced virtually no modification of the grains, must be regarded as the more primitive type.

The genus includes about 10 species of shrubs and small trees with pellucid-dotted leaves and white or whitish flowers, distributed in America from Mexico to the Straits of Magellan and in Australia, the Philippines, New Zealand, and adjoining islands. Included in it are such interesting plants as the aromatic pepper tree *D. aromatica*, of Tasmania; the pepper tree *D. axillaris*, of

New Zealand; and the pepper shrub *D. dipetala*, of New South Wales, Australia; besides the two following species:

Drimys Winteri Forst. Winter's bark or Cinnamon tree (Fig. 91; Plate V, Fig. 9) type. Tetrads generally tetrahedral, though occasionally they are found in other arrangements. Grains not closely pressed together, 34.2 μ in diameter; reticulum rather coarse but less so than in the grains of *D. piperita*.

A small tree, about 50 ft. high. Straits of Magellan in South America; with milk-white, jasmine-scented flowers. Occasionally cultivated.

Drimys piperita Hook. f. Grains similar to the type but always tetrahedral and more closely pressed together so that the tetrad is almost completely spherical. Reticulum more open, and its ridges conspicuously buttressed. The individual grains measure about 18.2 μ to 19.4 μ in diameter. These grains can easily be distinguished from those of *D. Winteri* by their more spherical tetrads, more open reticulum, and smaller size.

A bushy shrub with large, leathery leaves which are aromatic and peppery and small axillary white flowers. Native of the high mountains of Borneo, the Philippines, and New Guinea.

ILLICIUM L. CHINESE ANISE STAR ANISE

The pollen grains of the various species of *Illicium* exhibit two distinct types between which no obvious relationships are apparent. These are described under their specific headings.

The genus includes about 20 species of aromatic shrubs or small trees with thick evergreen leaves and small yellowish or purple flowers. In distribution they are mostly oriental (India, China, and the Philippines), with two species in the southern United States. The star anise used in flavoring is obtained from the Chinese species, *I. verum* Hook.

Illicium floridanum Ellis Anise tree, "Star anise," Poison bay (Fig. 92). Grains uniform, spheroidal, about 28.5 μ in diameter; tricolpate, occasionally dicolpate. Furrows long and slender, meeting at both poles, without germ pores. Exine completely covered by a system of anastomosing ridges bounding angular lacunae and ending with closed and somewhat smaller lacunae along the furrows, the ridges coalescing to form a sort of rim; mesh of the reticulum somewhat finer than in the grains of *Drimys Winteri*, otherwise similar.

When the grains expand the furrows broaden throughout their entire length, appearing as channels of uniform width, and display on each furrow membrane a central thickening extending its full length.   In their confluence at the poles and in their linear shape these furrows differ from those of other dicotyledons and may not even be homologous with them.   Instead, they suggest by their appearance and the fact that the grains readily split

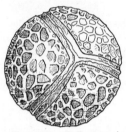

open along them, with the split starting at the poles, that they are lines of dehiscence, homologous with the triradiate crests of Pteridophyte spores.   To settle this point, however, it would be necessary to observe the orientation of these grains in their tetrads.

The anise tree is a shrub 6 to 10 ft. high,

Fig. 92.—Pollen grain of *Illicium floridanum,* 28.5 μ in diameter, fully expanded, polar view.   The opposite pole is exactly the same.

in swamps.   Florida to Louisiana.   It flowers early in spring, producing large, purple, nodding flowers.

Illicium religiosum (*I. anisatum* (L.) Sieb. & Zucc.) Shikimi, Japanese sacred anise tree.   Grains indistinguishable from those of the preceding species, about 28 μ in diameter.

Shikimi is a small tree, native of Japan, occasionally cultivated in the southern part of the United States.

Illicium yunnanense Franchet. Grains uniform, oblately flattened and more or less three-lobed in outline, about 30.8 μ in diameter, tricolpate, with furrows long and tapering but not quite meeting at either pole, deeply sunken, imparting to the grain its three-lobed appearance. Furrow membranes marked with median linear thickenings throughout their length but with no indication of germ pores.   Exine of the general surface uniformly reticulate, similar to that of the grains of *Schizandra* (Plate V, Fig. 10) but of heavier ridges and smaller and less angular lacunae.

I am unable to say whether or not the furrows of this grain are homologous with the long furrows of the two preceding species. The fact that they taper and do not meet at the poles suggests that they belong to the ordinary trischistoclasic system of the higher dicotyledons; but if this is so, the possession of such furrows by the grains of this species certainly denotes a very great genetic difference between it and the preceding species. This matter deserves further investigation and could be determined by finding out the orientation of the grains in their tetrads— whether the furrows are so arranged that they bound the faces of contact or pass through their centers.

A shrub or small tree about 10 ft. high, with yellowish, fragrant flowers, native of China; it has been collected in and about Yunnan, Tsangshan range, between Tatzang and Hsiakuan.

SCHIZANDRA Michx. BAY STAR VINE

Grains generally uniform, oblately spheroidal, 22.8 to 28.5 μ broad and about 18 to 19 μ deep. Provided with *six* meridionally

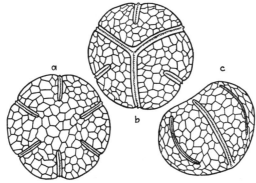

FIG. 93.—Pollen grain of *Schizandra chinensis* (*cf.* Plate V, Fig. 10); *a*, ventral; *b*, dorsal; *c*, side views.

arranged furrows; the whole surface adorned with a reticulate system of lacunae bounded by low, delicate ridges similar to those of the grains of *Illicium* but finer than in those of *Drimys*. The furrows are also the same as those of the grains of *Illicium floridanum* in their structure, their linear form, and the central thickening of the furrow membrane. They are sunken in the surface of the grain and, being perfectly symmetrical in arrangement, impart to it a six-lobed outline when seen in polar view.

The furrows are of two kinds: Three of them are long, fused at one pole and reaching in a meridional direction about two-thirds of the way toward the opposite pole; while the other three are short, ranged around the equator alternately with the three long furrows and also directed meridionally (Fig. 93). The short furrows are various in length in the different species but never meet at either pole, though they may approach as far as the long furrows toward the blank pole.   Both kinds of furrow are exactly alike, in structure, differing only in their length.   The long furrows appear to serve as lines of dehiscence, for the grains are frequently found breaking open along them, starting at the convergent pole, recalling the condition found in Pteridophyte spores.

When these grains expand and contract the furrows play no part in the volume-change accommodation; instead, the area about the blank pole dips in cup fashion when they dry and rounds out when they are moistened.   The rims of the furrows are thickened, and the intine underlying them is also slightly thickened, rendering the furrows inflexible so that they act like the ribs of an umbrella, serving to prevent the bending in of the walls of the grain except in the region beyond their ends.   The area that is permitted to invaginate is thus delimited by the ends of the furrows surrounding the blank pole.   The surface of this flexible area is reticulate, as is the rest of the grain, but it is clearly defined and obviously functions as an expansion mechanism for the accommodation of changes in volume.   It therefore seems justifiable to assume that it is homologous with the single furrow of the grains of *Drimys*.   If this is so it then follows that the blank pole must have been distal and the convergent pole proximal in the tetrad, as is the case in fern spores, lending strength to the belief that the three long furrows are homologous with the triradiate crest of fern spores and therefore represent the boundaries of the three contact faces that the grain made with its neighbors of the tetrad; this being so, the three short furrows pass through the centers of the three contact faces and are therefore homologous, in position at least, with the three furrows of ordinarily tricolpate pollen grains and others of the trischistoclasic system among the dicotyledons.   They do not function as furrows, either as expansion mechanisms or as places of emergence for the pollen tubes, the former function being retained by the area about the distal or blank pole, and the latter accomplished by dehiscence along the three long furrows at the proximal or convergent pole.   In this respect this grain is anomalous but is of the utmost interest because it shows the spatial relation between the furrows of the trischistoclasic or linear stress system, the single furrow of the monocolpate grain of the lower gymnosperms, and the three lines of dehiscence or triradiate crest of the pteridophyte spore.

Schizandra is a genus of about six or seven twining woody vines, in China and Japan, one in the United States, others in tropical Asia and Himalaya. Several species are cultivated for their bright-green leaves and cup-shaped white or crimson flowers which are followed by scarlet, berry-like fruits in autumn.

The genus is said to be an "anomalous member of the family" (Bailey 1924), but it is very closely related to *Kadsura* with which its pollen grains are identical. The similarity of its pollen grain, to that of *Illicium* and possibly to a certain extent of *Drimys* is also evidence of its genetic relationship with them.

Schizandra chinensis K. Koch. (Plate V, Fig. 10) type. Grains as in the generic description, uniform, 21.6 μ in diameter, short furrows not extending noticeably farther toward the blank pole than toward the convergent pole, thus approximately bisected by the equator.

A twining shrub, China and Japan. Flowers in May and June.

Schizandra coccinea Michx. Bay star vine. Grains uniform, 25 to 28 μ in diameter. The short furrows do not extend quite so far toward the convergent pole as toward the blank pole, thus are not bisected by the equator. The thickened rim of both the long and short furrows is a little broader than in the previous species.

A slender, high-climbing woody vine with monoecious crimson-purplish flowers and scarlet berries; in woods; South Carolina to Florida to Louisiana. Flowers in spring and summer.

Schizandra Hanceana Baill. (*Kadsura chinensis* Hance, *K. japonica* Benth.). Grains as in the type, uniform oblately spheroidal, about 24 μ in diameter. All six furrows end evenly around the area at the blank pole. The short furrows do not extend quite so far toward the convergent as toward the blank pole so are not bisected by the equator.

A woody climber, native of China and occasionally cultivated in the warmer parts of Europe.

KADSURA Juss.

Grains as in the *Schizandra* type, except for minor specific differences, showing less deviation from the type than is found within the genus *Schizandra* itself.

Woody climbers with mostly leathery leaves and axillary, rather inconspicuous, whitish or rose-colored flowers. Native of tropical Asia. Though the flowers are not showy, some species are cultivated for the beauty of their dark-green lustrous leaves and clusters of scarlet fruit in autumn.

Kadsura peltigera Rehder & Wilson. Grains as in *Schizandra* type, uniform, 25.1 to 26.2 μ broad and 18 μ deep. All six furrows end evenly around the area at the blank pole. The short furrows extend about as far toward the convergent pole as toward the blank pole, so that they are approximately bisected by the equator.

Climbing shrub 8 to 12 ft. high with solitary, axillary yellow flowers, about 2.5 cm. broad.

In forests in Kiangsi and Yunnan, China.

Kadsura scandens Blume. Grains uniform, oblate spheroidal, 22.8 to 24 μ broad. Essentially as in the *Schizandra* type, except that the blank area about the distal pole is, on the average, a little larger in proportion to the size of the grain.

A climbing shrub reaching a height of 75 ft. in Java, Sumatra, and Borneo.

Kadsura paucidenticulata Merr. Grains uniform, oblate spheroidal, 23.9 to 25.1 μ broad, essentially as in the *Schizandra* type. Polar area rather larger, and short furrows shorter, extending farther toward the blank pole than toward the convergent pole.

A climbing shrub, native of the Philippines, similar to *K. philippinensis* Merr. and *K. Macgregorii* Merr., also inhabiting the same region.

Kadsura japonica Juss. Grains as in the *Schizandra* type, uniform, 22.1 to 22.8 μ in diameter; short furrows rather long and bisected by the equator.

Japan and eastern China.

NYMPHAEACEAE Water-lily Family

Grains of various size and shape, provided with a single large furrow which is nearly closed by an operculum of similar character to the exine of the general surface but separated from the latter by a narrow strip of thin, flexible exine which generally completely surrounds the operculum and functions as the furrow. Exine thin, of warty-granular texture, and generally provided with conspicuous spines or nodules of widely various character (Fig. 94; Plate VI, Figs. 1, 6).

Morphologically the ring-shaped band of thin exine together with the islet of thicker exine that it surrounds seems to be homologous with the furrow. That this is the proper interpretation is borne out by the fact that the detached piece of exine is usually slightly different in texture, sculpturing, and thickness from the general exine of the grain, recalling the difference in texture and thickness encountered between the furrow floor and the general exine of the grains of the Cycadales. Consequently I shall regard it in this light and, for the convenience of the present discussion, shall call the ring-shaped strip of thin exine the furrow ring; and the enclosed islet of thicker exine, which is homologous with the furrow floor of the grains of the primitive gymnosperms, the operculum (Fig. 94).

In the grains of *Castalia* (Plate VI, Fig. 1) the operculum is broadly elliptical or circular in outline and so large that it occupies most of the ventral half of the grain. In the grains of *Nymphaea* it is elongate and extremely narrow (Plate VI, Fig. 6). Though these two types of furrow are strictly homologous, mechanically they act quite differently, so that at first sight the two forms appear to bear no relation to each other. When the grain of *Castalia* dries the furrow ring permits the operculum to be drawn into the dorsal hemisphere, causing the grain to assume the shape of a round-topped bun. When that of *Nymphaea* dries, the long elliptical furrow, together with its operculum, is invaginated as if it were a simple elongate furrow, causing the grain to simulate the familiar boat-shaped form of the primitive gymnosperms, Magnoliaceae, monocotyledons etc. Nevertheless, the only truly morphological difference between the grains of *Castalia* and those of *Nymphaea* is in the shape of the furrow; in one it is short and broad, and in the other long and narrow. Functionally in both, the operculum insures complete closure of the furrow; it finds its functional analogy in the strip-like thickenings on the furrow membranes of the grains of some of the Nassauvineae (Wodehouse, 1929). Its morphological homology, however, is with the floor of the furrow of the grains of the primitive gymnosperms.

The pollen grains of the Nymphaeaceae have been described by many authors. Thus Fischer (1890) regards the grains of

Castalia as provided with a single lid, but those of *Nymphaea* he regards as provided merely with a single furrow. Bauer has shown *"Nuphar advena"* (*i.e., Nymphaea advena*) as spherical and without any furrow. Heintze (1927), from evidence based partly on their pollen grains, associated the Nymphaeaceae with the Piperaceae and Magnoliaceae in his class Pseudo-dicotyledoneae, a group which seems to include most of the primitive dicotyledons.

The Nymphaeaceae are a family of aquatic plants with submerged or floating leaves and aerial flowers. Included in the family, besides the two genera treated here, are *Victoria* Lindl. *Euryale* Salisb. and *Barclaya* Wall., of which I have not been able to examine the pollen. According to Fischer (1890, page 62), however, the pollen of *Victoria regia* is similar to that of *Castalia*, except that its grains remain at maturity united in tetrahedral tetrads. They are smooth, and each has a single furrow occupying almost a half of its ventral side. From his description this form recalls in striking fashion the grains of *Drimys* among the Magnoliaceae.

Regarding the relationships of the Nymphaeaceae that are suggested by their pollen-grain forms, we have already seen that the Magnoliaceae, the several tribes of the Coniferae, and the monocotyledons (*e.g.,* the Palmaceae) inherited the broad, open, cycadean type of furrow, and each devised its own way of modifying, protecting, or eliminating it. Now, in the grains of the Nymphaeaceae, we see still another way of accomplishing the same end. Thus, as far as their pollen morphology is concerned, the Nymphaeaceae may represent a genetic line coordinate with the tribes of the Coniferales, the monocotyledons, and the lower dicotyledons.

KEY TO THE SPECIES

I. Furrow elongate, provided with a narrow operculum; exine finely warty-granular and covered with long, conical spines. Grains about 57 μ long.   *Nymphaea advena*

II. Furrow circular or broadly elliptical, occupying the major portion of the ventral side of the grain, almost completely closed by its operculum. Exine various.
    A. Exine bristly or nodular. Grains 30 by 28 μ.   *Castalia odorata*
    B. Exine nodular, not bristly.

40 to 42 μ long.   Castalia flava
34 to 38 to long.   Castalia mexicana
C. Exine smooth.   Grain 30 to 34 μ long. Castalia amazonum
                                           Castalia gracilis

Nymphaea advena Soland. (*Nuphar advena* Ait.) Yellow pond lily (Plate VI, Fig. 6) type. Grains rather uniform, about 51.3 μ long, provided with a single, longitudinal furrow closed by a narrow, linear operculum. Exine heavy, slightly granular, with long, sturdy, and obtusely pointed spines which are longer on the dorsal than on the ventral side, varying from 5 to 8.5 μ in length, irregularly arranged.

When dry the grains are more or less boat-shaped, with the furrow tightly closed and somewhat invaginated. When moistened the furrow becomes evaginated, causing the grain to assume an oblate spheroidal form, with the furrow extending a little less than half around it on the ventral side. In this condition the furrow can be seen to be provided with a narrow strip of exine, which is the operculum, of a texture similar to that of the rest of the grain but bearing spines a little shorter.

Nymphaea advena is an aquatic herb with floating leaves, submersed leaves seldom present, and large, showy yellow flowers appearing in June and July. Nova Scotia to the Rocky Mountains and southward to Florida, Texas, and Utah.

The flowers are insect pollinated but shed large amounts of pollen, which, when found in Postglacial silts, can easily be identified and is valuable in showing the local conditions under which such deposits were laid down, since its mode of pollination precludes the likelihood of its being transported far from its place of origin in effective quantities.

In his studies of the pollen grains of ancient sediments, Meinke (1926) has depicted this grain and states that the spicules are fairly far apart and that the surface between them is reticulate. Such a reticulate appearance of the exine I find tends to develop upon drying after being soaked in water; therefore it cannot be regarded as a morphological character. Von Mohl (1835) illustrates the grain of *Nymphaea* and draws attention to the fact that it has a single furrow.

The genus comprises about eight species, of rather wide distribution in the North Temperate Zone, all rather similar in habit and appearance. Of these I have examined the pollen of

N. hybridus and *N. bombacini* but was unfortunately not able to procure material in condition suitable for detailed studies. However, their grains appear to be the same as those of *N. advena* described on page 343.

CASTALIA Salisb. Water lily

Grains dome-shaped, 30 to 46 μ in diameter, monocolpate, with a large, circular or broadly elliptical furrow occupying the greater part of the ventral surface and almost completely closed by an operculum. Exine warty-granular and provided with rounded nodules and conspicuous spines extremely irregular in their size, shape, and arrangement, or smooth.

When moist and fully expanded the grains are approximately globular but slightly flattened on the ventral side and slightly elongate, with the furrow ring broad and encircling the grain

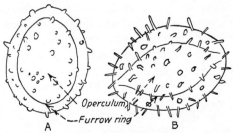

Fig. 94.—Pollen grain of white water lily, *Castalia odorata*, ventral view: *A*, a grain with its operculum completely surrounded by a furrow ring; *B*, with its operculum joined at the two ends to the general surface of the exine.

just below the equator. In this condition the large operculum occupies the major portion of the ventral side. When dry and contracted the operculum is drawn tightly inward and more or less flattened, but the dorsal part of the grain retains its spherical curvature. The grain in this condition suggests the appearance of a turtle with its appendages withdrawn. Underlying the margins of the furrow is a subexineous thickening which calls to mind the thickened furrow rim of the grains of *Podocarpus*, with which it appears to be homologous. In the grain of *Nymphaea* this rim furnishes a sort of seat for the operculum in its valve-like action in closing the orifice of the furrow.

When observed from the ventral side in the contracted condition (Fig. 94a) the grains may present a more or less circular outline, the invaginated furrow appearing as a smaller and complete circle, concentric with the periphery of the grain; but more often the grains in this condition are broadly elliptical in outline, in which case the furrow ring may be discontinuous, leaving the exine of the operculum connected with that of the general surface of the grain through two isthmuses (Fig. 94*b*). Such a furrow recalls that of the grains of the cycads and Bennettitales, and is further evidence that the operculum of the grain of *Castalia* is homologous with the furrow floor of the ancient cycadean type of pollen grain.

The pollen grains of *Castalia*, on account of their large size and characteristic appearance, are easy to recognize and yield valuable data in paleoclimatic studies. They have been studied by many investigators and variously interpreted. Meincke (1927) describes them as spiculed on one side and bulging and smooth on the other, one-half seeming without spicules. A grain stated to be that of *Castalia* in the fossilized form is illustrated by Lewis and Coke (1929), but their figure, which shows a grain with regular conical spines evenly distributed in serried ranks over its surface and with a single longitudinal furrow, precludes the possibility of its being that of *Castalia*. If the spines of their figure were a little less uniform in their arrangement, it would suit, however, the grains of *Nymphaea*. Grains of *Castalia Lotus* are illustrated in both the wet and dry condition by von Mohl (1835) and show admirably the mechanism whereby harmomegathy takes place. Hugo Fischer (1890) includes the grains of *Castalia* in his group of "grains with a single lid."

Castalia odorata (Soland.) Woodv. & Wood (*Nymphaea odorata* Soland.) White water lily, Water nymph (Plate VI, Fig. 1) type. Grains about 30 by 38 μ.

The entire surface is generally covered with long, conspicuous spines or with rounded, wart-like protuberances or both. The spines are unique: they have a resinous appearance and, when they reach their best development, are long, straight, cylindrical rods, not tapering but maintaining their full diameter almost or quite to their tips, which are generally rounded but may be truncated squarely or obliquely or bluntly pointed. They are set on the surface of the grain at all possible angles and are often extremely oblique. They are never uniform, in spacing, shape, or length, differing in these respects markedly from the spines encountered in the grains of most other plants. Sometimes they are well developed throughout the grain, imparting to the whole surface, except for the furrow ring which is always smooth, a bristly appearance, but nearly always they are better developed on the dorsal surface than on the ventral, and frequently on the operculum they are represented only by little wart-like nodules. When examined with high magnification the nodules have an appearance suggestive of spines that have been melted down and spread out into resinous-like lumps. But within the same flower may be found grains that are entirely spine covered and others that are entirely nodular.

Castalia odorata is an aquatic herb with submerged and floating leaves and aerial flowers, in ponds and slow streams. Newfoundland to Manitoba, southward to Florida, Louisiana, and Kansas. Flowers June to September. The flowers are entirely insect pollinated but shed large amounts of pollen.

Castalia flava (Leitner) Greene. Grains as in the type, except that they are provided with only poorly developed spines or are entirely nodular, 46.7 to 52 μ in diameter. The dorsal surface is generally covered with closely packed tubercles, but the operculum has only a few along its margin and is otherwise smooth.

An aquatic herb in lakes, lagoons, and slow streams. Florida. Flowers all summer.

Castalia zanzibarensis Casp. (*Nymphaea zanzibarensis* Casp.) Grains various in size, many empty and abortive, about 40 by 37.5 μ. Exine nodular, without spines.

Tropical Africa.

Castalia mexicana Zucc. Yellow water lily. Grains in general shape as in the type but without spines, 37.5 by 41 μ. Exine warty, with irregularly shaped nodules on the dorsal surface, resembling droplets of varnish that form when applied to a glassy surface, but nearly or quite smooth on the ventral.

Mexico.

Castalia amazonum (Mart. & Zucc.) Britt. & Wilson. Grains as in the type, except that they lack all trace of spines, the texture of the exine being quite smooth throughout; uniform in size, about 33.5 by 29.6 μ.

Haiti, Puerto Rico, Trinidad, Cuba, Santo Domingo.

Castalia gracilis Rose. Grains as in the type, except that the texture of the exine is quite smooth throughout; uniform in size, about 30.8 by 27.5 μ.

Mexico.

SALICACEAE Willow Family

The family Salicaceae consists of the two genera, *Salix* and *Populus*, which are unquestionably closely related but differ from each other in their modes of pollination. All species of *Populus* are completely limited to wind pollination, while those of *Salix* are primarily insect pollinated. In keeping with this are found great differences between the pollen grains of the two genera, despite their close relationship. Those of *Salix* are tricolpate and heavily reticulate (Plate VI, Fig. 2), characters which we have seen are associated with insect pollination, and they show no considerable deviation from the basic dicotyledonous form, while those of *Populus* are nearly smooth and entirely without furrows (Plate VI, Fig. 4), characters which we have seen are distinctly anemophilous.

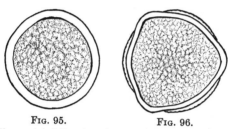

Fig. 95.   Fig. 96.

Fig. 95.—Pollen grain of *Populus nigra*, optical section.
Fig. 96.—Pollen grain of *Salix fragilis*, optical section in the plane of the equator.

The exine of the grains of *Salix* is thick, and this together with its heavily reticulate surface imparts to their walls considerable rigidity (Fig. 96). Associated with this are well-developed furrows which function as harmomegathi, opening and closing freely in response to the volume changes of the grain. The pattern of the reticulum is of a type found in the grains of many other species in widely separated groups. Its lacunae are rather large and angular, and their ridges high. The character of the mesh has a tendency to vary in different parts of the grain. Generally it is most open in the middle of the lunes, and closer toward the poles and toward the margins of the furrows along which it ends abruptly with closed lacunae, showing that the furrow is not torn through the reticulum but is developed simultaneously with it as a co-ordinate structure.

In the pollen grains of the poplars, in association with their mode of pollination by wind, the reticulum of the exine is either completely lacking or only barely recognizable, but there is some variation in this among the different species. Accompanying the reduction in thickness of the exine has gone the disappearance of furrows, which are entirely lacking in all species of *Populus*. The exine, however, is marked all over by small rifts, as if it were inelastic and too small to cover the grain as it attained its full size, an appearance which suggests that the exine of *Populus* is a vanishing structure.

There are grounds, other than the evidence of their pollen grains, for believing that the willows are in the transition stage in their mode of pollination, developing in the direction of anemophily. This is suggested by the arrangement of their flowers in catkins with both the anthers and styles exserted and by the separation of sexes and the abundance of their pollen which is blown freely about in the air. The opposite interpretation has been placed on these facts by Arber and Parkin (1907), who regard "*Populus* as the older genus and *Salix* as derived from a poplar-like ancestor at a more remote period," believing that "entomophily in *Salix* is but a recently acquired character." If Arber and Parkin's interpretation is correct and the tendency is toward entomophily, the pollen grains of *Salix* must have greatly outstripped the other characters of the plants in their evolutionary processes, becoming completely entomophilous even before the flowers themselves, a supposition which is highly improbable because, in evolutionary processes, the pollen grains are notoriously inert, generally lagging far behind the other organs of the plant. It seems to me much more likely that both *Salix* and *Populus* are derived from some willow-like ancestor which was entomophilous and that, while the poplars have become entirely wind pollinated, the willows have not yet proceeded far enough toward anemophily to effect any characteristic modification in their pollen grains.

KEY TO THE SPECIES

I. Grains spheroidal or oblate, about 17 to 18 μ in diameter, generally with three furrows or occasionally other numbers in the trischisto-clasic system. Exine heavily reticulate.   Salix fragilis
Salis discolor

II. Grains spheroidal or somewhat irregular, 24 to
    37 μ in diameter, exine thin, scarcely reticu-
    late, acolpate.

    A. Exine fragmentary or broken by rifts.

    B. Exine continuous, not broken by rifts.

Populus Sargentii
Populus Fremontii
Populus balsamifera
Populus Eugenei
Populus nigra
Populus grandidentata
Populus MacDougalii
Populus angustifolia

SALIX (Tourn.) L. Willow, Osier

Grains spheroidal, flattened, three-lobed, or, when dry, ellipsoidal; about 17.8 μ in diameter; prevailingly tricolpate. Exine reticulate, with sharply angular lacunae and vertical ridges which are thin and blade-like on their crests but thickened toward their bases (Plate VI, Fig. 2).

The mesh of the reticulum is generally coarser toward the centers of the lunes, finer toward the poles, and sharply bounded along the margins of the furrows with much smaller lacunae. The furrows are long and tapering, their membranes flecked as if covered with detached fragments of the reticulum, without a true germ pore but generally with a central bulge representing the point of emergence of the pollen tube.

The genus comprises about 150 species of trees and shrubs in nearly all moist temperate regions and well up into the Arctic Circle. Some of the species flower very early in spring, long before the first appearance of the leaves, while others flower at the same time as the unfolding of the leaves, and still others after the leaves are fully developed. Thus in many localities the different species of willow flower throughout a period extending over several months. They are obviously primarily insect pollinated, since the flowers are provided with nectar and sweet scent, and they succeed in attracting many bees and other insects. Nevertheless, the pollen of willows can be caught on atmospheric pollen slides in considerable quantities during the flowering period, and sometimes it becomes an important factor in hayfever; the pollen of *S. lasiolepis* is said by Chamberlain (1927) to be a common cause of hayfever in Oregon. On the whole, however, experience indicates that the willows can be regarded as only relatively unimportant in hayfever.

Willow pollen is frequently found in Postglacial silts.   In this connection the pollen of *Salix repens* has been described and illustrated by Erdtman (1923), and that of *S. serecia* by Sears (1930). Pollen grains of unnamed species are illustrated by Docturowsky and Kudrjaschow (1923) and by Meinke (1927), the latter author drawing attention to their resemblance to the grains of *Fraxinus* and *Adoxa*.   Fossilized pollen of willow is described and illustrated by Lewis and Coke (1930), who found it in the Dismal Swamp peat of Virginia and North Carolina at all levels, though the trees are nearly absent from the region at the present time.   In his studies of the pollen carried by bees, Høeg (1924) was able to recover willow pollen occasionally from bees collected in Novaya Zemlya, and he also found that it was the pollen most frequently occurring on bees from Ellesmere Land (1929).

Salix fragilis L. Crackle willow (Plate VI, Fig. 2) type.   Grains slightly oblate or spheroidal; tricolpate; uniform; about 17.8 μ in diameter; otherwise as in the generic description.

A large tree introduced from Europe but now widely distributed throughout much of the eastern part of the United States, generally along the borders of streams.   Flowers in May at the time when the leaves are unfolding.

Salix discolor Muhl. Pussy willow.   Normal grains spheroidal or slightly oblate; about 17.6 μ in diameter.   There are always some giant grains with six or four furrows and others that are entirely irregular.

A shrub or occasionally a small tree of moist places, consisting of several races.   Flowering very early in spring—March to May—before the first appearance of the leaves.   Nova Scotia to Saskatchewan, Delaware, and Missouri.

POPULUS (Tourn.) L. Poplar, Cottonwood, Aspen

Grains spheroidal or somewhat irregular in shape, 24 to 37 μ in diameter, acolpate, *i.e.*, without germinal furrows in the ordinary sense.   Exine extremely thin, sometimes even fragmentary, minutely reticulate, or granular in appearance.   Intine thick.

The only resemblance that these grains bear to those of *Salix* is in the vaguely reticulate character of their exine.   The latter is apparently a vanishing structure; in the pollen of some species it is not even a continuous coat, but is marked by a number of rifts irregular in size, shape and arrangement, and which give the impression of having been torn through the exine with the expansion of the grain, yet they are found as readily when the grains are dry and unexpanded as when moist and expanded. The absence of true furrows is a necessary corollary to the thinness of the exine; we have already seen that the formation of furrows is the result of stresses, and such an exine as this is too weak to transmit stresses. Moreover furrows are not needed to permit either pollen-tube emergence or volume-change accommodation in the presence of such a flexible and easily ruptured exine. The extreme thinness of the exine appears to be compensated by a corresponding increase in thickness of the intine which is uniformly much thicker than that of the grains of *Salix*.

The condition encountered here is an example of a principle of broad application. That is that pollination by wind tends to bring about a reduction of the exine with an attendant loss or reduction of its structures such as furrows, pores and sculpturing, and this tends to be compensated by an increase in thickness of the intine. A similar condition is found in the grains of *Fraxinus*, for example. *Fraxinus* is wind pollinated while belonging to a family of otherwise insect-pollinated plants, and its pollen grains have exines greatly reduced in thickness and intines greatly thickened as compared with those of other members of the family. We have already seen that pollination on or under water also tends to bring about a reduction of the exine, but in this case it is not attended with a corresponding increase in thickness of the intine. Many of the Gymnosperms, which are all wind pollinated, have developed this type of pollen grain. For example the pollen grains of the Taxodineae and Cupressineae have deviated far from the basic primitive form of the gymnosperms and developed a form of grain not unlike that of the poplars.

The poplars are mostly large trees, highly specialized in their adaptation to wind pollination, shedding huge quantities of light, air-borne pollen early in spring before the leaves unfold. In many regions where the trees are abundant they cause much hayfever. Thus *P. deltoides* is said to cause hayfever in Oklahoma (Balyeat, 1926) and in Colorado is credited with about 19 per cent of the hayfever cases (Mullen, 1922), while other species are important in Oregon (Chamberlain, 1927) and Colorado (Waring, 1926).   Still other species will be mentioned under their descriptions.

It is stated by Waring and Pope (1927) that the "cotton"— the copious tomentum borne by the seeds—of the cottonwood trees is a factor in hayfever.   This assertion is based upon experimental results obtained with seven hayfever patients in the neighborhood of Denver, Colorado, who gave positive skin tests to the cotton.   The species employed are not definitely stated, but *P. balsamifera, P. angustifolia, P. deltoides, P. nigra* var. *italica*, and *P. Sargentii* are mentioned as the species probably producing the cotton in the air at the time when the symptoms of hayfever were manifest.   On the other hand, it is emphatically denied by Phillips in Arizona (1923, p. 274) that the cotton of cottonwood trees can cause hayfever.   He likewise does not state which species, but it appears that he had reference, at least in part, to *P. Macdougalii*.

The fragile and unresistant nature of the exine of poplar pollen grains renders it doubtful if they can be recognized with any degree of certainty in peat deposits, but in this connection *P. deltoides* is described and figured by Sears (1930) and *P. tremula* by Docturowsky and Kudriaschow (1923).

Populus Sargentii Dode. Western cottonwood (Plate VI, Fig. 4) type.   Grains all normal, uniform in size and shape, spheroidal, averaging about 27 μ in diameter.   The surface texture would be described as scurfy, but upon minute examination it is found to be derived from a broken or fragmentary reticulum, though this is less apparent in this species than in some of the others.   Otherwise as in the generic description.

A large tree in semiarid regions, shedding much pollen very early in spring.   It has been found to give marked reactions with hayfever patients and causes some hayfever in regions where abundant, more so than *P. angustifolia* (Hall in Scheppegrell, 1917).   Flowers in March and April.   Saskatchewan to North Dakota, Nebraska, Kansas, and New Mexico.

Populus Fremontii S. Wats. Fremont's cottonwood.   Grains all normal and nearly uniform, averaging about 25.3 μ in diameter.   The reticulum of the exine is exceedingly fine but is more easily seen than in the type and, though much broken by irregular rifts, does not present a scurfy appearance.   Otherwise as in the type.

A large tree. Flowers very early in spring; throughout western California and Lower California. Exists in several varieties, some of which are planted as shade trees in California, where they are known to produce hayfever (Selfridge, 1920).

Populus MacDougalii Rose California cottonwood. Grains variously irregular in size and shape, many abortive, suggesting hybridity of origin; normal grains averaging about 36.4 μ in diameter. Surface reticulum slightly more marked than in the other species and without rifts. Otherwise as in the type.

A large tree in semiarid regions. Sheds much pollen very early in spring, causing some hayfever starting about Feb. 1 (Phillips, 1923). Abundant on the Colorado River delta, parts of California, Nevada, and Arizona. It is doubtful if this species is distinct from *P. Fremontii* S. Wats. It should probably be regarded as a variety of the latter.

Populus grandidentata Michx. Large-toothed aspen. Grains uniform in size and apparently nearly all normal, but irregular in shape, about 28.9 μ in diameter. They differ from the type in the extremely fine reticulate pitting of their exine which also lacks the rifts that are characteristic of the type.

A large tree flowering in April. Nova Scotia to Ontario and Minnesota. South to Delaware, North Carolina, and Tennessee.

Populus nigra L. Black poplar. Grains nearly all perfect. Spheroidal, averaging 24.4 μ in diameter. Exine covered by an extremely fine reticulum, more apparent than in the type and more suggestive of the pattern of *Salix*, broken by irregular rifts. Figured by Meinke (1927).

This species consists of several varieties and is perhaps better known in the variety *italica* Du Roi, Lombardy poplar, naturalized from Europe and much planted. Flowers in April and May.

Populus angustifolia James Narrow-leaved cottonwood. Grains mostly normal and uniform but generally accompanied by some that are abortive. Spheroidal, averaging about 25.7 μ in diameter. Surface reticulum coarser and not broken by rifts. Otherwise as in the type.

A large tree in moist soil, especially along streams. Flowers in April and May, before the opening of the leaves. Assiniboia to South Dakota, Nebraska, New Mexico, and Chihuahua. Is said to cause some hayfever in California, though less than *P. Sargentii* (Hall in Scheppegrell, 1917).

Populus balsamifera var. **virginiana** Sarg. (*P. deltoïdes Marsh.*) Necklace poplar. Grains irregular in size, many abortive. The normal grains average about 34.5 μ in diameter. Exine clearly reticulate. Otherwise as in the type.

A common tree, frequently planted about cities and probably responsible for some hayfever. Quebec to Manitoba, south to Connecticut, Florida, and Tennessee. Flowers April and May.

Populus Eugenei Simon Louis Carolina poplar. The pollen of this species is conspicuous for its large proportion of abortive grains constituting more than half of it. Normal and apparently healthy grains range in size from about 34.7 to over 40 μ in diameter, averaging about 36 μ. The texture of the exine is extremely fine, and reticulate markings cannot be discerned with certainty, but it is marked with rather conspicuous rifts. Otherwise as in the type.

A large tree, originated as a hybrid in cultivation and exists only in the male form; much planted about streets in cities. It sheds large amounts of pollen very early in spring but is not known to cause hayfever.

JUGLANDACEAE Walnut Family

The pollen grains of the Juglandaceae are characterized by extreme simplicity. The exine is always thin and entirely lacking in sculpturing but is more or less granular in texture. In keeping with this they lack germinal furrows but have, instead, a varying number of pores which are always surrounded by subexineous thickenings. In form the grains are more or less oblately flattened and with a circular or angular outline, depending upon the number, arrangement, and character of the pores.

In the grains of *Juglans* and *Carya* the pores tend to be crowded into one hemisphere, leaving the opposite quite void of pores. For convenience I shall call the former the dorsal and the latter the ventral hemispheres. In these grains the subexineous thickenings are rather thin but of large extent. In those of *Juglans* they are generally discrete, though they may touch each other, but in those of *Carya* the subexineous thickenings are completely fused except *C. Pecan*, over the whole of the dorsal hemisphere and encroach part way on to the ventral but always leaving a large area of the latter free of thickenings. When the grains dry and shrink they become invaginated on the ventral side, the unthickened area dipping inward and causing the grain to assume a cup shape. When they expand they become oblate-spheroidal or almost quite spherical through the bulging out of the ventral concavity. Immediately underlying this area is a large, globular, hyaline mass (Fig. 98), and it is principally to the contraction and expansion of this that the cupping in and bulging out of the ventral surface are due.

The grains of *Pterocarya*, *Platycarya*, and *Engelhardtia* have the pores equatorially arranged and show no distinction between the dorsal and ventral hemispheres. The subexineous thickenings surrounding the pores in the grains of these three latter genera are less extensive but more abruptly thickened and cause the pores to protrude, giving the grain an angular outline. These grains closely resemble those of the Betulaceae and, to a lesser extent, those of some species of the Urticaceae, such as *Momisia*. Indeed, it is often difficult to distinguish the species of these three families.

The Juglandaceae are represented in North America only by *Juglans* and *Carya*, the others being tropical and subtropical, but the remains of all five genera are found in North American Tertiary deposits. All are wind pollinated and shed enormous quantities of pollen, and several species of *Juglans* and *Carya* are known to cause some hayfever.

KEY TO THE SPECIES

I. Pores more or less confined to one hemisphere.
  A. Pores more than 3, their subexineous thickenings not fused. Grains conspicuously flattened dorsiventrally. 34 by 29.5 μ to 41.6 by 38.2 μ.   *Juglans*
    1. Pores 11 to 15 (most grains with 12), elliptical. Texture granular.

    Pores 12 or rarely 13; texture fine.   {J. nigra / J. major

    Pores 11 to 15 (most grains with 12). Texture coarse.   J. californica
    2. Pores various in number, only occasionally 12; apertures nearly or quite circular. Texture fine-granular or smooth.

    Pores 6 to 16, grains about 41.6 by 38.2 μ, fine granular.   J. regia

    Pores 5 to 9, grain about 35.3 by 33.3 μ, smooth.   J. cinerea.

 B. Pores generally 3, occasionally some grains
with 4 or 6. Grains nearly or quite spherical, 40 to 52 μ in diameter.   *Carya*

  1. Subexineous thickenings separate, texture
coarse-granular.   C. Pecan

  2. Subexineous thickenings united, covering
more than half the surface of the grain.
About one-half of the grains with 4 germ
pores.   C. glabra

   Nearly all grains with 3 germ pores.
Grains 52 by 45 μ.   C. minima

                   ⎧C. ovate
Grains 40 by 46 μ.   ⎨C. alba
                   ⎩C. myristicae-
                     formis

II. Pores equatorially arranged. Grains angular in
outline, with the pores at the angles.

 A. Pores 3 to 7, generally more than 3. Subexineous thickenings of small extent. 26 to 35 μ
in diameter.   Pterocarya
                     hupehensis
                     fraxinifolia
                     Paliurus
                     stenoptera

 B. Pores always three. 14 to 22 μ in diameter.

  1. Pores slit-shaped; exine conspicuously
warty-granular. About 14 μ in diameter. Platycarya strobila-
                     cea

  2. Pores elliptical to circular. Exine faintly
granular. 19 to 22 μ in diameter. Engelhardtia spicata

JUGLANS J. Walnut

 Grains, when expanded, decidedly flattened, oblate-spheroidal,
34 to 42 μ in diameter. Pores elliptical to circular, 2.3 to 3.3 μ in
length, always surrounded by subexineous thickenings which are
generally discrete, though they sometimes touch and are occasionally even partly fused with each other. There are always
more than 3 pores (about 6 to 15) confined mostly to the dorsal
hemisphere (Fig. 97) and, though encroaching somewhat upon
the ventral, always leaving the greater part of it free. The
orientation of the pores is not fortuitous but depends upon their
number and relative positions and is so ordered that the long
axes of their apertures tend to converge in twos or threes at
angles of 120 deg., suggesting that their arrangement is according
to the trischistoclasic system. The surface texture of the exine
is more or less granular.

The pollen of the walnuts is frequently caught on atmospheric pollen slides and is known occasionally to cause hayfever (Hall, 1922). In its fossil form it has been recorded from the Green River oil shales (Wodehouse, 1933*a*) and from Postglacial silts and has been illustrated in this connection by Erdtman (1927).

Juglans nigra L. Black walnut (Fig. 97; Plate VI, Fig. 9) type. Grains 34.2 to 30.8 *μ* in diameter. Germ pores elliptical, 12 or occasionally 13, about 2.85 *μ* in length, confined to an area covering a little more than the dorsal hemisphere, generally more or less regularly arranged; in the typical arrangement three of the pores are found around the dorsal pole with their long axes

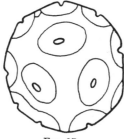

FIG. 97.   FIG. 98.

FIG. 97.—Pollen grain of *Juglans nigra*, diagram of dorsal surface (*cf.* Plate VI, Fig. 9).

FIG. 98.—Pollen grain of *Carya Pecan*, optical section passing through the ventral and dorsal poles, at the top and bottom respectively.

directed tangentially, *i.e.*, according to the sides of an equilateral triangle, and the remaining pores spaced at slightly unequal intervals on a circle slightly above the equator and so oriented that their long axes converge in pairs (Fig. 97). The exact relation of these with the three pores below them is virtually impossible to determine, because the apertures are too nearly circular to enable the direction of their axes to be discerned unless observed in nearly full view. Nevertheless, they appear to be arranged in the trischistoclasic system. Texture finely granular.

A large tree flowering in May. Ontario to Florida and westward to Minnesota, Nebraska, and Kansas. It sheds large quantities of pollen which in my own experience and that of Duke and Durham (1928) is frequently caught on pollen slides but is not known to cause hayfever.

Juglans major (Torr.) Hell. Arizona walnut, Nogal.   Grains as in the type, apparently offering no distinguishing features.

Southern New Mexico, Arizona, and Colorado.   Not known to cause hayfever.

Juglans californica S. Wats. California black walnut.   Germ pores 11 to 15 but generally 12, more or less regularly arranged, texture coarsely granular, almost papillate.   Otherwise as in the type.

A large tree, flowering in March and April, in southern California coastal region where it is known to be an important cause of hayfever (Hall, 1918) and is said to be the most important tree in this respect within its restricted range (Selfridge, 1920).

Juglans cinerea L. Butternut.   Grains spheroidal, uniform in size, averaging 35.3 by 33.5 μ.   Germ pores 5 to 9, their apertures more or less circular, averaging 3.9 μ in diameter, irregularly arranged around the equator and in the dorsal hemisphere. Texture smooth.

May.   New Brunswick to Georgia and westward to Minnesota and Arkansas.   Sometimes regarded as a contributory cause of hayfever.

Juglans regia L. English walnut.   Grains uniform, oblate-spheroidal, 41.6 by 48.2 μ.   Germ pores 6 to 16, with their apertures more or less circular, irregularly arranged, 3.3 μ in diameter, crowded more or less into one hemisphere.   Texture nearly or quite smooth.

A large tree extensively cultivated in California but not believed to cause hayfever.

CARYA Nutt. Hickory

Grains spheroidal or oblate, less flattened and larger than those of *Juglans*, 40 to 52 μ in diameter.   Germ pores generally three (occasionally some grains with four or six), apertures short, elliptical, or nearly circular, 3.4 to 5.7 μ in diameter, equally spaced on a circle a little dorsad of the equator and with their axes directed meridionally or, when there are four or six pores, converging at angles of approximately 120 deg.   Subexineous thickenings greatly extended and completely fused, except in *C. Pecan*.   Texture fine-granular or smooth.

These grains are easily distinguished from those of *Juglans* by their fewer germ pores and their larger size.   The trees are dioecious and shed large amounts of pollen in late spring, of doubtful importance in hayfever. The pollen has been shown to occur in abundance in the Dismal Swamp peat (Lewis and Coke, 1930). In the fossilized condition it can readily be distinguished by the three large germ pores in one hemisphere.

Carya cordiformis (Wang.) K. Koch (*Hicroia minima* Britt.) Bitternut (Plate VI, Fig. 8) type. Grains various in size, and some abortive. Normal grains oblate-spheroidal to nearly or quite spheroidal, averaging 52.4 by 45.6 μ. Pores three or, in some grains which may or may not be considerably larger than normal, four, equally spaced just dorsad of the equator, apertures circular or broadly elliptical, averaging 5.24 μ in diameter; the subexineous thickenings completely fused and extending over the whole surface of the grain, except a small area at the ventral pole. Texture slightly granular.

May. Eastern and central United States and Canada. Of doubtful importance in hayfever.

Carya glabra (Mill.) Spach Sweet pignut. Essentially as in the type, except that the grains are somewhat smaller—44.8 by 38.7 μ—a large proportion have four pores, and a few, which are always giants, have six. Apertures slightly elongate, 4.56 μ in length. When three they are meridionally arranged with their long axes converging toward the poles; but when four, converging in pairs.

May. Eastern and central United States and Canada. Of doubtful importance in hayfever.

Carya alba (L.) K. Koch Mockernut. Grains nearly spheroidal, 40.3 μ in diameter. Pores always three, with their apertures more or less elliptical, 4.5 μ in length. Texture slightly granular. Otherwise as in the type. Massachusetts, Florida, eastern Texas, Ohio, southwestern Ontario.

The most abundant hickory of the southern states. Of doubtful importance in hayfever.

Carya ovata (Mill.) K. Koch Shagbark hickory. Grains uniform spheroidal, 42 μ in diameter. Germ pores three (occasionally four, and such grains are not giants); apertures elliptical, 4.5 μ in diameter. Texture slightly granular. Otherwise as in the type. May. Northeastern United States and Canada. Of doubtful importance in hayfever.

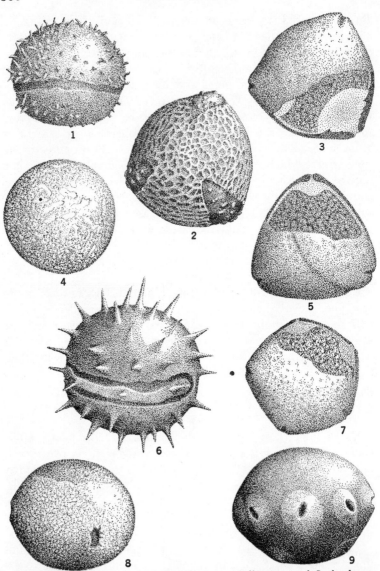

PLATE VI.—Pollen grains of Nymphaeaceae, Salicaceae, and Juglandaceae.
1, *Castalia odorata*, side view, expanded, 30 μ in diameter. 2, *Salix fragilis*,
polar view, expanded, 27 μ in diameter. 3, *Engelhardtia spicata*, polar view,
20 μ in diameter. 4, *Populus Sargentii*, 27 μ in diameter. 5, *Platycarya strobilacea*, 14 μ in diameter, upper portion shown in optical section. 6, *Nymphaea
advena*, ventral view, expanded, 51 μ in diameter. 7, *Pterocarya hupehensis*,
polar view, 30 μ in diameter, upper part shown in optical section. 8, *Carya
cordiformis*, side view, 52 μ in diameter. 9, *Juglans nigra*, side view dorsal side
uppermost, 34 μ in diameter.

Carya myristicaeformis (Michx.) Nutt. Nutmeg hickory. Grains uniform, slightly flattened, 45.6 by 41 μ. Germ pores circular or broadly elliptical, 5.7 μ in diameter. Texture slightly granular. Otherwise as in the type.

Southern Arkansas and adjoining states, where it is believed to be a minor cause of hayfever.

Carya Pecan Asch. & Graeb. Pecan (Fig. 98). Grains uniform, spheroidal, 44.4 μ in diameter. Germ pores three, their apertures elliptical, 3.4 μ in diameter; subexineous thickenings not fused but sometimes touching. Texture decidedly granular, more noticeably so than in the other species of the genus. These two characters—the separate subexineous thickenings and granular texture—serve to distinguish the grains of this species from others of the genus and suggest a somewhat closer relationship of this species with *Juglans*.

Flowers April and May. Indiana to Iowa and Kansas, southward to Alabama and Texas. Known to cause some hayfever.

Engelhardtia spicata Blume (Plate VI, Fig. 3). Grains much flattened, uniform, 19.4 to 21.6 μ in diameter, triangular in outline. Pores three, one at each angle, aspidate, their apertures elliptical to circular, 2.6 to 3.4 μ long, their membranes smooth or slightly flecked; pore diagram similar to that of *Myrica* (Fig. 99*b*). Subexineous thickenings extending deeply into the cell below the pores. Exine faintly granular.

A large tree, native of Asia from the Himalayas to Java and the Philippines. The genus is now represented in America by *Oreomunnea* in the mountains of Central America, but during the Tertiary period it was widespread in both Europe and America. All species are wind pollinated and shed large amounts of pollen but are not known to cause hayfever.

Platycarya strobilacea Sieb. & Zucc. (Plate VI, Fig. 5). Grains much flattened, uniform, 14 μ in diameter, triangular in outline. Pores three, one at each angle, aspidate, their apertures slit-shaped, 2.3 μ long. Pore diagram as in *Corylus* (Fig. 99*c*). Subexineous thickenings beneath the pores shallow and not laterally extensive. Exine coarsely but faintly granular; always crossed by two grooves, one on each side at right angles to each other.

A small tree, native of Japan and northern China.

PTEROCARYA Kunth.

Grains much flattened, 27 to 34 μ in diameter, occasional grains much smaller. Pores 3 to 7, never constant in number, one at each angle, aspidate, their apertures elliptical, 3 to 4.6 μ long, arranged around the equator and meridionally oriented or converging in pairs alternately above and below the equator, occasionally variously irregular in arrangement. Pore diagram as in *Carpinus* (Fig. 99*d*). Subexineous thickenings beneath the pores shallow. Exine faintly granular.

The genus consists of a few species of trees in Transcaucasian Federation, China, and Japan but is abundantly represented in Tertiary floras of both Europe and North America.

Pterocarya hupehensis Skan. (Plate VI, Fig. 7) type. Grains 29 to 30.5 μ in diameter, generally five pored, occasionally four or six. Otherwise as in the generic description.

Tree about 30 ft. high, native of China in the province of Hupeh.

Pterocarya Paliurus Bat. Grains about 33.1 μ in diameter. Pores six, seven, or five; in grains with the higher numbers not generally strictly equatorially arranged. Otherwise as in the type.

Tree native of China in the mountains of Ning-po.

Pterocarya caucasica C. A. Mey (*P. fraxinifolia* Spach.). Grains 33 to 35.3 μ in diameter. Pores six or five or occasionally four. Otherwise as in the type.

A beautiful tree along the rivers and mountains of Caucasia.

Pterocarya stenoptera C. DC. Grains 26.2 to 30.4 μ in diameter. Pores six or five, occasionally three or four. Otherwise as in the type.

Tree, native of China.

BETULACEAE Birch Family

Grains smooth or only faintly granular, spheroidal or more or less oblately flattened, 20 to 40 μ in diameter, provided with three to seven germ pores which tend to be equally spaced around the equator. In shape the germinal apertures differ in the different species, being circular, elliptical, or slit-shaped. When elongate they are meridionally oriented—when there are three—or with their major axes converging in pairs when more than three. The most distinctive character of these grains, however, is that their germ pores always protrude as rounded domes and give the grains an angular outline when seen in polar view. This character I have called "aspidate" owing to the resemblance of such a protruding pore to a small circular shield or *aspis*. The dome-shaped protrusions are due to a thickening of the intine underlying the region of the pore and frequently also to a lesser annular thickening of the exine.

All of these characters the grains of the Betulaceae share with those of the Myricaceae; *Myriophyllum* among the Haloragidaceae; *Platycarya*, *Engelhardtia*, and *Pterocarya* among the Juglandaceae; *Momisia* among the Urticaceae; and *Casuarina;* and they are also closely approached in the grains of *Broussonetia*, *Morus*, *Humulus*, and *Cannabis* among the Urticaceae. In fact the grains of the Betulaceae represent a form toward which those of many wind-pollinated species of diverse origins tend to approach. This together with a close intrafamily resemblance of the various genera makes the recognition of the pollen grains of the Betulaceae always difficult and occasionally uncertain. They can generally be distinguished, however, by certain minor characters which they possess individually.

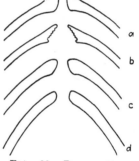

One such character is found in the annular thickening of the exine surrounding the pore. When seen in optical section the germinal aperture appears as a gap at which the walls on either side end with knob-like thickenings. In fossil material the underlying layers are absent, leaving little or no trace of their former position; consequently in such material we need be concerned only with the structure of the outer layers.

Fig. 99.—Pore patterns: *a*, broad-knob or *Betula* pattern; *b*, tarsus or *Myrica* pattern; *c*, club-shaped or *Corylus* pattern; *d*, unexpanded or *Carpinus* pattern.

Passing in review the grains of the various members of the Betulaceae and those of the families with which it is possible to confuse them, four fairly well-marked types of pore pattern may be distinguished. These are (1) the broad-knob or *Betula* pore pattern (Fig. 99*a*) in which the exine appears to end at the pore in a broad and abrupt expansion, and in grains with this type of pore pattern the pores are raised sharply above the surface of the grain. This pore pattern is characteristic of all species of *Betula*, *Myriophyllum*, and, with a slight modification toward the next type, of *Alnus;* (2) the tarsus or *Myrica* pore pattern in which the wall thickening suggests in appearance the terminal joint or tarsus of the hind legs of some insects (Fig. 99b). This pore pattern in its fullest development characterizes the grains of *Myrica* and *Comptonia* and is somewhat approached in those of *Engelhardtia* and *Alnus;* (3) the club-shaped or *Corylus* pore pattern (Fig. 99c) in which the exine is only slightly and gradually expanded at the pores. As a consequence the pores are only slightly raised above the surface. This characterizes the grains of *Corylus*, *Pterocarya*, *Platycarya*, *Momisia*, and, with a certain tendency toward the tarsus pattern, those of *Ostrya;* (4) the unexpanded or *Carpinus* pore pattern (Fig. 99d). In this the walls of the exine are not at all or only very slightly expanded at the pores. It must be admitted that the distinction between this and the previous pore pattern is often vague. This pore pattern characterizes the grains of *Carpinus* and, with a modification toward the tarsus type, those of *Engelhardtia*. Fortunately we are aided in the distinction of these two grains by the fact that that of *Carpinus* is the largest, while that of *Engelhardtia* is the smallest of all the grains possessing this pore pattern.

Jentys-Szafer (1928), after making extensive studies of the pollen of *Corylus*, *Myrica*, and *Betula*, describes the thickenings beneath the pores in all these genera as follows: "Sous l'exine, on voit s'étendre l'intine, mate et incolore, étroitmente accolée à la première; elle entoure le contenu du grain, à la surface duquel on distingue trois petites cuvettes caractéristiques qui se trouve au-dessous des pores." She finds that the grains of these three genera, though at first sight much alike, present certain differences which enable them to be distinguished, when they are caused to swell or disintegrate by treatment with sulphuric acid, dilute chromic, or potassium hydrate. By such means it can be shown that the exine of the grains of *Corylus* consists of five layers, two of which are rather thick and three very thin; while in the grain of *Myrica* one can recognize only three layers—one thick and two thin—yet the exine of the grain of *Myrica* is, in general, a little thicker than that of *Corylus*. She finds that these characters may be used in distinguishing the species in their fossil condition.

The *Betula* pollen grain may be recognized by the double nature of the exine around the pores, according to Dokturowsky and Kudrjaschow (1923). When seen in optical section, if the focus of the microscope is just right, they present the appearance of two serpents face to face with their mouths open ("deux gueules de serpent, ouvertes l'une en face de l'autre"). It is true that a similar appearance is produced in the grains of *Corylus* by appropriate focusing, but it is much less marked, and the lower jaws of the serpents are somewhat undershot.

Madame Szafer also shows that the pollen grains of the different species of *Betula* differ from each other in such minor characters as the thickness of the exine around the germinal apertures and in their sizes. The differences in size between the different species are slight, but if hundreds of grains are accurately measured and size-frequency curves plotted, each is found to have its characteristic shape. Such curves may be used to detect mixtures of different species of pollen in fossil material and give a fair estimate of the relative amounts of each.

The pollen grains of the Betulaceae are of frequent occurrence and well preserved in Postglacial silts, and in this connection the European species have been studied and described by many investigators. Docturowsky and Kudrjaschow (1923) give figures of *B. humilis* Schr., *B. verrucosa* Ehr., and *B. nana* L., which they point out may be distinguished from each other by their sizes. They find that there are minute but tangible differences between the species within the genera *Corylus*, *Betula*, and *Alnus* and give diagrams which bring out the differences. Erdtman (1923, 1927) illustrates a species of *Betula*. Von Mohl (1835) likewise illustrates a grain of *Betula*, describing the pores as "on the angles of the grain with large halos." Lewis and Coke (1929) illustrate fossil grains of *Betula*, *Alnus*, and *Myrica* and state, "The pollens of *Betula* and *Myrica* are much alike, though they may be distinguished with certainty in well-preserved specimens." Their figures of the fossilized remains of these grains show well-marked differences in outline which are by no means apparent in fresh material.

The Betulaceae are mostly dioecious trees or shrubs. They shed large quantities of light, air-borne pollen which is the cause of some hayfever in early spring. The pollen is found in large quantities in both recent and ancient bog deposits, and it is caught in great abundance on pollen slides exposed several miles from any trees.

KEY TO THE GENERA OF BETULACEAE AND MYRICACEAE

I. Germ pores mostly 3; a small proportion of the grains may have 4 or rarely more.

    A. Germinal apertures always more or less elliptical, equatorially arranged and equally spaced; some grains, which are generally giants, with 4 to 7 pores.   Betula
Carpinus

    B. Germinal apertures generally not elliptical, though they may occasionally be so, mostly approximately circular or somewhat irregular.

        1. Germ pores mostly 3, equally spaced on the equator.
        Pores circular or slightly elliptic.   Corylus
        Pores irregular in outline, tending to be circular.   Myrica
        2. Germ pores 3 or 4 or, occasionally, 5, not equally spaced.   Comptonia

II. Germ pores various in number, always a large proportion of the grains with 4, 5, or 6, elliptic.

    A. Grains without thickened bands connecting the pores; pores 3 or 4 (generally four in *Carpinus Betulus*); pore membranes marked by a central elongate thickening. Ostrya
Carpinus

    B. Grains with thickened bands connecting the pores; pores 4 or 5, rarely 6, their apertures narrowly elongate, their membranes without central thickening.   Alnus

BETULA L. BIRCH

Grains flattened, angular, 20 to 40 μ in diameter (generally less than 27 μ); pores three, occasionally, in some grains, four and higher numbers up to seven, strongly aspidate and somewhat protruding, imparting to the grain its angular appearance. Exine slightly granular or nearly smooth. Pore pattern as in Fig. 99a.

Mostly large trees flowering in early spring a little in advance of the unfolding of the leaves. They shed enormous quantities of light, wind-borne pollen which is one of the most prevalent causes of hayfever of the early spring type, in the production of which the different species are apparently not distinguishable. In the author's experience in New York State where the three species *B. populifolia*, *B. lutea*, and *B. lenta* are frequently associated and flower successively in the sequence named, those patients afflicted with birch hayfever exhibit their symptoms throughout the flowering periods of all three species.

Betula populifolia Marsh. Gray, White, or Poplar-leaved birch (Plate VII, Fig. 1) type. Grains uniform in size and appearance, except for an occasional four-pored giant. Normal grains about 20 by 28.2 μ. Germinal apertures elliptical, about 2.3 μ in length, with a somewhat wavy margin, their long axes directed meridionally, except when there are four pores, in which case they coverge in pairs.

A small tree shedding much pollen in May. Nova Scotia to southern Ontario, Pennsylvania, and Delaware.

Betula lutea Michx. f. Yellow or Gray birch. Essentially as in the type, except that more of the grains have four and occasionally more pores up to seven. Grains about 29.6 by 25.1 μ, length of aperture 3.14 μ.

A large tree shedding much pollen, beginning to flower at just about the time when *B. populifolia* ceases. The grains of this species are figured by Sears (1930), who does not find that they bear any characters that distinguish them from those of other species. Newfoundland to Manitoba, southward to Delaware, Illinois, and Minnesota, also in Tennessee and North Carolina.

Betula lenta L. Black or cherry birch. Grains as in the type, about 25.9 by 21.6 μ; pores about 2.3 μ long.

A large tree shedding an enormous amount of pollen in May, a little later than *B. populifolia*. Newfoundland to Ontario, southward to Delaware, Indiana, and Iowa, also along the mountains to Florida and Tennessee.

Betula alba L. European white birch. Grains various in size but always three-pored, 20.5 to 30.4 μ in diameter. Exine finely and faintly granular, slightly more so around the pores.

A small or large tree, native of Europe but extensively cultivated in the United States, occurring in many varieties. Flowers in May. An important cause of hayfever.

Betula alnoides Buch.-Ham. Grains uniform, as in the generic description, 22 to 26.5 μ in diameter.

A medium-sized tree. Temperate and subtropical Himalaya, in moist ravines. Flowers in April.

Betula utilis D. Don. Grains uniform, large, 36 to 40 μ in diameter, always three-pored. Exine faintly granular. Exceptional in the genus in their large size.

A shrub or small tree, northwestern Himalaya and western Tibet. Flowers with the young leaves in May.

CARPINUS L. HORNBEAM, IRONWOOD

Grains similar to those of *Betula* but more nearly spherical, various in size, 25.6 to 41 μ in diameter. Pores generally three, sometimes four, rarely five or six. Pore pattern similar to that of the grains of *Betula*, but exine surrounding the pore less thickened.

The genus comprises about 15 species of trees, widely distributed in the Northern Hemisphere. All are wind pollinated and in the early spring shed large quantities of pollen, which probably causes some hayfever.

Carpinus caroliniana Walt. Hop hornbeam. Grains various, 26.8 to 33.1 μ in diameter; pores three or four, occasionally five or six, their apertures circular, about 4 μ in diameter, often operculate. Exine smooth or faintly granular.

A small tree, shedding large quantities of pollen in the early spring. Nova Scotia to western Ontario and southward. The grains of this species have been figured by Sears (1930) showing three germ pores.

Carpinus Betula L. Hornbeam. Grains various, 36.4 to 41 μ in diameter. Pores generally four, occasionally three or five, their apertures circular or broadly elliptical, generally operculate. Exine smooth or faintly granular.

These grains may be distinguished from those of *Alnus*, which also have generally four pores, by their larger size and lack of connecting bands and from those of *Betula* and *Alnus* by their less protruding pores.

A small tree, native of Europe and western Asia, frequently planted in America. The grains of this species have been figured by Docturowsky and Kudrjaschow (1923), who state that the pores are four, rarely five; also by Erdtman (1923, 1927) and Meinke (1927), both stating that they have four or five pores.

Carpinus viminea Wall. Grains uniform, virtually as in *C. caroliniana*, about 25.6 μ in diameter. Pores three or rarely four, small and circular, generally operculate.

A small tree. Temperate Himalaya, from Chamba eastwards. Flowers March to April.

Ostrya virginiana (Mill.) K. Koch Blue beech. Pollen with a large proportion (about one-third) of its grains four-pored; 28 by 25 μ in diameter; apertures of the pores decidedly elliptical, often more than twice as long as broad, 4.5 μ long, pore membranes marked with a slight fleck. Otherwise as in the *Betula* type.

This species is figured by Sears (1930) showing three germ pores with apertures circular. The European *Ostrya carpinifolia* pollen is figured by Erdtman (1923).

A small tree, similar in habit to *Carpinus*. Flowers early in spring before the leaves unfold. Cape Breton, Indiana to Manitoba, Newfoundland, Florida, and Texas.

CORYLUS L. HAZEL

Grains essentially as in the *Betula* type, about 22 to 26.5 μ in diameter. Pores always three, their apertures slightly elliptical or quite circular, 3.4 to 3.7 μ in diameter.

Medium-sized shrubs shedding large amounts of air-borne pollen very early in spring—March to April—long before the leaves unfold. Suspected of being a minor cause of hayfever. The pollen of the various species is extremely abundant in Postglacial silts. Of it Erdtman (1929, page 114) says, "A peat deposit in the vicinity of Lake Constance holds the European record for pollen of hazel, which was laid down during the first half of the Boreal period. It is therefore a pioneer shrub." It is figured by Docturowsky and Kudrjaschow (1923), Meinke (1927), and Erdtman (1923), the latter stating that it "ist Morphologische nicht ganz sicher von der *Myrica* zu unterscheiden." Luersen (1869) has endeavored to show the structure of these grains.

Corylus americana Walt. Hazelnut. Grains uniform in size, 22.8 μ in diameter. Apertures of pores 3.42 μ in diameter.

Manitoba and Ontario to Saskatchewan, Florida, and Kansas.

Corylus Avellana L. Filbert, hazelnut. Grains somewhat various in size, averaging about 26.5 by 22 μ. Apertures of pores 3.7 μ in diameter.

Habit as in *C. americana*, native of Europe and north Africa but widely cultivated in North America.

ALNUS (Tourn.) Hill ALDER

Grains flattened, 19 to 27 μ in diameter, with four or five or rarely three or six germinal apertures which are narrowly elliptical or slit-shaped, 2.5 to 4.5 μ long, aspidate, *i.e.*, surrounded by subexineous thickenings. These cause the pores to protrude and give the grains an angular outline. Texture smooth or slightly granular (Plate VII, Figs. 2, 3).

The most distinctive characteristic of these grains is the presence of band-like thickenings beneath the exine, apparently of the same material as the thickenings of the exine surrounding the pores and extending out from them in geodetic curves from pore to pore on each side of the equator. These can generally be seen only with difficulty in unstained material, but when appropriately stained they become quite conspicuous. Similar band-like thickenings are not found elsewhere among the Betulaceae, as far as these studies have gone, and serve to distinguish the grains of all species of alder from all others of the Betulaceae.

Alder pollen is occasionally an important factor in hayfever. Thus *A. oregona* is stated by Chamberlain (1927) to be an important hayfever plant in Oregon and Washington. The pollen of various species of alder have been recorded in Postglacial silts and have been recorded and illustrated by Lewis and Coke (1929) from the Dismal Swamp in the United States. *Alnus* pollen is recorded from most European bogs that have been studied. It was figured by Erdtman (1923) showing the curved linear thickenings. He regards it as almost a pioneer, in the Boreal period, following closely *Corylus* and *Pinus*. It is also figured by Meinke (1927), omitting the curved linear thickenings because, he states, they do not show except in fossilized material.

Alnus rugosa (Du Roi) K. Koch (Plate VII, Figs. 2, 3) Smooth alder type. Grains flattened, about 21.5 by 17.8 μ. Germ pores four or five, rarely three or six, their apertures generally extremely narrow, often slit-shaped.

A shrub or small tree, along the shores of ponds and river banks. Maine to Florida and westward to Texas and Minnesota. Flowers very early in spring, long before the unfolding of the leaves.

Alnus sinuata (Regel) Rydb. Mountain alder. Grains as in the type, except that they are slightly larger—about 27 by 24 μ—and somewhat various; pores four or five, occasionally three, their apertures elliptical, about 4.5 μ long, converging in pairs.

A large shrub. May to July. Oregon, Wyoming, and Alberta.

Alnus incana (L.) Moench Speckled or Hoary alder. Grains about 24 μ in diameter. Pores four or five, occasionally three, apertures long-elliptic, 3.4 μ in length. Frequently the pores are not equatorially arranged, but the apertures tend to converge in pairs. Otherwise as in the type. The grains of this species have been figured by Sears (1930), Docturowsky, and Kudrjaschow (1923) without band-like thickenings. They have also been figured by Erdtman (1923), drawing attention to the connecting bands extending from pore to pore.

Flowers in April and May. Alaska to California to New Mexico to the Yukon.

Alnus nepalensis D. Don. Grains as in the generic description, uniform, 19.4 to 20.5 μ in diameter. Pores four, occasionally three; connecting bands rather faint.

A large tree, China, Burma, and Himalaya, in valleys and along streams. Flowers October and November.

MYRICACEAE Sweet-gale Family

Grains similar to those of the Betulaceae and discussed with them (p. 362 *et seq.*).

MYRICA L.

Grains similar to those of *Betula*, 25 to 27 μ in diameter, their apertures irregular, approximately circular, not generally elliptical, about 3.5 μ long, in optical section presenting a pore pattern as in Fig. 99*b*.

Myrica pollen is known to occur abundantly in Postglacial silts. Lewis and Coke (1930) state, "The pollen of *Betula* and *Myrica* are much alike, though they may be distinguished with certainty in well-preserved specimens (Figs. 20, 22)." These figures, which are of fossilized material, show differences in outline which are not apparent in fresh material. Jentys-Szafer (1928) gives several very interesting figures and states that the grains of *Myrica Gale* are most likely to be confused with those of *Corylus*. They may be distinguished, however, because the exine of those of *Myrica* is a little thicker than of *Corylus*, especially near the pores, and when treated with concentrated sulphuric acid, followed by dilute chromic acid, it is seen in the grains of *Myrica* to consist of three layers, two of which are thin, with one much

thicker in between.   The grains of *Myrica* are also a little smaller
than those of *Corylus*, measuring in glycerin 21 to 27.5 μ in
diameter, but the difference in size is too slight to be relied upon
in distinguishing them when found together in peats.   In the
fossil form, however, Jentys-Szafer states, these two species may
be distinguished from each other by the difference in the thickness
of their walls and by the presence in the grains of *Myrica* of three
arcuate thickenings, one underlying each of the pores but entirely
absent from the grains of *Corylus*.

It has frequently been stated that, though the grains of
Corylus are abundant in peat deposits, those of *Myrica* are not
preserved in such deposits, but Jentys-Szafer believes that, on
account of the similarity of the structure and the behavior of
the grains toward such destructive reagents as sulphuric acid
and potassium hydroxide, there is no reason to suppose that one
could be preserved while the other is destroyed under identical
conditions.   In fact, upon examining certain European peats,
she found as many grains presenting the characters of *Myrica* as
of *Corylus*.   Nevertheless, she admits, the differences are
slight and can be discerned only in typical grains.   Docturowsky
and Kudrjaschow (1923) give figures of *Myrica* pollen, but
these do not show that it can be distinguished from that of
Corylus.

Myrica Gale L. Sweet gale.   Grains as in the generic description, about 27 by 23.5 μ.   Pores three.   Exine slightly roughened, especially around the pores.

A low shrub in swamps and along ponds and streams, throughout most of the northern part of the United States and Canada,
also Europe and Asia.   Flowers in April and May.

Myrica cerifera L. Wax myrtle.   Grains as in the generic
description, uniform, 24 to 26.2 μ in diameter.   Pores always
three, broadly elliptical.   Exine faintly granular, especially
around the pores.

A shrub or small tree, reaching a height of about 40 ft.   In
sandy swamps or wet woods, southern New Jersey to Florida
and Texas.   March to April.

Myrica Nagi Thunb.   Grains as in the generic description,
about 22.8 μ in diameter.

A small tree.   Subtropical Himalaya.   Flowers August to
September.

Comptonia perigrina (L.) Coulter (*Myrica asplenifolia* L.) Sweet fern, Ferngale. Grains generally more or less flattened but various in this respect, about 27.1 μ in diameter. Germ pores three, four, or rarely six, their apertures circular, 3.5 μ in diameter, and slightly more protruding than in the grains of *Corylus* and *Betula*.

The pores may be equally spaced around the equator of the grain as in those of *Myrica*, but they are more often irregularly arranged, particularly when there are three when they are generally gathered into one hemisphere. They may be easily distinguished from those of *Betula* by the frequent occurrence of four pores and their frequently asymmetrical placement and from those of *Alnus* by the absence of linear thickenings which characterize the grains of that genus.

A small shrub. Flowers in April and May. Nova Scotia to Saskatchewan, North Carolina, Indiana, Michigan.

FAGACEAE Beech Family

The pollen grains of the Fagaceae are of two entirely different types. Those of *Quercus* and *Fagus* are similar, so also are those of *Castanea* and *Castanopsis*, but there is no obvious relationship between the two former and the two latter. Accordingly detailed descriptions are given of these under their generic headings.

Key to the Genera

Grains when moist flattened and angular. Furrows three or occasionally four or six, broadly expanded, one at each angle of the grain. Exine thin, warty-granular. Hyaline bodies underlying the furrows conspicuous.   Quercus

Grains when moist spheroidal. Furrows long, narrow, and tapering, their margins slightly raised, normally three, but some grains with two or a single furrow encircling the grain. Exine heavy and coarsely granular. Hyaline wedges underlying the furrows spherical and not conspicuous.   Fagus

Grains when moist ellipsoidal. Furrows three, slender and tapering, with a germ pore bulging through a well-marked transverse furrow. Exine smooth. Hyaline wedges none.   Castanea   Castanopsis

QUERCUS L. Oak

Grains spheroidal, or oblately flattened and angular in outline, according to the extent of their expansion; tricolpate or occasionally some grains with more than three furrows; beneath the center of each furrow an internal hyaline body. Furrows meridional in arrangement or, if 4 or 6, tetrahedral; long and tapering to pointed ends, their membranes smooth but generally ruptured and not observable in grains that have been prepared for microscopic examination in the ordinary way. Exine rather thin, more or less warty-granular. Intine thick (Plate VII, Fig. 6).

The most conspicuous and distinctive feature of the grains of *Quercus* is their possession of hyaline wedge-shaped plugs embedded in the cell contents, underlying the furrows, one beneath each, and radiating toward them from the center of the cell (Plate VII, Fig. 7). Their function appears to be to rupture the furrow membrane and spread open the furrows when the grain is moistened. When the grain is dry it is ellipsoidal in shape, with the furrows tightly closed, visible from the surface only as shallow grooves, and the hyaline plugs are small and inconspicuous, but as soon as the grain begins to take up moisture it assumes a spherical form, and the furrows gape slightly open. Immediately underlying the center of each furrow the end of the hyaline wedge may be seen apparently penetrating the furrow membrane. One cannot be certain, however, whether the opening in the membrane, which appears as an irregular break extending longitudinally, is a rupture caused by the protrusion of the hyaline wedge or a true germinal aperture. At any rate the furrow membrane is narrow and does not permit of much stretching. As the grain expands further the wedge underlying each furrow elongates and tears the furrow membrane wide open almost from end to end. Through these slits protrudes the expanding gelatinous cell content covered by its elastic intine. The grain in this condition is flattened and triangular in shape, with the three furrows appearing as more or less irregular slits torn through the exine. In the partly expanded condition when the grain is spherical it bears some resemblance to that of *Fagus;* the furrows are narrow and of medium length, with their margins slightly above the general level of the exine.

The grains of the different species are much alike, and there appear to be no reliable criteria for distinguishing them from each other. They vary somewhat in the texture of their exine and in their size range from 30 by 25 to 36 by 26 μ, measured in the expanded condition.

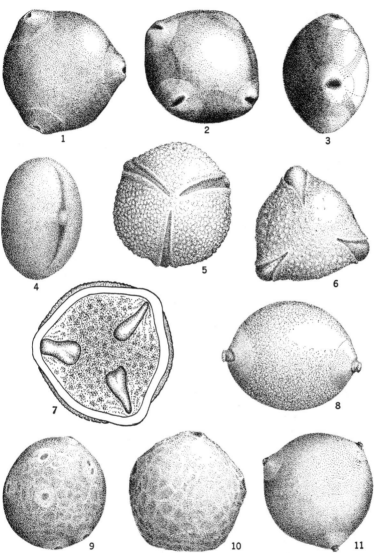

PLATE VII.—Pollen grains of Betulaceae, Fagaceae, and Urticaceae; 1, *Betula populifolia*, polar view, 20 μ in diameter. 2, *Alnus rugosa*, 21.5 μ in diameter, partly side view. 3, *Alnus rugosa*, side view. 4, *Castanea dentata*, 14.7 by 11 μ, side view, fully expanded. 5, *Fagus grandifolia*, polar view, fully expanded, 40 μ in diameter. 6, *Quercus alba*, 34 μ in diameter, polar view, fully expanded and furrow membranes ruptured. 7, *Quercus venustula*, optical section. 8, *Morus alba*, side view, 20 μ long. 9, *Celtis occidentalis*, 40 μ in diameter. 10, *Ulmus americana*, polar view, 37.2 μ in diameter. 11, *Maclura pomifera*, polar view, 22 μ in diameter.

It has frequently been stated that the pollen grains of oak are indistinguishable from those of violet, and this is cited as a remarkable example of morphological convergence. Beyond the fact that the grains of violet have a tendency to overexpand when moistened, causing the furrows to tear wide open, there is no resemblance. The exine of the violet grain is nearly smooth, lacking entirely the warty-granular texture characteristic of the oak grains; and the violet grain has no hyaline wedges. Its germinal apertures are well defined and quite conspicuous, unless the furrow membranes are ruptured. Furthermore, some species of violet have some or all of their grains provided with four, six, or even five furrows. In such cases the furrows are arranged around the equator and directed meridionally, unless there are four, in which case they converge in pairs. Some species of oak likewise have supernumerary furrows, but, unlike those of the violet, these are always arranged according to the trischistoclasic system. The supposed convergence of form between the oak and violet pollen grains is entirely superficial, based only on an accidental resemblance which results from the fact that both have a tendency to overexpand, accompanied by the rupture of the furrow membranes.

Oak pollen has been described and figured by several authors. For example, Meinke (1927) gives figures of *Q. robor* and *Q. sessilis* and states that the pollen of oak may be distinguished from that of violet by its more coarsely granular exine. Docturowsky and Kudrjaschow (1923) show a figure of the pollen grain of a species of oak, pointing out that it resembles that of maple but may be distinguished by its exine's being thinly papillate and not cleft as in the pollen of maple. Pollen of *Q. sessiliflora* is shown by Erdtman (1923, 1927). Fossilized oak pollen is figured by Lewis and Coke (1930), who regard it as similar to that of willow, but state that it may be distinguished by its lack of a reticulate surface, and its larger size.

Oak pollen is found at nearly all levels in Postglacial silts. For example, the work of Stark (1925), Budde (1930), Lewis and Coke (1930), and many others shows that the oaks have been prevalent in both Europe and America continuously since the last recession of the continental ice sheet. Erdtman (1929), in speaking of the Postglacial history of the British forests, states "Oak forests have generally played a prominent rôle since the immigrations of the oak in the Boreal period."

The oaks shed enormous quantities of pollen. In the vicinity of New York City it was found that for several weeks each spring the pollen grains of the various species of oak greatly outnumber all others (see Chart I). Similar observations have been recorded by other investigators; for example Duke and Durham (1928) have shown that the atmospheric pollen count of oak in Kansas City when at its maximum, about Apr. 27, outnumbered all others except elm. Oak pollen undoubtedly causes some hay-fever, but much less than would be expected from the enormous quantities that are found in the air. The relative importance in this respect of the many different species is not understood, but, in view of the close interrelationship existing among them, it is hardly to be expected that the specificity of their biological reaction would be very marked. *Q. marilandica* is said to cause some hayfever in the neighborhood of Oklahoma City (Balyeat, 1926); *Q. Garryana*, in western Oregon (Chamberlain, 1927). Several species are mentioned by Hall (1922) as of little or no importance in California, though shedding much pollen. This point will be discussed in connection with the several species as they are considered.

Quercus alba L. White oak (Plate VII, Fig. 6) type. Grains in the overexpanded condition, flattened, triangular in outline, about 34.2 by 26.2 μ in size, tricolpate, with the furrows appearing as rather short slits in the exine and gaping widely open, with the cell contents protruding as if forced out by pressure within; hyaline wedges conspicuous; texture warty-granular.

The grain of this species is figured by Sears (1930), who states that it is probably not possible to distinguish it from those of other species of oak.

A large tree, abundant in the northeastern United States and Canada. The flowers are borne in pendant racemes which emerge with the leaves in May, shedding large amounts of pollen which, with that of other species of oak, is one of the most frequent causes of the early spring or tree hayfever in the north-eastern United States.

Quercus borealis Michx. (*Q. rubra* Du Roi) Red oak. Grains indistinguishable from the type, 36.5 by 25.6 μ. Figured by Sears (1930).

A large tree, abundant in the northeastern United States and Canada. Frequently planted. Flowers in May.

Quercus velutina Lam. Black oak.   Normal grains essentially as in the type, except that the hyaline wedges are rudimentary, and the surface texture slightly finer.   The pollen upon which these observations were made exhibited many irregularities in form, such as generally denote hybridity of origin; many of the grains were obviously abortive; others were giants possessing supernumerary furrows and variously misshapen; and some were united in tetrads.   The furrows of these irregular grains when more than three (four or six) were found to be arranged in the trischistoclasic system.   I am not prepared to say whether such irregularities are inherent into the species or characterize only certain individuals.

A large tree, native of the eastern half of the United States. Flowers in May, shedding much pollen which causes some hayfever.

Quercus venustula Greene   Scrub oak.   Grains uniform, about 35 by 27.5 μ, as in the type, except that the hyaline wedges are more prominent, cigar-shaped with the large end outward.

A small shrub, 3 to 6 ft. high, abundant in Colorado and New Mexico, where it is known to cause some hayfever.

Quercus Engelmanii Greene   Evergreen oak, Mesa oak. Grains uniform, as in the type, about 31 by 24 μ.

A tree 50 to 60 ft. high, of limited distribution in California, "occupying with *Q. agrifolia* a belt about fifty miles wide and extending to within fifteen or twenty miles of the coast, from the neighborhood of Sierra Madre and San Gabriel, Los Angeles County, to the mesa east of San Diego; in northern Lower California" (Sargent, 1922).   Within this restricted area it is regarded as an important factor in hayfever (Selfridge, 1920).

Quercus bicolor Willd. Swamp white oak.   Normal grains essentially as in the type, about 27.5 μ in diameter.   A small proportion of the grains have four or six furrows, which are always in the tetrahedral arrangement.

A large tree, often 100 ft. high, shedding enormous quantities of pollen in May, common in moist places throughout almost the eastern half of the United States.

Quercus Prinus L. Chestnut oak.   Normal grains essentially as in the type, 31 by 25 μ.   Furrows rather long and sharply defined, regular in outline; hyaline wedges rather conspicuous. A large proportion of the grains are tetracolpate and hexacolpate, with the furrows in the tetrahedral arrangement.

A large tree with thick and deeply furrowed bark. It sheds enormous quantities of pollen in May. Of general distribution in the Atlantic coast states.

Quercus agrifolia Neé. California live oak, Encina. Grains all normal, except a few that are abortive, essentially as in the type, about 31 by 25 μ; furrows rather long and sharply defined.

A tree 80 to 90 ft. high, with evergreen leaves. In distribution confined to California and Lower California, where it is the largest and most generally distributed oak tree between the mountains and the sea, covering the lower hills and ascending to altitudes of 4,500 ft. (Sargent, 1922). It flowers through most of March and April, shedding rather large quantities of pollen which has been shown to give positive skin tests with hayfever patients (Hall, 1922) and is apparently an important factor in hayfever. It is stated by Selfridge (1920) to be the most important hay-fever tree in California. But by Rowe (1928) it is regarded as unimportant in the San Francisco Bay region.

FAGUS L. BEECH

The grains of *Fagus* in their general construction and their appearance in the unexpanded condition, are similar to those of *Quercus*, but their exine is thicker, the internal hyaline bodies are more spherical, and when the grains are moistened there is much less distortion of their form—they remain almost spherical —and, though the furrows gape somewhat open, their membranes do not rupture.

The genus comprises but a single American species, though the European *Fagus sylvatica* L. "is frequently planted for ornament in the eastern states, in several of its forms, especially those with purple leaves and pendulous branches" (Sargent, 1922). Beech pollen is commonly recorded from European Postglacial bog deposits. For example, it is recorded by Keller (1929), Stark (1925), and Budde (1930), and grains of *F. sylvatica* are figured by Erdtman (1923, 1927) in connection with his pollen-analysis studies. But it has apparently not yet been recorded from similar deposits in America.

Fagus grandifolia Ehrh. (*F. americana* Sweet, *F. ferruginea* Ait.) American Beech type (Plate VII, Fig. 5). Normal grains spheroidal, uniform, averaging 40 μ in diameter; exine heavy and decidedly roughened; furrows long, narrow, and tapering, equally spaced around the equator and meridionally arranged, their margins raised slightly above the general surface of the exine, each enclosing a germ pore which is rather small and elliptical. Underlying each is a hyaline body which is similar to those of the grains of *Quercus*, yet these grains do not tend to overexpand and rupture their furrow membranes as do those of *Quercus*, probably on account of the greater thickness of their exine.

In the pollen of some trees are found a large number of grains with only two furrows. Such furrows may either be in the normal tricolpate position, as if one of the usual three had failed to develop, or they may be exactly opposite, in which case they are confluent at the poles and encircle the grain as a single furrow which may or may not be provided with two germ pores. Such grains may or may not be smaller than normal.

The grains of this species have been figured by Sears (1930), who points out that they may be distinguished from those of oak by the thickened margins of the germinal furrows. To this I should add the further distinction that the general surface of the exine is more constantly and more coarsely roughened, the exine is heavier, and the hyaline wedges are much less conspicuous than in the grains of oak.

The American beech is a large tree, conspicuous for its grayish-white bark. It is of rather general distribution in the eastern United States and Canada, from New Brunswick and Ontario southward to Virginia and, in its variety *caroliniana*, southward to Florida.

The flowers open in May at about the same time as the unfolding of the leaves. They are obviously wind pollinated, though they appear to shed less pollen than most anemophilous trees. The pollen of beech appears to be a minor cause of hayfever, and it is caught on pollen slides at considerable distances from the trees.

CASTANEA Hill CHESTNUT, CHINQUAPIN

The grains of both *Castanea* and the next genus, *Castanopsis*, are characterized by their small size—about 14 by 10 μ. They bear no resemblance to those of *Fagus* or *Quercus;* they lack entirely the granular texture of these two, and they possess a well-developed germ pore emerging through a transverse furrow.

The chestnuts and chinquapins are unquestionably wind pollinated but shed much less pollen than most anemophilous trees. Their pollen is not known to cause hayfever, though that of *Castanea sativa* is listed by Hall (1922) as a probable cause. The grains of various species are occasionally reported from Postglacial silts. In this connection the fossil pollen of *C. sativa* is described and illustrated by Erdtman (1923).

Castanea is a small genus of large trees widely distributed throughout North America, and the European species *C. sativa* has recently been introduced into some parts of North America.

Castanea dentata Borkh. Chestnut (Plate VII, Fig. 4) type. Grains uniform, tricolpate; when fully expanded ellipsoidal in shape, 14.7 by 11.2 μ. Furrows long and tapering, almost meeting at the poles, each enclosing a well-marked germinal aperture and a distinct transverse furrow with a thickened rim. The latter is conspicuous in optical section, and serves as a useful means of identification in fossil material. In fresh material, when the grains are expanded, the pore membrane is always seen to bulge through its aperture. Exine perfectly smooth. When these grains dry the furrows close up tightly and appear as narrow grooves and hide the germ pore from view, the grains themselves becoming columnar in shape.

A large tree, occasionally 100 ft. high. Flowers in June and July. Formerly abundantly and widely distributed in the eastern part of the United States but now almost extinct throughout most of its range owing to the ravages of a parasitic fungus, *Endothia parasitica* Anders.

Castanea pumila Mill. Chinquapin. Grains as in the type, 14.5 by 18.9 μ.

A small tree or shrub, sometimes forming thickets. New Jersey to Indiana and southward to Florida, most abundant in southern Arkansas and eastern Texas. Flowers May and June.

Castanea floridana (Gray) Ashe Chinquapin. Grains as in the type, 13.5 by 10.5 μ.

A small tree sparingly distributed in the Gulf Coast states.

Castanea nana Muhl. Chinquapin. Grains uniform and exactly as in the type, 11.7 by 11.2 μ.

A low shrub forming thickets on sand hills and in barrens, Georgia and Florida to Louisiana. Flowers in early spring.

CASTANOPSIS Spach

A genus with two species in California and the Pacific coast states but a larger number of species in southern Asia. Similar in most respects to *Castanea* to which it is closely allied.

Castanopsis chrysophylla DC. Golden chinquapin. Grains exactly as in *Castanea dentata*, 13.7 by 11.9 μ.

A large tree, Washington to California.

URTICACEAE Nettle Family

The family is here considered in its broadest sense, including the groups Ulmaceae, Moraceae, and Cannabinaceae, which are frequently regarded as separate families. Their pollen grains may be described as spheroidal or oblately flattened, entirely lacking germinal furrows but provided with two to seven germ pores equatorially arranged.

In all species the grains are extremely simple, lacking any but the most rudimentary sculpturing, such as a granular or warty texture, and even this is present in only a few. This is in keeping with their habit of wind pollination.

The grains are extremely various in size in the different species, ranging in diameter from about 13 μ, in *Broussonetia* and *Urtica*, to over 40 μ, in some species of *Celtis*. The germ pores are likewise various in character and size. In most species they are decidedly aspidate, often approaching very closely to the form of the grains of the Betulaceae, but in the grains of *Ulmus*, *Planera*, *Holoptelea*, and *Zelkova* the grains are not aspidate or possess only rudimentary subexineous thickenings around the germ pores. These four genera which lack the aspidate character all belong to the group of Ulmaceae and are apparently rather closely related. Other members of the same group, however, differ in this respect. For example, the grains of *Celtis*, *Ptero-celtis*, and *Gironniera*, which likewise belong to the group of Ulmaceae, are decidedly aspidate, which shows that the character, in this family at least, is not of real phylogenetic value. The aspidate character is one that frequently appears in wind-pollinated groups of diverse origins; therefore it seems most likely that the degree to which it is expressed is a measure of the response of the species to that mode of pollination rather than an indication of relationship. Besides being characteristic of most of the Urticaceae, the aspidate form of pores is found in the grains of the Betulaceae, Myricaceae, Haloragidaceae, Casuarinaceae, and Juglandaceae, families which are for the most part widely separated; but all are wind pollinated.

The following Asiatic genera omitted from this discussion have grain similar to those of *Urtica: Pouzolzia,* 9.4 to 11 μ, pores two or three; *Debregeasia,* 14 to 16.5 μ, pores three; *Maotia,* 14.8 to 17 μ, pores two.

KEY TO THE GENERA

I. Germ pores 3 to 7, mostly 5; not aspidate, or surrounded by only inconspicuous subexineous thickenings, apertures elliptic, pore membranes not capped but occasionally slightly flecked.

   A. Exine marked by internal reticulate thickenings or with connecting bands between the pores. Texture smooth.

      1. Exine not marked by internal reticulate thickenings but with conspicuous band-like thickenings extending from pore to pore.   Planera aquatica

      2. Exine marked by internal reticulate thickenings, connecting bands between the pores absent or only faintly expressed (*Ulmus crassifolia*).   Ulmus

   B. Exine not marked by internal reticulate thickenings or by connecting bands between the pores. Texture more or less granular.

      1. Texture finely granular, 16 to 18.2 μ in diameter.   Gironniera

      2. Texture coarsely warty-granular, 25 to 32 μ in diameter.   Holoptelea
                                           Zelkova

II. Germ pores two to six, mostly three or two, more or less aspidate, *i.e.,* surrounded by quite conspicuous subexineous thickenings; their apertures circular, irregular, or broadly elliptic in outline. Pore membranes capped, flecked, or smooth.

   A. Germ pores mostly two, only occasionally three.

      1. Grains large, 20 to 25 μ in diameter, ellipsoidal, with the pores near the ends but not diametrically opposite.

         a. Texture warty-granular, pore membrane smooth.   Trema

         b. Texture smooth, pore membrane flecked.   Morus

      2. Grains small, less than 14 μ in diameter, spherical or irregular in form.   Broussonetia

B. Germ pores mostly three or four, only occasionally
    two.
    1. Grains small, mostly less than 14 μ in diameter. Urtica
    2. Grains larger, 20 to 31 μ in diameter (frequently
        some giants with supernumerary pores in
        Celtis and *Momisia*).

Pore membrane capped.	Maclura
Pore membrane not capped.	Humulus
	Cannabis
	Celtis
	Pteroceltis
	Momisia

ULMUS L. Elm

Grains oblate, 23 to 38 μ in diameter. Germ pores three to seven, generally five or four, rarely three, elliptical in shape, their apertures 3.5 to 6 μ in length, equatorially arranged, with their long axes converging in pairs. Subexineous thickenings absent or only faintly represented. Pore membranes smooth or slightly flecked but never capped. Texture of the exine smooth but marked by slight undulations which are due to internal thickenings and which present the appearance of being the result of impressions made on the inner surface of the exine by the pressure of the starch grains with which these grains are always packed. The impressions, however, are permanent and persist after the starch is dissolved away by sulphuric acid.

The grains of *Ulmus* are very similar to those of *Holoptelea*, *Zelkova*, and *Planera* but may be distinguished from those of *Planera* by the absence of curved linear thickenings reaching from pore to pore.

Large trees shedding prodigious quantities of pollen, in most species, generally very early in spring, preceding the leaves by several weeks. It is well known that elm pollen is the cause of much hayfever, but the relative importance of the different species is not yet fully understood.

In the experience of the author, also in that of Duke and Durham (1928), elm pollen is found greatly to outrank all others in abundance in the air during a short period in March. The pollen of several species of elm has been found in Postglacial silts (*e.g.*, Erdtman, 1922; Budde, 1930; Rudolph and Firbas, 1924), and that of *U. foliacea* has been illustrated by Erdtman (1923) and by Docturowsky and Kudrjaschow (1923).

Ulmus americana L. White elm (Plate VII, Fig. 10) type. Grains distinctly flattened, averaging about 37.2 by 29.6 μ. Germ pores three to seven, most commonly five, arranged around the equator; apertures short-elliptical, with their long axes converging in pairs alternately above and below the equator, pore membranes flecked. When there are five pores the interval between the unpaired pore and its neighbor on one side is generally visibly greater than between the others. Thus if such grains are observed in polar view, their outline suggests a pentagon with one side longer than the others. The heavy reticulate thickenings underlying the exine suggest the surface markings of a peanut shell. These are difficult to see when the grain is full of starch but become clearly discernible when treated with sulphuric acid which dissolves out the cell contents. The surface texture is otherwise quite smooth.

A large tree flowering very early in spring before the leaves, shedding an abundance of light, air-borne pollen which is the undisputed cause of some early spring hayfever. Widely distributed throughout most of the United States and Canada east of the Rocky Mountains.

Ulmus campestris L. English elm. Grains essentially as in the type. Germinal apertures generally five, occasionally four or six.

A large tree flowering in early spring. Native of England and Europe, extensively introduced into America.

Ulmus fulva Michx. Slippery elm. Grains essentially as in the type, except that they are slightly smaller, 29.1 by 23.4 μ in diameter, germ pores generally four, less commonly five, with their apertures converging in pairs.

A large tree flowering early in spring. Widely distributed in the northeastern United States and Canada.

Ulmus alata Michx. Winged elm. Grains essentially as in the type, 27.8 by 22.8 μ in diameter. Germ pores generally five, less commonly four, 4.3 μ in length. As the pore membranes bulge through the apertures they may be seen to be slightly flecked as in the type but not capped as in the grains of *Maclura* and *Morus*.

A large tree shedding much pollen which is known to be the cause of some hayfever in early spring. Widely distributed throughout the southeastern United States.

Ulmus floridana Chapm. Florida elm.   Essentially as in the type.   Germinal apertures generally five.

A small tree flowering in late winter and early spring.   North Carolina to Florida.

Ulmus crassifolia Nutt. Cedar elm.   Grains as in the type except that the subexineous thickenings around the pores are slightly more pronounced, and there is a suggestion of linear thickenings reaching from pore to pore, though much less pronounced than in the grains of *Planera*.   The grains are also somewhat smaller than in the type, averaging 23.5 μ in diameter, and germinal apertures 3.5 μ in diameter.

Flowers August to October and is known to cause some hay-fever.   The common elm tree of eastern Texas and adjoining states.

Planera aquatica Gmel. Water elm.   Grains as in *Ulmus*, flattened, averaging 35.3 by 30.8 μ in diameter: germ pores generally four, only occasionally five, their apertures ellipsoidal, with their long axes converging in pairs, averaging 5.9 μ in length, the pore membranes slightly bulging when moist and quite noticeably flecked.   The pores are surrounded by slight subexineous thickenings.   From these extend out band-like thickenings reaching from pore to pore, apparently following geodetic curves, after the fashion of those of the grains of *Alnus* but less pronounced.   The presence of these thickenings and the fact that the grains are generally provided with only four germ pores offer the only distinguishing features between these grains and those of *Ulmus americana*.

A small tree in river swamps.   Indiana and Missouri to North Carolina, Florida, and Texas.   Flowers in early spring.

Gironniera rhamnifolia Blume. Grains uniform, 16 to 18.5 μ in diameter, approximately spherical or somewhat triangular in polar view.   Pores three, not surrounded by subexineous thickenings, apertures nearly circular; pore membranes smooth.   Exine thin, slightly thickened around the pores, faintly warty-granular.

A small tree native of New Guinea.   The genus comprises about eight species of trees and shrubs in Malaya and East India.

Holoptelea integrifolia Planch.   Grains 25 to 28.5 μ in diameter; pores generally five, occasionally four.   Exine coarsely warty-granular.   Otherwise as in the *Ulmus* type.

A small tree native of the East Indies and Ceylon.

Zelkova acuminata Planch. Grains 29 to 32 μ in diameter. Otherwise indistinguishable from those of *Holoptelea*.

A small tree native of Japan.

Trema amboinensis Blume (*Sponia amboinensis* Dcne.). Grains uniform, 21.5 to 24 μ in diameter, broadly ellipsoidal. Germ pores two, one at each end, as in the grains of *Morus* but not directly opposite; apertures not elongate, circular or more or less irregular in outline; pore membranes smooth. Subexineous thickenings very deep, the two together occupying nearly half the cell. Exine rather thick, coarsely warty-granular, greatly thickened around the pores.

Morus alba L. Mulberry (Plate VII, Fig. 8) type. Grains ellipsoidal or spheroidal, about 20.6 by 17.1 μ in diameter. Germ pores two, occasionally three, not diametrically opposite each other. Apertures circular, 3.5 μ in diameter; pore membranes generally noticeably bulging and capped with a thickening of material, with the same staining properties as the general exine. Texture smooth or slightly granular. This grain bears a close resemblance to those of *Broussonetia* and *Urtica* but is distinguished from them by its larger size. It is likewise similar to those of *Trema* but is distinguished by its smooth texture and capped pores.

A small tree shedding in early June much pollen which may be detected in large quantities in the air. It has been shown to be the cause of hayfever (Bernton, 1928). Naturalized from the Old World in fields and waste places. Maine to Minnesota, Georgia, and Texas.

Broussonetia papyrifera Vent. Paper mulberry. Grains irregular in shape but tending to be spherical, thin-walled, usually somewhat collapsed, 13.4 μ in diameter. Germ pores two, usually not exactly opposite, aspidate and slightly protruding, and the subexineous thickenings extending deeply inward. Pore membranes not generally bulging through the apertures and not capped or flecked. Apertures circular or approximately so, 2.3 μ in diameter. Texture smooth.

These grains are characterized by their small size and two aspidate germ pores, characters which, however, they share with those of *Urtica*. In shape and structure they also closely resemble the grains of *Morus alba* (Plate VII, Fig. 8), but the latter may be distinguished by their much larger size.

A small tree, in June shedding much pollen, which it does by an explosive action in response to light (Balyeat, 1932). It has been shown (Bernton, 1928) to be a potent cause of hayfever. Introduced from Asia.   New York, Missouri, and Florida.

Urtica dioica L. Stinging nettle.   Grains spheroidal or irregular, thin walled and collapsing easily, 10.5 μ in diameter.   Germ pores two or three, aspidate, with subexineous thickenings extending deeply into the cell; apertures circular, 1.7 μ in diameter; pore membranes slightly protruding and capped.   Texture smooth.

These grains are scarcely distinguishable from those of *Broussonetia* but differ from those of *Morus alba* in their smaller size.

A low perennial herb, wind pollinated, flowering in summer and fall.   Nova Scotia to Minnesota, South Carolina, and Missouri. Naturalized from Europe and Asia.   Not known to cause hayfever.

Urtica vividis Rydb. Nettle.   Grains essentially as in *Urtica dioica*, differing only in their possession of three or four pores and their slightly larger size—13.7 μ in diameter.   Not known to cause hayfever.

Maclura pomifera Schneider, (*Toxylon pomiferum* Raf.). Osage orange (Plate VII, Fig. 11) type.   Grains slightly flattened, those with the same number of germ pores of uniform size averaging 22 by 19.6 μ.   Germ pores generally three, though a considerable proportion of the grains have four or occasionally two.   Four-pored grains generally larger than the three-pored, averaging 22.9 μ in diameter.   Pores circular or nearly so, about 1.7 μ in diameter, aspidate, the subexineous thickenings very thick.   Pore membranes bulging when moistened, always thickened in the center, presenting the appearance of a little cap. Texture smooth.

A large tree with inconspicuous greenish flowers, shedding in early June much pollen which may be readily caught on pollen slides.   It has been shown (Bernton, 1928) to cause some hayfever.   Virginia to Arkansas, Georgia, and Texas.

Humulus Lupulus L. Hop.   Grains similar to those of *Maclura* (Plate VII, Fig. 11).   Spherical or slightly flattened oblately, about 24.5 μ in diameter.   Germ pores three or four, occasionally six or two, aspidate, with the pore membranes protruding and the subexineous thickenings extending deeply into the cell. Apertures broadly elliptic or nearly circular, 3.1 μ in diameter; pore membranes only slightly flecked or smooth, not capped. Texture faintly granular or smooth. These grains differ from the type of *Maclura pomifera* only in the much weaker development or entire absence of pore caps and the more elliptic shape of their germinal apertures.

A climbing vine, dioecious, bearing greenish staminate flowers, shedding large amounts of light, air-borne pollen throughout most of the summer. Hop pollen is not known to cause hayfever but, on account of its kinship with such undoubted hayfever plants as *Broussonetia* and *Morus*, deserves further investigation. Native of Europe and Asia. Escaped from cultivation. Nova Scotia, Manitoba, Florida, Arizona, and elsewhere in America.

Cannabis sativa L. Hemp. Grains similar to those of *Maclura*, oblate, averaging about 25 μ in diameter. Germ pores generally three but often four and, occasionally, two, aspidate, with the subexineous thickenings extending deeply into the cell. Apertures circular or nearly so, 2.3 μ in diameter; pore membranes not capped and only occasionally slightly flecked. Texture smooth. The character which distinguishes this grain from that of *Maclura* is the much weaker development or entire absence of pore caps in the former.

CELTIS L. Hackberry, Nettle tree

Grains spheroidal, not appreciably flattened. Texture noticeably granular. Germinal apertures nearly circular; pores aspidate, not raised perceptibly above the surface of the grain. Subexineous thickenings less pronounced than in the grains of *Maclura;* pore membranes flecked. Internal reticulate thickenings of the exine faintly represented but not persisting when the cell contents are dissolved away by sulphuric acid.

Celtis laevigata K. Koch (*C. mississippiensis* Spach) Hackberry. Grains nearly or quite spherical, averaging 40 μ in diameter. Germ pores three equally spaced around the equator, aspidate but not protruding above the surface of the grain. Pore membranes marked by a single fleck but less so than those of the grains of *Maclura*. Texture slightly granular and appearing almost warty in the regions of the pores. This grain differs from the type (*M. pomifera*) principally in its thinner subexineous thickenings.

Celtis occidentalis L. Hackberry (Plate VII, Fig. 9). Grains spherical, packed with starch grains, texture slightly granular. Germ pores aspidate; apertures circular or more or less irregular but not elliptical; pore membranes sometimes marked by a single fleck. These grains show an enormous variation. In size they range from 25 to 55 μ in diameter; the germ pores range in number from 3, a number that is rare, upward to 10 or more. The pores exhibit no regularity of arrangement or size, and sometimes two or three appear to coalesce, but generally the larger grains have the larger numbers of pores. This great irregularity, together with a large number of abortive grains that are always found, suggests hybridity of origin.

A small tree, generally of gnarled appearance. The flowers open in early spring with the unfolding of the leaves. They shed large amounts of wind-borne pollen which probably causes some hayfever. This species is apparently not distinguished from *C. laevigata* in hayfever literature. The grains are described and illustrated by Sears (1930), showing only three germ pores, as in those of *C. laevigata*.

Pteroceltis Tatarinowii Maxim. Grains uniform, spheroidal or slightly triangular in outline, 23.5 to 27 μ in diameter. Pores three, their apertures circular or slightly elliptical. Otherwise as in *Celtis*.

Small tree, native of Mongolia and north China.

Momisia Iguanaea Rose & Standl. Cockspur. Grains somewhat various, 20 to 27.5 μ in diameter, spheroidal or oblately flattened and somewhat triangular in outline. Pores three, occasionally two, aspidate, equatorially arranged, their apertures broadly elliptic with their long axes directed meridionally. Exine thin, finely granular, especially around the pores.

These grains are scarcely distinguishable from those of *Celtis* and *Pteroceltis*, excepting in the slightly more elliptical shape of their germinal apertures.

A woody vine, Florida, West Indies, and tropical America.

Momisia aculeata (Lw.) Klotz. (*Celtis aculeata* Klotz.). Normal grains as in *M. iguanaea* but extremely various and irregular, with many of them giants or dwarfs and others obviously abortive and with various numbers of germ pores, in this respect similar to the pollen of *C. occidentalis.*

A small tree native of the West Indies and tropical America.

POLYGONACEAE Knotweed Family

The pollen grains of the Polygonaceae are extremely various, apparently without any general underlying similarities, so that it is useless to attempt to frame a definition for them. A study of the different forms, however, is of peculiar interest because it shows that they are related to each other and reveals several developmental tendencies which are remarkable and of far-reaching importance. In this family we see a suggestive illustration of how the ordinary tricolpate or three-furrowed type of grain with heavy walls and broad, deep furrows might have given rise to the thin-walled type with furrows reduced to thread-like grooves or entirely absent. Also, we discover how the same tricolpate form of grain could have given rise to the many-pored or cribellate form of grain which reaches perhaps its highest development in the Chenopodiaceae and Amaranthaceae. As regards the morphology of their pollen grains, the Polygonaceae are a transitional family.

The basic form of the grains of this family can be typified by that of *Eriogonum* (Plate VIII, Fig. 6). It is ellipsoidal, heavy-walled with a thick exine of granular structure but perfectly smooth on its surface, and gashed almost from pole to pole by three long, tapering furrows which function freely as harmomegathi, closing up tightly when the grain dries and gaping open widely when it is moistened, with a sort of hinge action at their pointed ends. In the middle of each furrow is a single roundish or elliptical germ pore, which is freely exposed when the furrow is open but more or less hidden when it is closed. This form of grain is always associated with insect pollination and can be regarded as the basic form not only of the Polygonaceae but also of most of the higher dicotyledons. In this family it characterizes, with relatively little modification, the pollen of such entomophilous species as *Eriogonum, Triplaris, Antigonum, Fagopyrum,* and some species of *Polygonum.* Generally there are just three furrows, but in the pollen of some species there are always to be found, besides the ordinary tricolpate grains, some with larger numbers. Among the pollen of the species that we have before us, that of *P. allocarpum* exhibits grains with 3, 4, 5, 6, 9, and 12 furrows, nearly always beautifully arranged in the trischisto-clasic system. The occasional possession of more furrows than the usual three must be regarded as a tendency inherent in the family, a vagary which, after all, is only an extension within the system of equal stress arrangements and characterizes the pollen of many unrelated dicotyledons which have tricolpate grains as the basic form.

An environmental modification of this form of grain is found in the pollen of the anemophilous members *Rumex*, *Rheum*, and *Muehlenbeckia*. The inevitable result of this mode of pollination is that their grains are thin walled, and its corollary that the furrows are much reduced, their harmomegathic function being unnecessary in association with a thin and flexible wall. In all of these the furrows are just linear grooves of negligible width even when expanded. When such grains dry, their surface dips in along the furrows, and they become deeply lobed, the furrows acting throughout their entire length as hinges for the bending of the thin exine. When the grains are moistened they become spheroidal, disclosing a small and weakly developed germ pore in the middle of each furrow. Owing to the hinge action of the furrows they are necessarily long, reaching almost from pole to pole when the grains are tricolpate or almost meeting each other at the centers of convergence when polycolpate. If the reduction in the thickness of the exine had been carried a little farther, it is quite conceivable that it would have resulted in the total disappearance of both pores and furrows, for they are organs of the exine. Indeed, so near the vanishing point have they approached in the grains of some species of *Rumex* that it seems likely that such is the origin of the furrowless and poreless forms of grain that are encountered here and there among the pollen of wind-pollinated plants of other families; but in this family I have not found grains of this type entirely devoid of furrows.

A directly opposite line of development is found among the pollen grains of some of the members of this family which have retained insect pollination, *e.g.*, those of *Persicaria*, *Tracaulon*, and some species of *Polygonum*. In these not only has the exine remained thick, but it has become built up into an elaborate system of high, vertical ridges which, anastomosing freely throughout, impart a stiffness to the exine, causing the grain to be encased in a shell of rigid inflexibility, which results in a loss of furrows and a great increase in the number of pores. The character of these grains has departed so far from the basic form that it would be difficult to see any relation between them, were it not for a few intermediate forms which clearly establish the connection. In the grains of *Polygonum californicum* (Plate VIII, Fig. 7), for example, part of the surface is alveolate, and part of it is unmodified. Though only a part of the surface is involved, it includes the areas over both poles—the regions which must take up most of the bending when the furrows open and close—and consequently their harmomegathy is necessarily greatly impeded. Associated with this—probably as a consequence of it—these grains have very short and ineffective furrows. Moreover, there is no compensating device to offset the reduction of the furrows; and I think that the reason for this is to be found in the size and shape of the grains, for they are very small, measuring, exclusive of the alveolate thickenings at the poles, 19.4 by 12.5 μ, the smallest in the family. Owing to the fact that in solid bodies volume is a function of the cube of the linear dimensions while surface area is a function of the square of the same dimensions, the small size of these grains results in a relatively small ratio between their volume and their surface area, and this ratio is still further reduced by their elongate shape; consequently, there is sufficient elasticity in their walls to accommodate whatever slight changes in volume there are, without any help from the furrows. In some ways this grain may be regarded as intermediate between the basic smooth type and the fully alveolate and suggests the mode of origin of the latter from the former, though itself—in its small size—divergent from both.

A more complete development of the alveolate structure is found in the grains of *Polygonum chinense* (Plate VIII, Fig. 8). Here the entire surface is covered with anastomosing upstanding ridges of such a character as to impart the utmost rigidity to the whole exine, which, it may readily be seen, would effectively prevent the opening and closing of any type of furrow, particularly the long, tapering one which characterizes the basic form of grain of this family. The furrows of the grains of *P. chinense* are three and moderately long, and it is obvious that their operation as expansion mechanisms is greatly impeded by the alveolate structure of the exine, for when the grains are fully expanded the furrows do not open wide throughout their full length but merely bulge out in the middle, pushed apart by the protrusion of the large germ pore, remaining pinched off toward their ends. These grains are large—43.2 μ in diameter—which means that their volume is about twenty times as great as that of the grains of *P. californicum*, while their surface area is only about nine times as great. As a consequence, in this case some compensating device is necessary to make up for the lack of harmomegathy of the furrows. This is apparently accomplished by an increase in the size of the pores, which are remarkable in this respect, measuring about 10.3 by 13.8 μ and bulging prominently when the grain is moistened. They appear to be quite large enough to accommodate changes in volume, thus taking over, to a large extent, the impaired harmomegathic function of the furrows.

In the grains of *Persicaria* (Plate VIII, Fig. 5) a still further advance in the same direction is found. Here the demobilization of the exine is complete, no trace of the furrows remains, and the pores are each completely enclosed in a single lacuna; but in this case the loss of the furrows is abundantly compensated by the large number of the pores. These cannot actually be counted, but their distance apart, taken in consideration with their arrangement, permits one to estimate their number at about 30. Their arrangement is plainly that which they would occupy if they were at the centers of furrows arranged in the trischisto-clasic system.

Briefly, then, it may be said that, in the evolution of these pollen-grain forms the tendency to develop an alveolate structure, with its resultant stiffening of the exine and demobilization of the furrows, stimulated a compensating increase in the number of the pores, a tendency manifestly already inherent in the family, and this resulted in the development of the extraordinarily beautiful form of grain of *Persicaria* and allied genera, decorated with a continuous reticulum of high ridges and provided with about 30 pores. This form is the culmination of this line of development in the family.

It is interesting to look ahead and see what the next step in such a line of development might be. There seems to be a widespread tendency among the angiosperms to abandon insect pollination and adopt wind pollination, a step which tends to induce a reduction of pollen-grain sculpturing. Anemophily has originated among the angiosperms many times quite independently. This is reflected in the classification of living species of wind-pollinated plants, for they are generally found in families which also include others which are insect pollinated, *e.g.*, the poplars in the willow family, the ragweeds and sagebrushes in the composite family, and the ashes in the olive family. In all such instances the change from insect to wind pollination was accompanied by a reduction of, or entire loss of, surface decorations of the pollen grains.

There are no wind-pollinated members of the Polygonaceae derived from ancestors with many-pored alveolate grains. (We have already seen that the forms of the grains of the wind-pollinated *Rumex*, *Rheum*, and *Muehlenbeckia* were derived from the ordinary tricolpate form of grain.) But the neighboring families, Chenopodiaceae and Amaranthaceae, are entirely wind pollinated, and consequently their grains are devoid of decorations. These two families may not have been derived from the Polygonaceae, but a consideration of their grains in association with those of the Polygonaceae is suggestive of the form to which an extension of the evolutionary sequence of forms established in the Polygonaceae might lead, under the influence of wind pollination. The grains of the Chenopodiaceae and Amaranthaceae are cribellate, *i.e.*, characterized by a large number of pores, giving the exine a sieve-like appearance. They are thin walled, and the exine is devoid of decorations other than the numerous round germ pores. It is likely that the many-pored character of the grains of these two families was called forth in some ancestral species by some form of sculpturing which brought about the demobilization of the exine but which has since been lost as the result of their adoption of wind pollination.

KEY TO THE SPECIES

I. Furrows present.
    A. Furrows long and extremely narrow linear
        channels; exine thin.
        1. Furrows always 3; germ pores circular;
           texture fine-granular.   Rheum officinale
        2. Furrows 3 or 4, generally both tri- and
           tetracolpate grains present; germ
           pores elliptical.

    a. 26.5 to 32 μ in diameter, pores 4.6 μ
       long.
       (1) Texture granular.   Muehlenbeckia vulcanica
       (2) Texture finely pitted.
          (*a*) Furrows generally 3, rarely
             4 or 5.   Rumex crispus
          (*b*) Furrows prevailingly 4, less
             frequently 3, and rarely 5
             or 6.   Rumex obtusifolius
    b. Grains 18.2 to 23.9 μ in diameter.
       (1) Furrows prevailingly 4, less fre-
          quently 3.   Rumex Acetosella
       (2) Furrows prevailingly 3, less fre-
          quently 4.   Rumex Acetosa
       (3) Furrows always 3.   Rumex scutatus

B. Furrows not linear, broader toward the
   middle, tapering toward their ends;
   exine thick.
   1. With the entire surface conspicuously
      granular or pitted or both. Germ
      pores circular or somewhat elliptical.
     a. Grains over 40 μ in length; texture
        very coarsely granular and pitted
        throughout.
       (1) Grains long-ellipsoidal, furrow
          membranes heavily flecked;
          germ pore decidedly elliptical. Fagopyrum esculentum
       (2) Grains nearly spherical; furrow
          membrane lightly flecked,
          germ pore somewhat ellipti-
          cal or circular.   Antigonum guatemalense
     b. Grains less than 40 μ in length.
       (1) Bulging between the furrows,
          therefore tending to be tri-
          angular in cross section.
          Furrow margins raised; pore
          circular; Texture granular
          throughout.   Chorizanthe pungens
                                        Chorizanthe Parryi
       (2) Not bulging between the furrows;
          furrow margins not raised.
          (*a*) Grains 32 to 39.5 μ long;
             germ pore nearly or quite
             circular; texture fine-
             pitted.   Triplaris americana
                                       Triplaris caracasana
                                       Triplaris felipensis

(b) Grains 27.5 to 31 μ long.
  (1) Germ pores circular
    Furrow membranes flecked.   Eriogonum gracile
    Furrow membranes smooth.   Erigonum galioides
  (2) Germ pore elliptical; furrow membranes smooth.   Polygonum buxiforme
    Polygonum allocarpum

2. Chimerical, with part of the surface granular and part alveolate.   Polygonum californicum
3. With entire surface alveolate; furrows always 3, short, not extending much beyond the pores; grains about 43 μ in diameter.   Polygonum chinense

II. Furrows absent; entire surface alveolate; pores about 30, disposed over the surface in the trischistoclasic system; grains 45 to 70 μ in diameter.

Persicaria Muhlenbergii
Persicaria pennsylvanica
Persicaria hydropiperoides
Persicaria Persicaria
Persicaria acuminata
Tracaulon arifolium
Tracaulon sagittatum

RUMEX L. Dock

Grains when moist spheroidal or tending to be somewhat ellipsoidal, slightly bulging between the furrows; somewhat various in size in the different species; those of *R. crispus* and *R. obtusifolius* 18 to 32 μ in diameter. Furrows long, very slender, and pointed at their ends, varying in number from three to six but generally three or four, arranged according to the trischistoclasic system. Furrow membranes smooth. Germ pores elliptical in shape, with their long axes directed in the same sense as those of the furrows, small, 3.4 to 4.6 μ long, sharply defined. Texture of the exine always distinctly pitted, though of somewhat various coarseness in the different species. Normal grains always tightly packed with starch, which shows plainly through the thin, transparent walls of the grain.

Rumex is a genus of about 140 species of mostly homely herbs, of wide distribution. Taxonomically they are grouped in the two sections, Acetosa and Lapathium. To the former belong the sorrels, *R. Acetosella*, *R. Acetosa*, and *R. scutatus*, and to the latter the docks proper, *R. crispus* and *R. obtusifolius*. The slight genetic difference between these two groups is reflected to a certain extent in the dimensions of their pollen grains, those of the ACETOSA group ranging, in the species here examined, from 18.2 to 23.9 μ in diameter, with their germ pores uniformly 3.4 μ in diameter, while those of the LAPATHIUM series range from 26.5 to 32 μ in diameter, with their germ pores 4.6 μ in diameter. The pollen of other species of these two groups should be examined to see if this difference holds for all and is really a character of sectional value.

All are wind pollinated, and some are counted as minor factors in hayfever. *R. hymenosepalus* Torr., Canaigre, is cultivated in California and is said to be an important cause of hayfever in San Fernandez valley (Selfridge, 1920). *R. conglomeratus* Murr. is stated by Hall (Scheppegrell, 1917) to be of only minor importance in California, though abundant and producing much pollen. The pollen of the various species possesses all the physical characters of hayfever pollen and, in my experience, is caught on the pollen slides in fairly large quantities almost throughout the summer. The reason why it should be so much less toxic to hayfever patients than the pollen of the grasses or even of plantain is probably bound up with its chemical make-up and deserves further inquiry.

The grains of six species are described and illustrated by Meinke (1927) in connection with his studies on Postglacial silts, but, as far as I am aware, they are seldom recorded from bog deposits; this is probably owing to the fragile nature of their exine which, in all the species of this genus, is very thin and tends to collapse beyond recognition when empty.

Rumex Acetosella L. Sour dock (Plate VIII, Fig. 1) type. Grains rather uniform in size, 22 to 24 μ in diameter. Furrows three, more frequently four or occasionally six. Germ pores 3.4 μ long. Exine coarsely pitted, more so than in the grains of *R. crispus* and *R. obtusifolius*, about the same as in those of *R. Acetosa* and *R. scutatus*. These grains may be distinguished from the two latter, which they resemble most closely, in being prevailingly tetracolpate.

Low herbs in dry fields and waste places. Wind pollinated, shedding large amounts of light, air-borne pollen, June and July;

throughout North America, except in the extreme north; introduced from Europe. Generally speaking, rather an unimportant factor in hayfever. Said to be important in California (Rowe, 1928; Selfridge, 1920) and in Oregon (Chamberlain, 1927).

Rumex Acetosa L. Green sorrel. Sour or Sheep dock. Grains essentially as in the type, rather uniform in size, 18.2 to 21.6 μ in diameter. Furrows three, or less frequently four. Germ pores 3.4 μ long.

A low herb, similar to though much larger than the preceding. Introduced from Europe or Asia, now widely distributed in the United States and Canada, wind pollinated, shedding rather large amounts of pollen in early summer. Not known to be a factor in hayfever but probably not distinguished from the preceding species.

Rumex scutatus L. Roman sorrel. Grains spheroidal, uniform, 23.9 μ to 25.1 μ in diameter, furrows nearly always three, texture more finely pitted than in the two preceding species. Otherwise as in the type. A low weed widely distributed in Europe; wind pollinated but not known to cause hayfever.

Rumex crispus L. Curled or Yellow dock. Grains spheroidal, rather uniform in size, 28.5 to 32.0 μ in diameter. Furrows three or rarely four or five; germ pore 4.6 μ in length. Otherwise as in the type. These grains may be distinguished from those of the three preceding species by their larger size and from those of *R. obtusifolius*, which they resemble more closely, by being prevailingly tricolpate and with a somewhat finer texture to their exine.

Tall rank herbs, roadsides and waste places almost throughout North America; wind pollinated but shedding relatively little pollen and constituting, outside a few restricted localities, only a minor cause of hayfever. It is, however, regarded as important in Oregon (Chamberlain, 1927). In California it is regarded as unimportant by Hall (Scheppegrell, 1917) but as important by Selfridge (1920). In my experience in the vicinity of New York City it sheds too little pollen ever to become a serious factor in hayfever.

Rumex obtusifolius L. Broad-leaved or Bitter dock. Grains spheroidal in shape, somewhat various in size, 26.4 to 31 μ in diameter. Furrows prevailingly four, less frequently three or six, rarely five. When more than three they are somewhat variously united or irregular in arrangement. Germ pores 4.6 μ long. Otherwise as in the type. This grain may be distinguished from that of *R. crispus*, which it resembles most closely, by being prevailingly tetracolpate and of a slightly more coarsely pitted texture.

A rank weed of roadsides and waste places. Similar in habit and appearance to the preceding. Regarded as a minor cause of hayfever in California (Hall in Scheppegrell, 1917).

Rheum officinale Baillon Tibetan rhubarb. Grains similar to those of *Rumex Acetosella*, spheroidal or ellipsoidal, rather uniform, about 30 μ in diameter; tricolpate, with furrows long and very slender, sunken in the surface of the grain to such an extent as to give it a three-lobed shape; each is provided with a single small, round or nearly round pore. Exine somewhat heavier, and pitting finer than in the type.

Native of Tibet and western China. Occasionally cultivated as a foliage plant and the source of at least part of officinal rhubarb. The genus *Rheum* L. includes about 20 species, native of Asia, from Siberia to Himalaya and Palestine. The best known species is the common garden rhubarb or wine plant, *R. Rhaponticum* L.

Muehlenbeckia vulcanica (Benth.) Endl. Grains resembling those of *Rumex Acetosella*, spheroidal or oblately flattened, 26 to 27.5 μ in diameter; texture granular, with the granules fused so as to form a more or less continuous reticulum. Otherwise as in the type.

The genus *Muehlenbeckia* comprises about 15 species of small shrubs and woody climbers, native of Australia, New Zealand, South America, and the Solomon Islands. The flowers are not showy and are unisexual, monoecious, or dioecious; they therefore appear to be wind pollinated, though I have not been able to determine this point with certainty. Among them are such well-known cultivated plants as the wire plant, *M. complexa* Meissn., a creeper from New Zealand, much cultivated in California and elsewhere; and the curious centipede plant, *M. platyclados* Meissn., a curiosity of the greenhouse, from the Solomon Islands.

ERIOGONUM Michx. ERIOGONUM, UMBRELLA PLANT

Grains uniform in shape and size, ellipsoidal, about 32 by 25 μ; tricolpate, with long, tapering furrows which gape open when the grain is moist, disclosing the circular germinal aperture through which the pore bulges prominently. The furrow membrane is for the most part smooth, though occasionally it may be lightly flecked with a few granules which tend to occupy a strip along its center. Exine thick, slightly thicker along the margins of the furrows and along three meridional strips between the furrows, recalling the thickenings in the grain of *Chorizanthe;* texture distinctly and rather coarsely granular, with the granules in the vicinity of the germ pores tending to be arranged in rows resembling thumb-print markings but unorganized in other parts of the grain.

These grains differ from those of the foregoing genera in their heavier exine and consequently better development of their furrows. The plants are insect pollinated, while those of *Rumex* and *Rheum* and probably *Muehlenbeckia* are wind pollinated. Thus we see, in the comparison of the grains of these two groups, an expression of an almost universal law—that when pollen becomes dispersed by wind the exine becomes thinner. This form of grain may be regarded as the least specialized in the family, the form from which the others were probably derived.

The genus comprises over 200 species of low herbs, native of America, mostly of the western states. All are insect pollinated, and none is regarded as a cause of hayfever.

Eriogonum gracile Benth. (Plate VIII, Fig. 6). type. Grains as in generic description, furrow membrane occasionally slightly flecked. Dry plains, valleys, and low hills: Great Salt valley and Coast Ranges to southern California and Lower California.

Eriogonum galioides I. M. Johnston. Grains as in generic description, furrow membrane smooth. Low, prostrate, perennial herb, common on San Luis Island, Gulf of California.

CHORIZANTHE R. Br.

Grains similar to those of *Eriogonum,* somewhat ellipsoidal, about 30 by 25 μ, tricolpate, with rather short, tapering furrows with their margins conspicuously raised, forming prominent ridges. Germ pore clearly defined, circular; furrow membrane smooth. The grain bulges quite conspicuously between the furrows, thus giving it something of a triangular shape in optical section (Plate VIII, Fig. 3). Exine thick and very coarsely granular, but granules without lineal arrangement. These grains differ from those of *Eriogonum* in the greater extent of their intercolpar thickenings, their more coarsely granular texture, and their shorter furrows.

About 30 species in western North America and Chile. Low, dichotomously branching desert herbs.

Chorizanthe pungens Benth. (Plate VIII, Fig. 3). As in generic description, indistinguishable from the preceding species. Low, prostrate herb, common in San Francisco Bay region of California and southward.

Chorizanthe Parryi Wats. As in the generic description. Low, flat-topped plants 3 to 15 in. broad, southern California, common on gravelly mesas near Crofton, San Bernardino County.

TRIPLARIS Löfl.

Grains ellipsoidal or nearly or quite spheroidal when fully expanded, tricolpate, with furrows long and tapering but narrower than in *Eriogonum*. Germ pores circular or slightly elliptical. Furrow membranes smooth. Exine rather thick but various in the different species, more or less granular and distinctly but finely pitted. These grains differ from those of *Eriogonum* in their more nearly spheroidal shape, thinner exine without thickenings between the furrows or along their margins, and fine pitting of the exine. In all of these characters they tend to resemble *Rumex*.

A genus of about 10 species of small trees, tropical South America.

Triplaris americana L. Grains uniform, spheroidal or short-ellipsoidal, about 35.3 by 33.1 μ, always tricolpate. Otherwise as in the generic description.

Native of South America, occasionally cultivated under glass or out of doors in the southern states.

Triplaris felipensis Wedd. Grains uniform, spheroidal when expanded, 35.3 to 36.5 μ in diameter. Otherwise as in generic description. Colombia, South America.

Triplaris caracasana Cham. Grains uniform, spheroidal, 31.4 to 34.2 μ in diameter. Pitting of the exine finer than in *T. americana*. Otherwise as in the generic description. Venezuela. Flowers in May.

Fagopyrum esculentum Moench. Buckwheat. Grains long-ellipsoidal in shape, extremely various in size, but the majority of them measuring about 57 by 47 μ; tricolpate, with furrows long and tapering; germ pores not sharply defined but decidedly elliptical; furrow membranes conspicuously flecked with large, coarse granules. Texture conspicuously pitted and with a coarse, underlying granular structure.

A low annual herb, native of Europe and northern Asia, much cultivated elsewhere and frequently escaped. June to September. Insect pollinated.

Antigonum guatemalense Meissn. Grains short-ellipsoidal to spheroidal, 57 to 62 μ long, tricolpate, with rather long, tapering furrows. Germ pores sharply defined, circular or slightly elliptical. Furrow membranes lightly flecked with a few loose, scattered granules. Exine thick and rugged with a coarse-granular and pitted texture. This grain may be distinguished from that of *Fagopyrum* by its more nearly spherical shape, coarse texture, and less conspicuously flecked furrow membranes. Woody climbers in Guatemala.

The genus *Antigonum* comprises three or four species of tendril-climbing vines, in Mexico and Central America. One species, the coral vine or corallita, is cultivated in the southern states for the beauty of its bright-pink flowers.

POLYGONUM (Tourn.) L. KNOTWEED, JOINTWEED

Several very different forms of grain are found among the species of this genus, and these exhibit characters both of the preceding genera and of the very different grains of the succeeding genera. The basic form of grain of *Polygonum* is tricolpate, with long tapering furrows, heavy granular exine, and decidedly ellipsoidal shape, essentially the same as that of *Eriogonum* (Plate VIII, Fig. 6) except that it lacks the intercolpar thickenings of the exine and the thickenings along the margins of the furrows of the latter. This form of grain is exhibited, among those members of this genus which we have before us, only by *P. buxiforme*. I have not been able to examine the pollen of more than a very few species and therefore cannot say from personal observation whether or not this form really does characterize the grains of the majority of them. Nevertheless, Fischer (1890)

finds that all 10 of the species that he examined "haben drei
parallele Falten mit je einer kreisrunden Keimpore; die Exine
ist doppelt die Zwischenstäbchen an den Polen feiner und dichter,
an den Seiten dicker und weitlänfiger gestellt; Oberfläche fast
glatt." It therefore seems safe to assume that such is the basic
form of the pollen grains of *Polygonum*.

This simple form undergoes, in some of the species, two highly
suggestive modifications. The first is the rather remarkable
multiplication of furrows, recalling the condition in *Rumex* and
others, *e.g.*, in the grains of *P. allocarpum*. In the grains of this
species the furrows are beautifully symmetrical and occur in
most of the theoretically possible arrangements of the trischistoclasic series of configurations up to that requiring 12 furrows,
and it is likely that an examination of the pollen of other species
or possibly a more extended examination of the pollen of this
species would discover some grains with higher numbers of
furrows in the same system.

The other modification that the simple basic tricolpate grain
undergoes in this genus is the development of an alveolate structure of its exine. This is partly expressed in the grains of
Polygonum californicum in which the alveolate and simple
granular characters are combined in chimerical fashion. It
reaches its fullest expression, however, in the grains of *P. chinense*,
in which the entire surface is alveolate, in this respect resembling
the grains of *Persicaria*.

Polygonum buxiforme Small Shore knotweed. Grains uniform ellipsoidal, averaging about 28 by 23 μ. Furrows three,
occasionally six, long and tapering, deeply depressed, giving the
grains a lobed appearance. Furrow membrane smooth, germ
pore elliptical, with its long axis directed in the same sense as
that of the furrow. Exine thick, with texture distinctly but
finely granular. These grains are similar to those of *Chorizanthe*
and *Eriogonum* but do not bulge between the furrows as in the
former, and their germ pores are distinctly elongate instead of
circular, as in the latter.

A prostrate, bushy weed, on shores and in waste places,
almost throughout the United States and Canada. August and
September.

Polygonum allocarpum Blake. Grains essentially as in *P.
buxiforme*, except that the majority have 6 furrows, relatively

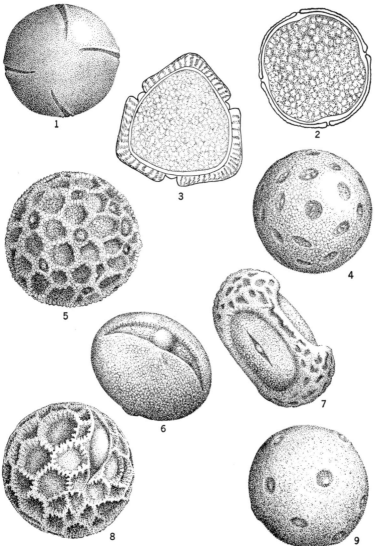

PLATE VIII.—Pollen grains of Polygonaceae and Chenopodiaceae. 1, *Rumex Acetosella*, polar view, 23 μ in diameter. 2, *Rumex Acetosella*, transverse optical section. 3, *Chorizanthe pungens*, optical section, 25 μ in diameter. 4, *Salsola Pestifer*, 27.5 μ in diameter. 5, *Persicaria Muhlenbergii*, 57 μ in diameter. 6, *Eriogonum gracile*, side view, 32 × 25 μ. 7, *Polygonum californicum*, side view, 19 by 12.5 μ. 8, *Polygonum chinense*, 43 μ in diameter. 9, *Sarcobatus vermiculatus*, 28 μ in diameter.

few have 3, and occasionally grains with 4, 5, 9, and 12 furrows are found. In nearly all of these the furrow configurations are beautifully regular, conforming almost exactly with the trischistoclasic system. The grains are uniform in size, 28.5 to 29.6 μ in diameter.

Branching annual herb, seacoasts and adjacent islands, Maine and New Brunswick.

Polygonum californicum Meissner (Plate VIII, Fig. 7). Grains uniform in size and shape, ellipsoidal, 19.0 by 12.5 μ. The exine of the two ends and three longitudinal strips, alveolate, almost as in *Persicaria*, but over three large elliptical areas surrounding the three furrows the exine is granular, as in the grains of *Polygonum buxiforme* and *P. allocarpum*. Furrows short and tapering, furrow membranes smooth, germ pore elliptical. This grain combines the characters of those of *Persicaria* and *Polygonum* in such a way that it may truly be spoken of as chimerical and suggests the mode whereby one form could have been derived from the other.

A slender, wiry annual, diffusely branching, 3 to 7 in. high. Dry foothills, Sierra Nevada and north Coast Ranges; north to Washington. July.

Polygonum chinense L. (Plate VIII, Fig. 8). Grains uniform, spheroidal, about 43.3 μ in diameter, tricolpate, with furrows short and sharply tapering, furrow membrane smooth, germ pore large, elliptical, occupying nearly the whole furrow. The entire surface of the grain is marked off into angular lacunae by a reticulate system of high ridges. In this respect the grain is almost exactly like the grains of *Persicaria*. The ridges have the appearance of being composed of vertical prisms partially fused together, making irregular, jagged, palisade-like partitions between the lacunae. The floors of the lacunae are studded here and there with a few little bead-like thickenings. The alveolar system abuts upon the furrows with mostly closed lacunae, showing that the furrows are not torn through the reticulum but are developed simultaneously with it as co-ordinate structures.

This form of grain is curiously intermediate between the basic form of the genus and the furrowless, alveolate form of *Persicaria* but tends more toward the latter. In its large size, spheroidal form, and alveolate surface it is persicarioid, but in its possession of three furrows with three germ pores it is polygonoid.

A shrubby perennial about 5 ft. high, with white, pink, or purplish flowers in small, panicled heads. Native of the Himalaya region and Ceylon to China and Japan and of the Philippines. Occasionally cultivated.

PERSICARIA (Tourn.) Mill.

Grains spheroidal, rather large, ranging from about 51 to about 70 μ in diameter; alveolate, with the whole or part of the surface marked off into angular lacunae by a reticulate system of well-defined ridges (Plate VIII, Fig. 5). The texture of the floor of the lacunae is more or less pebbled, always coarse but various in the different species. The pebbled structure also involves the ridges, which are extremely rough and jagged as a consequence, presenting the appearance of a breakwater built of closely packed but crookedly driven piles. Elements similar to those which go to make up this remarkable structure are encountered in a lesser degree of development in the granular and pitted texture of the grains of *Fagopyrum* and *Antigonum* and, to a lesser extent, of *Rumex;* so this structure, remarkable as is its appearance, cannot be said to have arisen *de novo* in this genus or in *Polygonum* but is in reality the culmination of a tendency variously expressed in the grains of most of the other species of the family.

Furrows are entirely absent in all species here considered; the germ pores are set here and there in the ordinary lacunae of the reticulum, and the lacunae occupied by them are frequently difficult to distinguish from those that are unoccupied but may generally be recognized by their smaller size and their smooth and slightly bulging floor. The system governing the arrangement of the pores is not readily apparent, because in all the species which we have before us the pores are round and consequently do not divulge their spacial orientation in the way that furrows do. It can readily be seen, however, that their arrangement is not isometric, as would be suggested by their rounded form; for if one pore is regarded as a center of a group, it is found not to be surrounded by five or six others at equal distances, as would be the case if their arrangement were isometric. Instead, they are arranged according to the trichistoclasic system, as in most furrow configurations. In these grains if one pore is regarded as a center, it is found to be flanked by two pairs of pores which are

equidistant and on opposite sides (Fig. 100). The pattern of
the arrangement of the group of five pores thus obtained resolves
itself into two equilateral triangles in which the initial or central
pore of the group serves as the apex of both; and we find that
each of the three pores of each triangular group is likewise the
member of a neighboring triangular group, thus forming a
continuous system throughout. The characteristic whereby

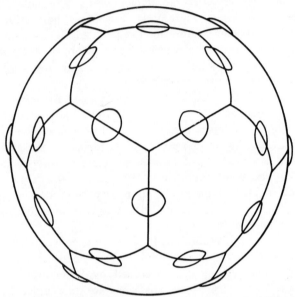

Fig. 100.—Diagram of the pore arrangement of a *Persicaria* pollen grain with
30 pores arranged in the trischistoclasic system. The lines drawn through the
pores represent the hypothetical furrow axes and correspond in arrangement to
the edges of a pentagonal dodecahedron.

this system may be recognized is the repetition of the triangular
group.

The circular form of the pores of the species of *Persicaria*, which
we have before us, makes it surprising that their arrangement
should be according to that of the trischistoclasic system, one
which is generally associated with elongate furrows rather than
circular pores. Much light, however, is thrown on their origin
by a consideration of the grains of *P. amphibium*, which, according to the description of Fritzsche (1837) and his beautiful figure,

are provided with 30 furrows, marking off the surface of the grain into 12 pentagonal areas corresponding exactly to the 12 faces of a pentagonal dodecahedron. If, in such a grain as this, the 30 elongate furrows were to be replaced by as many round germ pores, their arrangement would be exactly like that of the various species of *Persicaria* which we have before us (except that the number of pores is not always 30), and I have no doubt that such is the explanation of the peculiar arrangement of these pores. They should be regarded as shortened furrows, derived from a many-furrowed grain in which the arrangement of the furrows followed the ordinary trischistoclasic system. The cause of the shortening was probably due to the extraordinary development of the reticulate pattern, with its resultant demobilization. The large number of pores possessed by these grains (about 30) abundantly compensates for the loss of the harmomegathic action of the furrow, for changes in volume are readily accommodated by the bulging or invaginating of so many pores.

A large genus of about 125 species of annual or perennial herbs. Prince's-feather, *P. orientalis* (L.) Spach, is a familiar example in cultivation.

Persicaria Muhlenbergii (S. Wats) Small Swamp persicaria (Plate VIII, Fig. 5) type. Grains rather uniform in size, about 57 μ in diameter, ridges of the reticulum heavy, apparently composed of more or less vertical prisms. The floors of the lacunae quickly and coarsely pebbled. Otherwise as in the generic description. In swamps and moist soil almost throughout North America. July to September.

Persicaria pennsylvanica (L.) Small Pennsylvania persicaria. Grains uniform, 68 to 74 μ in diameter, essentially as in the type, except that the ridges are a little heavier. Nova Scotia to Ontario, Minnesota, Florida, and Texas. July to September.

Persicaria hydropiperoides (Michx.) Small Wild water pepper. Grains rather uniform, essentially as in the type, about 45.6 μ in diameter.

In swamps and wet soil. Almost throughout the United States and adjoining parts of Canada.

Persicaria Persicaria (L.) Small Lady's-thumb, Heartweed. Grains uniform, 43 to 51 μ in diameter, essentially as in the type.

In waste places throughout North America, except the extreme north. Naturalized from Europe. June to October.

Persicaria acuminata (H. B. K.) Grains uniform, about 51.3 μ in diameter. Essentially as in the type. In moist, shady places almost throughout South America.

Tracaulon arifolium (L.) Rap. Halberd-leaved tearthumb. Grains essentially as in *P. Muhlenbergii*, uniform, 51.3 μ in diameter. A slender, reclining, perennial herb with prickly stem, in moist places. New Brunswick and Ontario to Minnesota and south to Georgia. July to September.

Tracaulon sagittatum (L.) Small Arrow-leaved tearthumb. Grains as in *P. Muhlenbergii*, uniform, about 57 μ in diameter. Plants similar to the preceding except for the arrow shape of the leaf.

CHENOPODIACEAE GOOSEFOOT FAMILY

Grains when moist and expanded spheroidal, 19 to 33 μ in diameter. Exine thin and granular, psilate, cribellate. Furrows absent but represented by round pores varying in number from 14 to α (Plate VIII, Figs. 4, 9).

The grains of the Chenopodiaceae are rather uniform throughout the family and are indistinguishable from those of the related family Amaranthaceae. They are similar to those of the Nyctaginaceae but may easily be distinguished from the latter by their smaller size and thinner exine.

The pores are generally nearly circular in outline, though they may be somewhat irregular, but they are never elongate and never resemble furrows in the ordinary sense of the word. Their structure is simple; they are always crossed by a delicate membrane flecked with a number of granules which may be aggregated toward the center and even fused to form a central mass resembling an operculum, as in the grains of the Gramineae. The distribution of the pores over the surface of the grain is not isometric, though at first sight it often appears to be so, and, indeed, in those grains in which the pores are numerous, they closely approximate such an arrangement. On the other hand, in grains in which there are fewer, measurements of the intervals between them reveal great variation in this distance, and, under favorable conditions it can be seen that the pores tend to be grouped in threes in the trischistoclasic system. Consequently, we feel safe in drawing the same conclusion here that we did in the grains of *Persicaria*, that is, that these pores are morphologically furrows which are so shortened that they exactly coincide with their enclosed germ pore.

We have already seen that the multiple-pored condition arose among the grains of the Polygonaceae in response to the necessity of accommodating changes in volume in the face of an impaired harmomegathic function of the furrows. Yet among the Chenopodiaceae the pores play only a negligible part in this function. The pore membranes may be drawn in or pushed out in response to slight changes in volume, but when the grain dries to any extent it always becomes deeply concave on one side. The thin and flexible nature of the exine thus does away with any necessity for special organs of harmomegathy. Why, then, are the pores of these grains so numerous? The answer is probably to be found in the fact that the Chenopodiaceae are derived from some entomophilous ancestor the exine of whose pollen grains was heavily sculptured and demobilized, as in the grains of *Persicaria*, compelling a great increase in the number of the reduced furrows to accomplish harmomegathy. Then, with the subsequent reduction of the sculpturing in response to wind pollination, the large number of pores has remained because it is not in the nature of evolution to go backward. The many-pored condition of these grains must, therefore, be looked upon as a relic character of very ancient origin, whereas their psilate character is a much more recent response to anemophily.

It is interesting, and perhaps not without profit, to speculate further on this doctrine. If the evolution of these grains should continue further in the same direction, the exine would become progressively thinner, and the pore membranes, no longer requiring flexibility, might, with profit to the grain, become thicker and give greater protection, until a stage was reached where there could be no distinction between the exine and the pore membranes. Indeed, some of the many-pored grains of the Chenopodiaceae and Amaranthaceae have very nearly reached this condition. Or if, on the other hand, the plants should return to entomophily, and the grains, released from the necessity of retaining their buoyancy, should greatly increase in size, the pores would likewise increase in size and require some protection for their membranes. Such a condition is realized among the grains of the Nyctaginaceae, a family of plants which are closely allied to the Chenopodiaceae but highly specialized in insect pollination. The grains of many of these are exceedingly large; those of *Mirabilis Wrightii*, for example, are 187 μ in diameter and have a thick and rigid exine provided with spines and various other adornments. But they are cribellate like the grains of the Chenopodiaceae. As a consequence of the rigidity of the exine of these grains, harmomegathy is entirely taken over by the pores which are very large; they bulge prominently when the grain is moistened and sink deeply inward when it is dried. But on account of their large size the pores require protection. They are almost completely covered over by a conspicuous operculum which resembles a spiked helmet and suggests from its appearance that it could have been derived from the aggregation and coalescence of flecks similar to those that characterize the pore membranes of the grains of the Chenopodiaceae. The result is an armored pore possessing great flexibility and clearly excellently adapted to accommodating changes in volume.

The implication of this doctrine is that the Chenopodiaceae and the Nyctaginaceae represent two divergent lines originating from some ancestral form with many-pored grains like those of *Persicaria*, the Chenopodiaceae developing under the influence of anemophily and the Nyctaginaceae under the influence of entomophily.

The Chenopodiaceae include about 550 species in about 75 genera of annual and perennial herbs and shrubs, of wide geographical distribution. Of the American representatives all are wind pollinated, and many of them very serious causes of hayfever. Their pollen has rarely been identified from Postglacial silts, but Lewis and Coke (1930), without attempting to identify the grains, state that "a very considerable number [of pollen grains] of other herbs may be distinguished as belonging mostly to the Chenopodiaceae and related families."

For a discussion of the importance of these plants in hayfever the reader is referred to Lamson and Watry (1933*a, b*).

Salsola Pestifer A. Nels. (*S. Tragus* Reichnb.) Russian thistle, Saltwort (Plate VIII, Fig. 4) type. Grains nearly or quite spherical, rather uniform in size, averaging 27.6 μ in diameter. Pores large, the largest observed in the family, 3.7 μ in diameter and about 6.6 μ apart, measured from center to center.

The pore membranes are flecked with six or eight loosely distributed granules and are nearly circular but with slightly wavy margins. The texture of the exine is decidedly granular, more distinctly so than that of the grains of *Chenopodium* and *Amaranthus*, and this, together with the wavy margins of the germ pores, imparts to the grains a more rugged appearance.

Russian thistle is a common weed, particularly of the Great Plains region of the United States. It flowers during the latter part of summer and causes much hayfever; it has been reported among the worst hayfever weeds in Oklahoma (Balyeat, 1926), in Colorado (Mullen, 1922), in Oregon (Chamberlain, 1927), and in Arizona (Phillips, 1923).

Sarcobatus vermiculatus (Hook.) Torr. (*S. Maximiliani* Ness.) Greasewood, Chico (Plate VIII, Fig. 9) type. Grains spheroidal, 23.9 to 29.6 μ in diameter; germ pores rather small, averaging 2.9 μ in diameter, widely spaced, about 10.8 μ apart measured from center to center. In appearance the pores are somewhat irregular in outline and with their membranes marked by a single large fleck with a jagged outline, suggesting that it is composed of a number of smaller flecks fused together. The texture of the general surface is smooth, thus presenting a much less rugged appearance than that of *Salsola Pestifer*. The most distinguishing character of these grains is the wide distance apart of their pores and, consequently, their small number, which is generally about 14 or 16, varying with the size of the grain. The distance between the pores is also extremely various, a necessary corollary to their arrangement in the trischisticlasic system.

Greasewood is a common plant in saline and arid regions; Saskatchewan to Texas to California to Washington; flowering throughout the latter part of summer. The flowers are wind pollinated and shed rather large amounts of pollen which is probably an important cause of hayfever in some regions. It has not been reported from Postglacial silts, but growing in or near salt marshes, as it frequently does, it is likely that it will eventually be found.

Chenopodium album L. Goosefoot, Lamb's-quarters. Grains various in size, many obviously abortive. Normal grains about 28.4 μ in diameter. Germ pores uniform, 2.5 μ in diameter and regularly arranged over the surface, about 5.4 μ apart. Margins of the pores slightly wavy; pore membranes marked by several loosely distributed flecks. Texture of the general surface of the exine sharply but finely granular.

A common weed of gardens and roadsides throughout most of the United States, flowering in late summer. In the eastern part of its range goosefoot is of little or no importance in hay-fever, but in the western part it is believed to cause much hay-fever. Thus it is said to be important in Colorado (Mullin, 1922), California (Rowe, 1928; Selfridge, 1920), Oregon (Chamberlain, 1927), and southern Arizona (Phillips, 1922) but is stated by Balyeat (1926) to be of little consequence owing to the lack of toxicity of its pollen. In the author's experience, though its pollen occasionally gives slight reactions with hayfever patients, it has proved of no consequence in the northeastern United States.

Chenopodium ambrosioides L. Mexican tea. Grains somewhat various, averaging 22.8 μ in diameter; pores 1.2 μ in diameter, evenly distributed, about 3.8 μ apart, nearly or quite circular and with even margins, membranes marked by a single central fleck which appears to be composed of four or five flecks fused. Texture of the general surface of the exine slightly coarser than that of the grains of *C. album*. These grains also differ from the latter in their slightly smaller and more numerous pores, the tendency toward fusion of the granules of the pore membranes, and the slightly coarser texture of their exine.

A common weed of farms and gardens, flowering in late summer, shedding a large amount of pollen which is probably a minor cause of hayfever throughout most of its range. It is said by Selfridge (1920) to be an important cause of hayfever in California, but Hall (Scheppegrell, 1917) states that it is of minor importance in this region.

Kochia scoparia Schrad. Burning bush, Summer cypress. Grains various, 29 to 34 μ in diameter. Germ pores various about 2.9 μ in diameter and about 5.9 μ apart, approximately circular and with their membranes marked by a central group of small flecks which may be more or less fused. Exine coarsely and distinctly granular.

An ornamental garden plant, introduced from Europe and Asia and extensively cultivated in the United States. In some regions, particularly in parts of Colorado, it has escaped from cultivation and become a troublesome weed. It flowers in late summer, shedding much pollen which is known to be a frequent cause of hayfever (Mullin, 1922; Waring, 1926).

Eurotia lanata (Pursh) Moq. Winter fat, White sage, Winter sage. Grains various, 22 to 26 μ in diameter; germ pores 2.5 to 3.1 μ in diameter and 3.4 to 6.8 μ apart. Pore membranes marked by flecks tending to clump toward the center. General surface of the exine granular.

A whitish, tomentose undershrub, common in semiarid regions; Saskatchewan to Texas to California to Washington. Flowers in late summer, shedding relatively little pollen, but is occasionally considered to be a cause of hayfever (Waring, 1926).

DONDIA Adans. Sea blite

Grains rather various in size, 18 to 25 μ in diameter. Pores uniform in size and arrangement, their membranes marked with a single central fleck. Texture of the exine distinctly granular but less so than in the type (*Salsola Pestifer*) or most other members of the family.

The sea blites are common weeds, particularly in the warmer parts of the United States. They shed large amounts of pollen throughout most of the summer but are not generally regarded as hayfever weeds, though Hall (1922) regards *D. fruticosa* as important in this respect in California. In this connection, however, they are deserving of further study because, in their enormous abundance in many places in the southwestern United States, the huge quantities and buoyant character of their pollen, and their close relationship to such a toxic hayfever plant as Russian thistle they possess qualities which are strongly suggestive of hayfever plants.

Dondia suffrutescens Heller (*Suaeda suffrutescens* S. Wats.) Sea blite, Alkali blite. Grains various, 18 to 25 μ in diameter, pores about 2 μ in diameter and about 4.27 μ apart.

A common weed in alkaline valleys from southern California to the Rio Grande.

Dondia nigra (Raf.) Standl. (*Suaeda diffusa* S. Wats.). Grains uniform, 22.8 to 23 μ in diameter; pores about 2.28 μ in diameter and about 5.2 μ apart. Otherwise indistinguishable from the preceding species.

A common weed similar to the preceding species, in sagebrush plains and alkaline soils.   Wyoming to New Mexico to Arizona to Oregon to northern Mexico.

Spinacia oleracea L. Spinach, Spinage. Grains uniform, except a few that are abortive and a few that are dwarf, 30 to 35 μ in diameter, dwarfs 12 to 16 μ.   Pores uniform, 6.48 μ in diameter and 2.28 μ apart; pore membranes marked with a few fine flecks which tend to be aggregated toward their centers. Texture of the exine finely granular and marked with black specks which are clearly defined and widely spaced.

A common garden herb introduced from China.   Though it sheds much pollen during the summer it is not known to cause hayfever.

Allenrolfia occidentalis (S. Wats.) Ktze. (*Spirostachys occidentalis* S. Wats.) Burro weed. Grains remarkably uniform, 20.4 μ in diameter. Pores uniform in size and arrangement, 5.13 μ in diameter and 2.85 μ apart, flecked with a few small granules which are sometimes centrally placed. Exine diffusely granular.

A common plant of salt marshes.   Utah to Arizona to California to Nevada.   Flowers in July and September, but, though it sheds enormous quantities of pollen, it is not known to cause hayfever.   On account of its characteristics and associations, however, it deserves therapeutical study.

ATRIPLEX L. ORACH, SALTBUSH, SHAD SCALE

Grains spheroidal, rather various in size, 20.5 to 27 μ in diameter; germ pores uniform in size and distribution, 2 to 3.2 μ in diameter and 4 to 5.7 μ apart in the different species. Pore membranes always flecked with several small granules aggregated toward their centers and, in some species, tending to be fused. Texture of the exine slightly granular.

The grains of the different species are virtually indistinguishable from each other by inspection. Measurements of their diameters and of the diameters and distance apart of the pores show that, in many cases, those of a single species vary enormously, often covering the entire range of the genus. Nevertheless, it appears likely that if biometrical methods were applied to these measurements, as has been done for the birches by Jentys-Szafer (1928) and others, it would be found possible to distinguish the different species of *Atriplex* by their pollen, with a fair degree of accuracy.

The genus comprises about 130 species of general distribution. About 60 species are native of North America, occupying saline, arid, and semiarid soils throughout the continent. They are annual or perennial shrubs or herbs. Many of them shed enormous quantities of pollen which frequently causes much hayfever, particularly in the southwestern United States, where the larger shrubby members of the genus are prevalent. Besides the native American species, the Australian saltbush, *A. semibaccata*, has been extensively cultivated for fodder in America and is regarded as an important cause of hayfever in California (Selfridge, 1920).

Some of the species exist in several forms or races, and, though these present no reliable criteria of distinction, they are frequently regarded as separate species. The large number of species, together with their various forms and a lack of agreement among the different authors upon their specific limits, has led to much confusion in the classification of the species of *Atriplex*. The most recent and successful treatment of this large and difficult genus is that of Hall and Clements (1923). Their treatment recommends itself particularly to hayfever students because their broad species concept corresponds closely to the specificity of allergic reactions.

Atriplex patula L. Spear scale, Spear orach. Grains various, ranging in size from 22.8 to 27.5 μ in diameter. Pores 2 to 2.8 μ in diameter and 4 to 5.4 μ apart; pore membranes flecked. Texture granular.

A low, annual herb, abundant in saline soil and salt marshes almost throughout North America. It sheds relatively much less pollen than most species of the genus and, throughout the greater part of its range, cannot be considered a factor in hayfever, though it is said to be important in Oregon (Chamberlain, 1927). Its grains may occasionally be found in Postglacial silts and have been figured in this connection by Erdtman (1923). The plants are extremely various in form; Hall and Clements (1930) recognize eight subspecies and many minor variations, most of which are treated as separate species by other authors.

Atriplex Wrightii S. Wats. Orach, Annual saltbush. Grains uniform in size, excepting a few that are abortive, about 22 μ in diameter. Pores uniform in size and spacing, 2.28 μ in diameter and 4.56 μ apart, membranes slightly flecked. Texture granular right up to the edges of the pores.

A robust, erect or ascending, annual herb, abundant in saline soil in southwestern New Mexico, Arizona, and adjoining Mexico. Shedding much pollen which is a serious cause of hayfever in central Arizona (Phillips, 1923).

Atriplex bracteosa (Durand & Hillgard) S. Wats. Bractscale. Grains mostly uniform, except a few that are abortive and a few that are giants. Normal grains averaging 22.8 μ in diameter, giants 31.5 μ. Pores rather uniform in size and arrangement, 2.28 μ in diameter, 4.56 μ apart in normal grains and in the giants, showing that there is no correlation between the size of the grains and the size of the pores and their distance apart.

A robust annual herb, abundant in alkaline valleys, California, Lower California, and west-central Nevada. Flowers from April to October and sheds much pollen which is probably an important factor in hayfever, though in this connection it is not distinguished from other species of the genus.

Atriplex canescens (Pursh) Nutt. (*A. Nuttalii* S. Wats.) Wing scale, "shad scale." Grains uniform, excepting a few that are abortive. 23 to 25.5 μ in diameter. Pores 2.2 to 2.6 μ in diameter and 4.5 to 5.2 μ apart. Pore membranes flecked with a group of small granules aggregated toward the center. Texture granular.

A large, erect, woody shrub, exceedingly various, the most widely distributed of the shrubby species of the genus. It has a wide range of adaptability but is usually found in saline soils and alkaline flats. Alberta to Kansas, western Texas and adjacent Mexico, Washington, and Montana. It flowers throughout the summer, shedding enormous quantities of pollen. Owing to its wide range, great abundance, and large quantities of pollen, it is a very serious cause of hayfever in many regions, particularly in the southwestern states (Phillips, 1922, 1923; Watson and Kibler, 1922). This species is generally known in hayfever literature as "shad scale," but the name is not applicable and should be reserved for *Atriplex confertifolia*.

Beta vulgaris L. Beet, Sugar beet, Mangle. Grains rather uniform, except for a few that are abortive, about 19.4 μ in diameter. Pores uniform in size and arrangement, about 2.73 μ in diameter and 5.58 μ apart, their membranes flecked with small granules aggregated toward the center and sometimes fused. Texture of the exine distinctly granular.

A common garden herb, producing much pollen in summer. Not known to cause hayfever.

AMARANTHACEAE Amaranth Family

The grains of the Amaranthaceae, as a family, are not distinguishable from those of the Chenopodiaceae. This is entirely in keeping with the close relationship known to exist between the two families.

The Amaranthaceae are mostly weedy herbs, a few grown for ornament. The family comprises about 40 genera and 500 species, of wide distribution. All are wind pollinated, and many shed enormous quantities of pollen; as a consequence this family contains some of the worst hayfever weeds.

AMARANTHUS L. Amaranth

Grains as in the Chenopodiaceae, spheroidal, 23 to 35 μ in diameter, psilate, cribellate. Germ pores rather numerous, approximately equal in size, rather large, ranging, among the different species, from 2 to 4.5 μ in diameter, arranged in the trischistoclasic system, 5 to 9.1 μ apart. In shape they are generally circular, but sometimes their margins are wavy. The pore membranes are variously flecked with granules which are distributed at random over their surface, showing little tendency to be aggregated toward the centers. Though the size of the grains and the diameters of the pores and their distance apart show much variation within the species, such measurements afford attractive material for the application of the biometrical method and would probably reveal valuable interspecific differences.

The texture of the surface is always granular. In this there are some slight differences between the grains of the different species, but these are too slight and difficult of analysis to lend themselves readily to description.

The amaranths are mostly garden weeds, though some, for example, love-lies-bleeding (*A. caudatus* L.) and prince's-feather

(*A. hybridus hypochondriacus* Bailey), are well-known garden plants. All are wind pollinated, and several are troublesome hayfever weeds.

Amaranthus Palmeri S. Wats. Palmer's amaranth. Grains various, 22.8 to 25.3 μ in diameter; pores somewhat various in size and distance apart independently of the size of the grain, 2.28 to 4.56 μ in diameter and 5.1 to 8.0 μ apart. Apertures circular, with slightly wavy margins; pore membranes irregularly flecked.

A common weed in moist grounds. Kansas to Texas to Colorado to California and adjacent Mexico. Flowers from June to September, shedding much pollen which is a serious cause of hayfever in regions where abundant, *e.g.*, Oklahoma (Balyeat, 1926), California (Rowe, 1928), and Arizona (Phillips, 1922, 1923).

Amaranthus retroflexus L. Redroot pigweed, green amaranth, rough pigweed. Grains uniform, apparently all normal and healthy, 23 to 25 μ in diameter, pores uniform in size and evenly distributed, 2.28 to 3.7 μ in diameter and 5.4 to 8 μ apart, their membranes flecked with separate granules. Surface texture finely but distinctly granular, slightly finer than in the grains of *A. Palmeri*.

A common weed throughout North America. Flowers from August to October. It does not shed much pollen; consequently, it only occasionally becomes a factor in hayfever, though it is said to be important in this respect in Arizona (Phillips, 1922), Oklahoma (Balyeat, 1926), California (Rowe, 1928), and Oregon (Chamberlain, 1928). Its grains are not known to occur in Postglacial silts but are figured in this connection by Sears (1930).

Amaranthus spinosus L. Spiny amaranth. Grains as in *A. retroflexus*, 23 to 30.2 μ in diameter. Texture granular. Pores uniform, 2.84 μ in diameter and 7.1 μ apart. Pore membranes flecked with discrete granules.

A common weed throughout the United States and adjacent Canada and Mexico. From June to September it sheds much pollen which is a serious cause of hayfever in regions where the plant is abundant, *e.g.*, Oklahoma (Balyeat, 1926) and California (Hall in Selfridge, 1927).

Amaranthus hybridus L. Spleen amaranth. Grains somewhat various, 26.8 to 28.5 μ in diameter. Germ pores 2 to 3.4 μ in diameter, approximately circular but with wavy margins, their membranes variously flecked with discrete granules. Exine finely granular.

A weed in waste ground almost throughout the North American continent. Flowers August to October. Probably an important cause of hayfever, though in this connection not generally distinguished from *A. retroflexus* with which it is often associated.

Amaranthus graecizans L. (*A. sylvestris* Desf.) Tumbleweed. Grains various, 24.2 μ in diameter. Pores various in size and arrangement, 2.2 to 3.4 μ in diameter and 5.7 to 7.4 μ apart. Pore membranes flecked with discrete granules.

A common weed throughout North America. It sheds much less pollen than most other members of the genus and is, therefore, not generally important in hayfever, but it is said to be a minor factor in this respect in the Rocky Mountain and Pacific coast states (Hall in Scheppegrell, 1917) and an important factor in California (Selfridge, 1920).

Acnida tamariscina (Nutt.) Wood Western water hemp. Grains various, some abortive. Normal grains 21 to 28.5 μ in diameter; pores 2 to 2.8 μ in diameter and 3.4 to 4.6 μ apart, averaging about 4 μ, which is less than the interporal distance of any of the Amaranths. Pore membranes flecked with granules which tend to aggregate toward the center and fuse together.

A common weed of moist places. Illinois to South Dakota to Colorado to New Mexico to Louisiana. Flowers July to September shedding large amounts of pollen which causes much hayfever in regions where abundant. For example, in Oklahoma it is regarded as the worst hayfever weed (Balyeat, 1926). A drawing and photograph of this pollen grain are shown by Balyeat and Steaman (1927).

The genus includes about eight species of amaranth-like herbs, of wide distribution in moist places in the United States. They have not received sufficient study from the hayfever standpoint for us to be able to say to what extent they are responsible for this malady.

DROSERACEAE Sundew Family

Grains always united in tetrads which are generally tetrahedral. Component grains 31 to 67 μ in diameter. Pores 12 to 18, more or less concealed in the grooves between the grains, four or six on each of the contact faces. Exine of exposed surface thick, coarsely granular, and provided with characteristic spines, that of the contact surfaces thin and membranous.

The four cells are fastened together only at the center of the group, the greater part of their adjacent faces merely touching. Each grain is adapted to, and highly modified by, its union with its neighbors of the tetrad. Its three inner faces which are in contact with its neighbors are thin-walled and entirely lack the sculpturing which its fourth or outer face bears. Moreover, they are functionally interdependent, for the germ pores are so arranged that they open into the interstices between the grains, which mechanically serve the purpose of harmomegathi. The expansion and contraction of the grains with changes in moisture content cause the grooves to open and close in the same fashion in which furrows generally do.

Dionaea muscipula Ell. Venus's-flytrap (Plate IX, Fig. 7). Grains always arranged in tetrahedral tetrads; individual grains about 67 μ in diameter, each flattened on the three of its faces that are in contact with its three neighbors but broadly rounded on its outer face, possessing a curvature of shorter radius than that of the group as a whole, resulting in deep grooves between the adjacent faces of the grains. Texture of the exposed face of each cell, including that between the pores in the grooves, coarsely and sharply granular and adorned with short, rounded, peg-like spines of uniform size and shape but irregular arrangement. Germ pores about 12 to each grain, arranged along the outer margin of the flattened faces (four to each) in such a way that they open into the grooves between the cells.

The pores consist of circular holes cut sharply through the exine and each set in a small depression of its own, giving the margin of the cell a scalloped appearance when viewed from above. When the tetrads are moistened each cell expands and tends to become rounded, causing the grooves between them to open widely and expose the pores; but when the grains dry and contract they tend to flatten against each other, closing up the grooves and protecting the pores. Thus the mechanical action of the grooves between the adjacent faces of the grains of the tetrad, in opening and exposing the pores when moistened and closing and protecting them when dried, is the same as the action of the ordinary germinal furrows of the individual grains of other species.

A low bog herb, remarkable for its habit of capturing insects, to which purpose its leaves are admirably adapted. North and South Carolina. Flowers in Spring.

DROSERA L. SUNDEW

Grains uniform, always united in tetrads, generally tetrahedral in arrangement, rarely rhomboidal or square, of various sizes in the different species, individual grains 31.5 to 43 μ in diameter. Exine of outer surface of each cell thick, rigid, and of a granular texture, provided with close-standing sharp spines of characteristic shape, that of the proximal face of each grain soft and

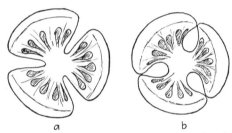

a   b

FIG. 101.—Tetrad pollen grains of *Drosera*, diagrammatic, with the upper cell of each removed to show the relative positions of the grains when the tetrad is *a*, moist, and *b*, dry.

flexible and thrown into plaits which converge toward the innermost point of the grain where it joins with its three neighbors at the center of the tetrad (Fig. 101).

Each grain of the tetrad has something the form of certain mushrooms, like *Lactarius* for example, in which the cap is the shape of an inverted pyramid with its gills decurrent a short way down the stalk. The arrangement of the four pollen cells can be visualized if we imagine four such mushrooms cut off their stalks at the point of termination of their decurrent gills and all four joined together by their cut ends. The outer surfaces of the four caps would then be in the relative positions of the four faces of a tetrahedron and correspond to the exposed faces of the four grains, while the decurrent gills on the mushrooms reaching toward the center of the group would correspond to the plaits on the proximal faces of the pollen grains.

When these grains are moistened the inner or soft part expands, causing the four cells to stand apart from each other and leaving a considerable gap between their rims; but when the grains are dry the flexible inner part of each becomes contracted and invaginated into the cap, thus drawing the four cells tightly together and closing the gaps between them.   The germ pores, which are arch-like openings between the plaits on the inner surfaces of the grains, are thus shut off from the outside when the grains are dry but freely exposed when moist.   In their function of harmomegathy, therefore, these four grains behave as a single unit.

The spines which cover the outer surface of the grains are sharp and generally short—about 1.1 μ long or occasionally as much as 2.3 μ in length.   The spine is conical, of two parts, as if truncated at about two-thirds of its height and the top third replaced by a smaller cone of more obtuse angle.   They are of uniform height but irregular in arrangement.

The genus includes about 85 species of wide distribution but best represented in Australia.   Seven are native of North America.   They are insect pollinated and flower during spring and summer.   Though they shed but little pollen, this is occasionally found in bog deposits.

Drosera capillaris Poir. Sundew.   Grains as in the generic description, individual cells measuring 30.8 to 34.2 μ in diameter, spines short and closely packed, about 1 μ in length.

In and about ponds, South Carolina to Florida.   Spring.

Drosera intermedia Hayne   Spatulate-leaved sundew.   Grains as in generic description.   Some tetrads are found in which the grains are in the tetragonal arrangement, and occasionally "tetrads" are found which are composed of four normal grains and a fifth dwarf.   Normal cells measure 32 to 37.6 μ in diameter. Spines short, about 1.1 μ in length.

In sandy swamps or ponds, Anticosti to Manitoba, south to Florida and Louisiana, also in West Indies and Europe. Summer.

Drosera filiformis Raf. Thread-leaved sundew.   Grains as in the generic description, each cell about 43.3 μ in width.   Spines about 2.3 μ long and clearly composed of two sections.   These grains may easily be distinguished from those of the preceding species by their larger spines.

In wet sand near the coast. Summer, Massachusetts to Florida and Mississippi.

HAMAMELIDACEAE Witch-hazel Family

Liquidambar Styraciflua L. Sweet gum, Red gum, Star-leaved gum, Bilsted, Alligator tree (Plate IX, Fig. 2). Grains spheroidal, about 38 μ in diameter; provided with 12 to 20 approximately circular pores; pore membranes generally bulging and conspicuously flecked; exine deeply pitted with minute round pits.

The germ pores are variously irregular in outline, though generally nearly circular; in size they are not uniform even on the same grain, 6.8 to 10.2 μ in diameter; in arrangement they appear to be as nearly isometric as possible. Clearly, the pores accommodate changes in volume by bulging out and dipping in, and it is likely that they should be regarded as reduced furrows.

A large tree shedding great quantities of anemophilous pollen in May. Connecticut to Texas, also Mexico and Central America. It is not known to cause hayfever, though it has often been suspected of doing so. Its pollen has the characteristics of hayfever pollens and is always caught on atmospheric pollen slides when exposed near the flowering trees.

Sweet gum is the only member of its genus, and its association with the witch-hazel family is of doubtful propriety. Indeed, its pollen grain suggests that it may not be correct. But the most conspicuous characters of the pollen grain are mainly those of reduction in response to wind pollination and cannot be applied without more extensive study.

PLATANACEAE Plane-tree Family

PLATANUS L. Plane tree, Sycamore

Normal grains, when fully expanded oblately flattened, various in size, 18 by 14 to 21 by 17 μ, tricolpate, with the furrows meridionally arranged, rarely tetracolpate, with the furrows converging in pairs, grains of the latter form sometimes giants; furrows extremely broad and of medium length, with their membranes copiously and uniformly flecked with granules with the same staining properties as the exine, without well-defined germ pores. Exine thin, easily collapsing as the grains dry, finely pitted throughout with angular pits of various size, and sometimes coarse enough to give the surface a reticulate appearance.   Intine thick and hyaline, uniform throughout.

When these grains dry the furrows are drawn deeply inward, causing the grain to assume a deeply three-furrowed ellipsoidal form, nearly twice as long as broad.   A fair proportion of the grains are abnormal—giants, dwarfs, abortive, and otherwise variously irregular.

The genus contains four or five species in eastern and western North America, Mexico, Central America, and southwestern Asia, all large, handsome trees resembling each other closely and apparently closely related.   In North America are found two other species, besides the two mentioned below.   One of these, the introduced species *P. acerifolia* Willd. (better known as *P. orientalis*), is believed to cause some hayfever in California (Hall, 1922).

Platanus occidentalis L. Sycamore, Buttonwood, Plane-tree (Plate IX, Fig. 5) type.   Grains as in the generic description.

Flowers in May, shedding large amounts of anemophilous pollen.   It has occasionally been suspected of causing hayfever and should probably be regarded as a minor contributing factor.

A large and handsome tree easily recognized by its outer bark's flaking off and leaving large, light-colored patches.   Abundant throughout most of its range, Maine to Ontario and Minnesota, Florida, Kansas, and Texas, also extensively planted in cities in the Pacific coast states.

Platanus racemosa Nutt. Western sycamore.   Grains indistinguishable from the type.

A large, beautiful tree, exceedingly common in all of the valleys of the California Coast Ranges, from Monterey to the southern border of the state, also to a lesser extent in the valleys and foothills elsewhere in California.   Flowers from February to April, shedding much light, anemophilous pollen, which is stated (Selfridge, 1920) to cause some hayfever.

ROSACEAE ROSE FAMILY

Grains ellipsoidal when dry but readily taking up moisture and expanding, when they become oblately flattened and angular in outline (Plate IX, Fig. 4).   This is the condition in which they are generally observed when mounted in glycerin jelly for microscopic examination.   In size they range from 25 to 52 μ

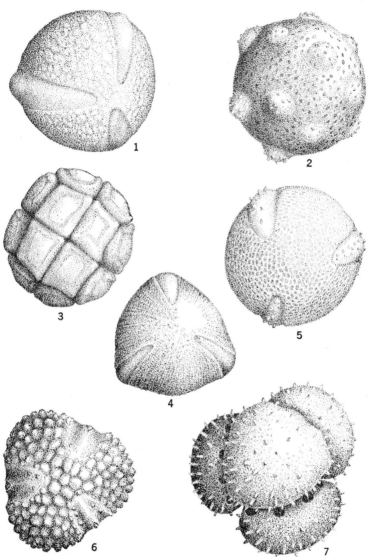

PLATE IX.—Pollen grains of Droseraceae, Hamamelidaceae, Rosaceae, Platanaceae, Mimosaceae, and Aquifoliaceae: 1, *Prosopis glandulosa*, 27 μ in diameter. 2, *Liquidambar Styraciflua*, 35 μ in diameter. 3, *Acacia longifolia* 16-celled, viewed from one of its flattened sides, 50 μ over all. 4, *Rosa rugosa*, polar view, 26 μ in diameter. 5, *Platanus occidentalis*, polar view, 20 μ in diameter. 6, *Ilex bronxensis*, polar view, 30 μ in diameter. 7, *Dionaea muscipula*, tetrad expanded, each grain about 67 μ in diameter.

in diameter. Normal grains are tricolpate, with rather long furrows tapering to pointed ends. In the unexpanded condition the furrow is crossed by a delicate, smooth membrane from which the germ pore bulges more or less prominently through a circular aperture, but in the moistened condition the furrow membrane is completely ruptured, and the boundary of the pore obliterated, the cell contents bulging prominently through the furrow. The texture of the exine is always more or less distinctly granular, with the granules generally arranged in rows, giving the surface a characteristically striate appearance, which is various in the different species and can sometimes be used as an aid in telling them apart.

The general form of this grain is almost exactly duplicated in those of the Leguminosae and Platanaceae and in other families of the Rosales. Thus it seems to be basic for the order.

Rosa rugosa Thunb. (Plate IX, Fig. 4) type. Grains somewhat various with a small proportion abortive. In the expanded condition flattened and more or less angular, with the cell contents bulging prominently through the furrows, 25.2 to 28.6 μ in diameter. Tricolpate, occasionally bicolpate; texture of the exine striate, vaguely suggesting the markings of a fingerprint.

The pollen of the different species of rose that I have examined is essentially all alike in the main morphological features. In that of some species the grains are uniform, in both size and shape, while in others there is considerable variation in size, with various irregularities in shape and a large proportion of the grains abortive—conditions that suggest hybridity of origin.* There are, however, slight differences in the texture of the different species. For example, the grains of *R. bracteata, R. centifolia,* and *R. rubiginosa* are like the type in their texture, exhibiting fingerprint markings, while the grains of *R. setigera, R. multiflora,* and *R. noisettiana,* though variously granular, show no trace of such markings.

Most roses shed only small amounts of pollen. Particularly is this true of the cultivated varieties, and a large proportion, even sometimes all of it, is abortive, consisting of empty skins. Of the different species that I have examined *R. rugosa* greatly outstrips all the others in both the quantity and the perfection

* For a discussion of this phase of the subject see Erlanson (1929) and Jeffrey (1916).

of its pollen. Since the roses are entirely insect pollinated, they are not an important factor in hayfever. Only by coming into actual contact with the flowers is it possible for a person to inhale enough pollen from them to produce an attack of hayfever; consequently cases of bona fide rose hayfever are very rare—in my own experience of over 2,000 cases I have encountered only two. It is therefore unfortunate that the name "rose cold" has been adopted for that type of hayfever which comes in the early summer when roses are blooming. Hayfever at that time of the year, as we have already seen, is practically always due to the pollen of the grasses which flower at the same time and, to a lesser extent, to that of plantain.

Pyrus Malus L. (*Malus sylvestris* Mill.) Apple. Grains when moist 27.5 to 28.5 μ in diameter. Texture without fingerprint markings. A large proportion of the grains are generally abortive and exhibit many irregularities. Similar to the type.

Pyrus japonica Thunb. (*Chaenomeles japonica* Lindl.) Dwarf Japanese quince. Grains rather uniform, except for a large proportion that are abortive, 34.2 to 36.5 μ in diameter. Texture granular-striate, with fingerprint markings more pronounced than in the type; otherwise similar to it.

A common garden shrub. Flowers in May, insect pollinated, not a factor in hayfever.

Prunus Persica Sieb. & Zucc. (*Amygdalus Persica* L., *Persica vulgaris* Mill.) Peach. Grains various in size and shape, with many abortive; normal grains 50 to 57 μ in diameter. Surface texture conspicuously marked with fingerprint striae. Otherwise as in the type.

A familiar tree of cultivation, existing in many varieties. Flowers in May, insect pollinated, and not a factor in hayfever, though the dust from the skin of the fruit appears occasionally to cause hayfever and asthmatic symptoms.

MIMOSACEAE Mimosa Family

The most outstanding character of the pollen grains of the Mimosaceae is their tendency to form in compound grains. The number of individuals that are fused together is not fixed but is generally some multiple of four. The grains of *Mimosa pudica* are always in closely knit groups of four. In most species of *Acacia* (Plate IX, Fig. 3), *Inga*, and *Vachellia* 16 is the characteristic number, though in the pollen of the three latter are found groupings of 4, 8, and 32 individuals, and in some species of *Inga* 8 is the characteristic number. Always the union of the cells is very close, and the individuals so interdependent that the group actually functions as an individual in all ways, except in fertilization. Morphologically each grain of the group is profoundly modified by its associations.

But this conglobate character is not universal in the family. There are a few genera, quite properly included in the Mimosaceae, in which the grains are always simple, and these appear to represent the primitive form of the family. The grains of *Prosopis* (Plate IX, Fig. 1), for example, probably furnish us with a fairly accurate conception of what those of all the Mimosaceae might look like if they had never been fused together to form compound grains. They are spheroidal, covered throughout with a heavy exine, and provided with three long, tapering furrows in the ordinary tricolpate configuration. In its appearance and general organization such a form or grain resembles those of the Leguminosae, to which the Mimosaceae are closely related, whereas in the grains of *Acacia*, *Inga*, and others in which compounding is the rule the units are so modified that they exhibit scarcely any characters that would suggest relationship to the Leguminosae or even to *Prosopis*.

Perhaps of even greater interest is the fact that this union has somewhat different effects upon the grains of the different genera. For example, in those of *Acacia* it has induced the formation of a few sketchy and nonfunctional furrows in the dodecacolpate configuration (Plate IX, Fig. 3) while in those of *Vachellia* it has induced the formation of three or four well-marked but still nonfunctional furrows in the hexacolpate configuration (Fig. 103). There are many questions that remain to be answered before our knowledge of these extraordinary pollen grains can be regarded as measurably complete. How is it that identical contact relations can produce furrows in one configuration in the grains of *Acacia* and in a different configuration in those of *Vachellia?* What arrangements do the phragmoplasts take during the formation of these compound grains? And what bearing do they have upon the presence of pore vestiges at some of the angles of the cells and their absence from others? Why should *Acacia, Inga,* and *Vachellia* have adopted the formation of compound grains while *Prosopis,* which is closely related and of similar habit, has not? In the answer to these questions and to the many others that cannot fail to occur to the investigator who undertakes the study of this fascinating group will be revealed much that is now obscure of cell organization and interrelationships.

The Mimosaceae include about 40 genera and 1,500 species of mostly shrubby plants or small trees, of wide distribution in the tropics but with a few species in temperate regions. They show a close affinity to the Leguminosae of which they are often treated as a tribe or subfamily. They form, however, a well-marked group, generally easily distinguished from true Leguminosae by their small, actinomorphic flowers with exserted stamens. They are probably mostly insect pollinated, though the structure of their flowers suggests that wind might also sometimes play a part in their pollination. Only *Acacia* and *Prosopis* have ever been suspected of causing hayfever, and it is doubtful if even these should be seriously so regarded. Rowe (1928, page 15) says, "*Acacia* pollen, though usually carried by insects, has been found on our plates, and it causes definite hayfever and asthma in some cases."

Prosopis glandulosa Torr. (*P. juliflora* DC.) Mesquite (Plate IX, Fig. 1). Grains spheroidal or somewhat triangular in outline when expanded but rather various in both shape and size, about 22.5 to 32 μ in diameter. Furrows generally three, broad and tapering to rounded ends, their boundaries not sharply defined. Germ pore represented by an elliptical bulge in the center of each furrow, surrounded by a vaguely defined annular thickening. Furrow membranes smooth. Texture of the general surface of the exine various, from nearly smooth to conspicuously warty but generally fine-granular.

Shrubs or small trees generally armed with sharp spines; common in plains and prairies, Kansas to Texas, Arizona, and Mexico. Not known to cause hayfever but occasionally suspected of doing so.

Besides the grains of *Prosopis,* those of *Leucaena glauca* Benth., *Entada scandens* Benth., and *Desmanthus virgatus* Willd. of this family also occur singly and are of this type (von Mohl, 1835).

ACACIA Willd. ACACIA

Grains compound (Plate IX, Fig. 3), consisting of a number of individuals firmly joined together. Generally there are 16, though groups of both larger and smaller numbers and even grains entirely dissociated are found to constitute various proportions of the pollen of the different species. In the normal 16-celled grains 8 cells are centrally placed, forming a sort of cubical block in which the individuals tend to be arranged in rectangular fashion. The central group is surrounded by eight peripheral cells, all in a plane at right angles to and bisecting the central group. The peripheral cells are so placed that their eight contacts with each other are alternately opposite and midway between the four contacts of the central group. As a consequence of the peripheral arrangement of the outer cells the group, as a whole, is flattened, lens- or biscuit-shaped, with a squarish or more or less rounded outline and with the intersecting lines between the individual grains crossing each other at right angles.

The individual grains of such a group are polyhedral, sometimes short wedge-shaped, each presenting a flat, angular, usually square or oblong face to the outside, with the body of the cell tapering abruptly inward toward the center of the group or truncated, depending upon its position in the group. The exine of the exposed surface is thick and rigid. Its corners are always rounded, leaving conspicuous interstices at the centers of convergence of the angles of adjacent cells. The exine of the inner part of the grain is thin and flexible, allowing it to be shaped by pressing against its neighbors and to fit snugly with them. Those individual grains which occur in abnormal groups of other numbers than 16 cells may differ slightly in shape in response to their different contact relations but, in the main, preserve their form.

In normal grains at the corner of each cell is nearly always found a slight thickening in the intine which causes a corresponding protrusion of the exine at that point (Plate IX, Fig. 3). These protrusions suggest by their appearance the former positions of connecting phragmoplasts between the adjacent cells and are probably to be regarded as germ pores. The furrows are represented by a linear depression in the exine of the cap, traversing a course parallel to its margin and generally giving off a short branch at each angle, corresponding in arrangement to one of the spherical squares in the dodecacolpate configuration of furrows in the trischistoclasic system. These furrows are vestigial and entirely functionless.

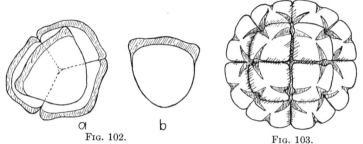

Fig. 102.   Fig. 103.

Fig. 102.—Abnormal *Acacia* pollen grains, diagrammatic: *a*, four cells united; *b*, a single cell.

Fig. 103.—Compound grain of *Vachellia Farnesiana*, diagram of the arrangement of the individual cells.

Pollen tubes are produced from the inner or protected sides of the grains and emerge from within the group through the interstices between the individual grains, forcing them apart in doing so. When these grains dry they draw a little closer together, the crevices between them becoming a little shallower, and the whole group becoming flatter and smoother. The mechanical accomplishment of these two important functions, *viz.*, pollen-tube emergence and harmomegathy, are both done by the grains' acting in concert and not as individuals. Truly this may be regarded as a colonial type of grain, in which the interstices at the angles of the cells function as germ pores and the intercellular grooves as harmomegathi.

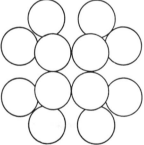

Fig. 104.—Diagram of the most compact arrangement of sixteen globular cells of the same size. The central group contains eight though only four are in view.

The rectangular arrangement of 16 cells encountered in *Acacia* pollen grains is surprising because at first sight it seems to be without regard for the law of least-surface configuration which is the guiding principle of cell arrangements. An analysis, however, shows that the arrangement really consists of four groups of four, each of which is tetrahedral.

If the form of an *Acacia* pollen grain be modeled in clay, the model will be found to break apart readily along two median lines which intersect each other at right angles, into four tetrads, each of which is approximately tetrahedral in arrangement. Each of the four groups is, therefore, within itself, a least-surface configuration. Or, if we reverse the procedure and construct four tetrahedral tetrads of uniform round balls and bring them together, we soon find that the most compact form that they can be made to assume is the same as the arrangement of the units of a 16-celled *Acacia* pollen grain (Fig. 104). There will always remain, however, spaces between the balls of the outer ring. It thus becomes evident that the spherical shape is not the best for units that are to fit together in such a configuration. Even if the balls are pressed together so as to flatten out their contact faces, gaps still remain between those of the outer ring, and large square holes between those of the central group. But if the units are block-shaped instead of spherical, the fitting is much more perfect. This is apparently what has happened in the compound grain of *Acacia*. The fact that there are 16 cells that must be grouped together, and the fact that 16 is an impossible number to group compactly, if the cells are spherical, has produced an environment for each in which isodiametric cells do not fit, and the effect of this environment is such as to induce a change in the form of the cells to one that does fit—hence the strange squared form of the components of this compound grain. The squared cells are like pegs that have been made square to fit into square holes.

So impressed upon the cell has its squared form become that it is retained even when not required to fit into a square hole. Occasionally, abnormal groups of four cells are found in which one cell is misplaced, applied by its side to its three neighbors, yet its form remains almost unchanged (Fig. 102a); it has its thick, stiff cap, and its body is covered by only a thin, flexible membrane, a form totally unadapted to its association in such a group. Even entirely dissociated individuals, which are occasionally found, present a thick, rigid, angular cap which tends to be squarish and a flaccid body which is rounded and bag-shaped (Fig. 102*b*). The form of these grains is clearly the result of environmental stimuli; yet it has become hereditary and is expressed even in the absence of the stimuli which called it forth. An exactly parallel case is found in the colonies of *Pediastrum*. Harper (1918) has shown that individuals of such a colony have acquired a part of their form from the necessity of being able to fit snugly together with a certain predetermined number of others and that this form has become fixed and hereditary and is expressed even when, as sometimes happens, the cell is dissociated or is associated with the other cells of the colony in some abnormal way to which its shape is not at all adapted.

The development of the pollen grains of *Acacia* has been studied by Rosanoff (1866) and Engler (1876), and they have shown that there take place in the pollen mother-cell two successive divisions resulting in the formation of four cells separated by clearly defined walls, and these four cells tend to be all in the same plane and rectangular in arrangement. Each of these daughter-cells appears to divide twice more, producing four cells which assume the tetrahedral arrangement.

The peculiar shape of the component units of the *Acacia* compound pollen grain is the result of the conflict between the law of bipartition and the law of least-surface configuration. The law of bipartition produces 16 cells, a number which, when of isodiametric units, cannot be made to pack together without leaving gaps; the law of least-surface configuration brings these 16 cells into the most compact form possible and fills in the interstices by shaping the cells to fit.

Acacia is a genus of about 450 species, not always clearly defined, of small trees or shrubs, widely dispersed throughout the tropics, especially in Australia. A large number of species are grown in cultivation in California and the warmer parts of the United States of America, and several species are grown elsewhere under glass. The flowers are insect pollinated, appearing very early in spring, and the pollen is said occasionally to cause a mild type of hayfever in California.

Acacia longifolia Willd. (Plate IX, Fig. 3) type. Sydney golden wattles. Grains nearly always 16-celled and grouped in the squared arrangement as in the generic description, though deviations from this are occasionally found. The individual grains measure about 17 μ in diameter, and the whole compound grain 48.5 to 54.7 μ.

A tall shrub or small tree producing bright-yellow flowers in early spring. It occurs in several varieties of which the grains of variety *floribunda* F. Muell. have been examined and are indistinguishable from those of the type.

Besides these the pollen of several unidentified species was examined and found to be likewise identical, except that in some a large proportion of the grains were composed of numbers of individuals other than 16.

Inga myriantha Poepp. & Endl. Grains compound as in *Acacia*, but the components not so closely united, the exposed part of each more rounded, and the exine thicker. The furrow vestiges tend to be formed on the sides of the bulging outer part of the grains. Diameter of the compound grain as a whole about 59 μ, and of its component individuals about 18 μ.

A tree about 30 ft. high, with white flowers. Native of Brazil, Peru, and Guiana.

The genus includes about 150 species of trees resembling the acacias but spineless, with pentamerous flowers having numerous exserted stamens which are generally red. Native of the West Indies and tropical South America. *Inga Feuillei* DC. is cultivated in California for its edible pods.

The grains of *Inga tergemina* Willd. are described by Rosanoff (1865) as eight-celled; those of *Inga anomala* Kunth. are described and figured by von Mohl (1835) as composed of eight functional cells, and the group provided with a stalk and sticky disk whereby it may become attached to insects. This is, perhaps, the highest development attained among the compound grains of dicotyledons, other than the milkweeds, and is quite comparable with that of the pollinia of the orchids.

Vachellia Farnesiana (L.) Wright & Arn. [*Acacia Farnesiana* (L.) Willd.] Frangipanni, Huisache, Casse, Yellow opopanax (Fig. 103). Grains compound and similar to those of *Acacia*, generally 16-celled, occasionally 4- or 8-celled. Individual grains 11.4 to 12.5 μ, and the group as a whole 41.5 to 52.5 μ in diameter. Exine thick and faintly granular, forming a sort of cap over the exposed surface of each grain. Furrows three or five, deep and conspicuous but nonfunctional and without pores, converging from the corners of the exposed surface of each cell toward one or two centers.

In the 16-celled grains, each of the eight central cells of the group presents to the outside a convex face which is square in outline. Underlying the exine can be seen three small thickenings in the intine, one at each distal corner (those remote from the center of the group). These are the germ pores, and from them extend three furrows converging toward a point near the center of the cap. But there is no furrow extending from the proximal or central corner of each cell, which lacks a germ pore. The eight peripheral cells are also four-sided in outline, either square or elongate in the direction of the circumference of the group, and the outer convex face of each is provided with either five or three furrows. Those cells which have three furrows are essentially the same as those of the central group, but those which have five furrows have pore vestiges at each of their four corners, and from these converge four furrows in pairs toward two centers which are joined together by a fifth furrow. In both the three-furrowed and five-furrowed cells the picture presented by their furrow system is that of part of the ordinarily hexacolpate configuration; the former presents one triconvergent center to the outside, while the latter presents two triconvergent centers.

A small proportion of the grains are irregular, presenting other arrangements than the squared one described for the grains of *Acacia*. Occasionally the peripheral row of cells exhibits a conspicuous gap. This is to be expected from purely mechanical reasons which will become clear from reference to the diagram (Fig. 104). It is interesting to note, however, that the gap may occur between any two cells of the peripheral row and is as likely to occur between those at the corners of the group as elsewhere, thus breaking up the tetrads. This is strong evidence that the 16-celled group should not be regarded as a loose assemblage of four better organized tetrads. Rather, the whole group should be regarded as complete within itself, and every cell interdependent with every other cell. A further study of these interesting relations would reveal much regarding the organization of the cell group and, incidentally, of the morphogenesis of pollen grains in general.

Huisache is a shrub or small tree with spreading, spiny branches. Plains and prairies, southern Texas and Mexico. Flowers in early spring, not known to cause hayfever.

AQUIFOLIACEAE Holly Family

A small family of trees and shrubs, related to the Ebenaceae.

Ilex L. Holly

Grains oblately flattened when moist, 26.8 to 33.1 μ in diameter. Furrows three, meridionally arranged, or occasionally four or six, tetrahedrally arranged, in which case the grains may or may not be giants. Furrows broad and long, somewhat tapering to rounded ends, their membranes heavy and conspicuously flecked with coarse granules; germ pores represented by hyaline thickenings, one below the center of each furrow, causing a rounded bulge which may or may not break through the furrow membrane when the grain is moistened. Exine very thick and rigid, presenting a coarsely pebbled appearance in surface view, structurally composed of rounded prisms embedded in a matrix of material of different refractive index.

The genus comprises about 280 species of shrubs, mostly America. The pollen of various species has been recovered from Postglacial silts, and in this connection that of *I. agrifolia* has been described and illustrated by Docturowsky and Kudrjaschow (1923) and Erdtman (1923). The hollys are not regarded as hayfever plants.

Ilex bronxensis Britt. Northern winterberry (Plate IX, Fig. 6) type. Grains uniform, 29.6 to 33.1 μ broad, 28.5 to 31.9 μ deep. Exine exceedingly coarsely granular, presenting a pebbled appearance.

A medium-sized shrub with evergreen leaves and orange-red berries. Flowers in June and July, insect pollinated but sheds rather a large amount of pollen.

Ilex decidua Walt. Swamp, meadow, or deciduous holly. Grains 26.8 to 28.5 μ broad and 22.8 to 23.9 μ deep. Furrows occasionally four or six. Some grains united in tetrahedral tetrads, with the three pores of each grain opposite and adjacent to one of each of its three neighboring grains. Exine heavy and coarsely granular but less so than in the type.

ACERACEAE Maple Family

A family of trees containing, besides the genus *Acer*, only the monotypic genus *Dipteronia* Oliv. of central China.

ACER L. Maple

Grains when moistened oblately spheroidal, ranging in size in the different species from about 28 to 36 μ in diameter, prevailingly tricolpate, but occasionally dicolpate or, less frequently, tetra-, penta-, and hexacolpate.

In normal tricolpate grains the furrows are equally spaced around the equator and directed meridionally (Plate X, Fig. 1), but in the grains with higher numbers of furrows they are not so arranged; instead they tend to conform to the tetrahedral configuration, though they are more often badly deformed, and their furrows unrelated to any system. When unexpanded the grains are ellipsoidal, with the furrows appearing as shallow, longitudinal grooves, but upon expanding they gape widely open, permitting the grain to become decidedly flattened. The furrow membranes are smooth or occasionally slightly flecked. They are not provided with germinal apertures; instead, the germ pore is represented only by a slight swelling in the center of each. The general surface of the exine is always conspicuously granular, and in the grains of all species, except those of *A. Negundo*, the granules are arranged or tend to be arranged in rows, giving the exine a more or less striate appearance. In this respect the grains of the maples resemble those of the roses. The patterns of the granular striae are not exactly duplicated in any two species, giving this character high diagnostic value.

The maples are mostly large or medium-sized trees. All, except *A. Negundo*, are primarily insect pollinated. Nevertheless, they are rather imperfectly adapted to this mode of pollination, and the pollen of several species of maple, besides those of *A. Negundo*, can often be caught on atmospheric pollen plates at considerable distances from the trees. The part that the maples play in the production of hayfever is not yet understood, but it is likely that they should be regarded as a contributory cause of the early spring type. Maple pollen is occasionally found in Postglacial silts; and in this connection are figured grains of *A. saccharum* (Sears, 1930) and unnamed species (Docturowsky and Kudrjaschow, 1923).

Key to the Species

I. Surface granules arranged in rows forming more or less distinct striae.

A. Striae always distinct and unmistakable (less
   distinct in A. *rubrum*).   A. Pseudo-platanus
                                                 A. platanoides
                                                 A. rubrum
B. Striae extremely faint and in some grains not
   present at all.   A. saccharum
II. Surface granules not arranged in rows, surface not
    striate.   A. Negundo

Acer Pseudo-platanus L. Sycamore maple (Plate X, Fig. 1)
type. Grains mostly uniform, when fully expanded spherical,
35.5 to 36.3 μ in diameter; tricolpate, with furrows meridionally
arranged, or rarely dicolpate, with the furrows opposite, fused
at the poles and encircling the grain as a single furrow. Furrows
normally long and tapering, their membranes smooth. Exine
granular-striate.

The surface texture of these grains is very characteristic; at
lower magnification it has the appearance of being striate, with
the striae forming patterns which resemble those of thumb-
prints. These striae have a tendency to run parallel to the
furrows and are obviously modified by them in their arrangement.
Seen with the higher resolving power of the microscope, the
texture may be described as coarsely granular, with the granules
arranged in rows of various length. The striate pattern, though
difficult to describe, is highly specific.

The sycamore maple is a medium-sized tree extensively planted
about city streets. It flowers in June, the flowers opening after
the leaves have fully expanded. The flowers are insect pollinated but rather imperfectly adapted to this mode of pollination,
so that much pollen is scattered in the air and probably should
be considered as a contributory factor in hayfever.

Acer platanoides L. Norway maple. Grains similar to the
type but slightly smaller and less uniform in size, 32 to 34 μ
in diameter, oblately spheroidal, always tricolpate. Surface
markings similar to but finer than in the type. Furrow membranes slightly flecked.

A large tree extensively planted about city streets. Flowers in
June. Insect pollinated but sheds much pollen which becomes
atmospheric and can readily be detected in the air and is probably
a contributory cause of hayfever. The pollen is also sometimes
found in Postglacial silts and in this connection has been figured
by Erdtman (1923).

Acer rubrum L. Red maple, scarlet maple. Grains similar to the type, except that the surface striae are much less distinct, always a large proportion of the grains abnormal; tetracolpate and pentacolpate giants, with the furrows in the tetrahedral position, some double zonate or more often irregular and asymmetrical. Normal grains 30.8 to 35.3 μ in diameter, tricolpate.

A large tree in swamps and low grounds and much planted elsewhere. Nova Scotia to Manitoba, Nebraska, Florida, and Texas. Flowers appearing before the leaves in March or April. Primarily insect pollinated but very imperfectly so. Its pollen is frequently caught on atmospheric pollen plates and is probably a contributory cause of early spring hayfever.

Acer saccharum Marsh. Sugar or rock maple. Grains essentially as in the type, occasionally dicolpate, with the furrows fused at the poles and encircling the grain as a single furrow, ellipsoidal, 36.5 to 40 μ in diameter. Texture extremely finely granular, with the granules tending to be arranged in striae, but less so than in the grains of *A. rubrum*, in this respect intermediate between the latter and those of *A. Negundo*.

Apparently these grains do not expand so much upon being moistened as the type, for they retain their ellipsoidal form, and the furrows do not gape widely open.

Acer Negundo L. (*Negundo aceroides* Moench., *N. fraxinifolia* Nutt.) Box elder, ash-leaved maple. Grains similar to the type, prevailingly tricolpate but frequently dicolpate with furrows opposite and fused, encircling the grain as a single furrow or in the position of the tricolpate furrows, as if one had been omitted; occasionally with more than three furrows, but such grains are usually irregular. Texture granular but not striate, in which character this species appears to be unique in the genus.

A large tree common along streams and much planted elsewhere. Maine and Ontario to Manitoba south to Florida, Texas, and Mexico. Flowers in April, wind pollinated, shedding large quantities of pollen which undoubtedly causes some hayfever in the early spring. Several varieties are recognized which greatly extend its range. Variety *violaceum* Kirch. in the eastern States, variety *texanum* Pax. in eastern Texas and adjoining states, variety *interior* Sarg. in the Rocky Mountain states, variety *arizonicum* Sarg. in southern Arizona and New Mexico, variety *californicum* Sarg. in the Pacific coast states. For a discussion of these different varieties the reader is referred to Sargent (1922).

The pollen of *Acer Negundo* in one or more of its varieties is said to be important in the production of hayfever in Oregon (Chamberlain, 1927), and its pollen has been shown to occur abundantly in the air in the neighborhood of Kansas City while the trees are in bloom (Duke and Durham, 1928).

TILIACEAE Linden Family

A large family of trees, shrubs, or rarely herbs, represented in northern regions by the single genus *Tilia*.

Tilia americana L. Basswood, Linden (Plate X, Fig. 2). Grains uniform in shape and size, oblately flattened and about 36.5 by 28 μ; germ pores three, rarely two or four, deeply sunken, elliptical in shape, and equally spaced on the equator. Exine reticulate pitted.

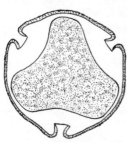

Fig. 105.—Pollen grain of *Tilia americana*, transverse optical section.

Furrows in the ordinary sense of the word are absent, but the pits in which the pores are situated are slightly elongate in a meridional direction and must undoubtedly be regarded as vestigial furrows. Underlying each pore is a relatively large thickening of the intine which forms a very conspicuous feature of the grain in optical section (Fig. 105) and causes the region surrounding the pore to be slightly elevated.

A large tree widely distributed throughout the eastern half of the United States. Flowers in May and June. Insect pollinated but generally shedding much pollen. It is not a factor in hayfever, but its pollen is frequently caught on atmospheric pollen plates and is found abundantly in Postglacial silts. In this connection this and other species of the genus have been described and illustrated by Sears (1930) and by Docturowsky and Kudrjaschow (1923), who describe the rudimentary furrows as false pores, merely pits in the exine.

VIOLACEAE Violet Family
VIOLA L. Violet

Grains when dry ellipsoidal or tending to be cylindrical with rounded ends, the furrows appearing as shallow grooves. When moistened becoming spheroidal, the furrows gaping widely open. Furrows generally three, occasionally four or six (in *V. tricolor* var. *hortensis* five, six, or four, never three) long and tapering to pointed ends; furrow membranes smooth, easily ruptured; germ pore circular or more or less irregular. Exine nearly or quite smooth.

The furrows when three are equally spaced around the equator, with their long axes meridionally directed, or, when there are four or six, in the tetrahedral configuration, except in the grains of *V. tricolor* var. *hortensis*, in which they are approximately equally spaced on the equator, with their long axes directed almost exactly meridionally, though they may tend somewhat to converge in pairs. Violet pollen grains have a strong tendency to overexpand when moistened, with the complete rupture of the furrow membrane, permitting the cell contents to protrude from the furrows, the grain becoming flattened and angular in outline. In this condition, which is, indeed, the one most generally encountered, unless precautions are taken to prevent its occurrence, they bear a superficial resemblance to the grains of *Quercus* but may easily be distinguished from the latter by the smooth texture of their exine and the absence of hyaline bodies.

A large genus of low shrubs and herbs, flowering in the early part of spring or, by cleistogamous flowers, throughout the summer; insect pollinated, producing only small amounts of pollen; not a cause of hayfever.

Viola lobata Benth. Violet type. Grains as in the generic description, spheroidal, tricolpate, 28.5 to 31.9 μ in diameter. Exine faintly granular.

California and southwestern Oregon.

Viola palmata L. Early blue violet. Grains as in the type, generally tricolpate or occasionally tetracolpate or hexacolpate, with the furrows in the tetrahedral configuration, about 30.8 μ in diameter. April and May. Massachusetts to Minnesota, southwest to Florida.

Viola hirsutula Brainard Southern wood-violet. Grains ellipsoidal when moist unless overexpanded, tricolpate, about 37.6 μ in diameter, otherwise as in the type. Flowers in April and May, southern New York to central Alabama and Georgia.

Viola cucullata Ait. Marsh. Blue violet. Grains spheroidal, tricolpate, 36 to 40 μ in diameter, exine smooth, otherwise as in type. April and June. Quebec to Ontario, southward to Georgia.

Viola odorata L. English or Sweet violet. Grains as in the type, 29.6 to 31.2 μ in diameter. Flowers March to May. Introduced from Europe and frequently planted in America.

Viola conspersa Reichenb. American dog violet. Grains spheroidal, generally tricolpate, occasionally tetra- or hexa-colpate, with furrows in the tetragonal configuration, about 30.8 μ in diameter, otherwise as in the type. Flowers April and May. Quebec to Minnesota, southward to Georgia.

Viola tricolor L. var. **hortensis** DC. Pansy, Heartsease. Grains various in size; when dry cylindrical with rounded ends, with the furrows showing as shallow, longitudinal grooves; when expanded decidedly oblately flattened, about 85 by 63 μ, with the furrows more or less equally spaced around the equator and nearly or quite meridionally arranged, except when there are four, in which case they tend to converge in pairs. Furrows long and tapering to pointed ends; furrow membranes flecked, easily ruptured by overexpansion. Germ pore irregular in outline but tending to be circular. Texture finely granular.

Flowers in early summer, cultivated.

HALORAGIDACEAE Water-milfoil Family

Aquatic or marsh plants with inconspicuous flowers in leafy spikes. The family includes about 100 species in eight genera.

MYRIOPHYLLUM L. Water milfoil

Grains similar to those of *Alnus* but lacking the connecting bands between the pores; uniform in size, oblately flattened and angular in outline, with the pores at the angles, 23 to 33 μ in diameter. Pores aspidate, with narrowly elongate or slit-like apertures, four, three, or rarely five, their number bearing no reference to the size of the grain, equally spaced around the equator—when three, meridionally arranged; when four or five, with their axes biconvergent. Texture of the exine slightly rough, especially around the pores.

These grains may be distinguished from those of *Alnus* by their narrower germinal apertures, less sharply defined aspides, and absence of connecting bands between the pores.

The genus is represented by about 10 species in North America and about 10 others elsewhere. All are perennial aquatic herbs, apparently wind pollinated but shedding little pollen. They are not a cause of hayfever, but their pollen is found in Postglacial silts, and, in this connection, that of four species has been described and illustrated by Meinke (1927, page 384).

Myriophyllum spicatum L. (Fig. 106) type. Grains uniform, 23.1 to 33 μ in diameter, germ pores four, three, or rarely five, their apertures 2.85 by 1.14 μ. About twice as many grains have four pores as have three.

Low, aquatic herb, growing in deep water, with submerged leaves and aerial flowers, widely distributed throughout most of North America, except the south-eastern United States and Mexico. Flowers in summer.

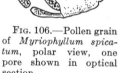

FIG. 106.—Pollen grain of *Myriophyllum spicatum*, polar view, one pore shown in optical section.

Myriophyllum heterophyllum Michx. Grains about 32 μ in diameter, essentially the same as the type, except that they have nearly always four pores, rarely five or three.

Aquatic herb of ponds and slow streams, mostly near the Atlantic and Gulf coasts of the United States.

CORNACEAE DOGWOOD FAMILY

Grains tricolpate. When moist, oblately flattened, 36 to 37.6 μ in diameter. Exine finely granular. Furrows long and tapering, reaching almost from pole to pole, equally spaced and meridionally arranged. Furrow membranes nearly smooth or slightly flecked, each provided with a well-defined aperture through which the germ pore bulges prominently. When dry the grains are spheroidal or ellipsoidal, the furrows closed tightly, assuming the form of shallow grooves.

Abortive grains and those which have lost their cell contents frequently retain the latter form even when wet, though not invariably so. Consequently, in attempting their identification in fossilized material, it must be borne in mind that shapes of these grains may be decidedly flattened, approximately spheroidal or ellipsoidal. Perhaps the most characteristic feature about them is the slight inwardly projecting subexineous thickening bordering the furrows, more pronounced around the pores. These thickenings are not conspicuous in normal, healthy grains, but in abortive grains and those which have lost their contents, as in fossil material, the thickened rims are conspicuous and serve as the most reliable diagnostic feature. The granular nature of the exine is about the same in the grains of both *Cornus* and *Nyssa* and is sometimes difficult to see, particularly in fossil material, but is of value in identification.

The Cornaceae are trees, shrubs, and perennial herbs, comprising about 10 genera, of which *Cornus* and *Nyssa* are the best known in the United States.

Nyssa sylvatica Marsh. Sour gum, Tupelo, Pepperidge (Plate X, Fig. 5) type. Grains uniform in size, all normal, tricolpate; when moistened oblately flattened, 37.2 by 27.4 μ, triangular in outline; the furrows at the angles long and tapering, expanding principally toward their centers, each provided with a distinct germinal aperture, elliptical in outline and with its long axis crossing that of the furrow. Furrow membrane flecked, pores bulging through with a ragged edge, as if having ruptured the furrow membrane. Exine finely but distinctly granular, with the granules appearing as the ends of fine, vertical rods of one material embedded in a matrix of another material of different refractive index, in optical section appearing radially striate.

Sour gum is a large tree inhabiting moist and swampy ground. Maine and Ontario to Florida, Michigan, Missouri, and Texas. Flowers in June. It is primarily insect pollinated but imperfectly so, some pollen becoming scattered in the air. In some experiments carried out by the author it was found that pollen slides exposed about 500 ft. from a tree caught a few grains of its pollen every day throughout its flowering period.

Sour-gum pollen is not known to cause hayfever but has been found by Lewis and Coke (1930) in great abundance in the Postglacial peat of the Dismal Swamp in the United States. These authors have also illustrated the pollen in its fossilized form.

Nyssa Ogeche Marsh. Ogeechee plum. Grains exactly as in the type.

A large tree in swamps. South Carolina to Georgia and Florida. Flowers in June.

Cornus florida L. (*Cynoxylon floridum* (L.) Raf.) Flowering dogwood. Grains essentially as in the type, except that they are a little larger, averaging 37 by 34 μ, and the texture of the exine is less distinctly granular.

A small or medium-sized tree, with large, showy white or pink flowers. Maine and Ontario to Florida, Minnesota, Kentucky, Kansas, and Texas. Flowers in July. Strictly insect pollinated and not a cause of hayfever.

OLEACEAE Olive Family

Grains spheroidal or somewhat oblately flattened, 19.5 to 30 μ in diameter, generally tricolpate or tetracolpate, with furrows conforming in arrangement to the trischistoclasic system. Furrows various in character among the different species. Furrow membranes smooth or variously flecked. Germ pores not sharply defined but represented in the grains of some species by a small swelling. Exine variously but always conspicuously reticulate.

The outstanding character of these grains is their reticulate exine. The pattern consists of a continuous and generally uniform lacework of elevated ridges, dividing the surface into angular lacunae. In the grains of some species the reticulum is simple; in those of others it is complex, the ridges which partition off the larger lacunae themselves bearing smaller lacunae. The smaller the lacunae the less angular they are—those borne in the ridges are almost circular in outline. This type of reticulum is not unique but characterizes the grains of such widely divergent groups as the Salicaceae, Platanaceae, Liliaceae, and others. It is thus typical of a class of phylogenetic characters which recur again and again with slight modifications in entirely different associations. We find it in the grains of *Salix*, with the lacunae smaller toward the furrows, and in those of *Platanus*, with the lacunae a little smaller and less angular throughout and associated with furrows which are more sharply defined. We find it again in the grains of the Liliaceae, associated with a single longitudinal furrow, and in those of *Potamogeton* in the absence of furrows.

In the Oleaceae the pattern is specifically constant but various among the different species. In the grains of *Ligustrum*, *Syringa*, *Forsythia*, and, to a lesser extent, *Olea* it is always rather coarse, consisting of large, hexagonal and pentagonal lacunae of uniform size and with high ridges.   In the grains of *Ligustrum* and *Syringa* the ridges are buttressed with rounded thickenings at their bases, while in those of *Forsythia* they are thick and bear within their walls much smaller, roundish lacunae.   This form calls to mind the structure of a soap foam consisting of large bubbles of rather uniform size in a matrix containing much smaller bubbles.   In the grains of *Olea* there is some trace of the buttressing, but it is much less pronounced than in those of *Ligustrum* and *Syringa*.   In the grains of *Fraxinus*, which is wind pollinated, the structure of the reticulum is less rugged, with the ridges lower and the lacunae smaller, roundish, and with no trace of buttressing.   The relation of the form of the grains of *Fraxinus* to that of *Ligustrum*, *Syringa*, and *Forsythia* is parallel to that existing between the grains of *Populus* and *Salix*, in which similar differences are definitely correlated with their modes of pollination, the former by wind and the latter by insects.   In the present instance *Ligustrum*, *Syringa*, and *Forsythia* are insect pollinated, and associated with this is the high degree of development of the surface reticulum; while *Fraxinus* is wind pollinated, and associated with this is a marked reduction in the reticulum.   If the degree of this reduction can be taken as a measure of the adaptation of these trees to anemophily, *Fraxinus* appears to be highly specialized in this respect, while *Olea* exhibits only a tendency toward anemophily.

Associated with the reduction of the reticulum in the former is found a flattening out of the furrow margins.   In the grains of *Olea* and other entomophilous members the furrows are sharply defined and harmomegathically functional, opening and closing with the changes in volume of the grain, while in the grains of the anemophilous *Fraxinus* they are poorly defined and with the furrow membranes flecked with what appear to be fragments of the reticulum.   Clearly, one of the functions of the furrows is to permit the contraction and expansion of the cell against the resistance of a rigid exine; therefore with the reduction of the reticulum and consequent loss of rigidity of the exine goes the need of a special structure to accomplish harmomegathy.   In any case it may be said of the Oleaceae that anemophily is associated with a reduction of the surface reticulum and a lessening in the degree of the development of the furrows.

FRAXINUS (Tourn.) L. ASH

Grains uniform, when fully expanded 20 to 25 μ in diameter, flattened and angular in outline, tetra-, tri-, or pentacolpate. Exine reticulate, the net simple and weakly developed, constant for all the grains of any given species but of various coarseness among the different species.

The reticulate pattern resembles that found on the grains of *Salix* and *Platanus*, but in those of *Fraxinus* it is more uniform throughout, not tending to become finer toward the poles and along the margins of the furrows, as is generally the case in the grains of *Salix*, and always it is much coarser than in the grains of *Platanus*. In the grains of *Fraxinus* the size of the mesh is maintained right up to the edge of the furrows, where it ends with open lacunae, suggesting that the furrows are torn through it with the expansion of the grain. This impression is heightened by the appearance of the furrows themselves. These are rather poorly defined; as seen in the expanded condition they are short and broad, with their membranes stretched and bulging and dotted with small flecks of material which look like fragments of the torn reticulum scattered over the surface. They are without germ pores, the whole surface serving as a place of exit for the pollen tube. They are always equally or approximately equally spaced around the equator. When there are four or five of them they cross the equator obliquely, with their axes converging in pairs alternately above and below the equator, but when there are three they cross the equator at right angles and converge toward the poles along meridional lines; thus, whatever their number they conform to the trischistoclasic system.

The grains of *Fraxinus* differ from those of the other members of the family in their finer reticulum, thinner exine, and more irregular and less sharply defined furrows. These are characteristic morphological modifications resulting from pollination by wind.

All species of *Fraxinus* are excellently adapted to pollination by wind and scatter enormous quantities of pollen in the air. In the author's experience in the vicinity of New York City and in that of Duke and Durham (1928) in the vicinity of Kansas City ash pollen becomes very abundant in the atmosphere during the short flowering period of the trees. Only occasionally, however, have any of the ashes been reported as factors in hayfever. Thus, *F. oregona* is regarded as one of the most important causes of the hayfever occurring in early spring in western Oregon (Chamberlain, 1927), and *F. attenuata* as one of the most important in February and March in Arizona (Phillips, 1922, 1923).

Fossilized grains of ash pollen have occasionally been found in European bog deposits, and in this connection a species of ash pollen has been illustrated by Meinke (1927), who points out its similarity to that of *Adoxa* (page 381), and the grains of *F. excelsior* are illustrated by Docturowsky and Kudrjaschow (1923). In similar studies in America the grains of *F. lanceolata* (*i.e.*, *F. americana* L.) are illustrated by Sears (1930). Hugo Fischer (1890, page 44) describes the grains of *F. excelsior* L. as generally tricolpate—"regelmässig dreifaltig."

The genus includes about 30 or 40 species of trees and shrubs widely distributed in the temperate regions of the Northern hemisphere and in Cuba and Java.

Fraxinus americana L. White ash, Cane ash (Plate X, Fig. 4) type. Grains uniform, when expanded about 24 μ in diameter, flattened and angular in outline. Furrows four, less often three, or rarely five, short and broad, gaping widely open as the grain expands and giving it its angular appearance. Furrow membranes distinctly flecked. Exine more finely reticulate than in the grains of *F. coriacea* and *F. Toumeyi*.

The white ash is a large forest tree in rich woods, almost throughout the United States and Canada. It sheds large quantities of pollen which is borne great distances in the air, in April and May, the flowers opening just before the leaves. It is, however, not known to cause hayfever.

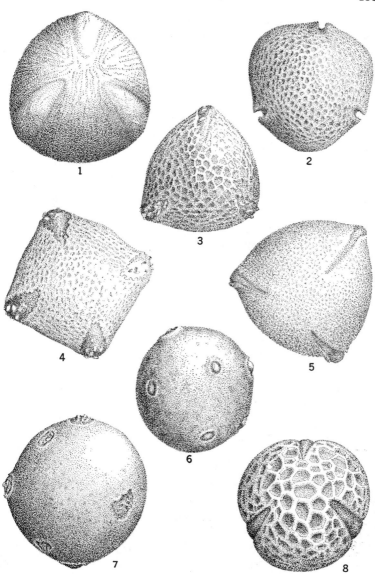

PLATE X.—Pollen grains of Aceraceae, Tiliaceae, Cornaceae, Oleaceae, and Plantaginaceae. 1, *Acer Pseudo-platanus*, polar view, 36 μ in diameter. 2, *Tilia americana*, polar view, 33 μ in diameter. 3, *Olea europaea*, polar view, 22 μ in diameter. 4, *Fraxinus americana*, polar view, 24 μ in diameter. 5, *Nyssa sylvatica*, polar view, 37 μ in diameter. 6, *Plantago lanceolata*, 35 μ in diameter. 7, *Plantago Rugelii*, 23 μ in diameter. 8, *Ligustrum Ibota*, polar view, 30 μ in diameter.

Fraxinus coriacea S. Wats. (*F. velutina* var. *coriacea* Rehd.) Desert ash. Grains as in the type, about 20 μ in diameter, always a few that are abortive, and with some variation in those that are normal, the latter nearly always tetracolpate, rarely tri- or pentacolpate. The reticulum is a little coarser than in the type.

A large tree shedding much pollen in early spring. Probably the cause of some hayfever in regions where abundant. It is one of the commonest ashes in southern Arizona, somewhat less abundant in adjacent parts of New Mexico and Mexico.

Olea europaea L. Olive (Plate X, Fig. 3) type. Grains flattened, about 22 μ in diameter, tricolpate, rarely tetracolpate, and those that are variously irregular and apparently abnormal. Exine reticulate, similar to that of the grains of *Fraxinus*, except that the mesh is much coarser and the ridges buttressed, in this respect resembling the grains of *Ligustrum*. Furrows broad, rather short, and vaguely defined, as in the grains of *Fraxinus;* their membranes flecked, without germinal apertures, the latter represented merely by a bulge which appears in the center of the furrow membrane when fully expanded.

Underlying the center of each furrow, embedded in the cell contents and radially oriented, is a hyaline rod, which expands upon being moistened, causing the bulge in the center of the furrow membrane. These organs are exactly homologous with those found in the grains of *Quercus*, though not quite so highly developed. The difference between the grains of *Fraxinus* and *Olea* lies principally in the better development of the ridges in the former and in the relatively unimportant, though conspicuous, haptotypic character of the number of germinal furrows, which are predominantly three in the grains of *Olea* and four in those of *Fraxinus*.

The olive is primarily insect pollinated, bearing flowers closely resembling those of privet, but sheds large amounts of pollen which becomes atmospheric. Flowers in April and May. It is native of Europe but has been introduced into some parts of California and Arizona where it is said to be a serious cause of hayfever and is stated by Rowe (1928) to be important in California. The genus includes about 40 species of trees and shrubs, native of the tropics and warm parts of the Old World and New Zealand.

LIGUSTRUM L. Privet

Grains similar to those of *Olea europaea* but considerably larger, ranging in the different species from 28 to 30 μ in diameter. Reticulum of the exine much coarser, with lacunae larger and ridges higher and buttressed, presenting a beaded appearance, as in the grains of *Olea* but much more pronounced. Toward the furrows the reticulum is a little finer than elsewhere, and it ends abruptly along the furrow margins with closed lacunae. Furrows generally three, occasionally four, a little shorter and more sharply defined than in the grains of *Olea*, an appearance obviously due to the more rugged character of the reticulum. Furrow membranes smooth, and each provided with a fairly well-defined germ pore.

The genus comprises about 50 species of both deciduous and evergreen shrubs, native of Asia, Australia, and the Mediterranean region. About a dozen species are cultivated as hedges or for their showy white flowers which open early in summer. They are all insect pollinated and are rarely a serious cause of hayfever, though they have occasionally been suspected of being so.

In the superficial appearance of the plants the privets bear little resemblance to the ashes, but their relationship to the latter is abundantly attested by the characters of their pollen grains. Those of the privets differ from those of the ashes only in the greater thickness of their exine and better development of the reticulum, characters which we have already seen are definitely correlated with their mode of pollination by insects.

Ligustrum Ibota Sieb. Privet (Plate X, Fig. 8) type. Grains averaging about 30.5 μ in diameter, ranging from 28 to 32 μ, otherwise as in the generic description.

A garden shrub closely resembling *L. vulgare.* Introduced into America from China and Japan. Flowers in June.

Ligustrum vulgare L. Common privet. Grains uniform, averaging about 28.5 μ in diameter, otherwise as in the generic description.

A garden shrub introduced into America from Europe and Asia, now common in the eastern United States and Canada. Flowers in June, occasionally suspected of causing hayfever.

Ligustrum ovalifolium Hassk. Privet. Grains about 30 μ in diameter, 28.5 to 31 μ, generally with three but occasionally with

four furrows which are a little shorter than those of the grains of
L. vulgare.   Otherwise as in the generic description.

A garden shrub existing in several forms with variegated leaves.
Native to Japan but extensively cultivated in America.

Syringa vulgaris L. Common lilac.   Grains spheroidal, similar
to the type (*Ligustrum Ibota*, Plate X, Fig. 8), about 26.3 μ in
diameter.   Furrows three or occasionally four, in which case
either strictly tetrahedral in arrangement or irregular and
entirely asymmetrical; normally sharply defined, long, slender,
and tapering, reaching almost from pole to pole, their membranes
smooth, but each provided with a germ pore appearing as a small,
rounded bulge at its center but without a well-defined aperture.

Underlying the pores is a small mass of hyaline material,
similar to but much smaller than the corresponding structures
in the grains of *Olea.*   In the great length of their furrows these
grains are quite distinct from those of both *Olea* and *Ligustrum*
but tend to resemble those of *Forsythia.*

The lilac is a garden shrub introduced into America from
Europe and Asia where the genus is represented by about
30 species.   Some half dozen of these are cultivated throughout
the United States and Canada.   All species are entirely insect
pollinated and shed but little pollen, but some have been suspected of occasionally causing hayfever.

Forsythia suspensa Vahl. Forsythia, Golden bells.   Grains
various, 19.4 to 37.6 μ in diameter, normally about 28.5 μ,
similar to the type (*Ligustrum Ibota*, Plate X, Fig. 8).   Furrows
three, long and tapering, their membranes smooth; germ pores
not sharply defined, represented by a slight bulge in the middle of
each furrow membrane.   Exine doubly reticulate.

The reticulum of these grains is remarkable and beautiful,
composed, for the most part, of a double system, consisting of
rather uniform lacunae separated by ridges which are broader
than those of the grains of *Syringa* and *Ligustrum* and bearing
within their walls a series of smaller lacunae.   As a result of this
the surface of these grains presents the appearance of lacework
delicately wrought in alabaster and studded with jewels.

Forsythia is a common garden shrub, insect pollinated and
flowering very early in spring before the unfolding of its leaves or
sometimes late in the autumn; not known to cause hayfever.
The genus includes four species, native of Japan, China, and

southern Europe. Of these, three have been introduced into cultivation in America.

PLANTAGINACEAE Plantain Family

PLANTAGO L. Plantain

Grains spheroidal, 16 to 40 μ in diameter. Furrows, in the ordinary sense of the word, absent. Pores 4 to 14, not elongate, circular or irregular in outline, scattered. Pore membranes flecked or with a single central thickening. Exine thin and more or less rough-granular. Intine thin and without conspicuous thickenings.

The pores of these grains should probably be regarded as shortened furrows; though they are not elongate, their furrow nature is suggested by their arrangement, which seems to conform to the trischistoclasic system. Harmomegathy is not required, because the exine is thin and flexible enough to accommodate all changes in volume. The thin exine and pore-like furrows suggest that these grains are reduced in form in response to wind pollination.

The genus contains over 200 species of low herbs, of wide distribution.

Plantago lanceolata L. English plantain (Plate X, Fig. 6) type. Grains approximately spheroidal when expanded, exceedingly various in size, 25 to 40 μ in diameter. Germ pores 7 to 14, distributed rather evenly over the surface and for the most part conforming to the trischistoclasic system, 10 to 14.8 μ apart, approximately circular in outline but sometimes with slightly wavy margins, 2.8 to 4.6 μ in diameter.

Each pore is encircled by a slight thickening of the exine which takes the stain a little more deeply than the rest of the surface, and each is crossed by a delicate membrane marked by a conspicuous central thickening. These two characters give the pores an appearance almost identical with the single pore of the grains of the grasses. There is much variation in the size of the pores on different grains, even among those of similar size, but on any single grain they are uniform. The grains of this species of plantain are notable for their great variation in size, a character which has been discussed at some length by Stout (1919). There appears to be no definite correlation between the size of the grain and the size, number, and distance apart of the germ pores. It can, however, be said that the larger grains tend to have larger pores, a greater number of them, and at greater distances apart.

The texture is characteristically mottled, but this is difficult to see unless the grains are well stained. Though this mottling is rather coarse, it is much less so than in the grains of the two following species.

A common weed of gardens and waste places almost throughout North America. Wind pollinated, flowering from April to November, shedding large amounts of pollen which is well known to be a potent cause of hayfever, generally in the early summer when the plants reach their best development. Plantain pollen is caught on pollen slides in large quantity almost throughout the summer.

Plantago Rugelii Dcne. Rugel's plantain (Plate X, Fig. 7). Grains approximately spheroidal, various in size but less so than those of *P. lanceolata*, 22.8 to 24.5 μ in diameter. Germ pores 6 to 10, very irregular in shape and with a jagged margin, various in size and not surrounded by an annular thickening; pore membranes flecked with a number of granules which tend to aggregate toward the centers of the membranes but are not generally fused. Texture similar to that of *P. lanceolata* but with the mottling coarser and sometimes almost warty.

This grain is easily distinguished from that of *P. lanceolata* by the ragged edges of its pores, the flecked character of the pore membranes, and the coarser texture of its exine.

A common weed distributed almost throughout North America. Flowers from June to September. It is wind pollinated but sheds so little pollen that it cannot be regarded as a factor in hayfever. It is occasionally caught on atmospheric pollen slides but in very much smaller quantity than the pollen of *P. lanceolata*.

Plantago major L. Common plantain. Grains somewhat various, approximately spheroidal, 16 to 21 μ in diameter. Germ pores four to six, according to the size of the grain, but generally five, irregular in shape; their membranes flecked with granules. Texture of the exine rough and warty.

In the texture of their exine, which is coarser even than that of the grains of *P. Rugelii*, and in the small number and irregular shape of their germ pores these grains are easily distinguished from those of the two preceding species.

A common weed, remarkably similar to *P. Rugelii;* in fact the plants themselves are more difficult to distinguish from each other than are their pollen grains. Of cosmopolitan distribution. May to September. Wind pollinated but shedding only a small amount of pollen which, though frequently caught on atmospheric pollen slides, is not regarded as a cause of hayfever.

COMPOSITAE Composite Family

CICHORIEAE Chicory Tribe

Grains globular, generally tricolpate, occasionally tetracolpate or, some abnormal grains, with higher numbers of furrows; echinolophate or occasionally simply echinate. Lacunae generally 12 to 20. Ridges high, generally vertically striate, never perforate, though occasionally appearing to be. Spines prominent, sharp and conical. Texture of the ridges and thickened parts of the exine more or less granular.

The pollen grains of the Cichorieae are generally characterized by an elaborate and beautiful system of sculpturing which, taken throughout the tribe, exhibits a wide range of variation but, in the majority of species, does not depart far from a certain form which may be considered basic for the tribe. Owing to the nature of the variations among the different species, and the fact that most of the forms encountered seem to be derivatives, through modification or reduction, from the basic form, a clear understanding of the relationship of the different forms to each other can best be gained by first examining in detail one typical form.

Such a form is that of the normal grains of *Taraxacum* (Plate XI, Fig. 2). These possess a characteristically trimerous pattern, but, if the sculpturing is stripped off, as sometimes happens when the pollen is prepared for microscopic examination, the underlying shape is found to be oblate-spheroidal, with three large germ pores bulging out as broad rounded papillae (Fig. 117). It is the presence of these three pores equally spaced around the equator of the grain which governs its trimerous pattern. The exine is thrown into an elaborate system of high ridges which anastomose enclosing variously shaped lacunae, the floors of which are covered by only the thinnest possible layer of smooth exine. The raised or thickened part of the exine is uniformly fine-granular and provided with long sharp conical spines, a condition designated as *echinolophate*.

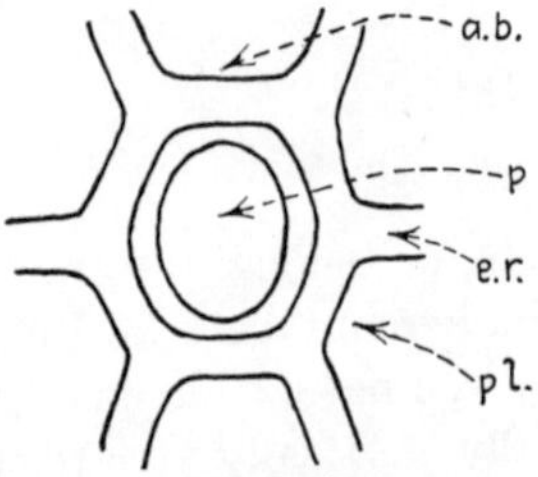

FIG. 107. 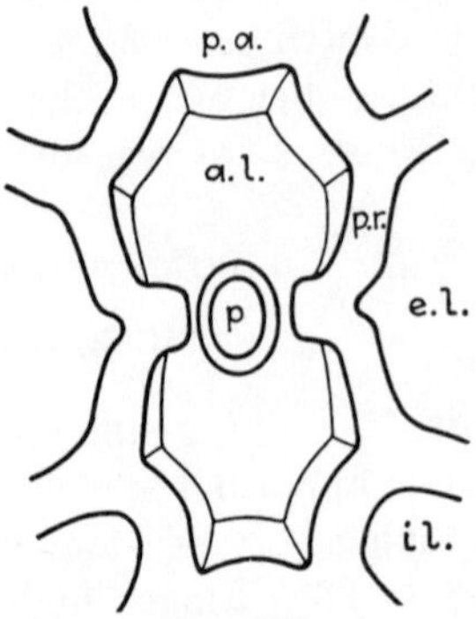   FIG. 108.

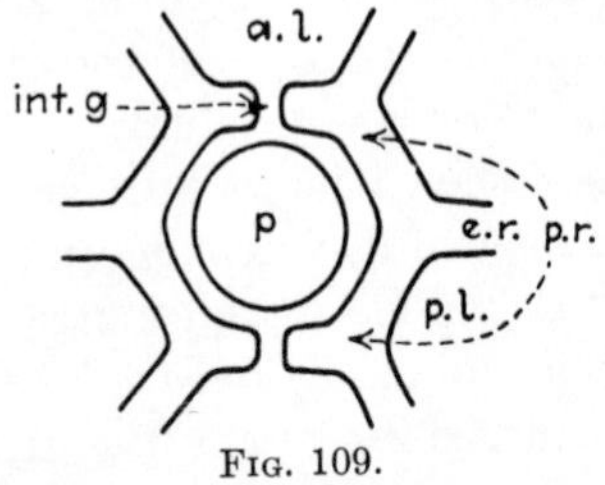

FIG. 109.

FIGS. 107–109.—Germ pores and surrounding ridges of pollen grains of Cichorieae: Fig. 107, *Scolymus hispanicus;* Fig. 108, *Tragopogon pratensis;* Fig. 109, *Taraxacum officinale:*— *a.l.*, abporal lacuna; *p*, germ pore; *p.l.*, paraporal lacuna; *p.a.*, polar area; *p.r.*, paraporal ridge; *e.l.*, equatorial lacunae; *int. g*, interlacunar gap; *e.r.*, equatorial ridge; *il.*, interporal lacuna. *tr*, transequatorial ridge.

The normal pattern in the grains of *Taraxacum* consists of 15 lacunae (Plate XI, Fig. 2), which are of definite shape and arrangement and can be readily identified from whatever direction the grain happens to be viewed. The three lacunae which encompass the three pores are hexagonal in form, but with two gaps in their ridges, and are known as the poral lacunae. If the grains be observed in polar view, *i.e.*, so oriented that the three pores are on the limb or edge of the apparent disk, and consequently one of the poles is uppermost, there will be seen six more lacunae (Fig. 110). Three of these are adjacent to and in meridional line with the poral lacunae. These are the abporal lacunae. They are pentagonal in form, and each communicates with its adjacent poral lacuna through a narrow gap in the separating ridge (Fig. 109); in the polar view (Fig. 110) the poral lacunae are in side view, so that only one bounding ridge of each is seen, but they are easily recognized by their interlacunar gaps. Alternating with the pores, and between the abporal lacunae, are the three broad paraporal lacunae. These are also pentagonal in form. On the limb of the grain (seen in side view in Plate XI,

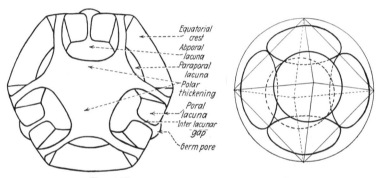

Fig. 110.   Fig. 111.

Fig. 110.—Diagram of the form elements of a pollen grain of *Taraxacum*. The large polar thickening varies in size and shape in the different grains of this species.

Fig. 111.—Diagram of the octahedral arrangement of six cells, which frequently occurs in the pollen mother-cells of *Taraxacum officinale* and some other species of the Cichorieae. The six cells are represented by heavy lines, the pollen mother-cell by the enclosing circle; and an octahedron is drawn in faint lines over the whole group to suggest the octahedral relation that the cells bear to each other.

Fig. 2) is the equatorial crest traversing the equator from poral lacuna to poral lacuna, separating from each other the adjacent paraporal lacunae of opposite hemispheres. In some cases it gives off a small projection into one or more of the paraporal lacunae. These, however, are omitted from the figures, because they seldom occur in the normal grains of *Taraxacum;* but they occur more frequently in the grains of other species, *e.g.*, those of *Scolymus* (Plate XI, Fig. 1). Over the pole is seen a rather large triangular or hexagonal area of thickened exine of variable extent—the polar thickening (Plate XI, Fig. 2). Since both hemispheres are alike, the whole pattern of the normal *Taraxacum* pollen grain comprises 3 poral, 6 abporal and 6 paraporal lacunae, making a total of 15. These are summarized in Table V. They correspond in arrangement to the faces of a pentakaidecahedron, with 12 pentagonal and 3 hexagonal faces.

The heaping of the material of the exine into vertical ridges serves to stiffen the exine to such an extent as nearly to demobilize the furrows, preventing them from opening and closing freely. Moreover, in the construction of the pattern of the grains of *Taraxacum*, the presence of the equatorial crests exerting a lateral thrust against the paraporal ridges bounding the furrows effectively prevents them from spreading apart to any extent despite the presence of gaps in the transverse ridges of the poral lacunae. As a consequence of this partial or complete demobilization of the furrows and their resultant loss of ability to accommodate changes in volume of the grain, the pores are very large and bulge prominently when the grain is moistened, thus taking over the greater part of the impaired harmomegathic function of the furrows.

We have already seen a similar example of the loss of harmomegathic function as a consequence of the development of high ridges on the exine, in the grains of *Polygonum* and *Persicaria*. In those of *Polygonum chinense* this was compensated by a great enlargement of the three pores, while in the various species of *Persicaria* it was compensated by increasing the number of pores up to 30 and more, all of which could bulge out as the grain increased in volume. In the grains of *Taraxacum* the compensation for the loss of harmomegathy of the furrows is made by an increase in the size of the pores and not by an increase in their number, for normally there are only three germ pores.

The basic form as exemplified by the grains of *Taraxacum* prevails, with little modification, among the majority of the species of the tribe. In the grains of *Hypochaeris*, *Sonchus* and *Nabalus* the pattern of the sculpturing is exactly as described for those of *Taraxacum*. In the grains of *Cichorium* (Plate XI, Fig. 6), *Crepis* and *Hieracium* the pattern differs only in the polar thickenings being less extensive and triradiate in outline owing to the encroachment upon them of the abporal lacunae. In the grains of *Haensèlera*, *Krigia*, *Cynthia*, and *Lactuca* the pattern differs in the polar thickenings being absent, represented only by the unexpanded confluences of three ridges at the poles. This latter is likewise true of the grains of *Scolymus* (Plate XI, Fig. 1), but these, besides, lack the interlacunar gaps between the poral and abporal lacunae. These grains are of particular interest because, with the closing of the interlacunar gaps, the furrow is completely demobilized, and it necessarily follows that its harmomegathic function devolves entirely upon the pores. As a consequence the latter are large. But it is true that they are no larger in proportion than the pores of the grains of *Taraxacum* and others, in which the interlacunar gaps are present. It, therefore, appears that the interlacunar gaps in such grains as these are only useless vestiges of vanishing furrows, and that the closing of the interlacunar gaps in the grains of *Scolymus* is the final stage in their elimination, and stamps these grains as representing a step further in advance along the evolutionary line which led to the production of the lophate character, with its resultant demobilization of the furrows.

In the grains of *Tragopogon pratensis* (Plate XI, Fig. 4) and *Scorzonera hispanica* (Plate XI, Fig. 5) are found the widest deviations from the basic form of pattern encountered in the tribe. Those of *Tragopogon* have 15 lacunae, and those of *Scorzonera* have 20 (Table V), and in neither case do they correspond at all closely to the 15 lacunae of the grains of *Taraxacum*. In both cases the poral lacunae are lacking (Figs. 108, 116), and each abporal lacuna communicates directly with its corresponding member of the opposite hemisphere through a rather broad gap in which the germ pore is situated, the two communicating abporal lacunae thus forming the germinal furrow. There are no equatorial crests; instead, the regions of the equator between the pores are occupied by large equatorial lacunae. In the grains of *Tragopogon* (Fig. 108) there is a single hexagonal equatorial lacuna in each of these regions, while in those of *Scorzonera hispanica* (Fig. 115) there are two pentagonal lacunae in each. The joining of the abporal lacunae to form a furrow and the absence of equatorial crests in both of these grains, permit lateral movement of the paraporal ridges, which resemble, in action and appearance, a crossbow (Figs. 108, 116). That in both cases the two joined abporal lacunae function as a furrow is obvious from the small size of the germ pore, for in the grains of these two species it is much smaller than in those of any other member of the tribe. Its mode of operation is truly unique and brings into

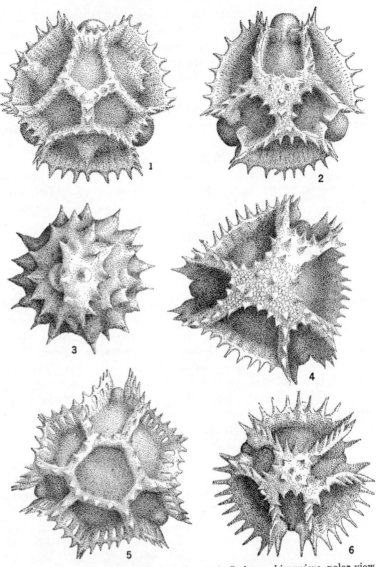

PLATE XI.—Pollen grains of Cichorieae. 1, *Scolymus hispanicus*, polar view, 35 μ in diameter. 2, *Taraxacum officinale*, polar view, 26 μ in diameter. 3, *Catananche caerulea*, side view, 27.4 μ in diameter. 4, *Tragopogon pratensis*, polar view, 32 μ in diameter. 5, *Scorzonera hispanica*, polar view, 37 μ in diameter. 6, *Cichorium Intybus*, polar view, 40 μ in diameter.

play a mechanism which is effective and beautiful in its simplicity. The pore in its interlacunar gap is tightly squeezed, in the one

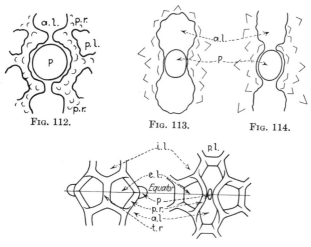

FIG. 112.   FIG. 113.   FIG. 114.

FIG. 115   FIG. 116.

FIGS. 112–116.—Details of pore patterns and surrounding ridges of pollen grains of Cichorieae: Fig. 112, *Dendroseris micrantha;* Fig. 113, *Catananche caerulea;* Fig. 114, *Catananche lutea;* Fig. 115, *Scorzonera hispanica,* with equatorial lacunae uppermost; 116, *Scorzonera hispanica,* with germ pore uppermost. Parts lettered as in figures 107–109.

case, between the projecting bosses of the lateral ridges (Fig. 108) and, in the other, between the ridges themselves (Fig. 116). It contains a plug of callose substance which upon absorbing water expands and in doing so pushes apart the two lateral ridges which are unhindered in their lateral movement owing to the presence of the equatorial lacunae into which they may move. When the grains are unexpanded the paraporal ridges are like bent crossbows with their backs pressing against the pores, but when the grains expand the paraporal ridges straighten like a bow that has been released. Such a movement, so nicely provided for in the grains of *Tragopogon* and *Scorzonera,* is entirely prevented in

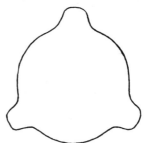

FIG. 117.—Pollen grain of *Taraxacum officinale* stripped of its exine to show the basic form upon which its elaborate pattern is built.

all grains like those of *Taraxacum* (Fig. 109) by the presence in these of equatorial crests which exert a thrust counteracting any lateral movement of the paraporal ridges.   The remarkably wide deviation of the forms of the grains of *Tragopogon* and *Scorzonera* from the basic form of the tribe suggests that they are genetically divergent from the rest of the tribe but rather close to each other.

The grains of *Dendroseris micrantha* and *Catananche* (Plate XI, Fig. 3) show the pattern of the Cichorieae reduced to its lowest terms, which suggests that they occupy isolated positions in the tribe.   But I think that their resemblance to each other is only superficial and without phylogenetic significance, because the forms of these grains are such as to suggest entirely different origins.   In the grains of *Dendroseris* the reduction of the sculpturing appears to be the result of the extension of the polar thickenings toward the equator leaving the lacunae, though reduced in size, fairly sharply defined in the region of the equator (Fig. 112); while in the grains of *Catananche*, though this might likewise be true, the rudimentary pattern appears more likely to be due to a partial development of the ridges throughout, resulting in the formation of unrecognizable vestiges of lacunae over all of the surface.   Moreover, the rudimentary lacunae appear to be quite different in the two cases (*cf.* Table V; Figs. 113, 114).   Both forms may be derivative, though the possibility of one of them being primitive must not be overlooked.   If one of them is primitive, it is most likely that of *Catananche*, in which case we witness here, in the clumping of the spines with irregularly shaped blank spaces between them, the initiation of the echinolophate system which characterizes the grains of almost the whole tribe; and in the grains of *Dendroseris micrantha* we witness the elimination of the echinolophate system by the encroachment upon it of the polar thickenings and the loss of spines.

The lacunar patterns of the Cichorieae resolve themselves into three well-marked types to which all but one of the forms may be referred as subsidiary or derived.   The cardinal types of pattern are the *Taraxacum* type (No. 1, Table V, Plate XI, Fig. 2), with 15 lacunae, including 3 poral but no equatorial lacunae; the *Tragopogon* type (No. 3, Table V, Plate XI, Fig. 4), also with 15 lacunae, including 3 equatorial but no poral lacunae; and the

Scorzonera type (No. 4, Table V, Plate XI, Fig. 5), with 20 lacunae, including 6 equatorial and no poral lacunae.

The *Taraxacum* type of lacunar pattern is represented in by far the greatest number of species. It characterizes, with certain modifications such as the fluctuation in extent of the polar thickenings, the grains of *Cichorium, Haenselera Krigia, Cynthia, Lactuca, Hypochaeris, Crepis, Hieracium,* and *Nabalus.* A four-pored tetraradiate derivative of this form, with 20 lacunae, characterizes about 90 per cent of the grains of *Sonchus oleraceus* (No. 1a, Table V) and a fair proportion of those of *Taraxacum, Cichorium, Hieracium aurantiacum,* and *H. pratense.* This differs from the basic trimerous pattern only in the addition of a fourth set of form elements. The tetraradiate pattern, in spite of its regular symmetry, should probably be regarded as entirely abnormal and will be discussed below. Another slight modification of this type is seen in the *Scolymus* form of pattern (No. 2, Table V), which characterizes both of the species of *Scolymus* here described. It differs from the *Taraxacum* pattern only in its closed poral lacunae (Fig. 107).

The *Tragopogon* type of lacunar pattern (Table V, Plate XI, Fig. 4), distinguished by its possession of three equatorial lacunae and no poral lacunae, is found only in the grains of *Tragopogon* and has no derivatives among the species here considered.

The *Scorzonera hispanica* type of lacunar pattern (No. 4, Table V), distinguished by the possession of six equatorial lacunae, two polar, and no poral lacunae, characterizes, without modification, only the grains of *S. hispanica,* but, with the replacement of the polar lacunae by polar thickenings, it characterizes the grains of *S. purpurea, S. graminifolia, S. nervosa;* by an enlargement of the polar thickenings, almost or quite obliterating the interporal lacunae, it characterizes the grains of *S. parviflora* and *S. humilis;* and, by a further encroachment of the polar thickenings, obliterating the equatorial lacunae, possibly those of *Catananche caerulea.*

The lacunar pattern of *Dendroseris micrantha* (Table V) is entirely aberrant in its possession of 12 paraporal lacunae. The extensive development of its polar thickenings suggests that it is a derived form but apparently not from one of the three cardinal forms mentioned above.

Tetraradiate Grains.—The pollen of many species in this tribe is characterized by the presence, in varying proportion, of abnormal grains. For the most part these are asymmetrical and malformed, often not identifiable. Notable among these, however, is the occurrence, mentioned above, of tetracolpate grains which are tetramerous and strictly tetraradiate. They constitute a fairly large proportion of the pollen of *Taraxacum*, *Cichorium*, several species of *Crepis*, and about 90 per cent of the pollen of *Sonchus oleraceus*. This condition has also been noted by Fischer (1890), who says, "Abweichungen von dreifaltigen Gestalt sind auch hier nicht häufig; ich fand vier parallele Falten, mit entsprechender Vermehrung der Flächen und Leisten, bei: *Hieracium aurantiacum*, *H. villosum*, *H. boreale*, *H. rigidum*, *Mulgedium Plumieri*, *Sonchus oleraceus*, bei letzterer häufiger als die dreifaltigen." Thus, the condition is apparently widespread in the tribe. This form is just as radially symmetrical as the typical forms, differing from them only in the possession of 4 pores and, as a consequence, 4 aporal and 4 interporal lacunae in each hemisphere, *i.e.*, a total of 20 on the grain, and with four- or eight-sided polar thickenings (No. 1a, Table V). Generally, the 4 furrows converge toward the poles at angles of exactly 90 deg. instead of the usual angle of 120 deg. These are the only examples that I have ever seen of truly tetraradiate pollen grains.

Such tetraradiate grains are of the utmost interest because they violate the law of equal triconvergent angles, which seems to be almost universal for furrow arrangements. Nevertheless, the reason for the tetraradiate configuration of the furrows of these grains is quite apparent if we inquire into the early stages of their formation. These I have observed in *Taraxacum*, the pollen mother-cell of which is notorious for its extraordinary and numerous irregularities of division. One of the commonest of these is the division of the mother-cell nucleus into six instead of the usual four daughter-nuclei. When these happen to be all of the same size, as they frequently are, they take up their positions in the mother-cell equidistantly from each other which results in their being octahedral in arrangement (Fig. 111). Then when the subsequent division of the mother-cell, which is simultaneous by furrowing, takes place, the result is that at the final separation each of the daughter-cells is connected with four of its neighbors of the hexad through four pit connections with the result that each daughter-cell comes to have four furrows equatorially arranged. Since each of these furrows originates through a separate impulse, each is independent of the others and receives a meridional orientation in the same way that the three furrows in ordinary tricolpate pollen grains receive meridional orientation through three independent contact impulses.

Among the numerous atypical forms that occur in this tribe, this is the only one that is radiosymmetrical. There are, besides these, four-pored grains bearing patterns which are asymmetrical and variously distorted—frequently so much that it is difficult to interpret them, but they appear to correspond to the ordinary tetracolpate form in which the furrows converge in pairs toward four centers, corresponding in arrangement to four of the six edges of a tetrahedron, the form of grain which we have seen results from daughter-cells' making *two* points of contact with their neighbors of a tetrad.

The numerous irregularities among the pollen grains of this tribe are generally, if indeed not always, to be associated with the widespread occurrence of an irregular distribution of chromosomes in the reduction divisions. Certainly this is true of some of the species of *Hieracium* and *Crepis* (Hollongshead and Babcock, 1930; Babcock and Clausen, 1929) and can generally be associated with hybridity of origin, and such pollen is known to be frequently sterile, the seeds forming apogamously. For example, Osawa (1913) finds that in *Taraxacum platycarpum* Dahlst. pollination is necessary for seed formation, while in *T. albidum* Dahlst. it is unnecessary. In the former the pollen mother-cells divide normally, forming four pollen grains in the usual way, while in the latter there is much irregularity in the meiotic divisions. Frequently the pollen mother-cell nucleus may give rise to fewer or more than the usual four daughter-nuclei, which, according to Osawa, is due either to lagging of the chromosomes in the first division, forming extranuclear chromosomes which later become cells, or to an amitotic division of the nucleus in the second division.

Since the patterns of the grains are largely the result of their relations with their neighbors during their formative period—whether they be formed in diads, tetrads, or hexads or whether they be smaller or larger than their neighbors—and since these relations depend largely upon the complement of chromosomes that each grain receives, it is likely that much can be learned regarding the distribution of chromosomes, in cases where such irregularities occur, by simply inspecting the pollen-grain patterns.

The lophate character, which is the outstanding feature of the Cichorieae, is not confined to this tribe alone. Among the Compositae it is also characteristic of the pollen grains of the tribe of Vernonieae, of *Barnadesia* in the tribe of Mutisieae, and of *Berkheya* in the tribe of Arctotidae. In the grains of the Vernonieae* an enormous range of variation occurs in the different species, but they can generally be distinguished from those of the Cichorieae by the greater number of lacunae which prevails almost throughout the tribe. Thus, there are 27 in that of *Stokesia* (Plate XII, Fig. 2), 30 in the grain of *Vernonia Wrightii* (Plate XII, Fig. 3) and 32 in that of *V. jucunda* (Table V), and in those of *Struchium*, and *Pacourina* (Plate XII, Fig. 1) they are too numerous to count with certainty. In *Barnadesia** patterns numerically similar to those of the Vernonieae are encountered; but the ridges are always without spines (Table V, Plate XII, Figs. 6 to 8).

Among the Arctotidae the grains of *Berkheya heterophylla* have a lophate pattern consisting of 29 lacunae of a quite distinctive form. The crests are without spines, as in *Barnadesia;* but the grains may be distinguished from these and all others by the curious bilateral nature of their pattern, in which there are two paraporal and two interporal lacunae in each hemisphere (Table V). In these grains the pattern is as fully and beautifully expressed as in any of the other groups but so different in the number and arrangement of its elements that it is scarcely comparable with any of the others, particularly those of the Cichorieae. Such a pattern, however, appears to be exceptional among the Arctotidae, for it is entirely absent in the grains of *Arctotis grandis.* The latter are simply echinate and spheroidal.

From a study of the occurrence of the lophate patterns among the Cichorieae and other groups of the Compositae, it thus appears that the presence or absence of this character is no criterion of relationship, any more than is the presence or absence of the ordinary reticulate pattern which we have seen to occur

* For a detailed account of the pollen grains of the Vernonieae see Wodehouse (1928*a*); of *Barnadesia*, Wodehouse (1928*b*).

again and again in unrelated groups, but the nature of the lophate character when present is of the highest phylogenetic value; and the divergences in number and spacial configuration of the pattern elements are also likely to prove of great value in the study of the irregular distribution of chromosomes.

KEY TO THE SPECIES

I. Equatorial ridges present, and equatorial lacunae absent; poral lacunae present; texture fine-granular or smooth.

    A. Lacunar pattern 1.* Interlacunar gaps present between the poral and abporal lacunae.

        1. Polar thickenings large, triangular or hexagonal.

a. Grains 19 to 25 μ in diameter.	Taraxacum officinale
	Hypochaeris radicata
b. Grains 26 to 30 μ in diameter.	Sonchus oleraceus
c. Grains 30 to 35 μ in diameter.	Nabalus altissimus

        2. Polar thickenings moderately developed, triradiate.

a. Grains 17 to 32 μ in diameter.	Crepis virens
	biennis
	japonica
	taraxacifolia
	tectorum
	Hieracium auricula
	venosum
	patens
	aurantiacum
	umbellatum
b. Grains 35 to 40 μ in diameter.	Cichorium Intybus

        3. Polar thickenings not developed, represented only by the unexpanded confluence of three ridges at the poles.

a. Grains 22 to 25 μ in diameter.	Krigia virginica
	Cynthia virginica
	Lactuca virosa
b. Grains 30 to 40 μ in diameter.	Haenselera granatensis

    B. Lacunar pattern 2.* Interlacunar gaps absent, poral lacunae hexagonal. Polar thickenings not developed, represented by the unexpanded confluence of three crests at the poles.

        1. Poral lacunae approximately isodiametric.

	Scolymus hispanicus
2. Poral lacunae meridionally elongate.	Scolymus grandiflorus

II. Equatorial lacunae present. Equatorial crests and poral lacunae absent. Texture coarsely granular. The pattern may be elaborate, represented by 15 or 20 lacunae, or may be greatly reduced, in which case the grains resemble those of Sec. III.

   A. Equatorial lacunae 3; polar thickenings large and hexagonal; lacunar pattern 3.*

      1. Ridges high.   Tragopogon pratensis
                                                   minor
                                                     porrifolius

      2. Ridges low.   orientalis

   B. Equatorial lacunae 6.

      1. Polar thickenings absent; polar lacunae present, triangular or hexagonal; lacunar pattern 4.*   Scorzonera hispanica

      2. Polar thickenings present but not greatly extended; polar lacunae absent. Lacunar pattern 4*a*.*   Scorzonera purpurea
                                                  graminifolia
                                                  nervosa

      3. Polar thickenings greatly extended lacunar pattern nearly obliterated, 4*b*.*   Scorzonera parviflora
                                                humilis

III. Equatorial lacunae absent. Lophate pattern represented only by the poral and a few other more or less rudimentary lacunae or entirely absent. Texture fine-granular.

   A. Poral lacunae present.

      1. Paraporal lacunae 6, clearly defined, each separated from its neighbor of the opposite hemisphere by a well-defined equatorial crest; lacunar pattern 7.* Spines sharp conical.   Dendroseris pinnata

      2. Paraporal lacunae 12 but vestigial. spines reduced or vestigial. Lacunar pattern 8.*   Dendroseris micrantha

   B. Lacunae absent, except a poorly defined vestige of the poral or abporal or both.

      1. Furrow constricted once in the middle, suggesting that it represents the union of 2 paraporal lacunae, with lacunar pattern 5.*   Catananche caerulea

      2. Furrow constricted twice, on either side of the pore, suggesting that it represents the union of a poral and abporal lacunae, with lacunar pattern of 6.*   Catananche lutea

* See table of lacunar patterns (p. 472).

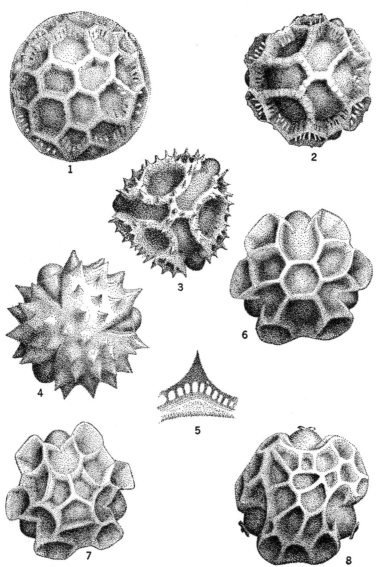

PLATE XII.—Pollen grains of Vernonieae, Astereae, and *Barnadesia*. 1, *Pacourina edulis*, 50 μ in diameter. 2, *Stokesia laevis*, polar view, 55 μ in diameter. 3, *Vernonia Wrightii*, polar view, 39.4 μ in diameter. 4, *Solidago speciosa*, polar view 23 μ in diameter. 5, Enlarged spine of the same as seen in optical section. 6, *Barnadesia trianae*, polar view, 50 μ in diameter. 7, *B. venosa*, polar view, 67.5 μ in diameter. 8, *B. berberoides*, polar view, 52 μ in diameter.

TABLE V.—LACUNAR PATTERNS

Lacunae	1. Taraxacum	1a. Sonchus oleraceus	2. Scolymus hispanicus	3. Tragopogon pratensis	4. Scorzonera hispanica	4a. Scorzonera purpurea	4b. Scorzonera parviflora	5. Catananche caerulea	6. Catananche lutea	7. Dendroseris pinnata	8. Dendroseris micrantha	9. Vernonia jucunda	10. Vernonia Wrightii	11. Barnadesia trianae	12. Barnadesia venosa	13. Berkheya heterophylla
Poral	3	4	3	0	0	0	0	0	3	3	3	3	3	3	3	3
Equatorial	0	0	0	3	6	6	6	0	0	0	0	3	3	3	3	6
Paraporal	6	8	6	0	0	0	0	0	0	6	12	12	12	12	12	4
Abporal*	6o	8o	6c	6o	6o	6o	6o	6o	6o	6o	6o	6c	6o	6o	6o	6o
Interporal	0	0	0	6	6	6	Faint	0	0	0	0	6	6	6	6	4
Polar	0	0	0	0	2	0	0	0	0	0	0	2	0	2	6	6
Total	15	20	15	15	20	18	12	6	9	15	21	32	30	32	36	29

* o, open; c, closed, in reference to the presence or absence of interlacunar gaps opening into the poral lacunae or abporal lacunae of the opposite hemisphere.

Taraxacum officinale Weber (*T. Taraxacum* Karst., *T. Dens-leonis* Desf. *Leontodon Taraxacum* L.) Dandelion (Plate XI, Fig. 2) type (see page 457). Grains extremely various; about one-half of them abnormal, *i.e.*, asymmetrical or deviating in various ways from the basic form of the family. Normal grains 24 to 27.5 μ in diameter, with ridges about 4.6 μ high and spines 2.3 μ long. Polar thickenings various in extent, hexagonal, triangular, or tending to be triradiate. Texture distinctly granular, and crests marked with conspicuous vertical striae.

Among the atypical grains are found many that are tetracolpate and hexacolpate. Most of these are extremely irregular and entirely asymmetrical, though some are strictly tetraradiate. This latter form has already been discussed at some length (see page 466).

The dandelion is a common weed of almost universal distribution. It is said to have lost its sexuality, its embryos developing by apogamy (Strasburger, 1908, pages 93, 518). Indeed, the appearance of most of its pollen grains suggests that they are incapable of effecting fertilization.

The genus consists of 20 or 25 species of low perennial or biennial herbs with radical pinnatifid or runcinate leaves; native of Europe, but some species widely distributed elsewhere.

Hypochaeris radicata L. Cat's-ear. Grains uniform, oblately spheroidal, 19.4 to 20.5 μ in diameter, as in *Taraxacum* type. Polar thickenings large; texture fine-granular, vertical striae of the crests faint; spines short but sharp, irregularly arranged over the greater part of the polar thickenings but serried along their margins.

A low herb with basal leaves and slightly branching scapes bearing a few small heads of yellow flowers. Introduced in fields and waste places in eastern North America. The genus contains about 40 or 50 species, native of Europe, the Mediterranean region, northern Asia, and South America.

Sonchus oleraceus L. Common or Annual sow thistle. Grains oblately spheroidal, 26.2 to 28.5 μ in diameter, ridges about 2.3 μ high, spines 2.3 μ long.

As in the case of dandelion pollen, both triradiate and tetra-radiate forms are found, the latter constituting about 90 per cent. Both forms are essentially the same as the corresponding forms of the dandelion pollen, except that in the tetraradiate form of

Sonchus the polar thickenings are more or less broken by small, asymmetrically arranged lacunae. The grains of *Sonchus* appear always to form in tetrahedral tetrads; therefore the explanation of the tetramerous forms is not the same as in the case of *Taraxacum* and deserves investigation.

A common weed with leafy stems, bearing small heads of pale-yellow flowers in summer; widely distributed in waste places. Native of Europe.

The genus includes about 45 species of herbs, native of the Old World.

CREPIS L. Hawk's-beard

Grains essentially as in the *Cichorium* type but generally smaller and with the polar thickenings larger in proportion. The pollen of some species is characterized by great lack of uniformity, often presenting many atypical grains. There is generally much variation in the character of the polar thickenings among the different species or even among the different grains of the same species; sometimes the polar thickening is only a small, triradiate expansion of the three convergent ridges at the poles, and sometimes it is as extensive as in the grains of *Taraxacum*. When large it is generally broken and occupied by one or more rudimentary and asymmetrically placed lacunae. The texture of the ridges is only faintly striate; that of the polar thickenings, faintly granular.

The genus comprises about 170 species of small or occasionally large herbs, with yellow or sometimes red flowers. Mostly of the Northern Hemisphere in the Old World, also in North America, tropical Africa, and one species in the Andes of Bolivia.

Crepis biennis L. (*Hedypnois biennis* Huds.) Rough hawk's-beard. Grains various in size and form, the majority abnormal. Normal grains oblately spheroidal, 20 to 27.5 μ in diameter, with ridges 3.5 μ high and spines 2.3 μ long. . Polar thickenings large, as in the *Taraxacum* type, but generally broken, provided with one or more rudimentary lacunae. Otherwise as in the *Cichorium* type.

A large proportion of the grains are tetracolpate, but these are not tetraradiate; they are, instead, variously irregular.

A low biennial herb, native of Europe but introduced into California.

Crepis japonica Benth. Grains somewhat various, a small proportion of them exhibiting irregularities of pattern. Normal grains about 18.2 μ in diameter, with ridges 3.4 μ high and spines 1.7 μ long. Otherwise as in the *Cichorium* type.

Tropical Asia and Australia.

Crepis taraxacifolia Thuill. (*C. praecox* Balb. *Barkhausia taraxacifolia* DC.). Grains uniform, 19.8 to 22 μ in diameter, ridges 2.3 μ high, spines 2.3 μ long. Polar thickenings more extensive than in the *Cichorium* type but less so than in that of *Taraxacum*.

This species is regarded by Hegi (1929) as a subspecies of *C. vesicaria*.

Europe.

Crepis tectorum L. (*Hieracium tectorum* Karsch.) Narrow-leaved or smooth hawk's-beard. Grains uniform in size and pattern, 19.4 to 20.5 μ in diameter; ridges 2.3 μ high; spines 2.3 μ long; paraporal lacunae generally provided with a small group of detached spines; texture scarcely granular, and ridges only faintly striate. Otherwise as in the *Cichorium* type.

A slender herb about 1 ft. high and branching from the base. In fields and waste places, naturalized in America from Europe.

Crepis capillaris (L.) Wallr. (*C. virens* L. *Lampsana capillaris* L.) Smooth hawk's-beard. Grains uniform, 19.4 to 20.5 μ in diameter, ridges 2.3 μ high, spines 1.7 μ long. Pattern of the ridges and lacunae as in the *Cichorium* type, except that the polar thickenings are larger, in some cases even larger than in the grains of *Taraxacum*.

A low herb 1 to 3 ft. high. Almost throughout Europe and in the Canary Islands. Introduced into California. It occurs in many different forms, some of which have received specific names.

HIERACIUM L. HAWKWEED

Grains indistinguishable from those of *Crepis*, 17 to 35 μ in diameter; ridges about 2.3 μ high, faintly or not at all striate on their sides or granular on their tops.

The grains of some species exhibit irregularities which are so extreme as to baffle analysis and make it impossible to relate them to any type form. Most of such grains are obviously abortive or otherwise defective.

Hispid or hirsute and often glandular perennial herbs, with single or panicled heads of showy, generally yellow flowers in summer and early autumn.

Hieracium auricula L.   Grains uniform, about 17 μ in diameter, ridges 2.3 μ high, and spines 2.3 μ long.   As in the *Cichorium* type but with the polar thickenings somewhat more extensive.

Small herbs with slender scapes bearing a few heads of yellow flowers throughout the summer.   Native of Europe.

Hieracium venosum L. Rattlesnake weed.   Grains uniform, about 22.1 μ in diameter, ridges 2.3 μ high, and spines 2.8 μ long, which is unusually long for grains of this genus.   Otherwise as in the *Cichorium* type.

Herbs with stem 1 to 2 ft. high arising from a basal rosette of purple-veined leaves.   Dry plains and woods, eastern United States and Canada.

Hieracium pratensis Tausch. Field hawkweed.   Grains various, many of them abnormal and obviously abortive.   Normal grains 19.4 to 20.5 μ in diameter, essentially as in the *Cichorium* type, except that the polar thickenings are more extensive, and the germ pores elliptical—elongate in the equatorial direction, an unusual condition in the family.

Many grains are tetracolpate, and some of these are strictly tetraradiate, as in the pollen of *Taraxacum*.

A low herb of Europe and northern Asia.

Hieracium aurantiacum L. Orange or Golden mouse-ear, Devil's-paintbrush, Tawny hawkweed.   Grains extremely various and irregular, more than half of them tetracolpate but not tetraradiate.   Normal grains about 22.5 μ in diameter, ridges 1.7 μ high, and spines 2.8 μ long.

The pattern of these grains is so much distorted that it is impossible to relate it to any type.   There is a marked tendency for the lacunae to become obliterated, the grain approaching the form of *Catananche*.   Such grains, however, are apparently always defective.

The plant is a low, hispid or hirsute herb, with deep orange-to flame-colored heads of flowers, borne in panicles or singly, on leafy scapes arising from a rosette of basal leaves.   A common weed of fields and roadsides.

New England to New York.   Naturalized from Europe.

Hieracium umbellatum L.   Grains extremely various, apparently all or nearly all defective, exactly as in *H. aurantiacum*.

A low herb with slender, leafy scape, 6 to 12 in. high, with one or a few large, showy heads of yellow flowers.

Throughout Europe, parts of Asia, Japan, and North America.

Nabalus altissimus (L.) Hook. (*Prenanthes altissima* L.) Rattlesnake root. Grains uniform, about 22 μ in diameter, ridges about 3.4 μ high and spines 3.4 μ long. Texture distinctly and rather coarsely granular, and ridges conspicuously striate. Pattern essentially as in the *Taraxacum* type, but ridges a little narrower; polar thickenings of various extent but generally rather large. Germinal lacunae rounded hexagonal, usually isodiametric, or occasionally elongate in the equatorial direction.

Tall, perennial herbs, with a slender, leafy stem rising to a height of 3 or 7 ft. and bearing numerous small heads of greenish or purplish flowers, in late summer.

Rich woods, New England to Minnesota and northward.

The genus comprises about 26 species, mostly of Europe, the Canary Islands, and Japan.

Haenselera granatensis Boiss. Grains uniform, spheroidal or somewhat oblately flattened, 28 to 35 μ in diameter, with ridges about 4 μ high and spines 3.4 μ long; pattern nearly always symmetrical, similar to the *Taraxacum* type, except that the polar thickenings are represented only by the unexpanded confluence of three crests at the poles, as in the grains of the *Scolymus* type (Plate XI, Fig. 1). The poral lacunae are elliptical, lengthened in a meridional direction, and each closely surrounds its bulging germ pore, which is large and has apparently entirely taken over the harmomegathic function. Interlacunar gaps are present but generally small and inconspicuous. The ridges are faintly striate and granular both on their tops and on their sides.

This grain is distinguished from that of *Tragopogon* by the presence of equatorial crests instead of lacunae, from those of *Scolymus* by the presence of interlacunar gaps and its heavier ridges, from those of *Taraxacum* and the species associated with it in the key by the lack of polar areas, and from those of *Krigia* and genera associated with it by its much larger size.

Perennial herb with a smooth, leafy scape, bearing a single head of yellow flowers. Regarded by Boissier as closely related to *Scolymus*.

The only species of the genus rather rare in southern Spain.

Krigia virginica (L.) Willd. Carolina dwarf dandelion.   Grains uniform 22.5 to 25.5 μ in diameter, ridges 4.0 μ high, spines 1.7 μ long.   Essentially as in *Haenselera,* excepting their smaller size and shorter spines, differing from the *Taraxacum* type in the lack of development of the polar thickenings, in which respect they resemble those of *Scolymus.*

Small herbs with lyrate leaves resembling those of the common dandelion.   Flowers yellow in small heads.   April to August. New England to Minnesota and southward.

Cynthia virginica (L.) D. Don (*Krigia amplexicaulis* Nutt.) Cynthia, Virginia goatsbeard.   Grains uniform, about 25.1 μ in diameter; ridges faintly striate, about 2.8 μ high, spines 1.7 μ long; in pattern indistinguishable from those of *Krigia*, sharing with them the unusually short spines.

Plants similar to *Krigia*, generally growing on moist banks, common.   Minnesota and southward, bearing small heads of yellow flowers.

Lactuca virosa L. (*L. scariola* L.) Prickly lettuce.   Grains uniform, 24 to 25 μ in diameter, ridges 3.5 μ high, spines 2.3 μ long; in pattern, etc., indistinguishable from those of *Krigia.*

A common weed with prickly leaves, generally vertically oriented, waste grounds and roadsides; flowers purplish in small heads, appearing in summer.   Introduced from Europe but now widely distributed throughout North America.

The genus contains about 100 species, mostly native of the Old World, and a few in North America and the West Indies.

Cichorium Intybus L. Chicory, Succory (Plate XI, Fig. 6) type.   Grains extremely various, many of them giants, tetra- and hexacolpate and sometimes tetraradiate.   These are of the utmost interest in throwing light on the origin of symmetry patterns of the Compositae and other groups (Wodehouse, 1929).   Normal grains are three pored and with a triradiate pattern, oblately spheroidal in form, about 40 μ in diameter, provided with vertical ridges about 5.7 μ high, conspicuously striate, and topped with conical, sharp spines about 2.3 μ long. The pattern is similar to that of the *Taraxacum* type, which has been fully described (page 457).   The poral lacunae are circular or hexagonal, each closely surrounding its large, bulging germ pore and communicating with the adjacent abporal lacunae through generally narrow interlacunar gaps. The three lacunae so joined form a germinal furrow which possesses partial harmomegathic function. The equatorial crests extend in a straight, unbroken line from poral lacuna to poral lacuna around the equator of the grain, occasionally giving off a short projection into one or more of the large, pentagonal, interporal lacunae. The three ridges which converge toward the poles are expanded at their confluence into a polar thickening which is triradiate and not triangular or hexagonal in shape, as in the *Taraxacum* type.

Chicory is a common weed with heads of delicate blue flowers appearing in summer. Introduced from Europe, it is now widely distributed in fields and along roadsides throughout most of the eastern half of the United States and Canada. Several varieties are cultivated and are of considerable culinary value.

SCOLYMUS L. GOLDEN THISTLE

Grains uniform, oblate-spheroidal, about 35 μ in diameter, with the pattern well developed, sharply defined, and beautifully symmetrical (Plate XI, Fig. 1). It consists of 15 lacunae separated by high uniform ridges which are conspicuously marked by vertical striae and topped with a row of conical sharp spines. Their pattern conforms, in general, with the basic pattern form of the tribe but is distinctive in its possession of closed poral lacunae (Fig. 107). These are hexagonal, isodiametric, or elongate in a meridional direction but do not communicate with the abporal lacunae through interlacunar gaps, as the poral lacunae do in the grains of most other members of the tribe. The paraporal lacunae are large and pentagonal, and the equatorial ridges which separate those of opposite hemispheres from each other generally give off into each a short projection bearing two or three spines. The abporal lacunae are elongate-pentagonal, their apexes converging toward the poles but separated from each other at the poles by a triradiate crest which is not expanded to form a polar thickening. The closed poral lacunae, together with the absence of polar thickenings, serves to distinguish the grains of *Scolymus* from those of all other members of the tribe so far examined.

The genus comprises three or four species of perennial herbs, native of the Mediterranean region.

Scolymus hispanicus L. Spanish oyster plant, Salsify (Plate XI, Fig. 1) type.   Grains about 34.2 μ in diameter.   Ridges 4 to 4.6 μ high, topped with spines of varying length, about 3.4 μ long. Germ pores large, about 11 μ in diameter, each tightly filling its hexagonal poral lacuna.

The poral lacunae are nearly isodiametric and are apparently too short to permit harmomegathy, this function being entirely taken over by the large, bulging germ pores.   The polar areas are generally occupied by the unexpanded confluences of three convergent ridges, but occasionally the confluence is spread apart to admit a polar lacuna at one or both poles.   This condition, however, is generally accompanied by various other irregularities and often asymmetry of pattern.

A biennial herb about 2 ft. high, with spiny, thistle-like leaves and a few heads of golden-yellow flowers.   Native of southern Europe, it is cultivated for its edible root which is similar to that of the true salsify (*Tragopogon porrifolius*).

Scolymus grandiflorus Desf.   Grains uniform, similar to the type but with ridges a little thinner, 3.4 to 4.6 μ high, topped with spines, 2.3 to 3.4 μ long.   The poral lacunae are always elongate in a meridional direction and appear to exercise some harmomegathy, for the pores are considerably smaller than those of the type.   The pattern is much less uniform and frequently exhibits a pentagonal or irregularly shaped lacuna at one or both poles, introducing various irregularities.

These grains may always be distinguished from those of the type by the lighter construction of their ridges and their elongate poral lacunae.   The grains of this species have been described and illustrated by Fritzsche (1837).

A perennial herb, occasionally cultivated for the beauty of its golden-yellow flowers.

TRAGOPOGON L. Goatsbeard

Grains generally symmetrical and uniform, spheroidal or somewhat oblately flattened, 28 to 38 μ in diameter; ridges rather broad, coarsely granular on top, conspicuously marked with vertical striae and topped with slender, conical, sharp-pointed spines (Plate XI, Fig. 4).

The lacunar pattern of these grains is unique, quite different from that of the grains of any other member of the family.   The ridges anastomose in such a way as to form 15 symmetrically arranged lacunae, some of which correspond to those of the grain of *Taraxacum*, and others of which do not. There are always three pores equatorially arranged but smaller than in the *Taraxacum* type and not enclosed in lacunae (Fig. 108); poral lacunae in these grains are entirely absent. The abporal lacunae are hexagonal in shape, and each communicates with its meridionally adjacent neighbor of the opposite hemisphere through a broad gap in which the germ pore is situated. The two lacunae, so connected, obviously serve as a germinal furrow possessing harmomegathy; and this is reflected in the small size of the pore, since it is not called upon to accommodate changes in volume. The equatorial crest is absent, unless two short bosses abutting against each pore on the equator be regarded as vestiges of it. The three areas on the equator between the pores are occupied by as many six-sided equatorial lacunae; and it is obviously the presence of these broad spaces, in place of the usual equatorial ridge, which permits the free expansion of the furrows. Alternating with the abporal lacunae in each hemisphere are three large, four-sided, interporal lacunae.

The lacunar pattern of this grain therefore includes six tetragonal and nine hexagonal faces. Relating this to polyhedrons, we find that no pentakaidecahedron with such a combination of faces can exist (see page 199). If, however, the two polar areas be regarded as filled-in hexagonal lacunae, making 17 lacunae in all, the pattern corresponds to a heptakaidecahedron with 6 tetragonal and 11 hexagonal faces, which appears to be the proper interpretation of this pattern.

These grains may be distinguished from those of all other members of the family so far investigated by their lack of poral lacunae together with their possession of three equatorial lacunae and their much coarser granular texture. These two former characters stamp *Tragopogon* as genetically distinct. Their grains thus represent the culminating development of the lophate character in the tribe, equaled only in the grains of *Scorzonera*.

The grain of a species of *Tragopogon* has been described and illustrated by Fritzsche (1837), but he regards the polar thickenings as lacunae filled with spines and so describes the grain as having 17 instead of 15 lacunae.

The plants are stout, glabrous biennials or perennials with entire grass-like clasping leaves and large, solitary heads of yellow or purplish flowers. The genus contains 30 or 40 species, in the Mediterranean region and central Asia.

Tragopogon pratensis L. Goatsbeard (Plate XI, Fig. 4) type. Grains uniform, about 32 μ in diameter, with ridges about 3.2 μ high and spines 3.4 μ long. Otherwise as in the generic description.

A weed of fields and roadsides. New England to New Jersey and Minnesota. Introduced from Europe. Flowers yellow, summer.

Tragopogon minor Mill. Grains uniform, 28 to 34.5 μ in diameter. Otherwise as in the type.

Regarded by Hegi (1929) as a variety of *T. pratensis*. Native of Europe.

Tragopogon porrifolius L. Salsify, Oyster plant. Grains uniform, about 28.5 μ in diameter, ridges about 5.7 μ high, spines 3.5 μ long. Otherwise as in the type.

Plant similar to *T. pratensis;* cultivated for its edible taproot. Introduced into America from Europe and occasionally escaped. Flowers purple, summer.

Tragopogon orientalis L. Grains uniform, about 32 μ in diameter, ridges about 4 μ high, spines 2.9 μ long. Otherwise as in the type. Regarded by Hegi (1929) as a variety of *T. pratensis*.

Native of Europe and northern Asia.

SCORZONERA L. Viper's-grass

Grains 28 to 42 μ in diameter, extremely various in the different species, from fully echinolophate almost to simply echinate with the pattern represented only by the lacunae of the equatorial region, and then reduced in size. Poral lacunae absent. Abporal lacunae of opposite hemispheres joined to form a single hour-glass-shaped lacuna (functionally the germinal furrow with the germ pore at the center of the constriction. Equatorial lacunae 6, arranged in pairs tandem fashion with their apexes impinging on the pores.

The most elaborate form of grain of the genus is that of *S. hispanica* (Plate XI, Fig. 5). In this the ridges are high, of uniform width, topped by short, conical spines, and frequently they present the appearance of being perforated by a row of small holes between the bases of the spines. The floors of the lacunae are covered with a thin layer of exine which exhibits a fine but distinctly granular texture. The pattern formed by the ridges is quite unique, as far as I am aware, not duplicated elsewhere in the tribe. The ridges anastomose in such a way as to form 20 lacunae instead of the usual 15 (Fig. 116). The poral lacunae are entirely absent. The abporal lacunae are hexagonal in shape, but the sixth side is missing because each communicates with its neighbor of the opposite hemisphere through a gap which replaces the sixth side. In this gap the germ pore is situated, recalling the condition in the grains of *Tragopogon* which they resemble, except that in the grains of *S. hispanica* the gaps are wider and without the projecting bosses. The two lacunae thus joined form an hourglass-shaped germinal furrow which is evidently effective in accommodating changes in volume because the pores are too small to serve this purpose. The polar area is occupied by a large, six-sided polar lacuna of which the three sides facing the pores are short and the three facing between the pores are long. The paraporal lacunae are absent; but between each pair of pores on the equator are two pentagonal equatorial lacunae arranged tandem fashion (Fig. 115), base to base, with their separating ridge crossing the equator in a meridional direction midway between the pores and forming a trans-equatorial ridge, and with their apexes rounded and impinging upon the pores. In each polar hemisphere are three large, interporal lacunae (Plate XI, Fig. 5), so called because they alternate with the abporal lacunae. Each is pentagonal, with its base on a long side of the polar lacuna, two of its sides against the abporal lacunae, two against the equatorial lacunae, and its vertex impinging upon the end of a transequatorial ridge. The complement of lacunae of these grains therefore consists of 2 polar, 6 abporal, 6 interporal, and 6 equatorial, giving a total of 20 lacunae, corresponding to the 20 faces of an eikosahedron with 12 pentagonal and 8 hexagonal faces. They lack the polar thickings, paraporal lacunae, and equatorial crests, elements that occur in the patterns of the grains of most Cichorieae.

In the other species of this genus the polar lacunae are absent, their places being occupied by polar thickenings similar to those of the grains of *Taraxacum* (Plate XI, Fig. 2) but enormously variable in extent. In fact, the main differences between the grains of the species of *Scorzonera* are due to the differences in extent of the polar thickenings. In some they are quite small, in which case the rest of the pattern is essentially the same as in the grains of *S. hispanica;* in others the polar areas are so extended that only vague fragments of the lacunae are represented in the region of the equator. But always the pattern about the pores is essentially the same, consisting of an hourglass-shaped furrow with the pore at its constriction and six equatorial lacunae. These serve to distinguish the grains of *Scorzonera* from those of all other genera, though the forms in which the extension of the polar thickening is excessive otherwise bear a strong resemblance to those of *Catananche lutea.*

The genus comprises about 100 species of large or small herbs, native of Europe, the Mediterranean region, and Central Asia.

Scorzonera hispanica L. Black salsify, Viper's-grass (Plate XI, Fig. 5) type. Grains somewhat various in size, 32 to 42 μ in diameter, but uniform in pattern. Ridges narrow, of uniform width, about 5.1 μ high, topped by short, conical spines about 2.8 μ long.

The ridges are conspicuously striate and present the appearance of bearing perforations between the roots of the spines, lacunar pattern 4 (Table V). This form is selected as the type of the genus and fully discussed above.

A branching perennial herb with yellow flowers borne on long peduncles, and a black-skinned edible fleshy root, for which it is cultivated, like that of the true salsify, *Tragopogon porrifolius.* Native of Central and Southern Europe; cultivated in America and occasionally escaped. Said to be closely allied to salsify.

Scorzonera graminifolia L. Grains oblately flattened, about 36 μ in diameter, with ridges about 4.6 μ high and spines 4 μ long. Essentially as in the type, except that the polar lacunae are absent, replaced by large polar thickenings, Lacunar pattern 4*a* (Table V) and not quite so sharply defined as in the type. Native of Siberia.

Scorzonera purpurea L. Grains uniform, oblately spheroidal, about 37 μ in diameter, with ridges about 4 μ high and spines about 3 μ long. Similar to the type, except that the polar areas are occupied by thickenings instead of lacunae. Lacunar pattern 4*a* (Table V).

The plant is a low herb with a leafy scape bearing one or a few large heads of showy purple flowers. Native of Europe and northern Asia.

Scorzonera nervosa. Trev. (*S. latifolia* DC.). Grains uniform, about 28.5 μ in diameter, with ridges about 5.7 μ high and spines 3.5 μ long. Similar to the type but with polar thickenings instead of lacunae, and these are so extensive as to occupy the greater part of the surface of the grain. Nevertheless, all of the lacunae except the polar are represented, though small and poorly defined. The lacunar pattern is expressed by 4a (Table V).

Native of Persia.

Scorzonera parviflora Jacq. (*S. caricifolia* Pall.). Grains oblately spheroidal, about 28 to 32 μ in diameter, with ridges about 3.4 μ high and spines 2.3 to 3.2 μ long. The polar thickenings are excessively extended, encroaching upon the rest of the grain to such an extent that almost its whole surface is evenly echinate, except the three furrows. These are hourglass-shaped, clearly representing the two abporal lacunae intercommunicating through a broad gap in which the pore is situated, as in the type. The equatorial lacunae are small and triangular in shape, separated from each other by a broad area of thickened exine which represents the greatly expanded transequatorial crest. The pores are larger than in the type, probably on account of the partial demobilization of this furrow—owing to its shortness and the stiffening effect of its well-developed paraporal ridges. The assemblage of lacunae around the pores, however, clearly indicates the relationship of this form of grain to the type. It is numerically expressed by the lacunar pattern 4b (Table V).

Native of Europe and northern and western Asia.

Scorzonera humilis Jacq. Grains uniform, approximately spheroidal, about 36.5 μ in diameter; almost the entire surface covered with sharp, conical spines about 4.6 μ long; texture granular.

These grains have been described by Fischer (1890) as "ringsum stachlig, wie *Catananche.*" In spite of the extreme reduction of their pattern they resemble the type of the genus in the hourglass shape of the furrow and the presence of equatorial lacunae, though the latter are small and poorly defined. Their lacunar pattern is numerically expressed by No. 4b (Table V).

The plant is a low herb with heads of yellow flowers borne singly on slender scapes rising from a cluster of basal linear leaves. Native of Europe.

CATANANCHE L.

Grains oblately spheroidal, rather uniform in size, 27 to 31 μ in diameter. The surface is without the pattern characteristic of the family; instead its rather thick exine is covered with short, conical, sharp spines. The only characteristics which hint at any connection of these grains with the rest of the Cichorieae are an irregular and clumped distribution of the spines, with small, irregular, blank spaces between them which suggest rudimentary lacunae and the constrictions of the furrows which suggest that they are composed of two or three fused lacunae.

The genus contains five species of low herbs, native of the Mediterranean region.

Catananche caerulea L. Blue succory (Plate XI, Fig. 3) type. Grains oblate-spheroidal, tricolpate or tetracolpate, 27.4 to 28.4 μ in diameter. Spines about 4.5 μ long. Furrows various but generally short, hourglass-shaped with a single constriction opposite the pore (Fig. 13). Lacunar pattern 5 (Table V).

In the tetracolpate grains the furrows are longer than in the tricolpate grains, equatorially arranged and converging in pairs alternately above and below the equator, in the ordinary hexacolpate configuration. Frequently they are fused at some or all of their points of convergence, and so traverse a broken or continuous zigzag course around the grain.

The plant is a perennial garden herb, cultivated for the beauty of its blue flowers, which it displays throughout most of the summer. Native of the Mediterranean region.

Catananche lutea L. f. Grains similar to the type, uniform and all tricolpate, about 30.8 μ in diameter; texture granular. Furrows longer and narrower than in the type and exhibiting two constrictions which vaguely suggest their derivation from the fusion of three lacunae (Fig. 114). This rudimentary pattern is numerically expressed by 6 (Table V).

DENDROSERIS D. Don

The grains of the two species here described are so far distinct that they are treated separately, under their species headings.

The plants are known only from the island of Juan Fernández. According to Bertero (Decaisne, 1835), who originally described these plants under the name of *Rea*, all of the species are small trees 10 to 20 ft. high, with the trunk or branches terminated with leaf clusters from the center of which arise large panicles of strange and exotic-looking flowers. The bark is smooth and green, and the flowers are snowy white, recalling in shape certain species of *Prenanthes*. Bertero describes the pollen as "pollen globosum, echinulatum," but in spite of its aberrant character, he regards the genus as most closely affiliated with *Sonchus*.

Bentham (1873) regards the genus as divergent from the rest of the tribe but associated with another arborescent genus, *Fitchia*. He says, "Both are truly Cichoriaceous in their corollas, anthers and styles, and *Dendroseris*, at least, in the milky juice of its bark; but their achenes are different from those of the Cichoriaceae generally, as well as their involucre and habit; and *Fitchia* in its receptacular paleae, awned achenes etc., recalls the Helianthoideae." I have examined the pollen grains of *Fitchia* and find that their form virtually excludes the possibility of the plants' belonging to the Cichorieae but conforms rather well to the pollen-grain form of the Heliantheae. I have therefore excluded *Fitchia* from this discussion of the Cichorieae.

Dendroseris micrantha Hook. & Arn. (*Rea micrantha* Bert.) type. Grains oblate-spheroidal, about 25 μ in diameter, generally tricolpate, but a small proportion tetracolpate. Lacunar pattern 5 (Table V), but greatly reduced by the excessive encroachment of the polar thickenings upon it. Poral lacunae present, communicating through interlacunar gaps with the small meridionally adjacent abporal lacunae (Fig. 112), the three lacunae so joined forming a short furrow. Paraporal lacunae small and poorly defined or, occasionally, absent. Spines mostly reduced or vestigial. Texture coarsely granular.

Altogether this form of grain is so far aberrant from the basic form of the tribe that, were it not for the peculiar form of its germinal furrow, consisting of three lacunae joined together, it would be difficult to recognize it as belonging to the Cichorieae.

An excessively branched tree, with leaves large and entire, somewhat alternate, though mostly collected at the ends of the branches. Flowers white, borne in small heads in large panicles. In cool and shady woods in mountains. Flowers in May.

Dendroseris pinnata Hook. & Arn. (*Rea pinnata* Bert.). Grains spheroidal or somewhat oblately flattened, uniform, about 27.5 μ in diameter. Lacunar pattern greatly reduced by the encroachment of the polar thickenings. Polar lacunae present, communicating through broad interlacunar gaps with the adjoining abporal lacunae forming a medium-sized furrow. Paraporal lacunae present, three in each hemisphere, each separated from its corresponding member of the opposite hemisphere by the well-developed equatorial crest which reaches from poral lacuna to poral lacuna around the equator. Spines conical and sharp, about 4.6 μ long. Texture minutely and faintly granular. The grains resemble the type (*D. micrantha*) only in the great extent of the polar thickenings which occupy the greater part of its surface. They differ from the type in the greater length and conical shape of their spines, their 6 instead of 12 paraporal lacunae, and their continuous equatorial crest reaching from pore to pore. These differences are such as to suggest that the two plants may be genetically unrelated.

A tree 10 to 15 ft. or more high, with pinnate leaves 1 ft. or more long, the pinnae unequally bifurcate. Flowers snowy white, borne in small heads in large, branching panicles.

ASTEREAE Aster Tribe

The grains of the Astereae are spheroidal or slightly flattened (Plate XII, Fig. 4). In size they range from about 16.5 to about 32 μ in diameter. They are always provided with well-developed and characteristic spines which are uniform in size and present the appearance of uniformity of distribution over the surface. The spines are short, broad at the base, and nearly conical in shape (Plate XII, Fig. 5). Sometimes they are strictly conical to their apexes, and sometimes they taper slightly into a more or less acuminate tip. Though the shape of the spines is occasionally obviously different in the different species this variation is generally too slight and intangible to lend itself to analysis. The length of the spines and their distance apart are somewhat various in the different species, and there is evidence that measurements of the spine lengths and spine intervals may be used to distinguish some of the genera.

The arrangement of the spines in the grains of most species of Astereae appears to be highly uniform and regular, arranged in the isometric system, patterned after the arrangement assumed by spherical bodies of uniform size when crowded together, as for example, when shot are caused to pack closely together in a single layer on a plane surface. This arrangement may be described by saying that if any one of the shot is regarded as a center, it will be surrounded by six others, all in contact with it and with each other. In other words, the centers of the shots are all equidistant from each other along the sides of an equilateral hexagon and equidistant from that of the shot at the center of the hexagon. In the distribution of the spines over the surface of the grains such an arrangement appears to be followed as faithfully as possible, but, owing to certain mathematical considerations which are discussed elsewhere, a continuous, regular, hexagonal pattern is impossible on the surface of a sphere. Thus we always find interspersed among the hexagonal groupings a few that are pentagonal, and we find upon measuring the angles and intervals between the spines, even in the most regular-appearing hexagonal configurations, that the variations are surprisingly great, so we are forced to the conclusion that the regularity of this arrangement is more apparent than real. Nevertheless, the intervals between the spines and their spacial configurations are almost as uniform as is mathemetically possible over the surface of a sphere.

The texture of the grains of the Astereae is always granular; the roughening is rather faint between the spines, but surrounding their bases it is coarser and somewhat more sharply defined; this granular appearance, however, does not extend far up the shaft of the spine, which throughout most of its upper part is quite smooth and homogeneous in appearance. Viewed in optical section, the structures which appear as granules in surface view are seen as radial striae of darkly staining material in a lightly staining matrix (Plate XII, Fig. 5).

The pollen of many species of Astereae is characterized by excessive abnormalities. Besides the usual number of abortive grains there are frequently found many giants with supernumerary furrows and some dwarfs with fewer or no furrows at all. Such abnormalities are encountered from time to time in nearly all groups of Compositae and many other plant families. Their origin is generally due to an irregular distribution of chromosomes in the maturation divisions (Beer, 1907), as the result of hybridity

(Jeffrey, 1916) or from other causes. The problem of the origin of such forms is a subject deserving further study.

A comparison of the dwarf, normal, and giant grains shows that the length of the spines and their distance apart bear no relation to the size of the grain; the dwarfs do not, as a consequence of their small size, have spines reduced or packed any closer together, and the giants do not have giant spines, nor are they more widely separated. It is as though each grain had at its disposal a quantity of exine of a standardized pattern; and of this it appropriates enough to cover its surface, which is accomplished by a little stretching here and there to fit the curvature or a little compressing to fit awkward corners, but uses it without other modification, whether the grain be a dwarf with only a small surface or a giant with several times the normal surface area. The total number of spines on these grains therefore is a function of their surface area. Hence it is useless to count or estimate the total number of spines per grain. The number of spines per unit area, however, or spine frequency is a definite and useful character. The spine frequency, spine length, and various other characters of the exine are emphytic. The basic morphogenetic principle involved is that the size of the pattern elements and the size of the grains are not positively correlated.

Throughout the entire tribe there is little variation in the emphytic characters, which is in keeping with the close relationship believed to exist between all the species. The interrelationships of these species are so close that their differences do not come to visible expression in basic characters such as those of the structure of the pollen grains.

SOLIDAGO L. GOLDENROD

Grains generally uniform in size and shape, 17 to 26 μ in diameter, spheroidal or slightly oblately flattened; prevailingly tricolpate, occasionally some grains tetra- or hexacolpate. Furrows of medium length, their membranes smooth and germinal apertures well defined and circular. Exine rather thick, finely and faintly granular. Spines apparently uniform in size and arrangement, typical of the tribe, short-conical and sharp pointed, 2.5 to 3.4 μ long and 4.6 to 5.7 μ apart.

The pollen grains of the different species are essentially all alike; there are slight differences in the average size of the grains, and in the size and distance apart of their spines; also some species show a greater tendency than others to produce grains with supernumerary furrows. But apart from these relatively minor differences, there is no means of distinguishing the pollen grains of the different species from each other.

The genus comprises over 125 species, almost entirely North American in distribution, except for a few in South America and two or three in Europe. The plants are branching perennial herbs producing showy yellow (occasionally white) flowers during the latter part of summer. The flowers are insect pollinated, though somewhat imperfectly adapted to this mode of pollination. Most species shed only minute quantities of pollen. Nevertheless, there are several species, notable among which are *S. speciosa* and *S. sempervirens*, that produce much pollen, which certainly becomes at times atmospheric.

The question of whether or not goldenrod is a cause of hayfever has received much discussion in the past, and there are still adherents to both the affirmative and negative sides. In the minds of many hayfever sufferers the goldenrods are inseparably associated with their affliction. But this is largely due to a misconception rising out of the fact that goldenrods flower during the latter part of the summer, during a time which very nearly coincides with the third and most serious hayfever season of each summer. It may be said, however, that, in the main, the conception of causal relationship between the two is not well founded, observers having overlooked the various wind-pollinated species such as ragweed, false ragweed, and cocklebur, which are nearly always associated with the goldenrods and escape attention because, they lack attractive coloring. And it may be safely said that nearly all late-summer hayfever, particularly in the eastern United States, is due primarily to the ragweeds and their allies and not to goldenrods.

On the other hand, the goldenrods, in some regions, unquestionably play a contributing part in the production of late-summer hayfever. Practically all hayfever patients who respond to ragweed pollen by means of the skin test respond to goldenrod pollen to the same or only a slightly lesser extent. Hence it follows that, should such patients breathe goldenrod pollen in quantities comparable to that of ragweed, they would get comparable hayfever symptoms. Under certain conditions this is possible, *e.g.*, when the hayfever sufferer gathers goldenrod flowers or otherwise comes in close proximity to one of the several species which produce a sufficient quantity of pollen. Hayfever from close association with goldenrod is well known. For instance, a flower gatherer carelessly whisking a bunch of goldenrod in front of the face of a hayfever victim can easily precipitate a spasm of sneezing. It is such obvious connection as this between cause and effect that has led goldenrod to assume more than its share of the blame for producing hayfever.

Even without coming in actual contact with the goldenrod flowers, hayfever patients may at times breathe a certain amount of goldenrod pollen. In experiments with atmospheric pollen I have found that, in the city of Yonkers, during the ragweed season, among the numerous ragweed-pollen grains caught by the slides there are nearly always a few grains that can be identified with almost positive certainty as belonging to goldenrod. Their number is very variable. For the most part it is quite small, averaging from day to day under normal weather conditions about 1 or 2 per cent of the total pollen caught. But in dry, windy weather their number rises considerably, and toward the end of the season when the ragweed plants are on the wane, which is the time when *Solidago speciosa* is at its height, the number of goldenrod-pollen grains caught on the atmospheric pollen slides may outnumber those of the ragweeds; consequently, there can be no doubt that goldenrod is at times a factor in hayfever, paling, it is true, by comparison with the enormously more abundant and prolific members of the ragweed tribe.*

Solidago speciosa Nutt. Showy or Noble goldenrod (Plate XII, Fig. 4) type. Grains uniform in size except for a very few that are abortive and a small proportion of aberrant forms. About 22.8 μ in diameter. Spines about 2.8 μ long and 5.1 μ apart. Texture finely and rather faintly granular.

Among the aberrant forms of grains are found some micro grains, some dicolpate grains with furrows opposite, a few hexacolpate, and a few giants which, judging from the pentagonal configuration which their furrows assume, are 30-colpate, with their furrows arranged after the fashion of a pentagonal dodeca-

---

* For a further discussion of this matter see p. 143.

hedron, though it is virtually impossible to count the furrows of such complicated configurations.

The showy goldenrod is a tall, showy plant with straight, columnar inflorescence, one of the most beautiful of the eastern species; abundant in rich soil, Massachusetts to North Carolina to Tennessee to Arkansas to Minnesota. Insect pollinated but shedding much pollen which, under favorable conditions, becomes atmospheric. This species sheds many times more pollen than any of the other species mentioned below, except *S. sempervirens*, which, however, is much scarcer and confined to salt and brackish places. Both species will shed pollen freely when cut and placed in water. August to October.

Solidago sempervirens L. Seaside goldenrod. Grains rather various in size, with a large proportion abortive or in other ways abnormal. Normal grains spheroidal or slightly flattened, 20.5 to 22.8 μ in diameter. Spines about 3.1 μ long and 5.1 to 6.2 μ apart. Otherwise as in the type.

Among the abnormal grains which constitute rather a large proportion of the pollen of this species are a few micro grains, grains with 2, 4, 6, and 12 furrows arranged in the trischistoclasic system, and some grains showing various degrees of reduction of their spines. Besides these there are a large number of grains united in tetrahedral tetrads. These appear to be abortive and are without spines. Among such "tetrads" are a few containing a fifth very small grain. The presence of a fifth grain in some of the tetrads which have brought their development to a successful conclusion suggests that it may be the cause of the aberrant forms, introducing asymmetrical contacts in the tetrad. The presence of the fifth grain is probably traceable to an irregular distribution of chromosomes in the reduction division, a matter which suggests hybridity of origin and invites further cytological study.

The seaside goldenrod is a tall, erect plant with thick, fleshy leaves rather abundant along seashores and in tidal marshes, New Brunswick to Florida and Mexico, also in Bermuda. August to December. It is insect pollinated but sheds large quantities of pollen which can easily be collected by placing the plants in water and allowing them to shed on sheets of paper. In hayfever a minor factor of only local importance.

Solidago rugosa Mill. Tall, Hairy, Wrinkle-leaved or Pyramid goldenrod. Grains uniform, except a few that are abortive, spheroidal or slightly flattened, about 26.2 μ in diameter, with spines 2.3 μ long and 3.4 to 5.7 μ apart. Otherwise as in the type.

A tall, handsome plant, from 1 to 7 ft. high, usually in dry places in fields and roadsides. Newfoundland to Western Ontario to Texas to Florida. July to November. Sheds much less pollen than the two preceding species and is of slight importance in hayfever.

Solidago altissima L. (*S. procera* Ait., *S. canadensis scabra* T. & G.) Tall or high goldenrod. Grains essentially as in the type, uniform except for a small proportion of abortive or aberrant forms, slightly flattened, 17.1 to 20.5 μ in diameter, with spines 2.3 to 2.9 μ long and 4.0 to 5.1 μ apart. Besides the grains of normal form, there are a few dicolpate grains, with furrows opposite and united encircling the grain as a single furrow with two apertures.

A tall, handsome plant, 2 to 8 ft. high, common in dry soil, Maine to Ontario to Texas to Georgia. August to November, shedding relatively little pollen, of secondary importance in hayfever.

Solidago juncea Ait Early or sharp-toothed goldenrod. Grains uniform, only very few abortive and no aberrant grains are seen; spheroidal in shape or slightly flattened, 17 to 19.4 μ in diameter, with spines uniform, about 2.5 μ long and 4 μ apart. Otherwise as in the type.

Plants 1½ to 4 ft. high, common in dry soil in waste places and roadsides. New Brunswick to Hudson Bay to Saskatchewan to Missouri to North Carolina. June to November. Sheds relatively little pollen, but the plants occur in enormous numbers. Of secondary importance in hayfever.

Solidago latifolia L. (*S. flexicaulis* L.) Zigzag or broad-leaved goldenrod.

Grains uniform, except for a few abortive and a few that are tetracolpate; spheroidal or slightly flattened, about 20 μ in diameter, with spines uniformly 3.4 μ long and 4.6 to 6.8 apart. Otherwise as in the type.

A small plant 1 to 3 ft. high, in rich woods. Nova Scotia to Missouri to Tennessee. July to September. Sheds insignificant amounts of pollen. Not a factor in hayfever.

Solidago bicolor L. White or pale goldenrod, Silverrod.

Grains uniform, except a very few that are abortive, slightly flattened, 21.6 to 22.8 μ in diameter, with spines uniformly 3.4 μ long and 4.6 to 5.7 μ apart. Otherwise as in the type. A low plant ½ to 4 ft. high, in dry soil. Prince Edward Island to Ontario to Minnesota to Tennessee to Georgia. July to September. Sheds insignificant amounts of pollen. Not a factor in hayfever.

Callistephus chinensis Ness. China aster. Grains as in *Solidago speciosa* (q.v.). Uniform except for a few abortive and a few tetracolpate grains, slightly flattened oblately, 21.6 to 23.9 μ in diameter, with spines 2.3 to 3.4 μ long and 4.6 to 6.4 μ apart.

China aster is a common garden annual introduced from China and Japan; with ray corollas of almost all colors except yellow. Flowers in late summer and fall. Insect pollinated but shedding rather large amounts of pollen which may cause hayfever if the flowers are handled.

ASTER L. ASTER

Grains in no way distinguishable from those of *Solidago* (q.v.). A genus of about 250 species of herbs, mostly of North America.

Aster patens Ait. Late purple aster. Grains rather uniform in size, except for a few that are abortive; spheroidal or slightly flattened, 27.5 μ in diameter, with spines about 2.9 μ long and 4.6 μ apart, texture finely granular, particularly at the base of the spines. New York, Minnesota, Florida, Louisiana, and Texas. August to October.

Aster novae-angliae L. New England aster. Grains essentially as in the type, uniform except for a few that are abortive, about 21.6 μ in diameter, with spines 2.8 μ long and 5.7 μ apart.

Eastern United States, August to October. Not a factor in hayfever.

Erigeron strigosus Muhl. (*E. ramosus* (Walt.) B.S.P.) Daisy fleabane. Grains extremely various, and many abortive. Many giants with furrow numbers ranging up to 12, furrows very irregular, frequently not conforming to any pattern. Normal grains 18.2 μ in diameter, spines about 2 μ long and about 3.2 μ apart. The grains of this species are the most irregular yet encountered in the Astereae.

A common weed of waste places, almost throughout North America. Flowers from May to November. Not an important factor in hayfever but may produce symptoms upon contact.

ANTHEMIDEAE MAYWEED TRIBE

Grains 17 to 34.2 μ in diameter, normally tricolpate, but some species with varying proportions of their grains with other numbers of furrows arranged according to the trischistoclasic system. Furrows of medium length, broad and tapering to pointed ends, their membranes smooth, each provided with a conspicuous germ pore. Exine moderately to exceedingly thick, coarsely and conspicuously granular; in insect-pollinated members provided with broad, conical spines; in wind-pollinated members, with spines greatly reduced or entirely absent.

The most distinctive and constant character of the grains of the Anthemideae lies in the *coarse-granular nature of their exine.* In the echinate forms, in which the exine is always extremely thick, the granules are most conspicuous, but even in the non-echinate forms, in which the exine is much less thick, they are quite pronounced. In the echinate grains the exine, if observed in optical section, is seen to consist of two layers (Plate XIII, Figs. 1, 2). The inner is the thicker and appears to be built up of large, vertical prisms presenting the appearance of coarse, radial striae. Overlying this is the much thinner layer of more transparent material marked with very fine radial striae. In surface view the inner layer shows plainly through the outer, presenting the coarse-granular appearance consisting of large, irregularly shaped, deeply staining bodies embedded in a less deeply staining matrix. The overlying fine-granular layer can be seen in surface view only with difficulty, even under the most favorable conditions, on account of its transparency and the optically disturbing effect of the underlying layer. In the non-echinate grains, in which the exine is thinner, the same sort of granular texture prevails, but usually it is much finer, and in optical section the outer layer appears as only a thin, structureless line, while in surface view it does not show at all. Nevertheless, there is a certain similarity between the granular nature of the two types of grain, which, though elusive of description, becomes recognizable from experience and is the best diagnostic character of the grains of the tribe.

The furrows are generally long and sharply defined and, owing to the thick and semirigid nature of the exine, are required to function freely as harmomegathi. They are deep and in most cases give the grain a three-lobed appearance. The furrow membranes are always smooth, and the germ pores circular in outline, rather large, and bulging prominently when the grains are expanded.

The *spines*, when present, are broadly conical, sharp pointed, and generally large in proportion to the size of the grain. They range, among the insect-pollinated species, from 1.1 to 4.6 μ in length and from 1.6 to 11.4 μ in distance apart. They are uniform in length on any given grain but somewhat various in their distance apart. Nevertheless, there is a rough correlation between these two dimensions. Thus, in a general way, it may be said that the shorter the spines the more closely together they are placed. For example, in the grains of *Leucanthemum Leucanthemum*, in which the spines are 4.6 μ long, they are 8 to 10.2 μ apart; while in those of *Tanacetum gracile*, in which they are only about 1.1 μ long, they are 4.5 to 5.7 μ apart; in the grains of the wind-pollinated *Crossostephium insulare*, in which the spines are only vestigial—too small to be measured—they are only a little over 1 μ apart. These differences are quite apparent to the eye, even unaided by measurements. For example, if the grains are observed in optical section and polar view, in those of *Leucanthemum* only 3 or 4 spines are seen on each of the three lobes at its limb; in those of *T. gracile* about 6 are seen on each lobe; while in those of *Crossostephium* 15 or more tiny protuberances are seen on each lobe. This relation between the length of the spines and their distance apart is not a peculiar property of the grains of the Anthemideae but likewise exists in the grains of the Ambrosieae and the Cynarieae and appears to be universal among the Compositae. But owing to the wide normal variation in the distance apart of the spines, the numerical relation between this distance and their size could be expressed only after making many measurements and striking averages for many different species. Until this is done, all that can be said on this point is that the smaller the spines the closer together and more numerous they are.

The cause of the wide difference in the number and size encountered among the grains of the members of this genetically rather compact group is most certainly due to their different modes of pollination. We have seen in other plant families that anemophily tends to induce a thinning of the exine and a loss of its external decorations. So it is in this group. The different species of *Anthemis, Leucanthemum,* and *Chrysanthemum,* which are insect pollinated, have grains in which the spines are well developed and the exine thick; while those of *Artemisia, Crossostephium,* and *Picrothamnus,* which are wind pollinated, have grains in which the spines are vestigial or absent and the exine much less thick. On this basis the members of this tribe may be divided rather sharply into two groups—those which are echinate grained and insect pollinated and those which are nearly or quite smooth grained and wind pollinated.

The genetic gap between the two groups is wide. I have not been able to find any really intermediate forms; and there appear to be now in existence no nicely intergrading series of forms, like those in the Ambrosieae, between the fully echinate-grained and the nearly smooth-grained forms. Nevertheless, there is considerable variation both in the size of the spines among the grains of the echinate group and in the prominence of the spine vestiges in the nonechinate group. Perhaps the most extremely echinate form is typified by the grains of *Leucanthemum* and *Chrysanthemum,* in which the spines are about 4 µ long; and the least echinate by those of *Artemisia* and *Chamartemisia,* in which the spines are vestigial and generally too small to be seen with certainty or are even entirely absent.

Though there are no truly intermediate forms, it is interesting to note that among the echinate-grained group the grains with the smallest spines are found in the genus *Tanacetum, e.g., T. gracile* and *T. camphoratum;* and among the nonechinate-grained group those with the most prominent spine vestiges are found in the genera *Crossostephium, Sphaeromeria, Vesicarpa,* and *Chamartemisia.* In a way this is in keeping with the classification of Rydberg (1916), who places these four genera between *Tanacetum* and *Artemisia.* At the same time, however, the characters of these pollen grains suggest that these four genera are much closer to *Artemisia* than to *Tanacetum.*

That the echinate character is closely associated with the mode of pollination is attested by the fact that the echinate pollen is always produced in relatively small amounts and is heavily impregnated with lipoid substances which cause the grains to adhere together, effectively preventing them from being carried by air currents. A corollary to this is that they cannot be counted among the serious causes of hayfever, but there is no doubt that several of the species may, upon close contact, cause hayfever symptoms with some people. Though I have on several occasions found on atmospheric pollen slides echinate grains of Anthemideae, which were probably those of *Leucanthemum*, it seems unlikely that these never occur in sufficient abundance to cause hayfever. When they are caught on the slides they generally occur adhering in groups of three or four. On the other hand, the nonechinate-grained species produce large amounts of pollen which is light and borne long distances by the wind; and among these are counted some of the most important hayfever plants of the western United States, *e.g.*, the sagebrushes and mugworts. The pollen of these possesses relatively little surface oil—not enough to cause them to adhere to each other—and when they are caught on atmospheric pollen plates they occur separately and in large numbers.

Grains with supernumerary furrows and aberrant furrow patterns are strikingly abundant in the pollen of most of the species of this group. It cannot always be assumed, however, that the irregularities of furrow pattern which are here recorded are universal for the species, because these records are based on too few observations. Sometimes such irregularities may be only individual peculiarities. Nevertheless, in the one instance in which this question was put to the test, *viz.*, that of *Picrothamnus desertorum*, it was found that plants collected in widely separated localities yielded grains with exactly the same aberrant furrow arrangements, just as numerous and in the same proportions. As we have seen (page 182), such aberrant forms arise from differences in size of the daughter-cells of a pollen mother-cell, an irregularity which, in turn, is generally due to an irregular distribution of chromosomes at the reduction divisions; these aberrant furrow patterns therefore point to a lack of genetic stability among the species which exhibit them. That such a lack of stability exists among the Anthemideae in general is abundantly attested by the large number of forms, varieties, and minor variations recorded in the literature (*cf.* Hall and Clements, 1923). Particularly is this true of the genus *Artemisia*.

The measurements of the grains here recorded were all made with them fully expanded. In each case they are the maximum and minimum of some half-dozen or dozen normal grains taken at random, avoiding only the aberrant forms. Consequently, they do not generally represent the entire range of size of even the normal grains and make no attempt to include that of the aberrant forms. The measurements of the grains do not include the spines but do include the thickness of the exine to the base of the spines. When only one dimension is given it is always the equatorial diameter.

The classification followed is essentially that of Rydberg (1916). The distribution of the pollen-grain characters throughout the tribe is, for the most part, quite consistent with it, but there are a few instances where they are found to be decidedly at variance. Unfortunately, in such cases the pollen-grain characters are of more negative than positive value; though they occasionally point rather definitely to a lack of consistency in the classification, they seldom suggest a better arrangement. Consequently, I have had to content myself with pointing out the instances of disagreement between the pollen-grain characters and Rydberg's classification, retaining his arrangement virtually unmodified. It is to be hoped, however, that other investigators will be stimulated by the suggestions of the pollen-grain characters to reopen the question of the classification of the Anthemideae.

KEY TO THE SPECIES

I. Echinate, with spines conspicuous, broadly conical, but sharply pointed. Exine very thick and coarsely granular, heavily impregnated with oil.

A. Grains 22.5 to 34.2 μ in diameter; spines 2.3 to 4.6 μ long and 4.6 to 1.4 μ apart.

Achillea
Cota
Anthemis
Maruta
Leucanthemum
Chrysanthemum
Tanacetum (in part)

B. Grains 19 to 26.2 μ in diameter; spines 1.1 to 2.3 μ long and 4.6 to 9.1 μ apart.

Chamomilla
Tanacetum gracile
Tanacetum artemisioides

II. Nonechinate; spines vestigial or entirely
  absent. Exine not excessively thick.
  Grains 17.5 to 29.6 μ in diameter.
  Exine generally sharply and coarsely
  granular but less so than in I.
  A. Spine vestiges distinctly visible,
    approaching in some cases the
    condition described as subechinate. Crossostephium artemisioides
    Artemisia norvegica
  B. Spine vestiges minute but large
    enough to be seen with certainty. Sphaeromeria
    Crossostephium insulare
    Crossostephium foliosum
    Crossostephium californicum
    Vesicarpa potentilloides
    Picrothamnus desertorum
    Artemisia frigida
    Artemisia camporum
    Artemisia canadensis
    Artemisia pycnocephala
  C. Spine vestiges represented by only a
    vanishing trace or, in some grains,
    apparently absent. Artemisia Bigelovii
    Artemisia gnaphalodes
    Artemisia Absinthium
    Artemisia dracunculoides
  D. Spine vestiges generally entirely
    absent, though a trace of them
    may occasionally be seen in some
    grains. Artemisia heterophylla
    Artemisia filifolia
    Artemisia tridentata
    Chamartemisia compacta
    Artemisiastrum Palmeri.

Anthemis nobilis L. (*Chamomilla nobilis* Gord., *Matricaria nobilis* Baill.) White or low camomile. Grains essentially as in the *Tanacetum* type (page 504), uniform, 24 to 25 μ in diameter, spines about 3.4 μ long and 8 μ apart. Exine thick and coarsely granular.

A low herb with daisy-like flowers. Native of Europe but extensively cultivated elsewhere and occasionally escaped. Flowers June to August.

Maruta Cotula (L.) DC. (*Anthemis Cotula* L.) Mayweed, dog fennel, fetid or wild camomile. Grains essentially as in the type, indistinguishable from those of *Anthemis nobilis*.   22.5 to 25.5 μ in diameter, spines about 2.8 μ long and about 8 μ apart.

A common weed with strongly aromatic odor, similar to the preceding species but less showy. Native of Europe, now naturalized throughout North America. Flowers June to November.

CHAMOMILLA (Hall) Gilib. Camomile

Grains similar to the *Tanacetum* type (page 504), 19.4 to 22.8 μ in diameter.   Spines 1.7 to 2.3 μ long and 4.6 to 6.8 μ apart. These are the smallest grains yet found among the echinate-grained Anthemideae, except those of *Tanacetum gracile*.

The genus includes about 20 species of daisy-like perennial herbs, of wide distribution.

Chamomilla Chamomilla (L.) Rydb. (*Matricaria Chamomilla* L.) Wild camomile.   Grains as in the generic description, except that a large proportion of them are giants with 4, 6, or 12 furrows, always arranged in the trischistoclasic system.   Normal grains 19.4 to 20.5 μ in diameter, with spines 2.3 μ long.

Native of Europe. Sometimes cultivated and in America extensively naturalized.   Flowers in Summer.

Chamomilla occidentalis (Greene) Rydb. (*Matricaria occidentalis* Greene).   As in the generic description, 19.5 to 22.8 μ in diameter, spines 1.7 μ long and 4.6 to 8 μ apart.

Middle California to southern Oregon.

Chamomilla suaveolens (Pursh.) Rydb. (*C discoidea* J. Gay, *Matricaria discoidea* DC., *M. matricarioides* (Less.) Porter) Rayless camomile or wild marigold.   Grains uniform, as in the generic description, about 20.5 μ in diameter, with spines 2.3 μ long and 5.7 to 6.8 μ apart.

Pacific coast and eastward to Arizona.   Also occasionally naturalized in the eastern United States and in Europe.   May to August.

Leucanthemum Leucanthemum (L.) Rydb. (*Chrysanthemum Leucanthemum* L.) Oxeye daisy.   Grains as in the type, uniform, about 24 to 28.5 μ in diameter, spines 4.6 μ long and 8 to 10.2 μ apart.

A common weed, native of Europe but naturalized almost throughout North America and elsewhere.   May to November. The daisy is entirely insect pollinated, but its pollen is recognized as an occasional cause of hayfever symptoms upon direct contact. It is also occasionally caught on atmospheric-pollen slides.

Leucanthemum arcticum (L.) DC. (*Chrysanthemum arcticum* L.) Arctic daisy. Grains indistinguishable from those of *L. Leucanthemum.*

Similar to the preceding species but somewhat smaller. Coast of Hudson Bay to Alaska, also in arctic Europe.

CHRYSANTHEMUM L.

Grains essentially as in the type, *Tanacetum.* In most of the species here recorded, however, they are somewhat various, and many of them abnormal. Normal grains 24.2 to 34.2 μ in diameter, spines 2.3 to 4.6 μ long and 5.7 to 11.4 μ apart.

The inner layer of the exine is extremely thick and very coarsely granular, but the outer layer is thinner than in the type yet sharply and distinctly granular and generally easily discernible. The furrows are long and pointed and, on account of the great thickness of the exine, are deeply depressed.

The genus comprises about 100 species of wide distribution in the Northern Hemisphere. All are entirely insect pollinated and, as a general rule, do not cause hayfever, though some of those which are cultivated are known to produce hayfever symptoms upon the patient's coming into direct contact with the plants. Also the leaves of some species are said occasionally to cause dermatitis (Goldstein, 1931).

Chrysanthemum coccineum Willd. (*Pyrethrum roseum* Sieb.) Common Pyrethrum. Grains rather various, many of them tetra- and hexacolpate, and many giants. Normal grains as in the generic description, 24.2 to 28.5 μ in diameter, spines 4.6 μ long and 5.7 to 8 μ apart.

The plant is a bushy herb, resembling the oxeye daisy and bearing white, pink, lilac, or crimson flowers. Native of Asia but extensively cultivated both as a source of insect powder and, in some of its varieties, as a garden perennial.

Chrysanthemum morifolium Ram. (*C. sinense* Sabine) Florists' chrysanthemum. Grains rather various; many tetra- and hexacolpate, and many variously irregular. Normal grains 31 to 34.2 μ in diameter, with spines 2.3 μ long and 8 to 11.4 μ apart.

The plant is a cultigen of unknown origin but believed to be a hybrid with an admixture of *C. indicum* L. The defective and variously irregular condition of its pollen points to hybridity of origin.

Chrysanthemum carinatum L. (*C. tricolor* Andr.) Tricolor chrysanthemum. Grains as in the generic description, uniform and all normal, except for a few abortives and dwarfs. Normal grains 28 to 30 μ in diameter, spines 3.4 μ long and 6.8 to 8 μ apart.

Annual, 2 to 3 ft. high. Disk flowers purple and rays banded with two other colors. Native of Morocco. Several garden races with different-colored ray flowers are in cultivation.

TANACETUM (Tourn.) L. Tansy

Grains approximately spheroidal but deeply three lobed by their furrows, 25 to 32 μ in diameter. Exine excessively thick and composed of two layers (Plate XIII, Figs. 1, 2), the inner coarsely granular and much the thicker of the two, the outer finely but distinctly granular and thicker than usual in this tribe.

There is considerable variation in the size of the spines among the different species; they are generally broadly conical and so large in proportion to the size of the grain that only four show on each lobe at the limb. The furrows are long and tapering to pointed ends, with their membranes perfectly smooth, but each provided with a round germinal aperture through which the germ pore may bulge prominently. Owing to the extreme thickness of the exine, the deep furrows impart to the grain a deeply three-lobed form, even when fully expanded.

The genus comprises about 30 species of coarse, aromatic, leafy perennial herbs, of wide distribution in the northern hemisphere. All species appear to be primarily insect pollinated, and none is known to cause hayfever. But they suggest a tendency toward anemophily in the reduction or suppression of the ligulate corollas of the marginal flowers, and there can be no doubt of their rather close relationship to *Artemisia* which is entirely anemophilous.

Tanacetum vulgare L. Tansy type. Fully one-half of the grains abortive, many of them dicolpate, fewer tetra- and hexa-colpate. Normal grains uniform, as in the generic description, 25 to 26.5 μ in diameter, with spines 2.8 μ long and 4.6 to 6.8 μ apart.

Among the abnormal grains those that are dicolpate are as large as those that are normal; their two furrows are opposite and united at the poles, thus encircling the grain as a single furrow with two germ pores. The tetra- and hexacolpate grains are apparently always giants, and the furrows are arranged in the trischistoclasic system.

Native of Europe and Asia but naturalized as a roadside weed throughout North America. Flowers July to September.

Tanacetum Camphoratum Less. (Plate XIII, Figs. 1, 2). Grains as in *T. vulgare*, except that they are a little larger—29.7 to 32 μ in diameter—with spines 2.2 μ long and about 9 μ apart. Di-, tetra-, and hexacolpate grains also present.

Beaches, California and Oregon.

Tanacetum bipinnatum (L.) Sch.-Bip. Grains essentially as in the type. A few tetracolpate grains are found.

Alaska, Yukon, and Mackenzie, also eastern Siberia.

Tanacetum Falconeri Hook. Grains essentially as in the type, all normal, 27.5 to 32 μ in diameter, with spines 3 to 4 μ long and 8 to 10.8 μ apart.

The Himalayas.

Tanacetum huronense Nutt. As in the type, 27.4 to 28.5 μ in diameter, spines 3 to 4 μ long and 8 to 10.3 μ apart. New Brunswick and Maine to Michigan and Hudson Bay.

Tanacetum longifolium Wall. As in the type, 27.5 to 28.5 μ in diameter. Spines 2.4 μ long and 6.5 to 8.0 μ apart.

The western Himalayas.

Tanacetum Douglasii DC. (*T. huronense* Gray). As in the type, 28.5 to 30 μ in diameter, with spines 2.8 μ long and 8 to 10.3 μ apart.

British Columbia to Oregon.

Tanacetum artemisioides Sch.-Bip. As in the type, a large proportion of the grains abortive. Normal grains 22.8 to 26.2 μ in diameter; spines about 2.2 μ long, 6.8 to 8.0 μ apart.

Western Tibet.

Tancetum gracile (Hook.) F. Thomas. Similar to the type, except that the spines are much smaller. 19.4 to 20 μ in diameter. Spines 1.1 μ long, and 4.6 to 5.7 μ apart. The grains of this species approach in character most closely to those of the non-echinate group.

Closely related to the preceding species. Native of western Tibet.

SPHAEROMERIA Nutt.

Grains similar to the *Crossostephium* type (Plate XIII, Figs. 3, 4) but with their spine vestiges smaller, standing in this respect intermediate between the *Crossostephium* and *Artemisia* types. The exine is rather thick and rigid but much less so than that of such echinate forms as *Tanacetum* and appearing to lack the overlying layer of fine, granular material characteristic of the latter. The furrows are long and rounded at their ends, but, on account of the much thinner exine, they do not impart a three-lobed outline to the grains, as do the furrows of those of *Tanacetum*. Nevertheless the furrows function freely in accommodating the exine to the changes in volume of the grain. When the grains are fully expanded they are approximately spheroidal or slightly flattened oblately, but when they are dry the furrows close, and the grains tend to become ellipsoidal. The furrow membranes are smooth, and each is provided with a rather small germ pore. The thinness of the exine and smallness of the spines are clearly correlated with their mode of pollination by wind and, at the same time, point to a closer relationship to the smooth-grained Artemisias than to the echinate-grained Tanacetums, unless, of course, anemophily was developed in this genus independently of *Artemisia*, which is unlikely.

The genus consists of about five species of low, cespitose perennials with woody base or small shrubs. In many ways these are intermediate in appearance between *Tanacetum* and *Artemisia* but resemble the latter more closely. Nevertheless, they are regarded by Hall and Clements (1923) as representing a section of the genus *Tanacetum*, associated with the plants which are treated here as *Chamartemisia*. Their pollen-grain characters confirm their relationships with *Chamartemisia* but suggest that both are more closely related to *Artemisia* than to *Tanacetum*. Furthermore, the marginal flowers are not ligulate, the heads lacking entirely the radiate character which marked all of the echinate-grained species. This, together with the smooth character of the pollen grains, seems ample justification for removing these plants from the genus *Tanacetum*.

Sphaeromeria argentea Nutt. (*Tanacetum Nuttalii* T. & G.). Grains uniform, similar to the *Crossostephium* type, 24 to 25.5 μ in diameter. Spine vestiges clearly visible though extremely minute—slightly smaller than in the type but more prominent than in the three succeeding species.

Arid hills, Wyoming and Montana.

Sphaeromeria cana (D. C. Eat.) Heller (*Tanacetum canum* D. C. Eat.). Grains uniform in size, 20 to 22.8 μ in diameter, essentially as in the *Crossostephium* type, except that the spine vestiges are slightly less prominent.

Nevada, eastern California, and Oregon.

Sphaeromeria capitata Nutt. (*Tanacetum capitatum* T. & G.). Grains uniform, 25.1 to 29.6 μ in diameter, essentially as in the *Crossostephium* type, except that the spine vestiges are slightly less conspicuous.

Wyoming and southern Montana.

Sphaeromeria simplex (A. Nels.) Heller (*Tanacetum simplex* A. Nels.). Grains similar to the *Crossostephium* type, except that the spine vestiges are much less conspicuous. They can be seen only with difficulty under the most favorable conditions and are distinctly smaller than in the preceding species.

Wyoming.

CROSSOSTEPHIUM Less.

The grains of three of the four species of this genus are practically indistinguishable from those of *Artemisia*, while those of the fourth, *C. artemisioides* (Plate XIII, Figs. 3, 4), differ in their spine vestiges, which are more prominent than those of any of the species of *Artemisia*. The grains of all four species are approximately spheroidal when expanded. The exine is rather thick and coarsely granular but much less so than that of the grains of *Tanacetum*. The furrows are only moderately long and not sharply pointed. They function freely as harmomegathi but do not impart a three-lobed outline to the normal grains, as do the furrows of the grains of *Tanacetum*. Abortive and empty grains, however, are deeply lobed, with the furrows tightly closed at the bases of the grooves.

According to the classification of Rydberg (1916, page 243), which is followed in this discussion, the genus includes the four species mentioned below, but Hall and Clements (1923, page 32) retain in it only *C. artemisioides*, which grows in Japan, the Philippines, and China, and they refer the other three species, which are American, to *Artemisia*. Apparently the latter treatment more correctly interprets the phylogeny of these plants, for in view of the striking difference in their pollen-grain characters it seems decidedly inappropriate to place the Asiatic *C. artemisioides* in the same genus with the three American species.

The plants are small or large shrubs of arid and semiarid regions, with the habit and appearance of the sagebrushes. All are wind pollinated, and one at least is the cause of much hayfever.

Crossostephium artemisioides Less. (*C. chinense* (L.) Merr., *Tanacetum chinenses* Gray, *Artemisia chinensis* Val.) (Plate XIII, Figs. 3, 4) type. Grains as in the generic description, 20 to 22.8 μ in diameter. Spine vestiges quite distinct, the largest found in the nonechinate group and occasionally almost reaching the proportions described as subechinate. In this respect this species seems to occupy a somewhat intermediate position between *Tanacetum* and *Artemisia*, though closer to the latter.

Much cultivated in Japan, China, the Philippines, and Indo-China, a native of China, currently known in Manila, where it is cultivated in pots, as *ajenjo*, which is a Spanish name for *Artemisia*.

Crossostephium insulare Rydb. (*Artemisia californica* Less.). Grains extremely various. Many of them abortive, giants or dwarfs, and some with two furrows. Normal grains differing from the *Crossostephium* type in their much smaller spine vestiges and thinner exine, resembling more closely the *Artemisia* type (Plate XIII, Fig. 5), 21.6 to 22.8 μ in diameter.

According to Hall (1923, page 54), this species should be regarded as a minor variation of *A. californica* Less. (*C. californicum* Rydb.). The presence in its pollen of a large proportion of abnormal and defective grains suggests that the plant is a hybrid, and the thinner exine and extremely vestigial nature of its spines suggest that it is more closely related to *Artemisia* than to the type of the present genus.

Crossostephium foliosum (Nutt.) Rydb. (*Artemisia foliosa* Nutt.). Grains uniform, as in the *Artemisia* type and indistinguishable from those of the preceding species.

A woody shrub regarded by Hall (1923, page 53) as a minor variation of the next species.

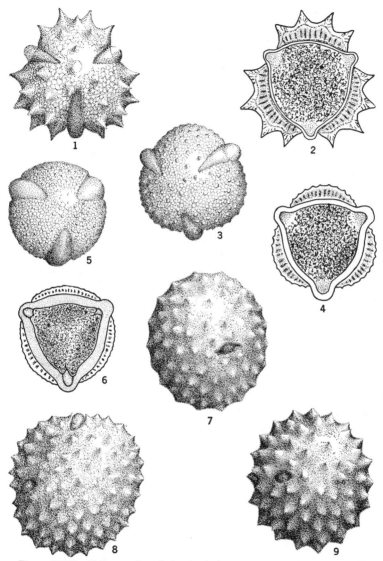

PLATE XIII.—Pollen grains of the Anthemideae and Ambrosieae. 1, *Tanacetum camphoratum*, polar view, 29.7 μ in diameter. 2, The same in optical section. 3, *Crossostephium artemisioides*, polar view, 20.9 μ in diameter. 4, The same in optical section. 5, *Artemisia tridentata*, polar view, 28.5 μ in diameter. 6, The same in optical section. 7, *Ambrosia elatior*, 18.3 μ in diameter. 8, *Ambrosia psilostachya*, 25 μ in diameter. 9, *Ambrosia trifida*, 17.7 μ in diameter.

Crossostephium californicum (Less.) Rydb. (*Artemisia californica* Less.) Coast sagebrush. Grains mostly uniform but accompanied by a small proportion of giants, and some with supernumerary· furrows. Normal grains as in the *Artemisia* type, with spine vestiges extremely minute, oblately flattened, 22 to 26.2 μ in diameter.

A shrub 3 to 9 ft. high, extremely abundant along the hills of the coast ranges from central California southward. Wind pollinated, shedding large amounts of pollen, which is the cause of much hayfever during the latter part of summer (Rowe, 1928; Selfridge, 1920; Hall 1917, 1923).

Vesicarpa potentilloides (Gray.) Rydb. (*Artemisia potentilloides* Gray, *Tanacetum potentilloides* Gray, *Sphaeromeria potentilloides* A. Heller). Grains as in the *Artemisia* type, 22.8 to 25.1 μ in diameter, with rather long, pointed furrows, fine but distinctly granular texture.

A perennial herb with woody root. The genus is regarded by Hall (1923) as most closely related to *Tanacetum*. The form of its pollen grain, however, in the absence of spines and its thin exine, points to a much closer relationship with *Artemisia*. The plant itself presents an appearance intermediate between *Tanacetum* and *Artemisia*.

Chamartemisia compacta (Hall.) Rydb. (*Tanacetum compactum* Hall). Grains uniform, as in the *Artemisia* type, with spines represented only by doubtful traces, apparently entirely absent in most grains, 20.5 to 22.8 μ in diameter.

A small, cespitose perennial, with woody root, resembling in appearance *Sphaeromeria*. Known only to occur at the head of Lee Canyon, Charleston Mountains, Nevada. The genus is most closely related to *Sphaeromeria*. Hall (1923) treats the two genera together as a section of *Tanacetum*. Their pollen grains, however, while in every way similar to each other, differ from those of *Tanacetum* in their lack of spines and in their much thinner exine and suggest that both *Chamartemisia* and *Sphaeromeria* are more closely related to *Artemisia* than to *Tanacetum*.

Picrothamnus desertorum Nutt. (*Artemisia spinescens* Eat.). Bud sagebrush. Grains extremely irregular, only a small proportion of them normal. Many are obviously abortive and empty, while others are dwarfs or giants. A large proportion of the latter are provided with supernumerary furrows, generally arranged in the trischistoclasic system. The furrow arrangements which are most in evidence are the tetracolpate, hexacolpate, octocolpate, nonacolpate, and dodecacolpate. Besides these there are a number of grains of the zonate type, and still others which are variously irregular.

The normal grains are exactly like the *Artemisia* type, with spine vestiges recognizable but extremely small, 21.6 to 27.4 μ in diameter. In the giants the diameter may reach as much as 43 μ.

Low, spiny shrubs of desert areas, somewhat similar to sagebrush when growing in similar habitats. Wyoming to New Mexico, Oregon, and California. Flowers from March to June, producing large quantities of pollen which is the cause of much hayfever (Scheppegrell, 1917; Hall, 1923).

This plant is regarded by Hall (1923) as a member of the genus *Artemisia* in the section DRACUNCULUS, in which he finds it in agreement in all important technical characters with *A. dracunculus* and *A. campestris*. The characters of the normal pollen grains certainly show no reason for separating it from *Artemisia*. The large proportion of abnormal and defective grains suggests that it may be a hybrid. Contrary to such a view, however, is the fact that the species exhibits a remarkable lack of variability, which has been noted by Hall (1923, page 133), who says, "Perhaps it is because of its fixed characters and incapacity for adaptation to new environments that the species has produced no forms that have received taxonomic recognition." It is difficult to see how a plant with such extreme variability of its pollen should exhibit such great somatic stability, unless, perchance, the pollen is not required for fertilization, the plant producing its seeds apogamously, as do the common dandelion and some species of *Hieracium*, a problem which deserves further study.

ARTEMISIA L. SAGEBRUSH, MUGWORT, WORMWOOD

Grains when expanded spheroidal or oblately flattened, 17.6 to 28.5 μ in diameter, normally tricolpate. Furrows long and tapering, fully functional, their membranes smooth, provided with a germinal aperture. Exine thick and coarsely granular, though much less so than in the *Tanacetum* type, the outer layer thin, occasionally slightly overlapping the furrow membranes along their margins.   Spine vestiges small or absent (Plate XIII, Figs. 5, 6).

In optical section the grains generally appear rounded-tri-angular in shape, with the pores bulging out on the three sides; the exine is seen to be thickest in the middle of the lunes, tapering in thickness gradually, in sweeping curves, to the edges of the furrows.   The coarsely granular nature of the exine appears coarsely striate in the optical section.

Perhaps the most noteworthy feature of the *Artemisia* pollen grains is the minuteness of their spines.   Nevertheless, in the pollen of nearly all species some vestige of them can be seen in at least some of the grains.   Moreover, there is considerable varia-tion in this character among the grains of the different species, and this is of such a nature that it is of some diagnostic value. Thus, on the basis of the size of the spine vestiges, it is possible to group the species which are considered here into four different classes as follows: (1) spine vestiges conspicuous, only slightly smaller than in the *Crossostephium* type (Plate XIII, Fig. 3), *Artemisia norvegica;* (2) spine vestiges minute but still quite large enough to be seen with certainty under favorable conditions, *A. frigida, A. camporum, A. Pycnocephala, A. canadensis;* (3) spine vestiges represented only by a vanishing trace or even entirely absent in some grains, *A. gnaphalodes, A. Bigelovii, A. Absinthium, A. dracunculoides;* (4) spine vestiges generally entirely absent, though a trace of them may occasionally be seen on some grains, *A. heterophylla, A. filifolia, A. tridentata.* The distinction among these groups is generally vague.   There is, however, no trouble in distinguishing the grains of group 1 from those of group 2 or those of group 2 from those of group 4; but the distinction between those of groups 2 and 3 and between those of 3 and 4 is somewhat uncertain.

The artemisias are all wind pollinated, and most of them shed large amounts of light pollen which may be borne long distances in the air.   Virtually all species that occur in sufficient abundance are generous contributors to the production of hayfever.

The taxonomy of the group is extremely complicated and difficult.   The number of species recognized by different authors varies from 17 to 72.   Many of them are unstable, occurring in a great array of forms, varieties, and minor variations.   It is largely owing to a lack of agreement among the different authors regarding the status of these that such disagreement originates in the numbers of species recognized by them. Nevertheless, the interrelationships between most of these is now exceedingly well understood, owing to the extraordinary and beautiful researches of Hall and Clements (1923). In the present treatment I am following the classification and terminology of Rydberg (1916), owing to its simpler nature and to the fact that this is not primarily a taxonomic work in which ultrataxonomic refinements are required.

Artemisia norvegica Fries. (*A. arctica* Less. *A. hyperborea* Macoun) Boreal sage. Grains somewhat various, some of them giants, abortive, or variously irregular. Normal grains 23.9 to 27.4 μ in diameter. Exine conspicuously but rather finely granular, provided with spine rudiments only slightly less conspicuous than those of *Crossostephium* (Plate XIII, Fig. 3).

A cespitose perennial herb, widely distributed in America and Europe in northern and mountainous regions. It occurs in many forms and varieties, some of which have been given specific names. Flowers from July to October and may cause some hayfever.

Artemisia Suksdorfii Piper (*A. heterophylla* Nutt., *A. vulgaris californica* Gray, *A. vulgaris litoralis* (Suksd.) Hall) California mugwort. Grains essentially as in the *A. tridentata* type, uniform, oblately flattened, 25.1 to 28.5 μ broad and about 23.9 μ deep. Exine distinctly and rather coarsely granular. Spine vestiges generally entirely absent.

Large, bushy perennial herb, 3 to 6 ft. high; common along stream banks and elsewhere. California to British Columbia. Flowers during the latter part of summer, shedding enormous quantities of pollen which is known to be an important cause of hayfever, particularly in the coastal regions of California (Hall in Scheppegrell (1917), Selfridge, 1920).

Artemisia gnaphalodes Nutt. (*A. vulgaris gnaphalodes* (Nutt.) Hall) Prairie or Western sage, Cudweed mugwort, Sagewort. Grains somewhat various, a small proportion of them giants, with four or six furrows or otherwise abnormal. Normal grains rather uniform, slightly flattened, 24 to 25.3 μ in diameter.

A low, cespitose perennial, attaining scarcely 3 ft. in height. Extremely abundant in prairie regions. Ontario and Michigan to Missouri, Texas, Coahuila, California, British Columbia, and

Saskatchewan and sparingly introduced in the eastern United States. Flowers during the latter part of summer and, in regions where abundant, is the cause of much hayfever.

Artemisia Bigelovii Gray. Flat or dwarf sagebrush. Grains extremely various, many of them dwarfs or giants with supernumerary furrows. Normal grains 24 to 25.6 μ in diameter. Texture conspicuously and rather coarsely granular; spine vestiges extremely minute, but generally visible.

Among the aberrant forms are dicolpate grains with furrows opposite, and hexa- and dodecacolpate grains, any of which may or may not be giants. In all, except the dicolpate forms, the furrow arrangements correspond rather closely to the trischisto-clasic system, though one or more of the furrows may be missing from any of the configurations without otherwise deforming their arrangement.

A low perennial shrub, 6 to 18 in. high, silvery canescent throughout. Western Texas to southern Colorado, Utah, and Arizona. Flowers August to October. Known to be a contributing factor in hayfever.

Artemisia Absinthium L. Common wormwood, Sagewort, Absinth. Grains uniform, as in the *Artemisia* type. Texture coarsely granular, spine vestiges scarcely visible or entirely absent.

A perennial herb with woody base and fragrant leaves; about 3 to 6 ft. high. Native of Europe, where it is much cultivated for the aromatic oil that may be obtained from its roots. Widely introduced into North America, particularly in the eastern states. July to October. At present it is only an unimportant factor in hayfever but is spreading rapidly.

Artemisia frigida Willd. Carpet, Pasture, or Prairie sage. Grains mostly uniform, essentially as in the type, spheroidal or slightly flattened when expanded, 21.6 to 25.1 μ in diameter. Spine vestiges extremely minute but visible. Besides the normal grains there are a few that are tetracolpate and larger (27.5 μ in diameter).

A low perennial 10 to 20 in. high, with woody base, silky canescent throughout. On dry plains and in rocky soil. Minnesota to Saskatchewan, Yukon, Idaho, Nebraska, Texas, and Arizona. July to October. An important cause of hayfever.

Artemisia dracunculoides Pursh. (*A. dracunculus glauca* (Pallas) Hall, *A. Dracunculus* Pursh.) Indian wormwood, Linear-leaved wormwood. Grains extremely various, many of them abortive, and many giants with three or higher numbers of furrows. Normal grains 20.5 to 27.9 μ in diameter. Spine vestiges extremely small but visible in most of the grains.

A glabrous perennial, 2 to 4 ft. high. Abundant on dry plains and prairies. Manitoba to British Columbia, Illinois, Missouri, Nebraska, Texas, Chihuahua, New Mexico, and California. July to November. Next to *A. tridentata* this is the most plentiful species in North America and is known to be an important cause of hayfever throughout a large part of its range (Rowe, 1928; Selfridge, 1920; Hall, 1917).

Artemisia canadensis Michx. (*A. campestris borealis* (Pallas) Hall, *A. peucedanifolia* Juss.) Field sagewort, Canada sage. Grains extremely various; many of them giants, abortive, and with supernumerary furrows (*e.g.*, 6, 9, and 12). Normal grains essentially as in the *A. tridentata* type, 19.4 to 21 μ broad and 17 to 18.5 μ deep. Spine vestiges extremely small but generally visible.

Stout herb 1 to 2 ft. high from a perennial creeping rootstock; in rocky soil. Newfoundland to Hudson Bay, Maine, Vermont, westward along the Great Lakes and to the Pacific Coast. July to August.

Artemisia camporum Rydb. (*A. campestris pacifica* (Nutt.) Hall, *A. pacifica* Nutt.) Field sagewort. Normal grains uniform, essentially as in the type, 17.6 to 19.8 μ in diameter but accompanied by many giant grains ranging in size from 24 to 33.6 μ in diameter and usually with supernumerary furrows (*i.e.*, tetra-, hexa-, and dodecacolpate) generally in the trischistoclasic system, though there are some in which they are entirely irregular. Texture coarse and conspicuously granular; spine vestiges minute but conspicuous enough to always be seen with certainty.

Ontario to Saskatchewan, Yukon, Arizona, and Nebraska.

Artemisia pycnocephala (Less.) DC. (*A. campestris pycnocephala* (Less.) Hall). Grains essentially as in the type, uniform, 19.4 to 21.6 μ in diameter and with furrows a little shorter than in the type. Texture finely granular; spine vestiges minute but always large enough to be seen with certainty.

A perennial with cespitose, woody base from which emerge stalks bearing the inflorescences. Common on sea beaches, central Oregon to Monterey, California. Said to be an important cause of hayfever in regions where abundant (Rowe, 1928).

Artemisia filifolia Torr. (*A. plattensis* Nutt.) Silvery worm-wood, Sand sagebrush. Grains as in the type, uniform, except for a few that are abnormal, 22.8 to 24.5 μ in diameter. Among the abnormal grains are bicolpate grains with furrows opposite and hexacolpate grains with furrows in the trischistoclasic system. Spine vestiges generally not visible, though occasionally a trace of them may be seen.

A coarse, bushy shrub 1 to 3 ft. high, shedding large quantities of pollen during the latter part of summer. Known to be the cause of much hayfever in regions where abundant. Nebraska and Wyoming to Nevada, Chihuahua, and Texas.

Artemisia tridentata Nutt. Common sagebrush (Plate XIII, Figs. 5, 6) type. Grains as in the generic description. When expanded oblately flattened, 25.1 to 28.5 μ in diameter and about 23.4 μ deep. Texture coarsely and distinctly granular. Spine vestiges generally entirely absent—in only a few grains can traces of them be seen.

A coarse, bushy shrub or small tree, extremely abundant in arid and semiarid regions: South Dakota and Montana to British Columbia, Lower California, and New Mexico. July to September. An important cause of hayfever. In some parts of Arizona outranking the ragweeds (Phillips, 1923). In regions of the Rocky Mountains, where the plant reaches its greatest size, it causes a type of hayfever known locally as "mountain fever."

Artemisiastrum Palmeri (Gray) Rydb. (*Artemisia Palmeri* Gray) Tall sagebrush. Grains uniform as in the *Artemisia* type, 18.8 to 21.1 μ in diameter. Spine vestiges entirely absent or represented by doubtful traces.

A tall shrub with herbaceous branches, rather rare and of local distribution in southern California and northern Lower California.

AMBROSIEAE RAGWEED TRIBE

Grains spheroidal or oblately flattened, 16.5 to 30 μ in diameter, generally tricolpate; but in the pollen of some species tetracolpate grains are frequent, and hexacolpate occasional. Furrows various, long and tapering, of medium length or merely rounded pits only slightly meridionally elongate, almost coinciding in extent with their enclosed germ pores. Exine rather thick but generally less so than in the grains of entomophilous Compositae, more or less distinctly granular; generally provided with spines which are short-conical or rounded, or vestigial, less frequently with spines well developed and sharp pointed.

In the following discussion the ragweeds and their allies will be treated as a tribe of the Compositae. In recent years Britton and Brown and other authors of floras have chosen to give the group the status of a family, making of the Compositae three families, Ambrosiaceae, Cichoriaceae, and Carduaceae. Bentham (1873) has truly stated that "the Compositae are at once the largest, the most distinct, and the most uniform, and therefore the most natural, of all orders of phenogamous plants"; and Bentham's statement still remains unchallenged. Since the business of taxonomy is to show relationships and suggest the trend of evolution, the breaking up of the most natural of all orders of flowering plants is not in the best interests of taxonomy.

The relationship of the Ambrosieae to the other tribes of the Compositae has been very definitely established as closest to the Heliantheae, though some investigators have regarded it as closer to the Anthemideae. Cassini (1834), the greatest of all the earlier synantherologists, regarded the Ambrosieae as related to the Heliantheae, also to the Anthemideae. Delpino (1871) believed that they were related to the Anthemideae through the Artemisias. Bentham (1873) stated, "They are, without doubt, connected with *Artemisia* as well as with the Melampodineae,* having much of the habit of the former and passing into the latter through *Parthenice;* but geographically as well as structurally, the relationship to the Melampodineae appears to me to be the closest." Small (1917) says, "The affinity between *Iva* and *Parthenice* is so close that there can be no doubt of the systematic position of the Ambrosiinae in the Heliantheae and . . . the origin of the subtribe . . . via *Parthenium* and *Parthenice.*" Moreover, the closeness of the relationship of the Ambrosieae to the Heliantheae is abundantly attested by the morphology of their pollen grains; consequently, the taxonomy might be even better expressed by treating the Ambrosieae as a subtribe of the Heliantheae, thus retaining the classification of Bentham and Hooker (1873).

* The Melampodineae are a subtribe of the Heliantheae, including *Parthenium* and *Parthenice.*

There is wide variation of form in the pollen grains of the Ambrosieac, and all the pollen characters which the members of the tribe possess in common are likewise found in the other tribes of the family, yet it is nearly always easy to recognize the pollen grains of the Ambrosieae by the characters which they possess individually.   In spite of their wide variation the different forms are clearly related to each other; they appear to represent stages in a progressive evolution of the pollen grains of this group away from the basic thick-walled, echinate form, which characterizes the family, and toward the smooth, thin-walled, highly specialized form of the Euxanthium section of *Xanthium.*

The pollen-grain characters of the different species of the Ambrosieae which appear to have distinctive or phylogenetic value are listed in Table, VI and some of them illustrated in Plate XIV.*   The important points brought out here are the marked differences in the size of the spines and length of the furrows in the grains of the different genera.   The spines show a more or less progressive reduction through the different groups, from the completely echinate form of the grain of *Oxytenia* (Plate XIV, Fig. 1) to the nearly smooth form of the grain of Euxanthium (Plate XIV, Fig. 7).   The furrow likewise shows a progressive reduction throughout the series.   It is long in the grains of most of the subtribe Iveneae but slightly reduced in those of *Euphrosyne* and greatly reduced in those of *Iva* (Plate XIV, Fig. 5).   It is short in those of all the subtribe Ambrosineae (Plate XIV, Figs. 6 to 8; Plate XIII, Figs. 7 to 9). Correlated with the reduction of the spines and the length of the furrow is a noticeable reduction in thickness of the exine.   This is not shown in the table, but it may be stated here that all the long-furrowed grains, *e.g.,* those of *Oxytenia* (Fig. 118), *Chorisiva* (Fig. 119), and *Cyclachaena* (Fig. 120), *i.e.,* those of all of the Iveneae except *Iva,* have a noticeably thicker exine than those of *Iva* and those of the Ambrosineae, which have reduced spines and short furrows, *e.g., Xanthium* (Fig. 122) and *Ambrosia* (Fig. 121).

Another point which is brought out by Table VI is that in genera which are represented by more than a single species the pollen

* The classification and nomenclature relating to the Ambrosieae (exclusive of *Xanthium*) are used here as expressed by Rydberg (1916, 1922); and that pertaining to *Xanthium,* by Millspaugh and Sherff (1916, 1922).

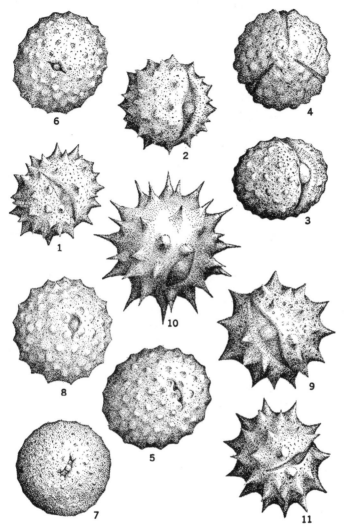

PLATE XIV.—Pollen grains of the Ambrosieae and allied genera. 1, *Oxytenia acerosa*, side view, 18.1 μ in diameter. 2, *Chorisiva nevadensis*, side view, 16.5 μ in diameter. 3, *Cyclachaena ambrosiaefolia*, side view, 19 μ in diameter. 4, The same in polar view. 5, *Iva axillaris*, side view, 20.9 μ in diameter. 6, *Ambrosia psilostachya*, side view, 23 μ in diameter. 7, *Xanthium pennsylvanicum*, side view, 23.4 μ in diameter. 8, *Xanthium catharticum*, side view, 20.9 μ in diameter. 9, *Anthemis nobilis*, side view, 23.1 μ in diameter. 10, *Helianthus annuus*, side view, 27.7 μ in diameter. 11, *Parthenice mollis*, side view, 15.8 μ in diameter.

grains exhibit marked uniformity throughout the genus, and the grains of most genera, except those which are admittedly very closely related, present some distinguishing character.   Thus it is seen that in the grains of all four species of *Cyclachaena* (Plate XIV, Figs. 3, 4) the furrows are long and constricted, the grains are subechinate and flattened, and in size they vary only from 17.8 to 19 μ in diameter.   In *Dicoria* the grains of the two

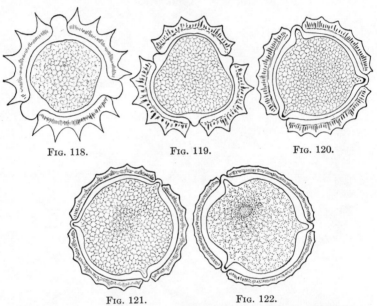

Fig. 118.   Fig. 119.   Fig. 120.

Fig. 121.   Fig. 122.

Figs. 118–122.—Pollen grains of Ambrosieae, diagrammatic equatorial sections, showing progressive thinning of the exine and reduction in the size of the spines through the ascending phyletic scale.   Figure 118, *Oxytenia acerosa;* Fig. 119, *Chorisiva nevadensis;* Fig. 120, *Cyclachaena xanthifolia;* Fig. 121, *Ambrosia elatior;* Fig. 122, *Xanthium speciosum.*

species recorded in the table are subechinate, with furrows long and constricted, and are practically identical with each other in all other observable respects.   In *Iva* the grains of all species are subechinate, with the spines still further reduced, and in size they range only from 19.1 to 21 μ in diameter.   Their most striking character is their uniformly short furrows, a character which separates them distinctly from the rest of the Iveneae and stands in sharp contrast with the long-furrowed grains of *Cyclachaena,* despite the fact that both *C. xanthifolia* and *C.*

ambrosiaefolia are regarded by many botanists as belonging to the genus *Iva*.

In the grains of *Ambrosia* (Plate XIV, Fig. 6), and *Acanthambrosia*, which is admittedly very closely related to it, the furrows are short in the grains of all species; the grains are subechinate, showing in this respect slightly less reduction in the spines than do those of *Hymenoclea* or even most of the Ivas. In size somewhat greater variation is found in the grains of these two genera than in the others; still it is not extreme, ranging only from 17.3 to 23 μ in diameter.

In *Franseria*, which is regarded as a transition genus between *Ambrosia* and *Xanthium*, the grains show a corresponding variation. In *Franseria tenuifolia* they are subechinate, with the spines quite as prominent as in those of *Ambrosia*. From this condition the spines range downward in size through the various species to those of the grains of *F. ilicifolia* and *F. deltoidea* in which they are represented by the merest traces. In fact the grains of *F. deltoidea* are scarcely distinguishable from those of the various species of Euxanthium (Plate XIV, Fig. 7) in which the spines are vestigial. It so happens that those species of *Franseria* which are most like *Ambrosia* in their grosser morphological characters have subechinate grains like those of *Ambrosia*, while those that are most like *Xanthium* have nearly smooth grains like those of Euxanthium.

In the grains of the genus *Xanthium* the most conspicuous thing is the wide difference in form existing between those of the two sections. In Acanthoxanthium the grains are small, with spines rather well developed, fully as prominent as in those of *Ambrosia*, while in Euxanthium the grains are larger, and invariably the spines are only vestigial. In view of the extreme uniformity of pollen-grain form found in most of the other genera of this tribe, this seems to be strong evidence that the two sections of *Xanthium* represent widely different genetic lines and should not be retained within the same genus. Indeed, the morphology of the plants themselves shows considerably more difference between these two sections of *Xanthium* than exists between the genera *Ambrosia*, *Franseria*, and *Acanthambrosia*, so on this ground alone, if these three genera are to be admitted, the classification would be much more consistent if the two sections of *Xanthium* were likewise given generic rank. The curious objection is offered to this procedure by American systematists that there is but a single American species belonging to the section Acanthoxanthium.

The grains of all species of the Ambrosieae are rather small, the average of the species listed in the table ranging from 14.8 to 26.4 μ in diameter. At first sight this might be regarded as an adaptation to wind pollination, but that this is not so is seen from the fact that the most highly specialized group, *Xanthium*, have the largest pollen grains, while the less highly specialized genera, *Oxytenia* and *Chorisiva*, have the smallest; in other words the development within the tribe has been toward an increase in pollen-grain size. Strange as it may seem, this increase in size in the development of the pollen grains of the Ambrosieae may actually be a response to wind pollination, for, from a study of wind-pollinated plants of other families, we find that neither those with very small nor those with very large pollen grains are ever wind pollinated but only those of intermediate size, ranging generally between 17 and 40 μ in diameter. The size of *Xanthium* pollen grains thus appears to be the optimum.

The reduction in the size of the spines and the thinning of the exine which are encountered among the Ambrosieae are almost certainly the result of their anemophilous habit. We have already seen that in groups where wind pollination is the rule the pollen grains are without spines or conspicuous adornments of any kind and with thin exines. This is true of such anemophilous families as the Gramineae, Cyperaceae, Juglandaceae, Betulaceae, and Chenopodiaceae and of *Populus* among the Salicaceae, of *Rumex* among the Polygonaceae, and of *Artemisia* and its allies among the Compositae. Here, again, among the Ambrosieae is further evidence of the law that anemophily leads to a thinning of the exine and a reduction of external adornments.

A graphical expression of the probable sequence of the characters discussed above is displayed in Fig. 123. The grain of *Oxytenia* is placed at the beginning of the sequence, representing the form least removed from the basic echinate form of the Compositae, *i.e.*, least affected by anemophily. Its spines are sharp and prominent, and its furrows are long and constricted at their ends. By a simple reduction of its spines this form could have given rise to that of *Chorisiva*, by a further reduction to those of *Cyclachaena* and *Dicoria*, and by a still further reduction to that of *Leuciva*. The derivation of these four forms from that of *Oxytenia* is accomplished solely by a reduction of their spines, together with a slight increase in size, the other characters remaining constant.

From such a form as that which characterizes the grains of *Cyclachaena* and *Dicoria*, by a reduction in the length of the furrows, could have arisen that of *Euphrosyne;* and by a still further reduction in the length of the furrows and of the size of the spines, together with a slight increase in the size of the grains, could have arisen that of the grains of *Iva*.

These seven genera constitute the subtribe Iveneae, which are characterized by monoecism with the staminate and pistillate flowers in the same heads, resembling in this respect section Dracunculus of the genus *Artemisia*, where the condition is associated with and probably induced by anemophily. In *Artemisia* it is associated with the most highly specialized forms and is as far as the separation of the sexes is carried in that genus. But in the Ambrosieae it is associated with the less highly specialized forms, characterizing the Iveneae and serving to distinguish them from the the more highly specialized Ambrosineae in which the staminate and pistillate flowers are always borne in separate heads.

The separation of the sexes into staminate and pistillate heads in the Ambrosieae is not accompanied by any abrupt change in the forms of their pollen grains. Those of *Ambrosia, Acanthambrosia, Hymenoclea*, and the *Ambrosia*-like *Franserias*, in all of which the sexes are separate, are almost the same as those of *Iva*, in which the sexes are united. Higher up the scale though, in the grains of the *Xanthium*-like Franserias and of Euxanthium, the reduction in size of the spine is resumed, and in the latter group the spines are almost obliterated. In this respect Euxanthium may be regarded as the climax development of the Ambrosieae.

Since the trend of development within the Ambrosieae is toward a reduction in the thickness of the exine and the size of the spines, a reduction of the length of the furrows, and an increase in size of the grain, by reversing this we are able to say that the ancestral form of grain must have been small, with thick exine and well-developed, sharp spines and with long, tapering furrows. Furthermore, the texture of the exine must have been finely but distinctly granular, for this character is fairly constant throughout the group.

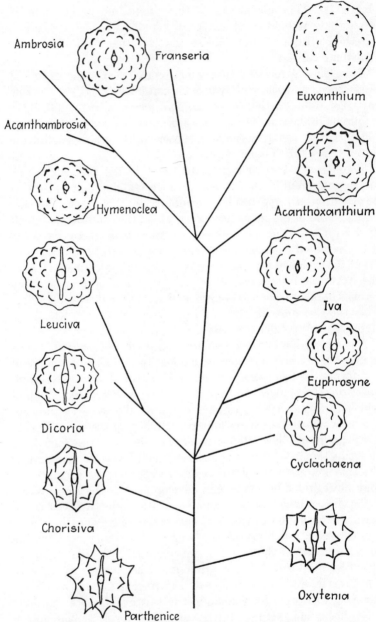

FIG. 123.—Phylogenetic arrangement of the genera of the Ambrosieae, as interpreted from the morphology of their pollen grains.

Which species among living forms comes nearest to satisfying these requirements? As we have already seen, it is claimed by Delpino and others that the relationship of the Ambrosieae is primarily with the Anthemideae and by Bentham and by Small that it is primarily with the Heliantheae through *Parthenium* and *Parthenice*. Let us see how near the grains of the Anthemideae come to fulfilling the requirements of the ancestral form. For example, the grain of *Anthemis nobilis* (Plate XIV, Fig. 9), which is characteristic of that tribe, has short, heavy spines; its furrows are rather long but are also very broad and not at all constricted at their ends; the texture of the exine is much more coarsely granular than that of any species of the Ambrosieae, and, in size, the grain of *Anthemis nobilis* is about 23.1 μ in diameter— much larger than demanded by the prototype. Clearly, this form of grain is quite remote and not at all in line with the trends within the Ambrosieae. Now let us see how near the grains of *Parthenice*, among the Heliantheae, come to satisfying the requirements of the prototype. For example, that of *P. mollis* (Plate XIV, Fig. 11) is small (15.4 μ in diameter)—smaller than those of either *Oxytenia* or *Choriseva*, as would be demanded by the upward trend in size within the group. The grain of *Parthenice mollis* is also echinate, provided with spines essentially the same as those of *Oxytenia*. It is tricolpate, with long furrows reaching almost from pole to pole and strongly constricted toward their ends, and with the surface texture only finely granular. In all of these characters it fulfills the requirements of the prototype almost perfectly—certainly much better than the grains of any of the Anthemideae. The grains of *Parthenium* are essentially the same as those of *Parthenice*, except for their size, which is somewhat larger (15.4 to 22.7 μ in diameter), in this respect, less in line with trend in size within the group. *Parthenice mollis* is regarded by Bentham as still closer to the Ambrosieae than *Parthenium;* in keeping with this it has a grain serving better as our hypothetical prototype. The evidence of the pollen grain therefore indicates that the Ambrosieae are connected with the Heliantheae through *Oxytenia* among the former and *Parthenice* among the latter.

KEY TO THE GENERA

I. Furrows more or less elongate, functioning as harmomegathi.

A. Furrows long and tapering, reaching almost from
   pole to pole.
   1. Echinate, provided with well-developed,
      sharp spines; 16.5 to 19.1 μ in diameter.
      a. Spines about 2.5 μ long and 4.6 μ apart. Oxytenia
      b. Spines about 1.1 μ long and 3.4 μ apart. Chorisiva
   2. Subechinate, with spines greatly reduced,
      and somewhat rounded; 16.5 to 19.0 μ in
      diameter.   Cyclachaena
   3. Not echinate, spines represented only by
      vestiges; about 20.9 μ in diameter; spines
      2.3 to 2.8 μ apart.   Leuciva
B. Furrows short to medium length but clearly
   functioning as harmomegathi. Grains about
   16.2 μ in diameter; spines greatly reduced,
   almost vestigial, about 2.3 μ apart.   Euphrosyne

II. Furrows greatly reduced, without harmomegathic
    function, generally represented only by pits in the
    exine and scarcely extending beyond their
    enclosed germ pores.
    A. Subechinate, with spines reduced but presenting
       a conspicuous feature of the exine, 17 to 26.2 μ
       in diameter.   Hymenoclea
                                                       Iva
                                                       Ambrosia
                                                       Acanthambrosia
                                                       ACANTHOXANTHIUM
                                                       Franseria (in part)

    B. Spines vestigial, usually represented only by
       inconspicuous papillae.
       1. Grains about 20.3 μ in diameter.   Franseria deltoidea
       2. Grains 22 to 30 μ in diameter.   EUXANTHIUM

Oxytenia acerosa Nutt. (Fig. 118; Plate XIV, Fig. 1). Grains
uniform, oblate-spheroidal, about 19.1 by 17.2 μ. Furrows long
and tapering, almost meeting at the poles; germ pores rather
large and generally somewhat bulging. Exine thick, finely
but distinctly granular. Spines conical and sharp, about 2.5 μ
long and 4.6 μ apart.

Monoecious shrubs 3 to 6 ft. high, with canescent, pinnatifid
leaves. In dry and sandy places; southern Colorado, southern
Utah, Arizona, and southeastern California. Flowers in August.
Not known to cause hayfever.

Chorisiva nevadensis (Jones) Rydb. (*Iva nevadensis* Jones)
(Fig. 119; Plate XIV, Fig. 2). Grains similar to those of *Oxytenia*,

uniform in size, less flattened, about 16.5 μ in diameter. Spines about 1.1 μ long and about 3.4 μ apart. Exine finely granular.

A low, diffusely branched annual 4 to 8 ft. high, with canescent, pinnately cleft leaves. Deserts, Nevada.

CYCLACHAENA Fresn.

Grains oblate-spheroidal, 16.7 to 19 μ in diameter, subechinate, with spines more or less conspicuous, 2.3 to 4 μ apart. The grains are generally tricolpate, but in the pollen of some species a small proportion are tetracolpate. The furrows are always long and tapering, almost meeting at the poles and obviously functioning as harmomegathi. Exine rather thick and finely but distinctly granular. These grains differ from those of *Oxytenia* and *Chorisiva* only in their smaller spines. Those of the four species of the genus are virtually indistinguishable from each other; the only observable differences between them are that the spines of *Cyclachaena xanthifolia* and *C. pedicellata* are slightly larger and farther apart than those of *C. ambrosiaefolia* and *C. lobata*, and in the pollen of *C. xanthifolia* are found a few grains with four instead of the usual three furrows. But these distinctions are too slight to be relied upon as criteria.

The genus includes four species of coarse annuals, mostly of arid and semiarid regions of the southwestern United States and Mexico. They are quite distinct from *Iva*, though frequently treated as a section of that genus. Though all possess the characters of hayfever plants, only *C. xanthifolia* is known to be a cause of hayfever.

Cyclachaena xanthifolia (Nutt.) Fresn. (*Iva xanthifolia* Nutt., *Euphrosyne xanthifolia* Gray) Prairie ragweed, Burweed, Horseweed, Careless weed (Fig. 120; Plate XIV, Figs. 3, 4). Grains as in the generic description, 17.6 to 19.8 μ in diameter, spines 2.3 to 3.4 μ apart.

A tall, coarse annual, 2 to 6 ft. high, in waste places, Illinois to Saskatchewan, Idaho, New Mexico, Texas, and Missouri. Flowers July and August, shedding large quantities of pollen which is the cause of much hayfever in regions where the plant is abundant. Mullin (1922) states that in Colorado 27 per cent of the hayfever patients react to this pollen; Hall (Scheppegrell, 1917) states that in the Rocky Mountain and Pacific coast states prairie ragweed ranks as a hayfever plant next in importance to *Artemisia*.

This plant is perhaps more frequently known by its synonym *Iva xanthifolia,* which is a misnomer. And, because of its mistaken association with the genus *Iva,* it is frequently called marsh elder. In hayfever studies it is generally known as "burweed marsh elder."

Cyclachaena pedicellata Rydb. Grains as in the generic description, 17.6 to 18.7 μ in diameter, about 15.4 μ measured through their polar axes. Spines 2.8 to 4 μ apart.

A tall annual herb, similar to the preceding but less common. New Mexico and western Texas.

Cyclachaena ambrosiaefolia (Gray) B. & H. (*Euphrosyne ambrosiaefolia* Gray, *Iva ambrosiaefolia* Gray) (Plate XIV, Figs. 3, 4). As in the generic description, 18.7 to 20 μ in diameter. Spines 2.3 to 2.8 μ apart.

A low annual herb, about 1½ ft. high. Texas to Arizona, Zacatecas, and San Luis Potosi.

Cyclachaena lobata Rydb. Grains as in the generic description, 16.5 to 18.7 μ in diameter. Spines 2.3 to 3.4 μ apart.

A little-known annual, California.

DICORIA T. & G. Dicoria

Grains similar to those of *Cyclachaena,* uniform, oblate-spheroidal, 16.5 to 18.7 μ in diameter; subechinate, spines 2.3 to 3.4 μ apart; tricolpate, furrows long and tapering but less extended than in the grains of *Cyclachaena.* Exine distinctly but finely granular. The grains of the two species here described are identical in appearance.

The genus contains about seven species of annual or biennial herbs, sometimes with a woody base; inhabiting the arid regions of southwestern United States and Mexico. Known to be capable of causing hayfever but unimportant in this respect owing to their restriction to desert regions.

Dicoria canescens Gray (*D. calliptera* Rose & Standl.). Annual herb 2 to 4 ft. high. Desert wastes. Arizona, southern California, and Utah. Flowers June to November.

Dicoria Brandegei Gray. A diffusely branching cinereous herb 1 to 3 ft. high. Sandy bottoms. Southern Colorado to southern Utah to Arizona. Flowers in August.

Leuciva dealbata (Gray) Rydb. (*Iva dealbata* Gray). Grains somewhat various, nearly one-half of them tetracolpate, with furrows arranged in the trischistoclasic system. Normal tricolpate grains similar to those of *Cyclachaena*, oblately flattened, about 22 by 19.4 μ, subechinate, with spines very small, almost vestigial and only slightly more prominent than those of the grains of *Cyclachaena*. Texture rather coarsely and distinctly granular.

Low tomentose annual, about 1½ ft. high. Of desert regions. Texas, New Mexico, Coahuila, and Chihuahua. This species was formerly included in the genus *Iva* but appears to be more closely related to *Cyclachaena*.

Euphrosyne parthenifolia DC. (*Gymnostyles parthenifolia* Moc.). Grains uniform, oblately flattened, subechinate, with spines almost vestigial. Furrows short and tapering but obviously functioning as harmomegathi, though less effectively than those of *Cyclachaena*. Germ pores slightly larger than in the preceding species.

Perennial herb about 2½ ft. high. Mexico.

HYMENOCLEA T. & G. Greasebush

Grains mostly uniform, oblately flattened, 18 to 19.6 μ in diameter, subechinate, with spines greatly reduced, almost vestigial. Furrows short but meridionally extended beyond the pore as pointed projections. Pores small, elliptical, about 2.7 μ long, with their long axes directed meridionally. Obviously, neither the pores nor the furrows of these grains are sufficiently developed to accommodate changes in volume. The exine, however, is thin, and when the grain contracts it is drawn inward, forming three deep meridional depressions with the pores at their bottoms. Exine finely but distinctly granular.

The grains of the three species here recorded are practically identical, except that a large proportion of those of *H. monogyra* are tetracolpate.

Dioecious shrubs with unisexual flower heads, the pistillate one-flowered and with the involucre dilated to form a number of transverse wings. In distribution confined to desert regions of southwestern United States and Mexico. The pollen of several species is known to be an active cause of hayfever, but, owing to their restriction to deserts, the shrubs are not often important in this respect.

Hymenoclea Salsola T & G. (*H. polygyra* Delpino). A large shrub 3 to 6 ft. high. Southern Utah and Arizona to California and Lower California.

Hymenoclea fasciculata A. Nels. A low shrub, 1 to 3 ft. high. Nevada.

Hymenoclea monogyra T. & G. A large shrub 3 to 12 ft. high. Western Texas and Coahuila to southern California and Sinaloa.

IVA L. MARSH ELDER, POVERTY WEED, BOZZLEWEED, SALT SAGE

Grains oblate-spheroidal, 19 to 21 μ in diameter, subechinate, with spines relatively small, less prominent than those of *Ambrosia elatior*. Furrows very short, merely pits slightly elongate meridionally and without harmomegathic function. Exine finely but distinctly granular. In general these grains are similar to those of *Hymenoclea* but somewhat larger. Those of the four species recorded here are practically identical, except for slight differences in the size and distance apart of their spines. Their size is always too small to measure, but they vary in distance apart from 2.3 to 4.9 μ.

The marsh elders are perennial or annual herbs or shrubs resembling the ragweeds but generally growing in swampy or moist places. The genus contains about 15 species, native of North America. They all shed large quantities of pollen which produces hayfever symptoms similar to those caused by ragweed.

Iva oraria Bart. (*I. frutescens* Bigel.) Marsh elder, High-water shrub. Grains as in the generic description, 21 to 22 μ in diameter. Spines 4 to 4.9 μ apart. July, August.

A common shrub on banks of tidal streams and in salt marshes, along the Atlantic coast from Massachusetts to Virginia. Its pollen produces skin reactions with ragweed-hayfever patients but, owing to the localized distribution of the plants, is not a serious cause of hayfever.

Iva frutescens L. Marsh elder, High-water shrub. Grains identical in every respect with those of the preceding species.

The plants themselves differ from the preceding species only in their geographical distribution which extends, in similar habitat, from Virginia to Florida and Texas, and in the slightly smaller size of their involucres and achenes, characters of doubtful value in specific distinctions.

Iva ciliata Willd. (*I. annua* Michx.) Rough marsh elder. Grains about 21 μ in diameter, similar to those of *I. oraria* but with their texture more coarsely granular and spines slightly larger, 3.4 to 4.6 μ apart.

A coarse annual 1 to 6 ft. high, resembling *Ambrosia*, generally in moist soil. Illinois to Nebraska, New Mexico, and Louisiana. Flowers August to September, shedding large quantities of pollen which is the cause of much hayfever.

Iva axillaris Pursh. (*I. foliosa* Nutt.) (Plate XIV, Fig. 5.) Small-flowered marsh elder, Poverty weed. Normal grains 19.8 to 22 μ in diameter, similar to those of *I. oraria*. Spines very small, about 2.8 μ apart. A large proportion of the grains tetracolpate or variously irregular.

Low, perennial weed with leafy, herbaceous stems. rising 1 to 2 ft. high from a woody base; common in alkaline or saline meadows. Manitoba to Oklahoma to New Mexico to California to British Columbia. Flowers from May to September, shedding much pollen which certainly causes some hayfever in regions where abundant. It is regarded by Rowe (1928) as unimportant in this respect in California but is stated by Hall (Scheppegrell, 1917) to be next in importance to sagebrush.

Iva Hayesiana Gray. Normal grains rather uniform in size, 21 to 22 μ in diameter. Spines small, almost vestigial as in *Xanthium*, 2.8 to 3.4 μ apart. Many grains tetracolpate or variously irregular.

A bushy perennial about 3 ft. high; southern California, Lower California, and adjacent islands. Its pollen probably causes some hayfever in regions where abundant.

Iva angustifolia Nutt. Grains uniform, about 19.2 μ in diameter. Spines similar to those of *I. oraria*, about 3.4 μ apart.

A slender annual 1 to 3 ft. high. Gravelly banks and ponds. Arkansas, Oklahoma, Louisiana, and Texas.

Iva cheiranthifolia H. B. K. Grains uniform, about 20 μ in diameter; subechinate, with spines rather prominent, 2.8 to 3.4 μ apart.

Bushy perennial. Banks of streams and coastal plains. Cuba and the Bahamas.

AMBROSIA L. Ragweed

Grains oblate-spheroidal, 17 to 24 μ in diameter, subechinate, with spines too short to be conveniently measured but various in size and various in their distance apart among the different species from 2.3 to 4.3 μ. Furrows short, not at all or only slightly elongate in a meridional direction, virtually coinciding in extent with the germ pores. Exine rather thin, always conspicuously granular. The pollen of the different species can occasionally be distinguished from each other by the diameter of the grains, the size and distance apart of their spines, and the presence or absence of tetracolpate grains. But these distinctions are generally rather slight and of difficult application.

The ragweeds are monoecious, branching herbs, notorious for the enormous quantities of pollen that they produce, and among them are counted the worst known causes of hayfever. The genus consists of about 15 species of wide distribution in North America.

KEY TO THE SPECIES

I. Grains 17 to 20 μ in diameter.

    A. Spines comparatively large, 3.4 to 4.3 μ apart.   A. bidentata
         A. trifida

    B. Spines comparatively small, 2.3 to 3.4 μ apart.   A. elatior
         A. aptera
         A. cumanensis
         A. tenuifolia
         A. peruviana

II. Grains 22 to 30 μ in diameter.   A. psilostachya
         A. coronopifolia
         A. hispida

Ambrosia elatior L. (*A. artemisiaefolia* T. & G.). Common or Short ragweed (Plate XIII, Fig. 7) type. Grains spheroidal or slightly oblate, uniform, nearly always tricolpate, rarely tetracolpate, 17.6 to 19.2 μ in diameter (average 18.3 μ), subechinate. Spines flat-conical, scarcely pointed at their tips, about 2.8 μ apart. Exine rather thin and flexible, distinctly, and comparatively coarsely, granular. Furrows short, merely small pits, almost coinciding with their enclosed germ pore.

These grains may be distinguished from those of *A. trifida* by their *larger* average diameter, and by the smaller size, less pointed character, and closer arrangement of their spines. They may be distinguished from those of *A. psilostachya* and *A. coronopifolia* by their *smaller* average size, smaller and more closely arranged spines, and the almost total absence of tetracolpate grains which characterize the pollen of the two latter species.

A coarse, branching annual with fibrous roots, a pernicious weed of cultivated fields throughout the northern part of the United States and adjacent Canada, though less abundant westward. It is known to consist of several slightly differing races, and, though all are probably equally active in producing hayfever, there is evidence that some of them possess slight immunological distinctions. August to October.

Ambrosia psilostachya DC. (Plate XIII, Fig. 8; Plate XIV, Fig. 6) Western ragweed. Grains spheroidal or oblately flattened, somewhat various in size, 22 to 24.7 μ in diameter, tricolpate or tetracolpate with about equal frequency. Spines larger than those of the grains of *A. elatior*, resembling those of *trifida*, 2.8 to 3.4 μ apart.

Bushy herbs from perennial, creeping rootstocks; similar in outward appearance to *A. elatior* but distinguished by their perennial habit. Louisiana to New Mexico and Tamaulipas. August to October. A frequent cause of hayfever.

Ambrosia coronopifolia T. & G. (*A. psilostachya* Gray) Western ragweed. Grains identical with those of the preceding species—a similar proportion of them tetracolpate.

The plants of this species are distinguished from those of *A. psilostachya* only by the relatively unimportant technical characters of the presence on their fruit of fewer and less pointed tubercles and the absence of pustulate bases to the hairs of their leaves. In view of the identity in form of their pollen grains and the presence of the same proportion of tetracolpate grains among both, it seems likely that these two species should be merged.

The present species (generally spoken of as *A. psilostachya*) is extremely abundant in lowland and waste places. Illinois to Saskatchewan, Texas, Mexico, and California. Throughout much of its range it is the cause of a large proportion of all the hayfever occurring during its flowering period, from July to October.

Ambrosia hispida Pursh. (*A. maritima* Ferrero). Grains oblate, rather various, 22.8 to 28.5 μ in diameter, many tetracolpate which may or may not be giants. Spines similar in appearance to those of *A. elatior*, 2.9 to 4 μ apart.

Sea beaches, southern Florida and West Indies. Flowers almost throughout the year but is not regarded as a serious cause of hayfever.

Ambrosia trifida L. Tall or Giant ragweed (Plate XIII, Fig. 9). Grains uniform, spheroidal or somewhat oblately flattened, 16.5 to 19.2 μ in diameter (average 17.7 μ), with spines relatively large and distinctly sharp pointed, about 3.4 μ apart. Texture distinctly granular.

These grains can be distinguished from those of *A. elatior* by their smaller average size and by their spines which are slightly larger, more sharply pointed, and farther apart. They can be distinguished from those of *A. psilostachya* and *A. coronopifolia* by their smaller size and the almost total absence of tetracolpate grains which characterize the pollen of the two latter species.

A coarse, annual weed, characteristically branching at the base, reaching a height of 13 ft.; with leaves undivided, three parted or five parted, and their petioles marginate. Exceedingly common throughout the northern part of the United States and adjacent Canada, less abundant westward. It sheds enormous quantities of pollen from early August until killed by frost. Its pollen and that of *A. elatior*, with which it is frequently associated, are the cause of most of the late summer hayfever in the northeastern United States.

Ambrosia aptera DC. (*A. trifida texana* Scheele). Grains oblate-spheroidal, about 18.2 μ in diameter, excepting a few giants which are about 22 μ in diameter; apparently always tricolpate. Spines distinctly sharp, resembling those of the grains of *A. trifida*, 2.6 to 3.1 μ apart.

A tall annual, 3 to 15 ft. high, closely resembling *A. trifida* but may be distinguished from it by the lack of lateral wings on its petioles and its habit of branching high up instead of at or near the ground. Louisiana to Arizona and adjoining Mexico. The cause of much hayfever in regions where abundant but not generally distinguished from *A. trifida* in hayfever studies.

Ambrosia cumanensis H. B. K. Grains oblate-spheroidal, uniform, 17.3 μ in diameter, with spines greatly reduced, similar to those of *A. elatior*, 2.8 to 3.4 μ apart.

A bushy perennial, $2\frac{1}{2}$ to 6 ft. high. Mexico to Colombia, Brazil, and Cuba. Not known to cause hayfever.

Ambrosia bidentata Michx. Grains uniform, oblate-spheroidal, 19.8 to 21 μ in diameter. Spines sharp and rather prominent, similar to those of *A. trifida*, about 4.3 μ apart.

A low, hirsute annual, usually much branched, 1 to 3 ft. high. Prairies, Illinois, Kansas, Louisiana, and Texas. July to September. Known to be the cause of some hayfever within its somewhat restricted range, though in hayfever studies it is not generally distinguished from the other species of *Ambrosia* with which it is usually associated.

Ambrosia tenuifolia Spreng. Grains uniform, oblately flattened, 19.8 to 25 μ in diameter, with spines rather prominent; similar to those of *A. trifida*, 2.8 to 3.4 μ apart.

A low annual 1 to 2 ft. high. Native of Argentina and Uruguay but naturalized in Louisiana and Puerto Rico.

Ambrosia peruviana Willd. (*A. artemisiaefolia* Benth.). Grains uniform, oblately flattened, 17.6 to 19.8 μ in diameter. Spines greatly reduced, similar to those of *A. elatior*, 2.6 to 3.4 μ apart.

An annual or perennial herb 2 to 6 ft. high. Jamaica, Puerto Rico, Mexico to Chile and Paraguay.

Acanthambrosia Bryantii (Curran) Rydb. (*Franseria Bryantii* Curran). Grains somewhat various, about one-quarter of them having four instead of the usual three furrows. Normal grains spheroidal or slightly oblate, 22 to 23.1 μ in diameter. Spines small, similar to those of *A. elatior*, 3.7 to 4.6 μ apart.

A low shrub. Lower California.

FRANSERIA Cav. (*Gaertneria* Medic.) FALSE RAGWEED

Grains similar to those of *Ambrosia*, oblate-spheroidal in shape, 18 to 23.5 μ in diameter, subechinate, the spines various in size, in some species vestigial.

The false ragweeds are annual or perennial herbs or shrubs, to be distinguished from the true ragweeds only on minor technical details. They likewise shed large amounts of pollen which causes much hayfever, mostly during the latter part of summer.

Franseria tenuifolia Harv. & Gray (*Gaertneria tenuifolia* Ktze., *Xanthium tenuifolium* Delpino). Slender ragweed. Grains various; many of them tetra- and hexacolpate, and these may or may not be giants. Normal grains 19.8 to 22 μ in diameter. Spines slightly more prominent than those of *Ambrosia trifida*, the most prominent observed in the genus, about 1.5 μ long and 3.3 to 3.4 μ apart.

A perennial herb, in general appearance resembling western ragweed and frequently confused with *Ambrosia tenuifolia*, which it resembles even more closely. "It grows in warm dry districts from the westerly part of the Mississippi valley to Colorado, Nevada and southern California and ranges southward to Texas." (Hall in Scheppegrell, 1917.)   Flowers May to November and is the cause of much hayfever in Arizona (Phillips, 1923) and in California (Selfridge, 1920).

Franseria dumosa Gray (*Gaertneria dumosa* Ktze.) Sandbur. Grains uniform, 19.8 to 24.2 μ in diameter.   Spines small, less prominent than those of *Ambrosia elatior*, 2.8 to 3.4 μ apart.

"A low spreading, white-stemmed shrub, with brittle, woody branches.   It grows in great abundance on the hot dry deserts from southern Utah to southeastern California and southern Arizona."   (Hall in Scheppegrell, 1917.)   Flowers March to June and is known to cause much hayfever.

Franseria acanthicarpa (Hook.) Coville (*F. Hookeriana* Nutt., *Gaertneria acanthicarpa* Britt., *Ambrosia acanthicarpa* Hook.) Bur ragweed.   Grains uniform, 18.7 to 20.3 μ in diameter. Spines less prominent than those of *Ambrosia elatior*, 2.8 to 3.7 μ apart.

A spreading, bushy annual or biennial weed with ashy-gray leaves, somewhat resembling western ragweed.   It inhabits sandy plains and is common in arid sections from the Rocky Mountains nearly to the Pacific coast.   In California, Oregon, and Washington it is restricted to the eastern or drier parts of the states.   Flowers from August to December and is the cause of much hayfever throughout a large part of its range (Phillips, 1922, 1923; Selfridge, 1920).

Franseria ilicifolia Gray (*Gaertneria ilicifolia* Ktze.).   Grains various, but apparently none has supernumerary furrows, 20.9 to 22 μ in diameter.   Spines vestigial, only slightly more prominent than those of the grains of Euxanthium, 2.8 to 2.9 μ apart.

A shrubby perennial about 3 ft. high.   Arizona, southern California, and Lower California.   Not known to cause hayfever.

Franseria albicaulis Torr.   Grains uniform, rarely tetra-colpate, about 18.7 μ in diameter.   Spines small, less prominent than in the grains of *Ambrosia elatior*.

A low, branching shrub, finely tomentose when young.   Southern California to southern Utah, Sonora, and Lower California. Not known to cause hayfever.

Franseria bipinnatifida Nutt. (*Gaertneria bipinnatifida* Ktze., *Ambrosia bipinnatifolia* Greene).   Beach   sandbur.   Grains rather uniform, 22.5 to 25.3 μ in diameter; a few tetracolpate. Spines almost vestigial only slightly more prominent than in the grains of Euxanthium.

A low, spreading herb of sea beaches and sand dunes, occasionally elsewhere in waste places. Flowers from April to December and is believed to be an important cause of hayfever in California (Rowe, 1928).

Franseria deltoidea Torr. (*Gaertneria deltoidea* Ktze.) Canyon ragweed, Rabbit bush. Grains uniform, 20.3 to 22 μ in diameter. Spines vestigial as in the grains of Euxanthium.

A shrubby perennial with finely tomentose branches. Southern Arizona. Flowers in spring and early summer and is an important cause of hayfever (Watson and Kibler, 1922; Phillips, 1923).

XANTHIUM L. Cocklebur

Section 1. Acanthoxanthium. Grains subechinate, with the spines prominent and sharp pointed, larger than those of the grains of *Ambrosia trifida*, 3.4 to 5.1 μ apart. Furrows extremely short, only slightly extended beyond the small germ pore which each encloses. Texture finely but conspicuously granular. The grains of the three species here included are virtually alike but are entirely dissimilar from those of all the species of the second section of the genus, Euxanthium, in their smaller size and much larger spines (Plate XIV, Fig. 8).

Xanthium spinosum L. (*Acanthoxanthium spinosum* Fourr.) Spiny clothbur, Clotweed, Burweed. A large, coarse annual herb with dark-green leaves, smooth and shining on the upper surface and armed with conspicuous three-pronged axillary spines.

Sporadically introduced almost throughout the United States, particularly abundant in California where it is regarded as an important cause of hayfever (Rowe, 1928). June to November. Native of the Mediterranean region and Australia.

Xanthium ambrosioides B. & H. Grains uniform, as in the sectional description.

Xanthium catharticum Kth. (Plate XIV, Fig. 8). Grains as in the sectional description.

Section 2. Euxanthium. Grains spheroidal, mostly larger than those of section Acanthoxanthium, 22.1 to 29.1 μ in diam-

TABLE VI.—POLLEN GRAINS OF THE AMBROSIEAE

Species	Furrows	Sculpturing	Shape	Size μ	Spine length, μ	Spine distance apart, μ
Iveneae:						
Oxytenia acerosa	Long	Echinate	Flattened	18.1	2.5	4.6
Chorisiva nevadensis	Long	Echinate	Spheroidal	16.5	1.1	3.4
Cyclachaena xanthifolia	Long	Subechinate	Flattened	18.7	.....	2.6-3.4
C. pedicellata	Long	Subechinate	Flattened	16.7	.....	2.8-4.0
C. ambrosiaefolia	Long	Subechinate	Flattened	19.0	.....	2.3-2.8
C. lobata	Long	Subechinate	Flattened	17.8	.....	2.3-3.4
Euphrosyne parthenifolia	Medium	Subechinate	Flattened	14.8	.....	2.3
Dicoria Brandegei	Long	Subechinate	Slightly flattened	17.6	.....	2.3-3.4
D. canescens	Long	Subechinate	Slightly flattened	17.8	.....	2.3-3.4
Leuciva dealbata	Long	Subechinate reduced	Flattened	20.3	.....	2.3-2.8
Iva ciliata	Short	Subechinate reduced	Spheroidal	20.9	.....	3.4-4.6
I. oraria	Short	Subechinate reduced	Spheroidal	20.9	.....	4.0-4.9
I. frutescens	Short	Subechinate reduced	Spheroidal	19.1	.....	2.3-4.0
I. angustifolia	Short	Subechinate reduced	Spheroidal	19.4	.....	3.4
I. cheiranthifolia	Short	Subechinate reduced	Slightly flattened	20.0	.....	2.8-3.4
I. Hayesiana	Short	Subechinate reduced	Slightly flattened	21.0	.....	2.8-3.4
I. axillaris	Short	Subechinate reduced	Spheroidal	20.9	.....	2.8
Ambrosineae:						
Hymenoclea fasciculata	Short	Subechinate much reduced	Flattened	18.1	.....	2.3-3.4
H. Salsola	Short	Subechinate much reduced	Flattened	19.6	.....	2.3-3.4
H. monogyra	Short	Subechinate much reduced	Flattened	18.8	.....	2.3-3.4
Ambrosia elatior	Short	Subechinate	Spheroidal	18.3	.....	2.3-3.4

Species					
A. trifida	Short	Subechinate	Spheroidal	17.7	3.4
A. aptera	Short	Subechinate	Spheroidal	18.5	2.6-3.1
A. cumanensis	Short	Subechinate	Slightly flattened	17.3	2.8-3.4
A. psilostachya	Short	Subechinate	Spheroidal	23.4	2.8-3.4
A. coronopifolia	Short	Subechinate	Spheroidal	24.5	3.4-4.0
A. hispida	Short	Subechinate	Flattened	25.0	2.9-4.0
A. bidentata	Short	Subechinate	Slightly flattened	19.5	4.3
A. tenuifolia	Short	Subechinate	Spheroidal	22.0	2.8-3.4
A. peruviana	Short	Subechinate	Slightly flattened	17.3	2.8-3.4
Acanthambrosia Bryantii	Short	Subechinate	Slightly flattened	22.8	3.7-4.6
Franseria tenuifolia	Short	Subechinate	Slightly flattened	20.7	3.3-3.4
F. bipinnatifida	Short	Subechinate much reduced	Spheroidal	23.3	2.3-2.8
F. acanthicarpa	Short	Subechinate reduced	Slightly flattened	19.8	2.8-3.7
F. dumosa	Short	Subechinate much reduced	Slightly flattened	20.6	2.8-3.4
F. albicaulis	Short	Subechinate much reduced	Slightly flattened	18.1	2.3
F. ilicifolia	Short	Subechinate much reduced	Slightly flattened	21.3	2.8-2.9
F. deltoidea	Short	Spines vestigial	Slightly flattened	20.3	2.3
Xanthium spinosum	Short	Subechinate prominent	Spheroidal	22.0	4.6
X. catharticum	Short	Subechinate prominent	Spheroidal	20.9	3.4-5.2
X. ambrosioides	Short	Subechinate prominent	Spheroidal	21.0	4.6
X. speciosum	Short	Spines vestigial	Spheroidal	26.4	2.3-2.8
X. strumarium	Short	Spines vestigial	Spheroidal	22.1	2.3-2.6
X. globosum	Short	Spines vestigial	Spheroidal	22.1	2.3-2.4
X. pennsylvanicum	Short	Spines vestigial	Spheroidal	25.0	2.6-2.8
X. chinense	Short	Spines vestigial	Spheroidal	23.4	2.6

eter, with spines vestigial, generally scarcely apparent, 2 to 2.8 μ apart. Furrows short, scarcely extending beyond their enclosed germ pore. Exine thin, collapsing easily as the grain shrinks, rather coarsely and conspicuously granular. There is scarcely any difference between the grains of the following species, except possibly in their size and in the distance apart of their spine vestiges.

Coarse, branching, rough, annual herbs. About 15 species of wide geographical distribution. Most of them produce large amounts of pollen which is known to give reactions by skin test with hayfever patients but generally less than the ragweeds, and several of them are important causes of hayfever.

Xanthium speciosum Kearney. Great clotbur (Fig. 122). Grains as in the sectional description.

A coarse and very stout weed 3 to 4½ ft. high. North Dakota to Wisconsin, Tennessee, Montana, Nebraska, and Texas. August to September. An important cause of hayfever, producing more pollen than most of the other species.

Xanthium strumarium L. (*X. brevirostre* Wallr.). Grains as in the sectional description.

Coarse, branching, pubescent herb about 3 ft. high. Native of Europe, introduced into California and Massachusetts.

Xanthium globosum Schull. Grains as in the sectional description.

Low, spreading herb with reddish, purple, or straw-colored stems. Missouri and Kansas.

Xanthium pennsylvanicum Wallr. (Plate XIV, Fig. 7). Grains as in the sectional description.

Coarse, scabrous herbs, about 2½ ft. high. Throughout the United States and adjoining Mexico and in the Hawaiian islands.

Xanthium chinense Mill. (*X. longirostre* Wallr., *X. canadense* Rowlee.). Grains as in the sectional description.

Coarse, robust herbs, reaching a height of 6 ft. Ontario to Massachusetts, Florida, Texas, and rarely California, Mexico, and throughout the West Indies.

GLOSSARY

Abporal lacuna, a lacuna meridionally opposite a germ pore. It may be closed as in the grain of *Scolymus* (Plate XI, Fig. 1), communicate with its adjoining poral lacuna as in that of *Taraxacum* (Plate XI, Fig. 2), or, if the poral lacuna is absent, it may communicate with its meridionally opposite abporal lacuna.

Acolpate, without furrows or pores. See Colpate.

Aspidate, bearing aspides.

Aspis, pl. **aspides,** a shield-shaped, subexineous thickening surrounding a germ pore.

Bladder, see Wing.

Cap or disk, the thickened dorsal surface of the winged grains of the Abietineae and Podocarpineae.

Circumpolar lacunae, those lacunae, generally six in each hemisphere, surrounding the polar lacuna or polar thickening in lophate grains.

Colpate, possessing germinal furrows or harmomegathi, generally used with numerical prefixes as mono-, di-, and tri-, signifying the number of furrows (Gr. κόλπος, a fold).

Cribellate, possessing a number of rounded germinal apertures more or less equally spaced. Example: *Salsola pestifer* (Plate VIII, Fig. 4) (Lat. *cribellum*, a little sieve.)

Disk, see Cap.

Dorsal, the side of the grain turned inward in the tetrad and opposite the furrow in monocolpate grains; opposed to ventral (q.v.).

Echinate, provided with long or conspicuous and generally sharp, pointed spines, *e.g.*, the grains of *Solidago* (Plate XII, Fig. 4) and *Oxytenia* (Plate XIV, Fig. 1) (Gr. ἐχῖνος, a hedgehog).

Echinolophate, lophate, with the ridges bearing spines on their crests.

Emphytic characters, those that are the result of a specifically inherited cell form (Gr. ἔμφυτος, innate).

Equator, the great circle midway between the two poles and dividing the grain into two polar hemispheres.

Equatorial lacuna, a lacuna situated on the equator between two germ pores and as much in one polar hemisphere as the other. It may be remote from contact with the pores or poral lacunae, as in the grains of *Vernonia jucunda*, or in contact with one of them, as in those of *Scorzonera* (Plate XI, Fig. 5), or with two of them, as in those of *Tragopogon* (Plate XI, Fig. 4).

Equatorial ridge, an interlacunar ridge extending from pore to pore along the equator in lophate grains. It may be continuous, as in the grains of *Taraxacum* (Plate XI, Fig. 2), or interrupted to admit the equatorial lacunae when these are present, as in the grains of *Scorzonera hispanica* (Plate XI, Fig. 5) and *Tragopogon pratensis* (Plate XI, Fig. 4).

Furrow, see Germinal furrow and Harmomegathus.

Furrow membrane, the area of the exine enclosed by the germinal furrow, generally a delicate elastic membrane which stretches as the furrow opens, *e.g.*, in the grains of *Solidago speciosa* (Plate XII, Fig. 4).

Furrow rim, the lip of the furrow, the edge or fold of exine bounding the furrow, sometimes thickened and in the winged grains of the Podocarpineae, bearing the ventral roots of the bladders.

Germinal aperture, a hole in the furrow membrane through which the germ pore protrudes. The term is also used to designate the rounded apertures which frequently occur in the general surface of the exine in the absence of germinal furrows, *e.g.*, in the grains of *Salsola pestifer*, though these should probably be regarded as germinal furrows which are rounded in form and coinciding in extent with their enclosed germ pores.

Germinal furrow, a longitudinal groove or opening in the exine, either enclosing a germ pore or serving directly as the place of emission of the pollen tube, also generally serving as a harmomegathus (q. v.).

Germ pore, a pollen-tube anlage or the place of emergence of the pollen tube, generally denoted by a rounded papilla, *e.g.*, in the grains of *Eriogonum gracile* (Plate VIII, Fig. 6). Germ pores are generally enclosed in a germinal furrow as in the above example, but they may penetrate the exine directly, *e.g.*, in the grains of *Salsola pestifer* (Plate VIII, Fig. 4). *Cf.* Germinal aperture.

Haptotypic characters, those which are due to internal or prenatal environment, such as the stimuli received by a developing pollen grain from contacts with its neighbors (Gr. ἅπτειν, touch, and τυπόω, make an impression).

Harmomegathus, an organ or mechanism which accommodates a semirigid exine to changes in volume, *e.g.*, the three germinal furrows of the grains of *Solidago speciosa* (Plate XII, Fig. 4).

Harmomegathy, volume-change accommodation (Gr. ἁρμόζω, accommodate or adapt, and μέγαθος, size).

Heterotasithynic, due to unequal lateral stresses, *i.e.*, bilateral stresses, the forces which produce vertical cracking in a wall. This is due to a lateral shrinking at right angles to the vertical thrust of gravity. Such an effect is encountered in the oblong pollen grains of *Impatiens*, with four furrows, one at each corner of the grain and not arranged in the trischistioclasic system (Gr. ἕτερος, other, τάσις, a straining, and ἰθύνετο, in a straight line).

Intercolpar, between the furrows.

Intercolpar thickening, thickened areas in the exine, *e.g.*, in the grains of *Chorizanthe pungens* (Plate VIII, Fig. 3).

Interlacunar ridge, one separating lacunae from each other in lophate grains, *e.g.*, those of *Taraxacum officinale* (Plate XI, Fig. 2).

Interporal lacuna, a lacuna situated between, and bounded on one or two sides by abporal lacunae and wholly within one polar hemisphere in lophate grains, *e.g.*, those of *Scorzonera hispanica* (Plate XI, Fig. 5).

Isometric, equal space appropriation, used here in a sense slightly modified from the usual meaning, characterized by equal measure, to describe the arrangement of spines and, occasionally, of pores which tend to be arranged at equal distances in all directions from each other.

Isotasithynic, due to equal lateral stresses, the forces which produce trischistoclasis, tending to form hexagons on a plane surface or hexagons, pentagons, squares, and triangles on a spherical surface, *e.g.*, cracks in a plaster wall, caused by the shrinking of the plaster equally in all directions. Stands in contrast to heterotasithynic (Gr. ἴσος equal, τάσις, a straining, and ἰθύνετο, in a straight line).

Lacuna, a large pit or depressed space in the exine of lophate or reticulate grains. Lacunae are never germ pores or furrows but may be occupied by one or the other of them.

Limb, the visual boundary or edge of the apparent disk of a sphere. In pollen grains it is the same as the equator only when the grain is viewed with one of the poles exactly uppermost.

Lophate, with the outer surface thrown into ridges, anastomosing or free, as for example in the grains of *Pacourina edulis* (Plate XII, Fig. 1) or *Taraxacum officinale* (Gr. λόφος, a crest).

Lune, an area on the surface of a sphere bounded by arcs of two great circles passing through the poles.

Marginal ridge, the slightly projecting rim of the cap or disk, *e.g.*, in the grains of *Pinus* (Fig. 78).

Monocolpate, having a single germinal furrow or harmomegathus on one side of the grain. Example: *Ginkgo biloba* (Plate II, Fig. 6). If the grain is encircled by a single furrow, it is regarded as dicolpate or zonate.

Operculum, a thickening, of measurable bulk and clearly defined, of the pore membrane. Example: grass pollen (Plate V, Figs. 2, 3), *Castalia* (Plate VI, Fig. 1).

Paraporal lacuna, a lacuna adjoining on one side a poral lacuna and wholly within one hemisphere, *e.g.*, in the grains of *Taraxacum officinale* (Plate XI, Fig. 2).

Paraporal ridges, the ridges bounding the germinal furrows and extended in a meridional direction, *e.g.*, in the grains of *Tragopogon pratensis* (Plate XI, Fig. 4).

Polar hemisphere. See Equator and Pole.

Polar lacuna, the one or more lacunae at the pole or center of symmetry in lophate grains in which the pattern is radiosymmetrical or nearly so. When there are more than one at each pole they are polar lacunae, unless, by definition, they are interporal or abporal lacunae. Example: the grain of *Barnadesia trianae* (Plate XII, Fig. 6) and *Barnadesia venosa* (Plate XII, Fig. 7).

Pole, one of the extremities of the axis of symmetry of radiosymmetrical pollen grains. If there is more than one such axis of symmetry, the word applies only to the extremities of the axis which is directed toward the center of the tetrad or was so directed during the grain's formation. From these tetrad relations the two poles and two hemispheres may be designated as inner and outer or proximal and distal, though in mature pollen grains that are not shed in tetrads the two hemispheres are rarely distinguishable.

Poral lacuna, a lacuna enclosing a germ pore. It may be open through a cleft, as in the grain of *Taraxacum* (Plate XI, Fig. 2), or closed, as in those of *Scolymus* (Plate XI, Fig. 1).

Pore, see germ pore.

Pore membrane, a delicate membrane covering a germ pore. It may be flecked or bear an operculum.

Psilate, unadorned—without spines ridges or projections of any kind, other than germ pores (Gr. ψιλός, smooth). Examples: *Phleum pratense* (Plate V, Fig. 2) and *Rumex Acetosella* (Plate VIII, Fig. 1).

Psilolophate, lophate, with the ridges smooth on their crests.

Reticulate, with the surface thrown into anastomosing ridges enclosing lacunae, generally smaller than in lophate grains, *e.g.,* in the grains of *Ligustrum* (Plate X, Fig. 8).

Ridge, see Interlacunar ridge.

Subechinate, provided with short and sometimes rounded spines, *e.g.,* the grains of *Ambrosia elatior* (Plate XIII, Fig. 7).

Subechinolophate, lophate, with the crests bearing reduced spines, *e.g.,* the grains of *Stokesia laevis* (Plate XII, Fig. 2).

Sublophate, with the surface thrown into ridges which are imperfectly defined, *e.g.,* in the grains of *Catananche caerulea* (Plate XI, Fig. 3).

Tasicolpate, bearing furrows in some systematic arrangement, apparently resulting from stresses acting over the surface of the grain; distinct from the furrow of a monocolpate grain which arises from the collapse of the grain on its unsupported side (Gr. τάσις, straining).

Tasithynic, due to lateral stresses, the stresses that arise from shrinking, as in plaster, mud, or pollen-grain surfaces (Gr. τάσις, a straining, and ἰθύνετο, in a straight line).

Transverse furrow, a short, elliptical or elongate opening in the intine underlying the true furrow and with its long axis crossing that of the latter at right angles.

Tricolpate, possessing three meridionally arranged germinal furrows.

Trischistoclasic, triradiate cracking, the system in which the furrows of the pollen grains of the higher dicotyledons tend to form, a system similar to the cracking of drying mud or shrinking plaster, as if produced by equilateral stresses (τρίς, three; σκιστός, branching or parted; κλάσις, -εως, a breaking).

Ventral. The side of a grain turned outward in its tetrad. In monopored or monocolpate grains it is the side upon which the pore or furrow is borne. In other grains the dorsal and ventral sides are generally not distinguishable from each other after the grains have separated from their tetrads.

Vestigial spines, those of less prominence than of subechinate grains. Example: *Xanthium* (Plate XIV, Fig. 7).

Wing, the bladdery projection flanking or surrounding, frill-like, the germinal furrow of the grains of some Abietineae and Podocarpineae. It is generally greatly distended and attached by its ventral roots along the furrow rim and by its dorsal roots just ventrad of the marginal ridge.

Zonate, provided with one or more furrows, each encircling the grain as a lesser circle, wholly in one hemisphere and usually parallel to the equator.

BIBLIOGRAPHY

AIRY, H. 1874. Microscopical examination of air. *Nature*, **9,** 439.

AMICI, J. B. 1824. Observations microscopiques sur diverses espèces de plantes. *Ann. Sci. Nat.*, **2**: 41–70, 211–248, *pl.* 4.

———. 1830. Note sur le mode d'action du pollen sur le stigmate; extrait d'une lettre à M. Mirbel, Modène, July 3, 1830. *Ann. Sci. Nat.*, **21**: 329–332.

ANDERSON, R. J. 1923. Composition of corn pollen; II, Concerning certain lipoids, a hydrocarbon and phytosterol occurring in the pollen of white flint corn. *Jour. Biol. Chem.*, **55**: 611–628.

——— and W. L. KULP. 1922. Analysis and composition of corn pollen. *Jour. Biol. Chem.*, **50**: 433–453.

ANDRONESCUE, D. J. 1915. The physiology of the pollen of *Zea Mays*, 36 pp. Department of Agriculture, Kingdom of Rumania.

ANONYMOUS. 1925. Plants which cause hayfever. The Arlington Chemical Co., Yonkers, N. Y.

ARBER, E. A. NEWELL, and JOHN PARKIN. 1907. The origin of the angiosperms. *Jour. Linn. Soc. Bot.*, **38**: 29–80, 4 *figs.*

ARMBRUSTER, L., and G. OENIKE. 1929. Die Pollenformen als Mittel zur Honigherkunftsbestimmung. *Bücherei f. Bienenkunde*, **10**: 1–116, 23 *pl.*, 2 *charts.*

ASSARSSON, G., and E. GRANLUND. 1924. En metod för pollenanalys av minerogena jordarter. *Geol. Fören. Förh.*, **46.**

BABCOCK, E. B., and J. CLAUSEN. 1929. Meiosis in two species and three hybrids of *Crepis*, and its bearing on taxonomic relationship. *Univ. Calif. Pub. Agric. Sci.*, **2** (15): 401–432, *pl.* 58–61, 1 *fig.*

BAILEY, L. H. 1924. A manual of cultivated plants. Macmillan Co., New York.

BAKER, RICHARD T., and HENRY G. SMITH. 1910. Pines of Australia. Tech. Mus. N.S.W. Tech. Ed. Ser. No. 16. Sydney, Australia.

BALL, C. R. 1910. The history and distribution of *Sorghum. Dept. Agric., Bur. Plant Industry, Bull.*, **175**: 1–62, 16 *figs.*

BALYEAT, R. M. 1927. Factors which determine the pollen content of the air. *Jour. Lab. and Clin. Med.*, **12** (12): 8 pp., 2 *charts.*

———. 1927a. Seasonal hayfever. Oklahoma City.

——— and T. R. STEMAN. 1926. The importance of Oklahoma's wind borne pollinated plants, 19 pp., 14 *figs.* Oklahoma City.

——— and ———. 1927. Hayfever and asthma. Distribution and importance of the acnidas. *Amer. Jour. Med. Sci.*, **175** (5): 639, 3 *figs.*

BANCROFT, NELLIE. 1913. On some Indian Jurassic gymnosperms. *Trans. Linn. Soc. Bot.*, 2 ser., **8**: 69–86, *pl.* 7–9.

547

BEER, RUDOLPH. 1907. The supernumerary pollen grains of *Fuchsia.* *Ann. Bot.*, **21**: 305–307.

BENNETT, A. W. 1875. Insects and flowers. *Pop. Sci. Rev.*, **14**: 113–126, *pl.* 119, 120.

BENSON, MARGARET. 1904. *Telangium Scotti,* a new species of *Telangium* (*Calymmatheca*) showing structure. *Ann. Bot.*, **18**: 161–177, 1 *pl.*, 1 *fig.*

———. 1908. On the contents of the pollen chamber of a specimen of *Lagenostoma ovoides.* *Bot. Gaz.*, **45**: 409–412, 2 *figs.*

BENTHAM, GEORGE. 1873. Notes on the classification, history, and geographical distribution of the Compositae. *Jour. Linn. Soc. Bot.*, **13**: 335–577, *pl.* 8–11.

——— and J. D. HOOKER. 1873. *Genera plantarum*, **2**: 166. Lovell Reeve & Co., London.

BERNTON, HARRY S. 1928. Hayfever and asthma caused by the pollen of the paper mulberry (*Papyrius papyrifera* Ktze.). *Jour. Lab. and Clin. Med.*, **13** (9): 829–836.

BESSEY, C. E. 1915. The phylogenetic taxonomy of the flowering plants. *Ann. Missouri Bot. Gard.*, **2**: 109–164.

BIOURGE, P. 1892. Recherches morphologiques et chimiques sur les grains de pollen. *La Cellule*, **8**: 47–80, *pl.* 1, 2.

BLOSSFELDT, K. 1928. Urformen der Kunst, 18 pp., 120 *pl.*, Ernst Wasmuth, Berlin.

BOUILLENNE, M., and R. BOUILLENNE. 1930. Recherches expérimentales sur l'agent toxique du pollen d'*Ambrosia div. sp.* (Compositacées). *Bull. Classe Sci. Acad. Roy. Belgique*, sér. 5, **16**: 1052–1073, 3 *figs.*

———. 1931. Recherches expérimentales sur l'agent toxique du pollen d'*Ambrosia div. sp.* (Compositacées) *Bull. Classe Sci. Acad. Roy. Belgique*, sér. 5, **17**: 318–338.

BOWERS, C. G. 1931. The development of pollen and vicin strands in *Rhododendron catawbiense.* *Bull. Torrey Bot. Club*, **57**: 285–313, *pl.* 11–15, *figs.* 26, 27.

BRITTON, N. L., and A. BROWN. 1913. Illustrated flora of the Northeastern United States and Canada, ed. 2. New York.

BRONGNIART, ADOLPHE. 1827. Mémoire sur la génération et le développement de l'embryon dans les végétaux phanérogamiques. *Ann. Sci. Nat.*, **12**: 14–53; 145–172; 225–298.

———. 1828. Nouvelles recherches sur le pollen et les granules spermatiques des végétaux. *Ann. Sci. Nat.*, **15**: 381–401, *pl.* 13, 14.

———. 1831. Observations sur le mode de fécondation des Orchidées et les Cistinées. *Ann. Sci. Nat.*, **24**: 113–130, *pl.* 5–12.

BROWN, ROBERT. 1811. On the Proteaceae of Jussieu. *Trans. Linn. Soc.*, **10**: 15–226, *pl.* 2, 3.

———. 1820. An account of a new genus of plants named *Rafflesia.* *Trans. Linn. Soc.*, **13**: 201–234, *pl.* 15–22.

———. 1828. Exposé sommaire des observations microscopiques faites dans les mois de juin, juillet et août, 1827, sur les particules contenues dans le pollen des plantes, et sur l'existence générale de molécules actives dans les corps organisés et inorganisés. *Ann. Sci. Nat.*, 1 sér. **14**: 341–362.

―――. 1833. Observations of the organs and mode of fecundation in the Orchideae and the Asclepideae. *Trans. Linn. Soc.*, **16**: 685–745.

BROWN, WILLIAM H., and RAYMOND KEIMHOLZ. 1925. *Cycas Chamberlinii. Philippine Jour. Sci.*, **26** (1): 47–51, 2 *pl.*, 1 *fig.*

BUDDE, H. 1930. Pollenanalytische Untersuchungen im Weissen Venn, Münsterland. *Ber. Deut. Bot. Ges.*, **48**: 26–40, 27 *figs.*, 1 *map.*

BURLINGAME, L. I. 1908. The staminate cone and male gametophyte of *Podocarpus. Bot. Gaz.*, **46** (3): 161, 178, *pl.*, 8–9.

BUTLEROW, A. 1872. Carl Julius Fritzsche. *Ber. Deut. Chem. Ges.*, **5**: 132–136.

CALDWELL, OTIS W. 1907. *Mycrocycas calocoma. Bot. Gaz.*, **44**: 118–140, *pl.* 10–13.

CAMERARIUS, RUDOLPH J. 1694. Ueber das Geschlecht der Pflanzen (De sexu plantarum epistola). Translated by M. Möbius. Wilhelm Engelmann, Leipzig. 1899.

CAMPBELL, D. H. 1897. A morphological study of Naias and Zannichellia. *Proc. Calif. Acad. Sci.*, ser 3, **1**: 1–62.

CAPELLINI, G., and E. SOLMS-LAUBACH. 1892. I Tronchi di Bennettitee dei Musei Italiani. *Mem. R. Accad. Sci. Inst. Bologna*, ser. 5, **2**: 161–215, *pl.* 1–5.

CASSINI, H. 1826. Oposcules phytologiques. Vol. **2**. Paris.

―――. 1828. Nouvelles observations sur les granules spermatiques des végétaux. *Ann. Sci. Nat.*, **13**: 146–153.

CHAMBERLAIN, C. J. 1909. *Dioon Spinulosum. Bot. Gaz.*, **48**: 401–413.

―――. 1912. Morphology of *Ceratozamia. Bot. Gaz.*, **53**: 1–19, 1 *pl.*, 7 *figs.*

―――. 1915. A phylogenetic study of cycads. *Proc. Nat. Acad. Sci.*, **1**: 86–90.

―――. 1919. The living cycads. University of Chicago Press, Chicago.

CHAMBERLAIN, C. T. 1927. Hayfever in the Pacific North West. *Ann. Otol. Rhinol. and Laryngol.*, **36**: 1083–1092.

COCA, A. F., MATHEW WALTZER, and AUGUST THOMMEN. 1931. Asthma and hayfever in theory and practice, 850 *pp.* Charles C. Thomas, Springfield, Ill.

COULTER, J. M. 1898. The origin of the gymnosperms and the seed habit. *Bot. Gaz.*, **26**: 153–168.

――― and C. J. CHAMBERLAIN. 1910. Morphology of the gymnosperms. Chicago University Press, Chicago.

DALLIMORE, WILLIAM, and A. B. JACKSON. 1923. A handbook of Coniferae. London.

DALLINGER, W. H. 1901. The microscope and its revelations, ed. 8. London.

DECASINE, M. J. 1835. Note sur un nouveau genre de Cichoracées, recueilli par M. Bertero dans l'île de Juan Fernandez. *Guill. Arch. Bot.*, **1**: 513.

DELPINO, F. 1871. Studi sopra un lignaggio anemofilo delle Composite ossia sopra ill gruppo delle Artemisiaceae. Florence.

DOCTOROWSKY, B. C., and B. B. KUDRJASCHOW. 1923. Pylca w torfie. *Izw. Naucz. Eksp. Inst. Torf. Moskwa.*, **5**: 33–44, *pl.* 1–4.

DUKE, WILLIAM W. 1926. Allergy, asthma, hayfever, urticaria, 344 *pp.*, 74 *figs.* C. V. Mosbey Company, St. Louis.

———. 1928. Pollen content of still air. *Jour. Amer. Med. Assoc.*, **91**: 1709–1711.

——— and O. C. DURHAM. 1928. Pollen content of still air. *Jour. Amer. Med. Assoc.*, **90**: 1529–1532.

DUNBAR, W. P. 1903. Weiter Beitrag zur Ursache und spezifischen Heilung des Heufiebers. *Deut. Med. Wochenschr.*, **29**: 149–152.

———. 1903. Zur Frage betreffend die Aetiologie und spezifische Theropie des Heufiebers. *Berlin Klin. Wochenschr.*, **40**: 537–539; 569–572; 596–599.

EDGEWORTH, M. P. 1877. Pollen. London.

EHRENBERG, C. G. 1831. Ueber das Pollen der Asclepiadeen; ein Beitrag zur Auflösung der Anomalieen in der Pflanzen-Befruchtung. *Abhl. Akad. Berlin.*, **1829**: 21–40, *pl.* 2.

ENGLER, A. 1876. Beiträge zur Antherbildung der Metaspermen. *Jahrb. Wiss. Bot.* **10**: 275–316, *pl.* 20–24.

ERDTMAN, G. 1922. Pollenanalytische Untersuchungen von Torfmooren und marinen Sedimenten in Sudwest-Schweden. *Arkiv. för Botanik*, **17**(10): 1–173.

———. 1923. Beitrag zur Kenntnis der Mikrofossilien in Torf und Sedimenten. *Arkiv. för Botanik*, **18**(14): 1–9, 2 *pl.*, 1 *fig.*

———. 1927. Literature on pollen statistics published before 1927. *Geol. Fören.* 1 *Stockholm Förh.*, March-April.

———. 1929. Some aspects of the postglacial history of British forests. *Jour. Ecology*, **17**(1): 112.

———. 1930. Literature on pollen statistics published during the years 1927–1929. *Geol. Fören.* 1 *Stockholm Förh.*, March-April.

———. 1932. Literature on pollen statistics and related topics published 1930 and 1931. *Geol. Fören.* 1 *Stockholm Förh.* November-December.

———. 1934a. Über die Verwendung von Essigsäureanhydrid bei Pollenuntersuchungen. *Svensk. Bot. Tid.*, **28**(2): 354–361.

———. 1934b. Literature on pollen-statistics and related topics published 1932–1934. *Geol. Fören. Förh.*, **56**(3): 463–481.

——— and H. ERDTMAN. 1933. The improvement of pollen analysis technique. *Svensk Bot. Tid.*, **27**(3): 347–357.

ERLANSON, EILEEN W. 1929. Cytological conditions and evidences for hybridity in North American wild roses. *Bot. Gaz.*, **87**: 443–506, *pl.* 16–19.

FARR, C. H. 1916. Cytokinesis of the pollen mothercells of certain dicotyledons. *Mem. N. Y. Bot. Gard.*, **6**: 253–317, *pl.* 27–29.

FEINBERG, S. M. 1929. Progress in hayfever. *Jour. Lab. and Clin. Med.*, **14**(8): 726–746.

BIBLIOGRAPHY 551

BIBLIOGRAPHY 551

FISCHER, HUGO. 1890. Beiträge zur vergleichenden Morphologie der Pollen-körener, 72 pp., *pl.* 1–3. Berlin.

FRANZ, F. K. E. 1908. Beiträge zur Kenntniss der Portulacaceen und Basillaceen, 50 pp., *figs.* 1–43. Halle.

FRITZSCHE, C. J. 1832. Beiträge zur Kenntniss des Pollen, 48 pp., 2 *pl.* Berlin.

——. 1833. De Plantarum polline. Berlin, Aug. 10.

——. 1834. Ueber den Pollen der Pflanzen und das Pollenin. *Poggendorf's Ann. Physik u. Chemie*, **32**(31): 481–492.

——. 1837. Ueber den Pollen. *Mém. Sav. Étrang. Acad. St. Petersburg*, **3**: 649–672, *pl.* 1–13.

FULLER, G. D. 1929. Peat bogs and postglacial vegetation. *Bot. Gaz.*, **87**: 560–562.

GATES, R. R. 1925. Pollen tetrad wall formation in *Lathraea*. *La Cellule*, **35**: 49–51, *pl.* 1.

GERASIMOV, D. A. 1930. On the characteristics of the pollen of *Larix* and *Pinus cembra* in peat. *Geol. Fören. Förh.*, **52**(1): 111–115, *figs.* 1, 2.

GLEICHEN, WILHELM. 1764. Das Neuste aus dem Reiche der Pflanzen. Erben.

GREEN, J. R. 1891. Diastase in pollen. *Ann. Bot.*, **5**: 511–512.

GREW, NEHEMIAH. 1682. The anatomy of plants. London.

GRIFFITH, J. W., and A. HENFREY. 1875. Micrographical dictionary. John van Voorst. London.

GRIFFITHS, DAVID. 1912. The grama grasses, *Bouteloua* and related genera. *Contributions Nat. Herbarium*, **14**(3): 343–428, *pl.* 67–83, *figs.* 19–36.

GROOM, PERCY. 1916. A note on the vegetative anatomy of *Pherosphaera Fitzgeraldi. Ann. Bot.*, **30**: 211–314, 3 *figs.*

GUILLEMIN, ANTOINE. 1925. Recherches microscopiques sue le pollen. *Mém. Soc. Hist. Nat. Paris*, **2**: 101–124, *pl.* 8.

HALL, H. M. 1917. The relation of farm weeds to hayfever. *Monthly Bull. (Sacramento, Calif.)*, **6**(2): 44–47, *figs.* 8–9.

——. 1918. Walnut pollen as a cause of hayfever. *Science*, **68** (221): 516–517.

——. 1922. Hayfever plants of California. *Pub. Health Rep.*, **37**(14): 803–822.

——. 1928. The genus *Haplopappus*, a phylogenetic study in the Compositae. *Carnegie Inst. Wash. Pub.*, **399**: 1–391, *pl.* 1–16, *figs.* 1–14.

——, and F. E. CLEMENTS. 1923. The phylogenetic method in taxonomy. *Carnegie Inst. Wash. Pub.*, 355 pp., 58 *pl.*, 47 *figs.*

HARPER, R. A. 1908. The organization of certain coenobic plants. *Bull. Univ. Wis. Sci. Ser.*, **3**: 279–334, *pl.* 1–4.

——. 1918. Organization, reproduction and inheritance in *Pediastrum. Proc. Amer. Phil. Soc.*, **57**: 375–438.

HEGI, GUSTAV. 1929. Illustrierte Flora von Mitteleurope, vol. 6, pt. 2.

HEINTZE, AUGUSTUS. 1927. Cormofyternas Fylogeni, 170 pp. Håkan Ohlssons Boktryckeri. Lund.

HEYEL, F. W. 1919. The protein extract of ragweed pollen. *Jour. Amer. Chem. Soc.*, **41**: 670–682.

HITCHCOCK, A. S. 1905. North American species of *Agrostis*. *Dept. Agric., Bur. Plant Industry, Bull.* **68**.

———. 1920. The Genera of the grasses of the United States (America) with special reference to economical species. *Dept. Agric., Bull.* **772**, 307 pp., 18 *pl.*

———. 1935. Manual of the Grasses of the United States. U. S. Gov. Printing Office, Washington.

HØEG, OVE ARBO. 1924. Pollen of humble-bees from Novaya Zemlya. Report of the scientific results of the Norwegian expedition to Novaya Zemlya, 1921, No. 27. Christiania.

———. 1929. Pollen on the humble-bees from Ellesmere Land. *Det Kongelige Norske videnskabers selskab. Forhändlinger*, **2** (16) 55–57.

HOLLINGSHEAD, LILLIAN, and ERNEST BABCOCK. 1930. Chromosomes and phylogeny in *Crepis*. *Univer. Calif. Pub. Agric. Sci.* **6** (1): 1–53, 24 *figs.*

HOOKER, J. D. 1863. On *Welwitschia*, a new genus of Gnetaceae. *Trans. Linn. Soc.*, **24**: 1–48, *pl.* 1–14.

HÖRMANN, HANS. 1929. Die pollenanalytische Unterscheidung von *Pinus montana, P. silvestris* and *P. cembra. Oesterr. Bot. Zeitschr.*, **78**: 215–228, 1 *pl.*

IBRAHIM, AHMET CAN. 1933. Sporen des Aegirhorizontes des Ruhrreviers. pp. 1–46, *pl.* 1–8. (Diss. Techn.) Hochschule Berlin.

JEFFREY, E. C. 1916. Hybridism and the rate of evolution. *Amer. Nat.*, **1**: 129.

———. 1917. The anatomy of woody plants. University of Chicago Press, Chicago.

JENTYS-SZAFER, J. 1928. La structure des membranes du pollen de *Corylus*, de *Myrica* et des espèces européennes de *Betula* et leur dètermination à l'état fossile. *Bull. Acad. Polen. Sci. Lettr., Classe Sci. Mathém. et Nat.*, sér. B; *Sc. Nat.*, pp. 75–125, 3 *pl.*

JURÁNYI, LUDWIG. 1872. Ueber den Bau und die Entwickelung des Pollens bei *Ceratozamia longifolia. Jahrb. Wiss. Bot.* **8**: 382–400, *pl.* 31–34.

———. 1882. Beiträge zur Kenntnis des Pollenentwickleung der Cycadeen und Conifereen. *Bot. Zeit.*, **40**: 814–818; 835–844.

KAMMAN, OTTO. 1904. Zur Kenntnis des Roggen-Pollens und das derin enthaltenen Heufiebergiften. *Beit. z. Chem. Physiol. u. Pathol.*, **5**: 346–354.

KELLER, P. 1929. Pollenanalytische Untersuchungen an einigen Mooren des St. Gallischen Rheintales. *Jahrb. St. Gall. Naturw. Ges.*, **64**: 74–88.

———. 1929. Analyse pollinique de la Tourbière de Pinet. *Arch. Botanique*, **4**: 57–63.

KELLY, JAMES W. 1928. Methods of collecting and preserving pollen for use in the treatment of hayfever. *Dept. Agric., Bur. Plant Industry, Circ.* **46**: 1–9. *figs.* 1–7.

KEY, S. N. 1918. The etiology of winter hayfever in Texas. *Texas State Jour. Med.*, January.

KIDSTON, R. 1906. On the microsporangia of the Pteridosperms. *Phil. Trans. Roy. Soc. Lond. B.*, **198**: 413–445, *pl.* 25–28.

KILDAHL, N. J. 1908. Affinities of *Phyllocladus*. *Bot. Gaz.*, **46**: 464.

KIRCHHEIMER, F. 1932. On pollen from the Upper Cretaceous Dysodil of Banke, Namaqualand (South Africa). *Trans. Roy. Soc. South Africa*, **21**(1): 41–50, *figs.* 1–6, *pl.* 5, 6.

——. 1934. Über Tsuga-Pollen aus dem Tertiär. *Planta, Arch. Wiss. Bot.*, **22**(2): 171–191, *figs.* 1–9.

KNOWLTON, F. H. 1927. Plants of the past, 275 pp., 90 *figs.* Princeton University Press, Princeton.

KOESSLER, J. H. 1918. An analysis of ragweed pollen. *Jour. Biol. Chem.*, **35**: 415–424.

KÖLREUTER, J. G. 1761–1766. Vorläufige Nachricht von einigen das Geschlecht der Pflanzen betreffenden Versuchen und Beobachtungen, nebst Fortsetzungen 1, 2, und 3. Wilhelm Engelmann, Leipzig.

KRÄUSEL, R. 1929. Die paläobotanischen Untersuchungsmethoden. Jena.

LAMSON, R. W., and ALVA WATRY. 1933a. Anemophilous plants of Seligman, Arizona. *Jour. Allergy*, **4**(3): 207–219, *figs.* 1–14.

——. 1933b. The importance of the Chenopodiaceae in pollinosis, with special reference to Winslow and Hollbrook, Arizona. *Jour. Allergy* **4**(4): 255–283, *figs.* 1–27, *tabs.* 1, 2.

LEE, ARTHUR BOLLES. 1921. The microtomist's vade-mecum. Philadelphia.

LEWIS, I. F., and E. C. COCKE. 1929. Pollen analysis of Dismal Swamp peat. *Jour. Elisha Mitchel Sci. Soc.*, **45**: 36–58, *pl.* 3–5.

LINDLEY, JOHN. 1830. The genera and species of Orchidaceous plants. London.

LOGAN, JAMES. 1739. Experimenta et Meletemata de plantarum generatione. Leyden. (Experiments and considerations of the generation of plants. London, 1749.)

LOPRIORE, G. 1905. Ueber die Vielkörnigkeit der Pollenkörn von *Araucaria Bidwillii* Hook. *Ber. Deut. Bot. Ges.*, **23**: 335–346, *pl.* 15.

LUERSEN, CHRISTIAN. 1869. Zur controverse über die Einzelligkeit oder Mehrzelligkeit des Pollens der Onagrarieen, Cucurbitaceen und Corylaceen. *Jahrb. Wiss. Bot.*, **7**: 34–35, 3 *pl.*

MALPIGHI, MARCELLO. 1687. Opera omnia. London.

MANGIN, LOUIS. 1886. Recherches sur le pollen. *Bull. Soc. Bot. France*, **33**: 337–442.

——. 1889. Observations sur la membrane du grain de pollen mûr. *Bull. Soc. Bot. France*, **36**: 274–283.

MARKGRAF, FRIEDRICH. 1929. Monographie der Gattung *Gnetum*. *Bull. Jard. Bot. Buitenzorg*, ser. 3, **10** (4): 407–511, 4 *pl.*, 8 *figs.*

MASTERS, MAXWELL T. 1900. *Glyptostrobus*. *Jour. Bot.*, **38**: 37–40.

MEINKE, H. 1927. Atlas und Bestimmungsschlüssel zur Pollenanalytik. *Bot. Arch.*, **19**: 380–449.

MEYEN, F. J. F. 1828. Anatomisch-physiologische Untersuchungen über den Inhalt der Pflanzen-zellen. Berlin.

————. 1839. Neues System der Pflanzenphysiologie, vol. 3: 155. Berlin.

MILLSPAUGH, C. F., and E. E. SHERFF. 1919. Revision of the North American species of *Xanthium*. *Field Mus. Nat. Hist. Pub. Bot. Ser.*, **4**: 9–42, *pl.* 7–13.

————. 1922. *Xanthium*. *North American Flora*, **33**: 37–44.

MIRBEL, C. F. 1802. Anatomie végétal. Paris.

————. 1833. Recherches anatomiques et physiologiques sur le *Marchantia polymorpha* pour servir à l'histoire du tissu cellulaire de l'épiderme et des stomates, pp. 55–100, *pl.* 9, 10.

MOHL, HUGO VON. 1835. Sur la structure et les formes des grains de pollen. *Ann. Sci. Nat.*, **3**: 148–180; 220–236; 304–346. *pl.* 9–11.

————. 1851. Grundzüge der Anatomie und Physiologie der vegetabilischen Zelle, p. 123. Braunschweig.

MULLIN, W. V. 1922. Pollen and hayfever—a regional problem. *Trans. Amer. Acad. Ophthalmology and Otolaryngology*, 10 pp.

NÄGELI, K. 1842. Zur Entwickelungsgeschichte des Pollens bei den Phanerogamen, 36 pp. 3 *pl.* Zurich.

NATHORST, A. G. 1908. Paläobotanische Mitteilungen 4, Ueber die Untersuchung kutinisiter fossiler Pflanzenteile. *Kungl. Svensk. Vet.-Akad. Handl.*, **43** (6), 28 pp., 4 *pl.* 1 *fig.*

————. 1909. Paläobotanische Mitteilungen 8, Ueber *Williamsonia*, *Wielandia*, *Cycadocephalus* und *Wiltrichia*. *Kungl. Svensk. Vet.-Akad. Handl.*, **45** (4), 38 pp. 8 *pl.*

————. 1911. Neue Beiträge zur Kenntnis der *Williamsonia* Blüten. *Kungl. Svensk. Vet.-Akad. Handl.*, **46** (4), 29 pp., 6 *pl.*

NAUMAN, E. 1925. Plankton. Abderhalden's Handbuch der biologischen Arbeitsmethoden. Süsswasserbiologie, 1.

NEEDHAM, M. 1750. Nouvelles observations microscopiques, 525 pp., 8 *pl.* Paris.

NORÉN, C. O. 1908. Zur Kenntnis der Entwickelung von *Saxegothea conspicua* Lindl. *Svensk. Bot. Tid.*, **2**: 101–122, 3 *figs.*, *pl.* 7–9.

OLIVER, F. W. 1904. On the structure and affinities of *Stephnospermum*. *Trans. Linn. Soc. Lond.* II, **6**: 361–400, 4 *pl.*, 1 *fig.*

————. 1909. On *Physostoma elegans*, an archaic type of seed from the Palaeozoic rocks. *Ann. Bot.*, **23**: 73–116, *pl.* 5–7, 10 *fig.*

———— and D. H. SCOTT. 1904. On the structure of the Palaeozoic seed *Lagenostoma Lomaxi*. *Phil. Trans. Roy. Soc. Lond. B*, **197**: 193–247, *pl.* 4–10.

OSAWA, J. 1913. Studies on the cytology of some species of *Taraxacum*. *Arch. Exp. Zellforsch.*, **10**: 450–469, 2 *pl.*

PATON, JULIA B. 1921. Pollen and pollen enzymes. *Amer. Jour. Bot.*, **8** (10): 471–501.

PATTERSON, PAUL M., and LESLIE N. GAY. 1930. The pollen content of the air and its relation to hayfever in Baltimore, Md. during 1930. *Jour. Allergy*, **3** (3): 282–295, *figs.* 1–9.

PEARSON, H. H. W. 1906. Some observations on *Welwitschia mirabilis*. *Phil. Trans. Roy. Soc. Lond.*, ser. *B.*, **198**: 265–304, *pl.* 18–20.

―――. 1912. On the microsporangium and microsporogenesis of *Gnetum*. *Ann. Bot.*, **26**: 603–620, 6 *figs*.

―――. 1929. Gnetales, 194 pp., 90 *figs*. Cambridge Univer. Press, Cambridge.

PENFUND, W. T., and B. G. EFRON. 1929. A standardized method for pollen air analysis. *Proc. Soc. Exp. Biol. and Med.*, **27**: 650–654, 2 *figs*.

PHILLIPS, E. W. 1922. Treatment of hayfever with Arizona pollens. *Southwestern Medicine*, Ap. 9.

―――. 1923. Hayfever in central Arizona. *Southwestern Medicine.*, **7** (8): 273–281.

PILGER, R. 1903. Taxaceae. A. Engler, Das Pflanzenreich, vol. 18 (IV, 5): 1–119. Wilhelm Engelmann, Leipzig.

―――. 1916. Die Taxales. *Mitt. Deut. Dendrol. Ges.* **25**: 1–28, *pl.* 10.

PIPER, C. V. 1918. The agricultural species of the bent grasses. *Dept. Agric. Bull.*, 692: 1–14, *figs*. 1, 2.

POHL, FRANZ. 1928. Der einfaltige Pollen, sein Verbreitung und phylogenetische Bedeutung. *Beihefte z. Bot. Centralb.*, **45** (1): 59–73, 1 *fig*.

POLLENDER, ALOYS. 1867. Ueber das Entstehen und die Bildung der kreisrunden Oeffnungen in der aüssern Haut des Blütenstaubes, 20 pp., 2 *pl*. Bonn.

POPE, MAXY ALICE. 1925. Pollen morphology as an index to plant classification; 1, Morphology of pollen. *Bot. Gaz.*, **45**: 63–72, 1 *pl*.

POTONIÉ, ROBERT. 1931*a*. Zur Mikroskopie der Braunkohlen Tertiäre Blütenstaubformen. *Braunkohle*, **16**: 1–9, 2 *pl*.

―――. 1931*b*. Zur Mikroskopie der Braunkohlen. Tertiäre Sporen- und Blütenstaubformen. *Braunkohle*, **27**: 554–556, 16 *figs*.

―――. 1931*c*. Die mikrobotanische Untersuchung der Kohlen Pollenformen. *Sitzungs. Preuss. Geol. Landesanstalt*, **6**: 15–16.

―――. 1931*d*. Pollenformen aus tertiären Braunkohlen. *Jahrb. Preuss. Geol. Landesanstalt*, **52**: 1–7, 1 *pl*.

―――. 1934. Zur Mikrobotanik der Kohlen und ihrer Verwandten. *Arbeiten Inst. f. Paläobotanik u. Petrographie Brennsteine*, **4**: 1–125, *pl.* 1–6, *figs*. 1–44.

―――― and JOHANN GELLETICH. 1933. Ueber Pteridophyten-Sporen einer eocänen Braunkohle aus Dorog in Ungarn. *Sitzungs. Ges. naturforsch. Freunde ausgegeben*, 15 März.

PRANTL, K. 1891. *Magnoliaceae*. Engler & Prantl. Die natürlichen Pflanzenfamilien, Vol. 3 (1): 12–19. Wilhelm Engelmann, Leipzig.

PRINGSHEIM, N. 1854. Untersuchungen über den Bau und Bildung der Pflanzenzelle, p. 50. Berlin.

PURKINJE, JOHANNES E. 1830. De cellulis antherarum fibrosis nec non de granorum pollinarum formis commentationis phytotomica. Breslau.

RADLKOFER, L. 1883. Ueber den systematischen Werth der Pollenbeschaffenheit bei den Acanthaceen. *Sitzungs. Mathem.-Phys. Classe K. bayer. Akad. Wiss.*, **13**: 256–314.

RAMIREZ, M. A. 1930. *Pyrethrum* as an etiologic factor in vasomotor rhinitis and asthma. *Jour. Allergy*, **1**: 142.

RASPAIL, F. V. 1826. Recherches sur les tissus organiques. *Mém. Soc. Hist. Nat. Paris*, **3**: 209–313.

———. 1828. Observations sur l'explosion du grain de pollen. *Mém. Soc. Hist. Nat. Paris*, **4**: 347–362.

RECORD, S. J. 1919. Identification of the economic woods of the United States (America), ed. 2, 157 pp. John Wiley & Sons, Inc., New York.

RENAULT, M. B. 1876. Bassin Houiller et Permien d'Autun et d'Epinac. vol. 4 of Gâtes minéreaux de la France flore fossil 2.

———. 1879. Structure compaére flore Carbonifère. *Nouvelles Arch. Muséum*, II; sér. 2: 28–34, 17 *pl.*

ROBERTSON, AGNES. 1907. The Taxoideae, a phylogenetic study. *New Phytol.*, **6**: 92–102, 1 *pl.*

ROBINSON, VICTOR. 1929. Johannes Evangelista Purkinje. *Sci. Monthly*, September, 1929.

ROSANOFF, SERGIUS. 1866. Zur Kenntniss des Baues und der Entwickelungsgeschichte des Pollen der Mimoseae. *Jahrb. Wiss. Bot.*, **4**: 441–450, *pl.* 31–32.

ROWE, ALBERT H. 1928. A study of the atmospheric pollen and botanic flora of the east shore of San Francisco bay. *Jour. Lab. and Clin. Med.*, **13** (5): 416–439, *figs.* 1–25.

RUDOLPH, K., and F. FIRBAS. 1926. Pollenanalytische Untersuchung subalpiner Moore des Riesengebirges. *Ber. Deut. Bot. Ges.*, **44**: 227–238, 3 *figs.*

RYDBERG, P. A. 1918. Anthemideae. *North American Flora*, **34**: 217–228.

———. 1922. Ambrosiaceae. *North American Flora*, **33**: 3–44.

SAPORTA, DE G., and A. F. MARION. 1885. L'évolution du règne végétal, les phanérogames, vol. 2, Felix Alcan, Paris.

SARGENT, CHARLES SPRAGUE. 1922. Manual of the trees of North America. Houghton Mifflin Company, Boston.

SAXTON, W. T. 1930. Notes on conifers; 7, *Pherosphaera Hookeriana*. *Ann. Bot.*, **44**: 957–963, *figs.* 1–8.

SCHACHT, H. 1860. Ueber den Bau einiger Pollenkörner. *Jahrb. Wiss. Bot.*, **2**: 109–168.

SCHEPPEGRELL, WILLIAM. 1917. Hayfever, its cause and prevention in the Rocky Mountain and Pacific states. *Public Health Repts.*, reprint **412**: 1135–1152.

———. 1922. Hayfever and asthma, 274 pp., 108 *figs.* Lea and Febiger, Philadelphia.

SCHLECHTENDAHL, D. F. L., and C. G. EHRENBERG, 1829. De antheris et polline Asclepiadearum. *Linnaea*, **4**: 94–97.

SCHMIDT, E., and E. GRAUMANND. 1921. Zur Kenntnis pflanzlicher Inkrusten. 1. Mitteilung: Method zur Reindarstellung pflanzlicher Skelettsubstanzen (1). *Ber. Deut. Chem. Ges.*, **54**: 2.

SCHNARF, KARL. 1929. Embryologie der Angiospermen, in K. Linsbauer, Handb. der Pflanzenanatomie, vol. 11 (2); Archegoniaten: 48–52.

SCOTT, D. H. 1905. The early history of seed bearing plants. *Mem. and Proc. Manchester Litt. and Phil. Soc.*, **49** (3): 32 pp.

————. 1907. The present position of Palaeozoic botany. *Progressus Rei Botanicae*, **1**: 139–217, 37 *figs.*

————. 1923. Studies in fossil botany. A. & C. Black, Ltd., London.

SEARS, PAUL B. 1930. Common fossil pollen of the Erie basin. *Bot. Gaz.*, **89** (1): 95–106, *pl.* 1–3.

SELFRIDGE, GRANT. 1920. Vaso-motor disturbances of the nose with special reference to hayfever—with a report for the year of 1919. *Laryngoscope*, **30** (10): 611–625, 2 *figs.*

SEWARD, A. C. 1917. Fossil plants, vol. 3. Cambridge University Press, Cambridge.

———— and S. O. FORD. 1906. The Araucarineae, recent and extinct. *Phil. Trans. Roy. Soc. Lond.* ser *B.*, **198**: 305–411, *pl.* 23, 24.

———— and J. GOWAN. 1900. The maidenhair tree. *Ann. Bot.*, **14**: 109–154, *pl.* 8–10.

SMALL, JAMES. 1917. The origin and development of the Compositae. *New Phytol.*, **18**: 201–234.

————. 1928. The Ma Huang of commerce. *Quart. Jour. Pharm.*, **1** (2): 163–167, *figs.* 1–7.

SMALL, JOHN K. 1926. Cycads. *Jour. N. Y. Bot. Gard.*, **27**: 121–129, 2 *figs.*

————. 1931. The Cypress, southern remnant of a northern fossil type. *Journ. N. Y. Bot. Gard.*, **31**: 125–135, 5 *figs.*

SMITH, CORNELIA M. 1929. Development of *Dionaea muscipula*. *Bot. Gaz.*, **87**: 507–530, *pl.* 20–24, 1 *fig.*

SMITH, W. G. 1876. Notes of pollen. *Gardener's Chron.*, **40** (n.s. 6): 516 *et seq.*

SOLMS-LAUBACH, H. GRAF. 1891. Fossil botany. Clarendon Press, London.

SPRENGEL, KURT. 1812. Von dem Bau und der Natur der Gewächse, 654 pp., 14 *pl.* Halle.

STAPF, OTTO. 1889. Die Arten der Gattung *Ephedra*. Vienna.

STARK, P. 1925. Der Gegenwärtige Stand der pollenanalytischen Forschung. *Zeits. Bot.*, **17**: 89–125.

————. 1927. Ueber die Zugehörigkeit des Kiefernpollens in den verschiedenen Horizonten der Bodenseemoore. *Ber. Deut. Bot. Ges.*, **45**: 40–47.

STILES, W. 1908. The anatomy of *Saxegothea conspicua*. *New Phytol.*, **7**: 209–222.

STOUT, A. B. 1919. Intersexes in *Plantago lanceolata*. *Bot. Gaz.*, **68**: 109–133, *pl.* 12, 13.

STRASBURGER, EDUARD. 1872. Die Coniferen und die Gnetaceen. Leipzig.

————. 1882. Ueber den Bau und das Wachsthum der Zellhäute, 264 pp. 8 *pl.* Jena.

————. 1884. Das Botanische Practicum. Jena.

————. 1889. Ueber das Wachsthum vegetabilischer Zellhäute. *Histol. Beiträge*, **2**: 36–93, *pl.* 3, 4.

————. 1892. Ueber das Verhalten des Pollens und die Befructungsvorgänge bei den Gymnospermen. *Histol. Beiträge*, **4**: 1–158, *pl.* 1–3.

———. 1902. Ein Beitrag zur Kenntniss von *Ceratophyllum submersum* und Phylogenetische Eröterungen. *Jahrb. Wiss. Bot.*, **37** :477.

———, FRITZ NOLL, H. SCHENK, and GEORGE KARSTEN. 1908. Textbook of botany. London.

SULTZBERGER, M B. and C. B. WEINBERG. 1930. Dermatitis due to insect powder. *Jour. Amer. Med. Assoc.*, **95** (2): 111–112, 1 *fig.*

SYKES, M. G. 1910. The anatomy of *Welwitschia mirabilis* in the seedling and adult stages. *Trans. Linn. Soc. London II. Bot.*, **7** : 327–354, *pl.* 34–35, 5 *figs.*

TAMMES, P. M. L. 1930. On the origin of the number and arrangement of the places of exit on the surface of pollen grains. *Rec. Travaux Bot. Néerlandais*, **2.** 82 pp., *pl.* 1–3, *figs.* 1–21.

THOMPSON, D'ARCY W. 1917. Growth and form, 793 pp., *figs.* 1–408. Cambridge University Press, Cambridge.

THOMSON, R. B. 1908. Notes on the pollen of *Microcachrys*. *Bot. Gaz.*, **46** : 465, 466.

———. 1909. On the pollen of *Microcachrys tetragona*. *Bot. Gaz.*, **47** : 26–29, *pl.* 1, 2.

———. 1913. On the comparative anatomy and affinities of the Araucarineae. *Phil. Trans. Roy. Soc. Lond.* ser. *B.*, **204** : 1–50, *pl.*, 3–7.

TISCHLER, G. 1908. Zellstudien an sterilen Bastardpflanzen. *Arch. Exp. Zellforsch.*, **1** : 33–151, *figs.* 1–120.

TISON, A. 1909. Sur le *Saxegothaea* Lindl. *Mém. Soc. Linn. Normandie*, **23** : 139–160, *pl.* 9–10.

TRELA, J. 1928. Zur Morphologie der Pollenkörner der einheimischen Tilia-arten. *Bull. Acad. Polon. Sci. Lettr. Classe Sci. Mathém. et Nat.*, sér *B. Sci. Nat.*: 45–54, *figs.* 1–4.

TSCHISTIAKOFF, J. 1876. Ueber die Entwickelungsgeschichte des Pollens bei *Epilobium angustifolium*. *Jahrb. Wiss. Bot.*, **10** : 7–48, *pl.* 1–5.

TURPIN, P. J. F. 1820. Essai d'une iconographie végétale. Paris.

VEITCH, JAMES, and sons. 1881. A manual of the Coniferae. Chelsea.

VESQUE, J. 1883. Sur l'organization mécanique du grain de pollin. *Compt. Rend. Acad. Sci.*, **96** : 1684–1687.

WARING, JAMES J. 1926. Report of the hayfever research committee of the state historical and natural history society of Colorado, 75 pp., 26 *figs.* Denver.

——— and MAXY POPE. 1927. The cotton of the cottonwood tree as a factor in hayfever, a preliminary report. *Colorado Medicine*, July, 3 pp., 1 *fig.*

WARMING, EUGENE. 1881–1888. Familien Podostemaceae. Mém. *Acad. Roy. Copenhagne, Classe Sci.*, **2** (1), (3), **14** (8), **9** (2), **11** (1).

WATSON, S. H., and C. S. KIBLER. 1922. Hayfever with special reference to its etiology in the Southwest. *Jour. Amer. Med. Assoc.*, Mar. 11.

WEBBER, H. J. 1901. Spermatogenesis and fecundation of *Zamia*. *Dept. Agric. Bur. Plant Industry, Bull.*, **2** : 7–98, 7 *pl.*

WEIMEL, THEODOR. 1850. Zur Entwickelungsgeschichte des Pollens. *Zeits. Bot.*, **8** (12): 225–235, 241–248, 265–270, 289–294, 313–332, *pl.* 5.

WIELAND, G. R. 1906. American fossil cycads. *Carnegie Institute, Pub.* Vol. 1.

——. 1916. American fossil cycads, *Carnegie Institute, Pub.* Vol. 2, Taxonomy.

——. 1929. Antiquity of the angiosperms. *Proc. Intern. Congr. Plant Sci.*, **1**: 429–456, 5 *pl.*

WODEHOUSE, R. P. 1916. A simple method of obtaining ragweed pollen in large quantities. *Boston Med. and Surg. Jour.*, **174**: 430.

——. 1926a. Pollen-grain morphology in the classification of the Anthemideae. *Bull. Torrey Bot. Club*, **53**: 479–485. *figs.* 1, 2.

——. 1926b. Morphology of pollen grains in plant classification. *Jour. N. Y. Bot. Gard.*, **27**: 145–154, 1 *pl.*

——. 1928a. The Phylogenetic value of pollen-grain characters. *Ann. Bot.*, **42**: 891–934, *pl.* 20, 21, *figs.* 1, 2.

——. 1928b. Pollen grains in the identification and classification of plants, II. Barnadesia. *Bull. Torrey Bot. Club*, **55**: 449–462, *pl.* 13, *figs.* 1, 2.

——. 1929. The origin of symmetry patterns of pollen grains. *Bull. Torrey Bot. Club*, **56**: 339–350, *pl.* 16, *figs.* 7–10.

——. 1930. Pollen grains in the identification and classification of plants—V. *Haplopappus* and other Astereae: the origin of their furrow configurations. *Bull. Torrey Bot. Club*, **57**: 21–46, *pl.* 1, *figs.* 11–24.

——. 1931b. The origin of the six-furrowed configuration of *Dahlia* pollen grains. *Bull. Torrey Bot. Club*, **57**: 371–380, *pl.* 19.

——. 1932. Tertiary pollen; I. Pollen of the living representatives of the Green River flora. *Bull. Torrey Bot. Club*, **59**: 313–340, *pl.* 20–22.

——. 1933a. Tertiary pollen; II. Pollen of the Green River oil shales. *Bull. Torrey Bot. Club*, **60**: 479–524. *figs.* 1–54.

WOODRUFF, J. G. 1930. Studies of the staminate inflorescence and pollen of *Hicoria Pecan*. *Jour. Agric. Res.*, **40** (12): 1059–1104.

WOODWORTH, ROBERT H. 1929. Cytological studies of the Betulaceae. *Bot. Gaz.*, **87**: 331–363; **88**: 383–399.

YOUNG, MARY S. 1910. The morphology of the Podocarpineae. *Bot. Gaz.*, **50**: 81–100, *pl.* 4–6.

ZIRKLE, CONWAY. 1932. Some forgotten records of hybridization and sex in plants. *Jour. Heredity*, **23** (11): 433–448, 3 *figs.*

——. 1934. More records of plant hybridization before Koelreuter. *Jour. Heredity*, **25** (1): 3–18, *figs.* 1–3, *frontispiece.*

INDEX

Numbers in **bold face** indicate pages bearing principal entries; numbers in *italics* indicate pages bearing synonyms

A

Abies, **263**–266
Abietineae, 243, 247, 256
Abortive tetrads, 163
Absinth, 514
Acacia, 427, 430, **432**–*436*
Acanthambrosia, 521, 535
Acanthoxanthium, 521, **537**
Acer, 438–442, 451
Aceraceae, **438**, 451
Acid-oxidation method of treating peat, 115
Acnida tamariscina, 421
Acolpate grains, 169
Actuopaleontology, 123
Adoxa, 350, 450
Aetheotesta, 211, 221
Agathis, 246, 255
Agropyron, 318
Agrostideae, 309
Agrostis, 130, **313,** 314, 329
Ailanthus glandulosa, 132
Ajenjo, 508
Alder, 131, 364, **369**–371, 375
Alenda, 292
Alkali blite, 415
Alkali method of treating peat, 114
All scale, 148
Allenrolfia occidentalis, 416
Alligator tree, 425
Alnus, 131, 364, **369**–371, 375
Alpino, Prosper, 26
Alternaria spores, 133
Amaranth, 133, 147, 148, **419**–421
  family, 419
  Palmer's, 420
Amaranthaceae, 419

Amaranthus, 133, 147, **419**–421
Ambrosia, 130, 509, 520, 521, **531**–535, *536*
  elatior, 130, 509, 520, 532
  psilostachya, 509, 519
  tenuifolia, 535
  trifida, 130, 509
  in hayfever, 130
Ambrosiaceae, *517*
Ambrosieae, 509, **516**
Ambrosineae, 523
Amici, Giovanni Battista, 47, 53
Amygdalus Persica, *429*
Anacardiaceae, 208
Andropogon, *314, 315*
Andropogonieae, 309
Angiospermae, 295
Aniline-oil gentian-violet method, 109
Anis tree, Japanese sacred, 336
  Chinese, 335
  star, 335
Annona tripetala, 325
Annual bluegrass, 312
Annual saltbush, 418
Anthemideae, **496,** 509
Anthemis, 498, **501,** 519
Anthoxanthum odoratum, 129, 319
Antigonum, 391, 403
Apple, 429
Aqueous fuchsin, 108
Aquifoliaceae, 427, **438**
Araucaria, 245, 246, 255
Araucariales, 246
Araucarineae, 245, 255
Arborvitae, 271
Arctic daisy, 503
Arctotidae, 468

Gesner, Konrad von, 26
Giant ragweed, 130, **534**
Ginkgo, 241
Ginkgoales, 240
Gironniera, 382, 386
Gleditsch, J. G., 28
Gleichen Russworm, Baron von, 37, 46
Glyptostrobus, 270
Gnetales, 283
Gnetum, 283, 284, **291**–295
Goatsbeard, 480, 482
Goethe, 41
Golden bells, 454
Golden thistle, 479
Goldenrod, 133, 490
 as a cause of hayfever, 491
Goldenrod fever, 143
Goose grass, 130
Goosefoot, 413
 family, 410
Grama grass, blue, 317
Gramineae, **303**–320, 329
Grass family, **303**–320, 329
Grass hayfever, 138
Grasses, flowers of, 139
 tribes of, 308
Greasebrush, 529
Greasewood, 148, 413
Green amaranth, 420
Greenland peats, 115, 119
Grew, Nehemiah, 16–20
 portrait, 17
Guillemin, Jean Baptiste, 48
Gymnosperms, living, 233–295
Gymnostyles parthenifolia, *529*

H

Hackberry, 389, 390
Hackberry hayfever, 138
Haenselera, 460, 465, **477**
Half-zonate grain, 175
Haloragidaceae, 444
Hamamelidaceae, 425, 427
Haplopappus, 167, 168
Haptotypic characters, 158
Hawk's-beard, 474

Hawkweed, 475
Hayfever, 134–152
 diagnosis, 149
 early spring, 135
 early summer, 138
 late summer, 143
Hazel, 131, 369
"Hazel forests," 122
Hazelnut, 369
Heartsease, 444
Heartweed, 409
Hedypnois, *474*
Heliantheae, 206
Helianthus annuus, 133, 154, 519
Hemicycadales, *227*
Hemlock, 131
 Canada, 266
Hemp, 389
Heptahedron, 191
Herd's-grass, 313
Hereditary characters, 153
Heredity, 155
Herodotus, 25
Heterotasithynic system of cracking, 187
Hexacolpate grains, 172
Hexad arrangement of daughter nuclei, 466
Hexahedron, 191
Hickory, 132, 358
 nutmeg, 361
 shagbark, 359
Hicoria, *359*
Hieracium, 460, 465, 467, **475,** 476
High-water shrub, 146, 530
Hila, 43
Hill sage, 147
Hiller peat auger, 110
Holcus, 314, *315*
Holly family, 438
Holoptelea, 382, 384, **386**
Hooke's microscope, 15, 16
Hop, 133, **388,** 389
Hop hornbeam, 368
Hordeae, 308
Hornbeam, 368
Horned pondweed, 301
Horseweed, 527